Homework

4.76
4.73
4.74

SI Prefixes

Multiplication Factor	Prefix†	Symbol
$1\ 000\ 000\ 000\ 000 = 10^{12}$	tera	T
$1\ 000\ 000\ 000 = 10^{9}$	giga	G
$1\ 000\ 000 = 10^{6}$	mega	M
$1\ 000 = 10^{3}$	kilo	k
$100 = 10^{2}$	hecto‡	h
$10 = 10^{1}$	deka‡	da
$0.1 = 10^{-1}$	deci‡	d
$0.01 = 10^{-2}$	centi‡	c
$0.001 = 10^{-3}$	milli	m
$0.000\ 001 = 10^{-6}$	micro	μ
$0.000\ 000\ 001 = 10^{-9}$	nano	n
$0.000\ 000\ 000\ 001 = 10^{-12}$	pico	p
$0.000\ 000\ 000\ 000\ 001 = 10^{-15}$	femto	f
$0.000\ 000\ 000\ 000\ 000\ 001 = 10^{-18}$	atto	a

† The first syllable of every prefix is accented so that the prefix will retain its identity. Thus, the preferred pronunciation of kilometre places the accent on the first syllable, not the second.

‡ The use of these prefixes should be avoided, except for the measurement of areas and volumes and for the nontechnical use of centimetre, as for body and clothing measurements.

Principal SI Units Used in Mechanics

Quantity	Unit	Symbol	Formula
Acceleration	Metre per second squared	. . .	m/s^2
Angle	Radian	rad	†
Angular acceleration	Radian per second squared	. . .	rad/s^2
Angular velocity	Radian per second	. . .	rad/s
Area	Square metre	. . .	m^2
Density	Kilogram per cubic metre	. . .	kg/m^3
Energy	Joule	J	$N \cdot m$
Force	Newton	N	$kg \cdot m/s^2$
Frequency	Hertz	Hz	s^{-1}
Impulse	Newton-second	. . .	$kg \cdot m/s$
Length	Metre	m	‡
Mass	Kilogram	kg	‡
Moment of a force	Newton-metre	. . .	$N \cdot m$
Power	Watt	W	J/s
Pressure	Pascal	Pa	N/m^2
Stress	Pascal	Pa	N/m^2
Time	Second	s	‡
Velocity	Metre per second	. . .	m/s
Volume, solids	Cubic metre	. . .	m^3
Liquids	Litre	L	$10^{-3}\ m^3$
Work	Joule	J	$N \cdot m$

† Supplementary unit (1 revolution $= 2\pi$ rad $= 360°$).

‡ Base unit.

Vector Mechanics
for Engineers

STATICS

2nd SI Metric Edition

Vector Mechanics
for Engineers

Statics

Ferdinand P. Beer
Lehigh University

E. Russell Johnston, Jr.
University of Connecticut

Metric Edition adapted by
G. Wayne Brown
Sir Sandford Fleming College

McGraw-Hill Book Company
Singapore   New York   St. Louis   San Francisco   Auckland   Bogotá   Caracas
Colorado Springs   Hamburg   Lisbon   London   Madrid   Mexico   Milan
Montreal   New Delhi   Oklahoma City   Panama   Paris
San Juan   São Paulo   Sydney   Tokyo   Toronto

ABOUT THE AUTHORS

"How did you happen to write your books together, with one of you at Lehigh and the other at UConn, and how do you manage to keep collaborating on their successive revisions?" These are the two questions most often asked of our two authors.

The answer to the first question is simple. Russ Johnston's first teaching appointment was in the department of civil engineering and mechanics at Lehigh University. There he met Ferd Beer, who had joined that department two years earlier and was in charge of the courses in statics and dynamics. Born in France and educated in France and Switzerland (he holds an M.S. degree from the Sorbonne and a Sc.D. degree in the field of theoretical mechanics from the University of Geneva), Ferd had come to the United States after serving in the French army during the early part of World War II and had taught for four years at Williams College in the Williams-MIT joint arts and engineering program. Born in Philadelphia, Russ had obtained a B.S. degree in civil engineering from the University of Delaware and a Sc.D. degree in the field of structural engineering from MIT.

Ferd was delighted to discover that the young man who had been hired chiefly to teach graduate structural engineering courses was not only willing but eager to help him reorganize the courses in statics and dynamics. Both believed that these courses should be taught from a few basic principles and that the various concepts involved would be best understood and remembered by the students if they were presented in a graphic way. Together they wrote lecture notes, to which they later added problems they felt would appeal to future engineers, and soon they had produced the manuscript of the first edition of *Mechanics for Engineers*.

The second edition of their text found Russ Johnston at Worcester Polytechnic Institute and the third at the University of Connecticut. In the meantime, both Ferd and Russ had assumed administrative responsibilities in their departments, and both were involved in research, consulting, and the supervision of graduate students, Ferd in the area of stochastic processes and random vibrations, and Russ in the area of elastic stability and structural analysis and design. However, their interest in improving the teaching of the basic mechanics courses had not subsided and they both taught sections of these courses as they kept revising their texts. .

This brings us to the second question: How did the authors manage to work together so effectively after Russ Johnston had left Lehigh? Part of the answer may be provided by their phone bills and the money they spend on postage. As the publication date of a new edition approaches, they call each other daily and rush to the post office with express-mail packages in order to double-check their work. There are also frequent visits between the two families. At one time there were even joint camping trips, with both families pitching their tents next to each other. The Beers were the first to graduate to a trailer, which was used to illustrate a problem in one of the early editions of their text, but was replaced by the Johnstons' trailer in the next one. Now this trailer has also been replaced, both authors preferring the comforts of a motel and its dining room to those of a camping ground and its fireplaces.

Contents

Preface

The main objective of a first course in mechanics should be to develop in the engineering student the ability to analyze any problem in a simple and logical manner and to apply to its solution a few, well-understood basic principles. It is hoped that this text, designed for the first course in statics offered in the sophomore year, and the volume that follows, *Vector Mechanics for Engineers: Dynamics*, will help the instructor achieve this goal.

Vector algebra is introduced early in the text and used in the presentation and the discussion of the fundamental principles of mechanics. Vector methods are also used to solve many problems, particularly three-dimensional problems where their application results in a simpler and more concise solution. The emphasis in this text, however, remains on the correct understanding of the principles of mechanics and on their application to the solution of engineering problems, and vector algebra is presented chiefly as a convenient tool.

One of the characteristics of the approach used in these volumes is that the mechanics of *particles* has been clearly separated from the mechanics of *rigid bodies*. This approach makes it possible to consider simple practical applications at an early stage and to postpone the introduction of more difficult concepts. In this volume, for example, the statics of particles is treated first (Chap. 2); after the rules of addition and subtraction of vectors have been introduced, the principle of equilibrium of a particle is immediately applied to practical situations involving only concurrent forces. The statics of rigid bodies is considered in Chaps. 3 and 4. In Chap. 3, the vector and scalar products of two vectors are introduced and used to define the moment of a force about a point and about an axis. The presentation of these new concepts is followed by a thorough and rigorous discussion of equivalent systems of forces leading, in Chap. 4, to many practical applications involving the equilibrium of rigid bodies under general force systems. In the volume on dynamics, the same division is observed. The basic concepts of force, mass, and acceleration, of work and energy, and of impulse and momentum are introduced and first applied to problems involving only particles. Thus the student may familiarize himself with the three basic methods used in dynamics and learn their respective advantages before facing the difficulties associated with the motion of rigid bodies.

Since this text is designed for a first course in statics, new concepts have been presented in simple terms and every step explained in detail. On the other hand, by discussing the broader aspects of the problems considered, a definite maturity of approach has been achieved. For example, the concepts of partial constraints and of static indeterminacy are introduced early in the text and used throughout.

The fact that mechanics is essentially a *deductive* science based on a few fundamental principles has been stressed. Derivations have been presented in their logical sequence and with all the rigor warranted at this level. However, the learning process being largely *inductive*, simple applications have been considered first. Thus the statics of particles precedes the statics of rigid bodies, and problems involving internal forces are postponed until Chap. 6. Also, in Chap. 4, equilibrium problems involving only coplanar forces are considered first and solved by ordinary algebra, while problems involving three-dimensional forces and requiring the full use of vector algebra are discussed in the second part of the chapter.

Free-body diagrams are introduced early, and their importance is emphasized throughout the text. Color has been used to distinguish forces from other elements of the free-body diagrams. This makes it easier for the students to identify the forces acting on a given particle or rigid body and to follow the discussion of sample problems and other examples given in the text. Free-body diagrams are used not only to solve equilibrium problems but also to express the equivalence of two systems of forces or, more generally, of two systems of vectors. This approach is particularly useful as a preparation for the study of the dynamics of rigid bodies. As will be shown in the volume on dynamics, by placing the emphasis on "free-body-diagram equations" rather than on the standard algebraic equations of motion, a more intuitive and more complete understanding of the fundamental principles of dynamics may be achieved.

A large number of optional sections have been included. These sections are indicated by asterisks and may thus easily be distinguished from those which form the core of the basic statics course. They may be omitted without prejudice to the understanding of the rest of the text. Among the topics covered in these additional sections are applications to hydrostatics, shear and bending-moment diagrams for beams, equilibrium of cables, products of inertia and Mohr's circle, mass products of inertia and principal axes of inertia for three-dimensional bodies, and the method of virtual work. The sections on beams are especially useful when the course in statics is immediately followed by a course in mechanics of materials, while the sections on the inertia properties of three-dimensional bodies are primarily intended for the students who will later study in dynamics the motion of rigid bodies in three dimensions.

The material presented in the text and most of the problems require no previous mathematical knowledge beyond algebra, trigonometry, and elementary calculus, and all the elements of vector algebra necessary to the understanding of the text have been carefully presented in Chaps. 2 and 3. In general, a greater emphasis has been placed on the correct understanding of the basic mathematical concepts involved than on the nimble manipulation of mathematical formulas. In this connection, it should be mentioned that the determination of the centroids of composite areas precedes the calculation of centroids by integration, thus making it possible to establish the concept of moment of area firmly before introducing the use of integration.

This version of *Vector Mechanics for Engineers* uses exclusively the international system of units (SI units) and the SI units most frequently used in mechanics have been introduced in Chap. 1

In several parts of the text the presentation of numerical solutions has been modified to take into account the universal use of calculators by engineering students. Instructions on the proper use of calculators for the solution of typical statics problems have been substituted in Chap. 2 for the notes on the use of the slide rule which were contained in the previous editions of *Vector Mechanics for Engineers*.

The text has been divided into units, each consisting of one or several theory sections, one or several sample problems, and a large number of problems to be assigned. Each unit corresponds to a well-defined topic and generally may be covered in one lesson. In a number of cases, however, the instructor will find it desirable to devote more than one lesson to a given topic. The sample problems have been set up in much the same form that a student will use in solving the assigned problems. They thus serve the double purpose of amplifying the text and demonstrating the type of neat and orderly work that the student should cultivate in his own solutions. Most of the problems to be assigned are of a practical nature and should appeal to the engineering student. They are primarily designed, however, to illustrate the material presented in the text and to help the student understand the basic principles of mechanics. The problems have been grouped according to the portions of material they illustrate and have been arranged in order of increasing difficulty. Problems requiring special attention have been indicated by asterisks. Answers to all even-numbered problems are given at the end of the book.

The authors wish to acknowledge gratefully the many helpful comments and suggestions offered by the users of the previous editions of *Mechanics for Engineers* and of *Vector Mechanics for Engineers*.

FERDINAND P. BEER
E. RUSSELL JOHNSTON, JR.

List of Symbols

a	Constant; radius; distance
A, B, C, . . .	Reactions at supports and connections
$A, B, C,$ . . .	Points
A	Area
b	Width; distance
c	Constant
C	Centroid
d	Distance
e	Base of natural logarithms
F	Force; friction force
g	Acceleration of gravity
G	Center of gravity; constant of gravitation
h	Height; sag of cable
i, j, k	Unit vectors along coordinate axes
$I, I_x,$ . . .	Moment of inertia
$\bar{I}$	Centroidal moment of inertia
$I_{xy},$ . . .	Product of inertia
J	Polar moment of inertia
k	Spring constant
k_x, k_y, k_O	Radius of gyration
$\bar{k}$	Centroidal radius of gyration
l	Length
L	Length; span
m	Mass
M	Couple; moment
$\mathbf{M}_O$	Moment about point O
$\mathbf{M}_O^R$	Moment resultant about point O
M	Magnitude of couple or moment; mass of earth
M_{OL}	Moment about axis OL
N	Normal component of reaction
O	Origin of coordinates
p	Pressure
P	Force; vector
Q	Force; vector
r	Position vector

r	Radius; distance; polar coordinate
$\mathbf{R}$	Resultant force; resultant vector; reaction
R	Radius of earth
s	Position vector
s	Length of arc; length of cable
$\mathbf{S}$	Force; vector
t	Thickness
$\mathbf{T}$	Force
T	Tension
U	Work
$\mathbf{V}$	Vector product; shearing force
V	Volume; potential energy; shear
w	Load per unit length
$\mathbf{W}, W$	Weight; load
x, y, z	Rectangular coordinates; distances
$\bar{x}, \bar{y}, \bar{z}$	Rectangular coordinates of centroid or center of gravity
α, β, γ	Angles
ε	Elongation
$\delta \mathbf{r}$	Virtual displacement
δU	Virtual work
$\boldsymbol{\lambda}$	Unit vector along a line
η	Efficiency
θ	Angular coordinate; angle; polar coordinate
μ	Coefficient of friction
ρ	Density
ϕ	Angle of friction; angle

Vector Mechanics
for Engineers

STATICS

Introduction

1.1. What Is Mechanics?   Mechanics may be defined as that science which describes and predicts the conditions of rest or motion of bodies under the action of forces. It is divided into three parts: mechanics of *rigid bodies*, mechanics of *deformable bodies*, and mechanics of *fluids*.

The mechanics of rigid bodies is subdivided into *statics* and *dynamics*, the former dealing with bodies at rest, the latter with bodies in motion. In this part of the study of mechanics, bodies are assumed to be perfectly rigid. Actual structures and machines, however, are never absolutely rigid and deform under the loads to which they are subjected. But these deformations are usually small and do not appreciably affect the conditions of equilibrium or motion of the structure under consideration. They are important, though, as far as the resistance of the structure to failure is concerned and are studied in mechanics of materials, which is a part of the mechanics of deformable bodies. The third division of mechanics, the mechanics of fluids, is subdivided into the study of *incompressible fluids* and of *compressible fluids*. An important subdivision of the study of incompressible fluids is *hydraulics*, which deals with problems involving liquids.

1

Mechanics is a physical science, since it deals with the study of physical phenomena. However, some associate mechanics with mathematics, while many consider it as an engineering subject. Both these views are justified in part. Mechanics is the foundation of most engieering sciences and is an indispensable prerequisite to their study. However, it does not have the *empiricism* found in some engineering sciences, i.e., it does not rely on experience or observation alone; by its rigor and the emphasis it places on deductive reasoning it resembles mathematics. But, again, it is not an *abstract* or even a *pure* science; mechanics is an *applied* science. The purpose of mechanics is to explain and predict physical phenomena and thus to lay the foundations for engineering applications.

1.2. Fundamental Concepts and Principles. Although the study of mechanics goes back to the time of Aristotle (384–322 B.C.) and Archimedes (287–212 B.C.), one has to wait until Newton (1642–1727) to find a satisfactory formulation of its fundamental principles. These principles were later expressed in a modified form by d'Alembert, Lagrange, and Hamilton. Their validity remained unchallenged, however, until Einstein formulated his *theory of relativity* (1905). While its limitations have now been recognised, *newtonian mechanics* still remains the basis of today's engineering sciences.

The basic concepts used in mechanics are *space*, *time*, *mass*, and *force*. These concepts cannot be truly defined; they should be accepted on the basis of our intuition and experience and used as a mental frame of reference for our study of mechanics.

The concept of *space* is associated with the notion of the position of a point *P*. The position of *P* may be defined by three lengths measured from a certain reference point, or *origin*, in three given directions. These lengths are known as the *coordinates* of *P*.

To define an event, it is not sufficient to indicate its position in space. The *time* of the event should also be given.

The concept of *mass* is used to characterize and compare bodies on the basis of certain fundamental mechanical experiments. Two bodies of the same mass, for example, will be attracted by the earth in the same manner; they will also offer the same resistance to a change in translational motion.

A *force* represents the action of one body on another. It may be exerted by actual contact or at a distance, as in the case of gravitational forces and magnetic forces. A force is characterized by its *point of application*, its *magnitude*, and its *direction*; a force is represented by a *vector* (Sec. 2.3).

In newtonian mechanics, space, time, and mass are absolute concepts, independent of each other. (This is not true in *relativistic mechanics*, where the time of an event depends upon its position, and where the mass of a body varies with its velocity.) On the other hand, the concept of force is not independent of the other three. Indeed, one of the fundamental principles of newtonian mechanics listed below indicates that the resultant force acting on a body is related to the mass of the body and to the manner in which its velocity varies with time.

We shall study the conditions of rest or motion of particles and rigid bodies in terms of the four basic concepts we have introduced. By *particle* we mean a very small amount of matter which may be assumed to occupy a single point in space. A *rigid body* is a combination of a large number of particles occupying fixed positions with respect to each other. The study of the mechanics of particles is obviously a prerequisite to that of rigid bodies. Besides, the results obtained for a particle may be used directly in a large number of problems dealing with the conditions of rest or motion of actual bodies.

The study of elementary mechanics rests on six fundamental principles based on experimental evidence.

The Parallelogram Law for the Addition of Forces. This states that two forces acting on a particle may be replaced by a single force, called their *resultant*, obtained by drawing the diagonal of the parallelogram which has sides equal to the given forces (Sec. 2.2).

The Principle of Transmissibility. This states that the conditions of equilibrium or of motion of a rigid body will remain unchanged if a force acting at a given point of the rigid body is replaced by a force of the same magnitude and same direction, but acting at a different point, provided that the two forces have the same line of action (Sec. 3.3).

Newton's Three Fundamental Laws. Formulated by Sir Isaac Newton in the latter part of the seventeenth century, these laws may be stated as follows:

FIRST LAW. If the resultant force acting on a particle is zero, the particle will remain at rest (if originally at rest) or will move with constant speed in a straight line (if originally in motion) (Sec. 2.10).

SECOND LAW. If the resultant force acting on a particle is not zero, the particle will have an acceleration proportional to the magnitude of the resultant and in the direction of this resultant force.

As we shall see in Sec. 12.2, this law may be stated as

$$\mathbf{F} = m\mathbf{a} \tag{1.1}$$

where $\mathbf{F}$, m, and $\mathbf{a}$ represent, respectively, the resultant force acting on the particle, the mass of the particle, and the acceleration of the particle, expressed in a consistent system of units.

THIRD LAW. The forces of action and reaction between bodies in contact have the same magnitude, same line of action, and opposite sense (Sec. 6.1).

Newton's Law of Gravitation. This states that two particles of mass M and m are mutually attracted with equal and opposite force $\mathbf{F}$ and $-\mathbf{F}$ (Fig. 1.1) of magnitude F given by the formula

$$F = G\frac{Mm}{r^2} \tag{1.2}$$

where r = distance between the two particles

$\quad\quad G$ = universal constant called the *constant of gravitation*

Fig. 1.1

Newton's law of gravitation introduces the idea of an action exerted at a distance and extends the range of application of Newton's third law: the action $\mathbf{F}$ and the reaction $-\mathbf{F}$ in Fig. 1.1 are equal and opposite, and they have the same line of action.

A particular case of great importance is that of the attraction of the earth on a particle located on its surface. The force $\mathbf{F}$ exerted by the earth on the particle is then defined as the *weight* $\mathbf{W}$ of the particle. Taking M equal to the mass of the earth, m equal to the mass of the particle, and r equal to the radius R of the earth, and introducing the constant

$$g = \frac{GM}{R^2} \tag{1.3}$$

the magnitude W of the weight of a particle of mass m may be expressed as†

$$W = mg \tag{1.4}$$

The value of R in formula (1.3) depends upon the elevation of the point considered; it also depends upon its latitude, since the earth is not truly spherical. The value of g therefore varies with the position of the point considered. As long as the point actually remains on the surface of the earth, it is sufficiently accurate in most engineering computations to assume that g equals 9.81 m/s^2.

---

†A more accurate definition of the weight $\mathbf{W}$ should take into account the rotation of the earth.

The principles we have just listed will be introduced in the course of our study of mechanics as they are needed. The study of the statics of particles, carried out in Chap. 2, will be based on the parallelogram law of addition and on Newton's first law alone. The principle of transmissibility will be introduced in Chap. 3 as we begin the study of the statics of rigid bodies, and Newton's third law in Chap. 6 as we analyze the forces exerted on each other by the various members forming a structure. It should be noted that the four aforementioned principles underlie the entire study of the statics of particles, rigid bodies, and systems of rigid bodies. In the study of dynamics, Newton's second law and Newton's law of gravitation will be introduced. It will then be shown that Newton's first law is a particular case of Newton's second law (Sec. 12.2) and that the principle of transmissibility could be derived from the other principles and thus eliminated (Sec. 16.5). In the meantime, however, Newton's first and third laws, the parallelogram law of addition, and the principle of transmissibility will provide us with the necessary and sufficient foundation for the study of the entire field of statics.

As noted earlier, the six fundamental principles listed above are based on experimental evidence. Except for Newton's first law and the principle of transmissibility, they are independent principles which cannot be derived mathematically from each other or from any other elementary physical principle. On these principles rests most of the intricate structure of newtonian mechanics. For more than two centuries a tremendous number of problems dealing with the conditions of rest and motion of rigid bodies, deformable bodies, and fluids have been solved by applying these fundamental principles. Many of the solutions obtained could be checked experimentally, thus providing a further verification of the principles from which they were derived. It is only recently that Newton's mechanics was found at fault, in the study of the motion of atoms and in the study of the motion of certain planets, where it must be supplemented by the theory of relativity. But on the human or engineering scale, where velocities are small compared with the velocity of light, Newton's mechanics has yet to be disproved.

1.3. International System of Units (SI Units†). With the four fundamental concepts introduced in the preceding section are associated the so-called *kinetic units*, i.e., the units of *length*, *time*, *mass*, and *force*. These units cannot be chosen independently if Eq. (1.1) is to be satisfied. Three of the units may be defined arbitrarily; they are

† SI stands for *Système International d'Unités* (French).

then referred to as *base units*. The fourth unit, however, must be chosen in accordance with Eq. (1.1) and is referred to as a *derived unit*. Kinetic units selected in that way are said to form a *consistent system of units*.

In this text, we shall use exclusively the **International System of Units** in which the base units are the units of length, mass, and time, and are called, respectively, the *metre* (m), the *kilogram* (kg), and the *second* (s). All three are arbitrarily defined. The second, which is supposed to represent the 1/86 400 part of the mean solar day, is actually defined as the duration of 9 192 631 770 cycles of the radiation associated with a specified transition of the cesium atom. The metre, originally intended to represent one-ten-millionth of the distance from the equator to the pole, is now defined as 1 650 763.73 wavelengths of the orange-red line of krypton 86. The kilogram, which is approximately equal to the mass of 0.001 m^3 of water, is actually defined as the mass of a platinum standard kept at the International Bureau of Weights and Measures at Sèvres, near Paris, France. The unit of force is a derived unit. It is called the *newton* (N) and is defined as the force which gives an acceleration of 1 m/s^2 to a mass of 1 kg (Fig. 1.2). From Eq. (1.1) we write

Fig. 1.2

$$1 \text{ N} = (1 \text{ kg})(1 \text{ m/s}^2) = 1 \text{ kg} \cdot \text{m/s}^2 \qquad (1.5)$$

The SI units are said to form an *absolute* system of units. This means that the three base units chosen are independent of the location where measurements are made. The metre, the kilogram, and the second may be used anywhere on the earth; they may even be used on another planet. They will always have the same significance.

The *weight* of a body, or *force of gravity* exerted on that body, should, like any other force, be expressed in newtons. From Eq. (1.4) it follows that the weight of a body of mass 1 kg (Fig. 1.3) is

Fig. 1.3

$$\begin{aligned} W &= mg \\ &= (1 \text{ kg})(9.81 \text{ m/s}^2) \\ &= 9.81 \text{ N} \end{aligned}$$

Table 1.1 SI Prefixes

Multiplication Factor	Prefix†	Symbol
$1\ 000\ 000\ 000\ 000 = 10^{12}$	tera	T
$1\ 000\ 000\ 000 = 10^{9}$	giga	G
$1\ 000\ 000 = 10^{6}$	mega	M
$1\ 000 = 10^{3}$	kilo	k
$100 = 10^{2}$	hecto‡	h
$10 = 10^{1}$	deka‡	da
$0.1 = 10^{-1}$	deci‡	d
$0.01 = 10^{-2}$	centi‡	c
$0.001 = 10^{-3}$	milli	m
$0.000\ 001 = 10^{-6}$	micro	μ
$0.000\ 000\ 001 = 10^{-9}$	nano	n
$0.000\ 000\ 000\ 001 = 10^{-12}$	pico	p
$0.000\ 000\ 000\ 000\ 001 = 10^{-15}$	femto	f
$0.000\ 000\ 000\ 000\ 000\ 001 = 10^{-18}$	atto	a

†The first syllable of every prefix is accented so that the prefix will retain its identity. Thus, the preferred pronunication of kilometre places the accent on the first syllable, not the second.

‡The use of thse prefixes should be avoided, except for the measurement of areas and volumes and for the nontechnical use of centimetre, as for body and clothing measurements.

Multiples and submultiples of the fundamental SI units may be obtained through the use of the prefixes defined in Table 1.1. The multiples and submultiples of the units of length, mass, and force most frequently used in engineering are, respectively, the *kilometre* (km) and the *millimetre* (mm); the *megagram*† (Mg) and the *gram* (g); and the *kilonewton* (kN). According to Table 1.1, we have

$$1 \text{ km} = 1000 \text{ m} \qquad 1 \text{ mm} = 0.001 \text{ m}$$
$$1 \text{ Mg} = 1000 \text{ kg} \qquad 1 \text{ g} = 0.001 \text{ kg}$$
$$1 \text{ kN} = 1000 \text{ N}$$

The conversion of these units into metres, kilograms, and newtons, respectively, can be effected by simply moving the decimal point three places to the right or to the left. For example, to convert 3.82 km into metres, one moves the decimal point three places to the right:

$$3.82 \text{ km} = 3820 \text{ m}$$

†Also known as a *tonne*.

Similarly, 47.2 mm is converted into metres by moving the decimal point three places to the left:

$$47.2 \text{ mm} = 0.0472 \text{ m}$$

Using the scientific notation, one may also write

$$3.82 \text{ km} = 3.82 \times 10^3 \text{ m}$$
$$47.2 \text{ mm} = 47.2 \times 10^{-3} \text{ m}$$

The multiples of the unit of time are the *minute* (min) and the *hour* (h). Since

$$1 \text{ min} = 60 \text{ s} \quad \text{and} \quad 1 \text{ h} = 60 \text{ min} = 3600 \text{ s}$$

these multiples cannot be converted as readily as the others.

By using the appropriate multiple or submultiple of a given unit, one may avoid writing very large or very small numbers. For example, one usually writes 427.2 km rather than 427 200 m, and 2.16 mm rather than 0.002 16 m.†

Units of Area and Volume. The unit of area is the *square metre* (m^2), which represents the area of a square of side 1 m; the unit of volume is the *cubic metre* (m^3), equal to the volume of a cube of side 1 m. In order to avoid exceedingly small or large numerical values in the computation of areas and volumes, one uses systems of subunits obtained by respectively squaring and cubing not only the millimetre but also two intermediate submultiples of the metre, namely, the *decimetre* (dm) and the *centimetre* (cm). Since, by definition,

$$1 \text{ dm} = 0.1 \text{ m} = 10^{-1} \text{ m}$$
$$1 \text{ cm} = 0.01 \text{ m} = 10^{-2} \text{ m}$$
$$1 \text{ mm} = 0.001 \text{ m} = 10^{-3} \text{ m}$$

---

† It should be noted that when more than four digits are used on either side of the decimal point to express a quantity in SI units — as in 427 200 m or 0.002 16 m — spaces, never commas, should be used to separate the digits into groups of three. This is to avoid confusion with the comma which is used in many countries in place of a decimal point.

the submultiples of the unit of area are

$$1 \text{ dm}^2 = (1 \text{ dm})^2 = (10^{-1} \text{ m})^2 = 10^{-2} \text{ m}^2$$
$$1 \text{ cm}^2 = (1 \text{ cm})^2 = (10^{-2} \text{ m})^2 = 10^{-4} \text{ m}^2$$
$$1 \text{ mm}^2 = (1 \text{ mm})^2 = (10^{-3} \text{ m})^2 = 10^{-6} \text{ m}^2$$

and the submultiples of the unit of volume are

$$1 \text{ dm}^3 = (1 \text{ dm})^3 = (10^{-1} \text{ m})^3 = 10^{-3} \text{ m}^3$$
$$1 \text{ cm}^3 = (1 \text{ cm})^3 = (10^{-2} \text{ m})^3 = 10^{-6} \text{ m}^3$$
$$1 \text{ mm}^3 = (1 \text{ mm})^3 = (10^{-3} \text{ m})^3 = 10^{-9} \text{ m}^3$$

It should be noted that when the volume of a liquid is being measured, the cubic decimetre (dm^3) is usually referred to as a *litre* (L).

Other derived SI units used to measure the moment of a force, the work of a force, etc., are shown in Table 1.2. While these units will be introduced in later chapters as they are needed, we should note an important rule at this time: When a derived unit is obtained by dividing a base unit by another base unit, a prefix may be used in the numerator of the derived unit but not in its denominator. For example, the constant k of a spring which stretches 20 mm under a load of 100 N will be expressed as

$$k = \frac{100 \text{ N}}{20 \text{ mm}} = \frac{100 \text{ N}}{0.020 \text{ m}} = 500 \text{ N/m} \qquad \text{or} \qquad k = 5 \text{ kN/m}$$

but never as $k = 5$ N/mm.

Table 1.2 Principal SI Units Used in Mechanics

Quantity	Unit	Symbol	Formula
Acceleration	Metre per second squared	. . .	m/s^2
Angle	Radian	rad	†
Angular acceleration	Radian per second squared	. . .	rad/s^2
Angular velocity	Radian per second	. . .	rad/s
Area	Square metre	. . .	m^2
Density	Kilogram per cubic metre	. . .	kg/m^3
Energy	Joule	J	$N \cdot m$
Force	Newton	N	$kg \cdot m/s^2$
Frequency	Hertz	Hz	s^{-1} /s
Impulse	Newton-second	. . .	$kg \cdot m/s$
Length	Metre	m	‡
Mass	Kilogram	kg	‡
Moment of a force	Newton-metre	. . .	$N \cdot m$
Power	Watt	W	J/s
Pressure	Pascal	Pa	N/m^2
Stress	Pascal	Pa	N/m^2
Time	Second	s	‡
Velocity	Metre per second	. . .	m/s
Volume, solids	Cubic metre	. . .	m^3
Liquids	Litre	L	$10^{-3} m^3$
Work	Joule	J	$N \cdot m$

†Supplementary unit (1 revolution = 2π rad = 360°).
‡Base unit.

1.4. Method of Problem Solution.   The student should approach a problem in mechanics as he would approach an actual engineering situation. By drawing on his own experience and on his intuition, he will find it easier to understand and formulate the problem. Once the problem has been clearly stated, however, there is no place in its solution for the student's particular fancy. *The solution must be based on the six fundamental principles stated in Sec. 1.2 or on theorems derived from them.* Every step taken must be justified on that basis. Strict rules must be followed, which lead to the solution in an almost automatic fashion, leaving no room for the student's intuition or "feeling." After an answer has been obtained, it should be checked. Here again, the student may call upon his common sense and personal experience. If not completely satisfied with the result obtained, he should carefully check his formulation of the problem, the validity of the methods used for its solution, and the accuracy of his computations.

The *statement* of a problem should be clear and precise. It should contain the given data and indicate what information is required. A neat drawing showing all quantities involved should be included. Separate diagrams should be drawn for all bodies involved, indicating clearly the forces acting on each body. These diagrams are known as *free-body diagrams* and are described in details in Secs. 2.11 and 4.2.

The *fundamental principles* of mechanics listed in Sec. 1.2 *will be used to write equations* expressing the conditions of rest or motion of the bodies considered. Each equation should be clearly related to one of the free-body diagrams. The student will then proceed to solve the problem observing strictly the usual rules of algebra and recording neatly the various steps taken.

After the answer has been obtained, it should be *carefully checked*. Mistakes in *reasoning* may often be detected by checking the units. For example, to determine the moment of a force of 50 N about a point 0.6 m from its line of action, we would have written (Sec. 3.12)

$$M = Fd = (50 \text{ N})(0.60 \text{ m}) = 30 \text{ N} \cdot \text{m}$$

The unit N · m obtained by multiplying newtons by metres is the correct unit for the moment of a force; if another unit had been obtained, we would have known that some mistake had been made.

Errors in *computation* will usually be found by substituting the numerical values obtained into an equation which has not yet been used and verifying that the equation is satisfied. The importance of correct computations in engineering cannot be overemphasized.

1.5. Numerical Accuracy. The accuracy of the solution of a problem depends upon two items: (1) the accuracy of the given data; (2) the accuracy of the computations performed.

The solution cannot be more accurate than the less accurate of these two items. For example, if the loading of a bridge is known to be 300 kN with a possible error of 400 N either way, the relative error which measures the degree of accuracy of the data is

$$\frac{400 \text{ N}}{300 \times 10^3 \text{ N}} = 0.0013 = 0.13 \text{ percent}$$

In computing the reaction at one of the bridge supports, it would then be meaningless to record it as 57.288 kN. The accuracy of the solution cannot be greater than 0.13 percent, no matter how accurate the computations are, and the possible error in the answer may be as large as $(0.13/100)$ $(57.288 \text{ kN}) \simeq 0.08 \text{ kN}$. The answer should be properly recorded as $57.29/\text{kN} \pm 0.08 \text{ kN}$.

In engineering problems, the data are seldom known with an accuracy greater than 0.2 percent. It is therefore seldom justified to write the answers to such problems with an accuracy greater than 0.2 percent. A practical rule is to use 4 figures to record numbers beginning with a "1" and 3 figures in all other cases. Unless otherwise indicated, the data given in a problem should be assumed known with a comparable degree of accuracy. A force of 40 N, for example, should be read 40.0 N, and a force of 15 N should be read 15.00 N.

Pocket electronic calculators are widely used by practicing engineers and engineering students. The speed and accuracy of these calculators facilitates the numerical computations in the solution of many problems. However, the student should not record more significant figures than can be justified, merely because they are easily obtained. As noted above, an accuracy greater than 0.2 percent is seldom necessary or meaningful in the solution of practical engineering problems.

Statics of Particles

2.1. Introduction. In this chapter we shall study the effect of forces acting on particles. First we shall learn how to replace two or more forces acting on a given particle by a single force having the same effect as the original forces. This single equivalent force is the *resultant* of the original forces acting on the particle. Later we shall derive the relations which exist among the various forces acting on a particle in a state of *equilibrium* and use these relations to determine some of the forces acting on the particle.

The use of the word "particle" does not imply that we shall restrict our study to that of small corpuscles. What it means is that the size and shape of the bodies under consideration will not significantly affect the solution of the problems treated in this chapter, and that all the forces acting on a given body will be assumed applied at the same point. Since such an assumption is verified in many practical applications, we shall be able to solve a number of engineering problems in this chapter.

The first part of the chapter is devoted to the study of forces contained in a single plane, and the second part to the analysis of forces in three-dimensional space.

FORCES IN A PLANE

2.2. Force on a Particle. Resultant of Two Forces. A force represents the action of one body on another and is generally characterized by its *point of application,* its *magnitude,* and its *direction.* Forces acting on a given particle, however, have the same point of application. Each force considered in this chapter will thus be completely defined by its magnitude and direction.

The magnitude of a force is characterized by a certain number of units. As indicated in Chap. 1, the SI units used by engineers to measure the magnitude of a force are the newton (N) and its multiple the kilonewton (kN), equal to 1000 N. The direction of a force is defined by the *line of action* and the *sense* of the force. The line of action is the infinite straight line along which the force acts; it is characterized by the angle it forms with some fixed axis (Fig. 2.1). The force itself is represented by a segment of that line; through the use of an appropriate scale, the length of this segment may be chosen to represent the magnitude of the force. Finally, the sense of the force should be indicated by an arrowhead. It is important in defining a force to indicate its sense. Two forces, such as those shown in Fig. 2.1*a* and *b*, having the same magnitude and the same line of action but different sense, will have directly opposite effects on a particle.

Experimental evidence shows that two forces **P** and **Q** acting on a particle *A* (Fig. 2.2*a*) may be replaced by a single force **R** which has the same effect on the particle (Fig. 2.2*c*). This force is called the *resultant* of the forces **P** and **Q** and may be obtained, as shown in Fig. 2.2*b*, by constructing a parallelogram, using **P** and **Q** as two sides of the parallelogram. *The diagonal that passes through A represents the resultant.* This is known as the *parallelogram law* for the addition of two forces. This law is based on experimental evidence; it cannot be proved or derived mathematically.

2.3. Vectors. It appears from the above that forces do not obey the rules of addition defined in ordinary arithmetic or algebra. For example, two forces acting at a right angle to each other, one of 4 N and the other of 3 N, add up to a force of 5 N, *not* to a force of 7 N. Forces are not the only expressions which follow the parallelogram law of addition. As we shall see later, *displacements, velocities, accelerations, momenta* are other examples of physical quantities possessing magnitude and direction and which are added according to the parallelogram law. All these quantities may be represented mathematically by *vectors*, while those physical quantities which do not have direction, such as *volume, mass,* or *energy,* are represented by ordinary numbers or *scalars.*

Vectors are defined as *mathematical expressions possessing magnitude and direction, which add according to the parallelogram law.* Vectors are represented by arrows in the illustrations and will be distinguished from scalar quantities in this text through the use of boldface type (**P**). In longhand writing, a vector may be characterized by drawing a short arrow above the letter used to represent it ($\vec{P}$), or by underlining the letter ($\underline{P}$). The last method may be preferred since it can also be used on a typewriter. The magnitude of a vector defines the length of the arrow used to represent the vector. In this text, italic type will be used to denote the magnitude of a vector. Thus, the magnitude of the vector **P** will be referred to as *P.*

A vector used to represent a force acting on a given particle has a well-defined point of application, namely, the particle itself. Such a vector is said to be a *fixed,* or *bound,* vector and cannot be moved without modifying the conditions of the problem. Other physical quantities, however, such as couples (see Chap. 3), are represented by vectors which may be freely moved in space; these vectors are called *free* vectors. Still other

(a)

(b)

Fig. 2.1

(a)

(b)

(c)

Fig. 2.2

Fig. 2.4

Fig. 2.5

−P

P + Q

P

Q

A

Fig. 2.6

physical quantities, such as forces acting on a rigid body (see Chap. 3), are represented by vectors which may be moved, or slid, along their line of action; they are known as *sliding* vectors.†

Two vectors which have the same magnitude and the same direction are said to be *equal*, whether or not they also have the same point of application (Fig. 2.4); equal vectors may be denoted by the same letter.

The *negative vector* of a given vector **P** is defined as a vector having the same magnitude as **P** and a direction opposite to that of **P** (Fig. 2.5); the negative of the vector **P** is denoted by −**P**. The vectors **P** and −**P** are commonly referred to as *equal and opposite* vectors. Clearly, we have

$$\mathbf{P} + (-\mathbf{P}) = 0$$

2.4. Addition of Vectors. We saw in the preceding section that, by definition, vectors add according to the parallelogram law. Thus the sum of two vectors **P** and **Q** is obtained by attaching the two vectors to the same point *A* and constructing a parallelogram, using **P** and **Q** as two sides of the parallelogram (Fig. 2.6). The diagonal that passes through *A* represents the sum of the vectors **P** and **Q**, and this sum is denoted by **P** + **Q**. The fact that the sign + is used to denote both vector and scalar addition should not cause any confusion if vector and scalar quantities are always carefully distinguished. Thus, we should note that the magnitude of the vector **P** + **Q** is *not*, in general, equal to the sum *P* + *Q* of the magnitudes of the vectors **P** and **Q**.

Since the parallelogram constructed on the vectors **P** and **Q** does not depend upon the order in which **P** and **Q** are selected, we conclude that the addition of two vectors is *commutative,* and we write

$$\mathbf{P} + \mathbf{Q} = \mathbf{Q} + \mathbf{P} \tag{2.1}$$

† Some expressions have magnitude and direction, but do not add according to the parallelogram law. While these expressions may be represented by arrows, they *cannot* be considered as vectors.

A group of such expressions are the finite rotations of a rigid body. Place a closed book on a table in front of you, so that it lies in the usual fashion, with its front cover up and its binding to the left. Now rotate it through 180° about an axis parallel to the binding (Fig. 2.3a); this rotation may be represented by an arrow of length equal to 180 units and oriented as shown. Picking up the book as it lies in its new position, rotate it now through 180° about a horizontal

180°

(a)

180°

(b)

Fig. 2.3 Finite rotations of a rigid body.

From the parallelogram law, we can derive an alternate method for determining the sum of two vectors. This method, known as the *triangle rule*, is derived as follows: Consider Fig. 2.6, where the sum of the vectors **P** and **Q** has been determined by the parallelogram law. Since the side of the parallelogram opposite **Q** is equal to **Q** in magnitude and direction, we could draw only half of the parallelogram (Fig. 2.7a). The sum of the two vectors may thus be found by *arranging* **P** *and* **Q** *in tip-to-tail fashion and then connecting the tail of* **P** *with the tip of* **Q**. In Fig. 2.7b, the other half of the parallelogram is considered, and the same result is obtained. This confirms the fact that vector addition is commutative.

The *subtraction* of a vector is defined as the addition of the corresponding negative vector. Thus, the vector **P** − **Q** representing the difference between the vectors **P** and **Q** is obtained by adding to **P** the negative vector −**Q** (Fig. 2.8). We write

$$\mathbf{P} - \mathbf{Q} = \mathbf{P} + (-\mathbf{Q}) \qquad (2.2)$$

Here again we should observe that, while the same sign is used to denote both vector and scalar subtraction, confusion will be avoided if care is taken to distinguish between vector and scalar quantities.

We shall now consider the *sum of three or more vectors*. The sum of three vectors **P**, **Q**, and **S** will, *by definition*, be obtained by first adding the vectors **P** and **Q**, and then adding the vector **S** to the vector **P** + **Q**. We thus write

$$\mathbf{P} + \mathbf{Q} + \mathbf{S} = (\mathbf{P} + \mathbf{Q}) + \mathbf{S} \qquad (2.3)$$

Similarly, the sum of four vectors will be obtained by adding the fourth vector to the sum of the first three. It follows that the sum of any number of vectors may be obtained by applying repeatedly the parallelogram law to successive pairs of vectors until all the given vectors are replaced by a single vector.

Fig. 2.7

Fig. 2.8

axis perpendicular to the binding (Fig. 2.3b); this second rotation may be represented by an arrow 180 units long and oriented as shown. But the book could have been placed in this final position through a single 180° rotation about a vertical axis (Fig. 2.3c). We conclude that the sum of the two 180° rotations represented by arrows directed respectively along the z and x axes is a 180° rotation represented by an arrow directed along the y axis (Fig. 2.3d). Clearly, the finite rotations of a rigid body *do not* obey the parallelogram law of addition; therefore they *cannot* be represented by vectors.

Fig. 2.9

Fig. 2.10

Fig. 2.11

Fig. 2.12

Fig. 2.13

If the given vectors are *coplanar*, i.e., if they are contained in the same plane, their sum may be easily obtained graphically. In that case, the repeated application of the triangle rule will be preferred to the application of the parallelogram law. In Fig. 2.9 the sum of three vectors **P**, **Q**, and **S** was obtained in that manner. The triangle rule was first applied to obtain the sum **P** + **Q** of the vectors **P** and **Q**; it was applied again to obtain the sum of the vectors **P** + **Q** and **S**. The determination of the vector **P** + **Q**, however, could have been omitted and the sum of the three vectors could have been obtained directly, as shown in Fig. 2.10, by *arranging the given vectors in tip-to-tail fashion and connecting the tail of the first vector with the tip of the last one.* This is known as the *polygon rule* for the addition of vectors.

We observe that the result obtained would have been unchanged if, as shown in Fig. 2.11, the vectors **Q** and **S** had been replaced by their sum **Q** + **S**. We may thus write

$$\mathbf{P} + \mathbf{Q} + \mathbf{S} = (\mathbf{P} + \mathbf{Q}) + \mathbf{S} = \mathbf{P} + (\mathbf{Q} + \mathbf{S}) \tag{2.4}$$

which expresses the fact that vector addition is *associative*. Recalling that vector addition has also been shown, in the case of two vectors, to be commutative, we write

$$\begin{aligned}
\mathbf{P} + \mathbf{Q} + \mathbf{S} &= (\mathbf{P} + \mathbf{Q}) + \mathbf{S} = \mathbf{S} + (\mathbf{P} + \mathbf{Q}) \\
&= \mathbf{S} + (\mathbf{Q} + \mathbf{P}) = \mathbf{S} + \mathbf{Q} + \mathbf{P}
\end{aligned} \tag{2.5}$$

This expression, as well as others which may be obtained in the same way, shows that the order in which several vectors are added together is immaterial (Fig. 2.12).

Product of a Scalar and a Vector. Since it is convenient to denote the sum **P** + **P** by 2**P**, the sum **P** + **P** + **P** by 3**P**, and, in general, the sum of n equal vectors **P** by the product n**P**, we shall define the product n**P** of a positive integer n and a vector **P** as a vector having the same direction as **P** and the magnitude nP. Extending this definition to include all scalars, and recalling the definition of a negative vector given in Sec. 2.3, we define the product k**P** of a scalar k and a vector **P** as a vector having the same direction as **P** (if k is positive), or a direction opposite to that of **P** (if k is negative), and a magnitude equal to the product of P and of the absolute value of k (Fig. 2.13).

2.5. Resultant of Several Concurrent Forces. Consider a particle A acted upon by several coplanar forces, i.e., by several forces contained in the same plane (Fig. 2.14*a*). Since the forces considered here all pass through A, they are also said to be *concurrent*. The vectors representing the forces acting on A may be added by the polygon rule (Fig. 2.14*b*). Since the use of the polygon rule is equivalent to the repeated application of the parallelogram law, the vector **R** thus obtained represents the resultant of the given concurrent forces, i.e., the single force which has

Fig. 2.14

(a)   *(b)*

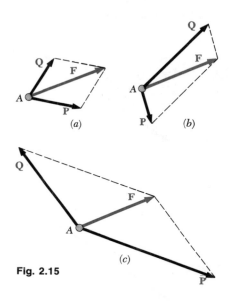

(a)   *(b)*

(c)

Fig. 2.15

the same effect on the particle A as the given forces. As indicated above, the order in which the vectors **P**, **Q**, and **S** representing the given forces are added together is immaterial.

2.6. Resolution of a Force into Components. We have seen that two or more forces acting on a particle may be replaced by a single force which has the same effect on the particle. Conversely, a single force **F** acting on a particle may be replaced by two or more forces which, together, have the same effect on the particle. These forces are called the *components* of the original force **F**, and the process of substituting them for **F** is called *resolving the force **F** into components*.

Clearly, for each force **F** there exist an infinite number of possible sets of components. Sets of *two components* **P** *and* **Q** are the most important as far as practical applications are concerned. But, even then, the number of ways in which a given force **F** may be resolved into two components is unlimited (Fig. 2.15). Two cases are of particular interest:

1. *One of the Two Components, **P**, Is Known.* The second component, **Q**, is obtained by applying the triangle rule and joining the tip of **P** to the tip of **F** (Fig. 2.16); the magnitude and direction of **Q** are determined graphically or by trigonometry. Once **Q** has been determined, both components **P** and **Q** should be applied at A.

2. *The Line of Action of Each Component Is Known.* The magnitude and sense of the components are obtained by applying the parallelogram law and drawing lines, through the tip of **F**, parallel to the given lines of action (Fig. 2.17). This process leads to two well-defined components, **P** and **Q**, which may be determined graphically, or trigonometrically, by applying the law of sines.

Many other cases may be encountered; for example, the direction of one component may be known while the magnitude of the other component is to be as small as possible (see Sample Prob. 2.2). In all cases the appropriate triangle or parallelogram is drawn, which satisfies the given conditions.

Fig. 2.16

Fig. 2.17

SAMPLE PROBLEM 2.1

The two forces **P** and **Q** act on a bolt A. Determine their resultant.

Graphical Solution. A parallelogram with sides equal to **P** and **Q** is drawn to scale. The magnitude and direction of the resultant are measured and found to be

$$R = 98 \text{ N} \qquad \alpha = 35° \qquad R = 98 \text{ N} \angle 35° \quad \blacktriangleleft$$

The triangle rule may also be used. Forces **P** and **Q** are drawn in tip-to-tail fashion. Again the magnitude and direction of the resultant are measured.

$$R = 98 \text{ N} \qquad \alpha = 35° \qquad R = 98 \text{ N} \angle 35° \quad \blacktriangleleft$$

Trigonometric Solution. The triangle rule is again used; two sides and the included angle are known. We apply the law of cosines.

$$R^2 = P^2 + Q^2 - 2PQ \cos B$$
$$R^2 = (40 \text{ N})^2 + (60 \text{ N})^2 - 2(40 \text{ N})(60 \text{ N}) \cos 155°$$
$$R = 97.73 \text{ N}$$

Now, applying the law of sines, we write

$$\frac{\sin A}{Q} = \frac{\sin B}{R} \qquad \frac{\sin A}{60 \text{ N}} = \frac{\sin 155°}{97.73 \text{ N}} \tag{1}$$

Solving Eq. (1) for $\sin A$, we have

$$\sin A = \frac{(60 \text{ N}) \sin 155°}{97.73 \text{ N}}$$

Using a calculator, we first compute the quotient, then its arc sine, and obtain

$$A = 15.04° \qquad \alpha = 20° + A = 35.04°$$

We use 3 significant figures to record the answer (cf. Sec. 1.6):

$$R = 97.7 \text{ N} \angle 35.0° \quad \blacktriangleleft$$

Alternate Trigonometric Solution. We construct the right triangle BCD and compute

$$CD = (60 \text{ N}) \sin 25° = 25.36 \text{ N}$$
$$BD = (60 \text{ N}) \cos 25° = 54.38 \text{ N}$$

Then, using triangle ACD, we obtain

$$\tan A = \frac{25.36 \text{ N}}{94.38 \text{ N}} \qquad A = 15.04°$$

$$R = \frac{25.36}{\sin A} \qquad R = 97.73 \text{ N}$$

Again, $\qquad \alpha = 20° + A = 35.04° \qquad R = 97.7 \text{ N} \angle 35.0° \quad \blacktriangleleft$

SAMPLE PROBLEM 2.2

A barge is pulled by two tugboats. If the resultant of the forces exerted by the tugboats is a 25 kN force directed along the axis of the barge, determine (a) the tension in each of the ropes, knowing that $\alpha = 45°$, (b) the value of α such that the tension in rope 2 is minimum.

a. **Tension for $\alpha = 45°$.** *Graphical Solution.* The parallelogram law is used; the diagonal (resultant) is known to be equal to 25 kN and to be directed to the right. The sides are drawn parallel to the ropes. If the drawing is done to scale, we measure

$$T_1 = 18.50 \text{ kN} \qquad T_2 = 13.00 \text{ kN} \blacktriangleleft$$

Trigonometric Solution. The triangle rule may be used. We note that the triangle shown represents half of the parallelogram shown above. Using the law of sines, we write

$$\frac{T_1}{\sin 45°} = \frac{T_2}{\sin 30°} = \frac{25 \text{ kN}}{\sin 105°}$$

With a calculator, we first compute and store the value of the last quotient. Multiplying this value successively by sin 45° and sin 30°, we obtain

$$T_1 = 18.30 \text{ kN} \qquad T_2 = 12.94 \text{ kN} \blacktriangleleft$$

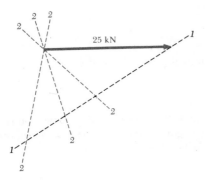

b. **Value of α for Minimum T_2.** To determine the value of α such that the tension in rope 2 is minimum, the triangle rule is again used. In the sketch shown, line *1-1* is the known direction of $\mathbf{T}_1$. Several possible directions of $\mathbf{T}_2$ are shown by the lines 2-2. We note that the minimum value of T_2 occurs when $\mathbf{T}_1$ and $\mathbf{T}_2$ are perpendicular. The minimum value of T_2 is

$$T_2 = (25 \text{ kN}) \sin 30° = 12.50 \text{ kN}$$

Corresponding values of T_1 and α are

$$T_1 = (25 \text{ kN}) \cos 30° = 21.7 \text{ kN}$$
$$\alpha = 90° - 30° \qquad\qquad \alpha = 60° \blacktriangleleft$$

22

2.1 and 2.2 Determine graphically the magnitude and direction of the resultant of the two forces shown, using (a) the parallelogram law, (b) the triangle rule.

Fig. P2.1

Fig. P2.2

2.3 Two structural members B and C are bolted to bracket A. Knowing that both members are in tension and that $P = 10$ kN and $Q = 15$ kN, determine graphically the magnitude and direction of the resultant force exerted on the bracket.

2.4 Two structural members B and C are bolted to bracket A. Knowing that both members are in tension and that $P = 30$ kN and $Q = 20$ kN, determine graphically the magnitude and direction of the resultant force exerted on the bracket.

Fig. P2.3 and P2.4

2.5 Solve Prob. 2.3, assuming that $P = 15$ kN and $Q = 12$ kN.

2.6 The force **F** of magnitude 1500 N is to be resolved into two components along lines a-a and b-b. Determine by trigonometry the angle α, knowing that the component of **F** along line a-a is to be 1200 N.

Fig. P2.6 and P2.7

2.7 The force **F** of magnitude 240 N is to be resolved into two components along lines a-a and b-b. Determine by trigonometry the angle α, knowing that the component of **F** along line b-b is to be 90 N.

2.8 A trolley which moves along a horizontal beam is acted upon by two forces as shown. (*a*) Knowing that $\alpha = 25°$, determine by trigonometry the magnitude of the force **P** so that the resultant force exerted on the trolley is vertical. (*b*) What is the corresponding magnitude of the resultant?

a) 3660
b) 3730

15°

A

1600 N

α

P

Fig. P2.8 and P2.13

2.9 A disabled automobile is pulled by means of two ropes as shown. The tension in *AB* is 2500 N and the angle α is 25°. Knowing that the resultant of the two forces applied at *A* is directed along the axis of the automobile, determine by trigonometry (*a*) the tension in rope *AC*, (*b*) the magnitude of the resultant of the two forces applied at *A*.

$\frac{2500}{30} = \frac{a}{\sin 25}$

B

30°

A

α

C

Fig. P2.9 and P2.12

$\frac{A}{\sin 30} = \frac{C}{\sin 20}$

2.10 Solve Prob. 2.9, assuming that the tension in rope *AB* is 4 kN and that $\alpha = 20°$.

a) 8.85
b) 8.96

2.11 Solve Prob. 2.8, assuming that $\alpha = 35°$

2.12 A disabled automobile is pulled by means of two ropes as shown. Knowing that the tension in rope *AB* is 3750 N, determine by trigonometry the tension in rope *AC* and the value of α so that the resultant force exerted at *A* is a 6000-N force directed along the axis of the automobile.

3330 and 34.3

2.13 A trolley which moves along a horizontal beam is acted upon by two forces as shown. Determine by trigonometry the magnitude and direction of the force **P** so that the resultant is a vertical force of 2500 N.

2.14 Solve Prob. 2.2 by trigonometry.

2.15 Determine by trigonometry the magnitude and direction of the resultant of the two forces shown.

2.16 If the resultant of the two forces exerted on the trolley of Prob. 2.8 is to be vertical, determine (*a*) the value of α for which the magnitude of **P** is minimum, (*b*) the corresponding magnitude of *P*.

a) 90°
b) 1545

25° 45° 1500 N

1000 N

Fig. P2.15

Fig. 2.18

Fig. 2.19

Fig. 2.20

Fig. 2.21

2.7. Rectangular Components of a Force. Unit Vectors.† In many problems it will be found desirable to resolve a force into two components which are perpendicular to each other. In Fig. 2.18, the force **F** has been resolved into a component **F**$_x$ along the x axis and a component **F**$_y$ along the y axis. The parallelogram drawn to obtain the two components is a *rectangle*, and **F**$_x$ and **F**$_y$ are called *rectangular components*.

The x and y axes are usually chosen horizontal and vertical, respectively, as in Fig. 2.18; they may, however, be chosen in any two perpendicular directions, as shown in Fig. 2.19. In determining the rectangular components of a force, the student should think of the construction lines shown in Figs. 2.18 and 2.19 as being *parallel* to the x and y axes, rather than *perpendicular* to these axes. This practice will help avoid mistakes in determining *oblique* components as in Sec. 2.6.

We shall, at this point, introduce two vectors of magnitude 1, directed respectively along the positive x and y axes. These vectors are called *unit vectors* and are denoted by **i** and **j**, respectively (Fig. 2.20). Recalling the definition of the product of a scalar and a vector given in Sec. 2.4, we note that the rectangular components **F**$_x$ and **F**$_y$ of a force **F** may be obtained by multiplying respectively the unit vectors **i** and **j** by appropriate scalars (Fig. 2.21). We write

$$\mathbf{F}_x = F_x\mathbf{i} \qquad \mathbf{F}_y = F_y\mathbf{j} \tag{2.6}$$

and

$$\mathbf{F} = F_x\mathbf{i} + F_y\mathbf{j} \tag{2.7}$$

While the scalars F_x and F_y may be positive or negative, depending upon the sense of **F**$_x$ and of **F**$_y$, their absolute values are respectively equal to the magnitudes of the component forces **F**$_x$ and **F**$_y$. The scalars F_x and F_y are called the *scalar components* of the force **F**, while the actual component forces **F**$_x$ and **F**$_y$ should be referred to as the *vector components* of **F**. However, when there exists no possibility of confusion, the vector as well as the scalar components of **F** may be referred to simply as the *components* of **F**. We note that the scalar component F_x is positive when the vector component **F**$_x$ has the same sense as the unit vector **i** (i.e., the same sense as the positive x axis) and negative when **F**$_x$ has the opposite sense. A similar conclusion may be drawn regarding the sign of the scalar component F_y.

Denoting by F the magnitude of the force **F** and by θ the angle between **F** and the x axis, measured counterclockwise from the positive x axis (Fig. 2.21), we may express the scalar components of **F** as follows:

$$F_x = F\cos\theta \qquad F_y = F\sin\theta \tag{2.8}$$

† The properties established in Secs. 2.7 and 2.8 may be readily extended to the rectangular components of any vector quantity.

We note that the relations obtained hold for any value of the angle θ from 0° to 360°, and that they define the signs as well as the absolute values of the scalar components F_x and F_y.

Example 1. A force of 800 N is exerted on a bolt A as shown in Fig. 2.22a. Determine the horizontal and vertical components of the force.

In order to obtain the correct sign for the scalar components F_x and F_y, the value $\theta = 180° - 35° = 145°$ should be substituted for θ in the relations (2.8). However, it will be found more practical to determine by inspection the signs of F_x and of F_y (Fig. 2.22b) and to use the trigonometric functions of the angle $\alpha = 35°$. We write therefore

$$F_x = -F \cos \alpha = -(800 \text{ N}) \cos 35° = -655 \text{ N}$$
$$F_y = +F \sin \alpha = +(800 \text{ N}) \sin 35° = +459 \text{ N}$$

The vector components of $\mathbf{F}$ are thus

$$\mathbf{F}_x = -(655 \text{ N})\mathbf{i} \qquad \mathbf{F}_y = +(459 \text{ N})\mathbf{j}$$

and we may write $\mathbf{F}$ in the form

$$\mathbf{F} = -(655 \text{ N})\mathbf{i} + (459 \text{ N})\mathbf{j}$$

Example 2. A man pulls with a force of 300 N on a rope attached to a building, as shown in Fig. 2.23a. What are the horizontal and vertical components of the force exerted by the rope at point A?

It is seen from Fig. 2.23b that

$$F_x = +(300 \text{ N}) \cos \alpha \qquad F_y = -(300 \text{ N}) \sin \alpha$$

Observing that $AB = 10$ m, we find from Fig. 2.23a

$$\cos \alpha = \frac{8 \text{ m}}{AB} = \frac{8 \text{ m}}{10 \text{ m}} = \frac{4}{5} \qquad \sin \alpha = \frac{6 \text{ m}}{AB} = \frac{6 \text{ m}}{10 \text{ m}} = \frac{3}{5}$$

We thus obtain

$$F_x = +(300 \text{ N})\tfrac{4}{5} = +240 \text{ N} \qquad F_y = -(300 \text{ N})\tfrac{3}{5} = -180 \text{ N}$$

and write

$$\mathbf{F} = (240 \text{ N})\mathbf{i} - (180 \text{ N})\mathbf{j}$$

(a)

(b)

Fig. 2.22

(a)

Fig. 2.23

(b)

Fig. 2.21 *(repeated)*

When a force $\mathbf{F}$ is defined by its rectangular components F_x and F_y (see Fig. 2.21), the angle θ defining its direction can be obtained by writing

$$\tan \theta = \frac{F_y}{F_x} \tag{2.9}$$

The magnitude F of the force may be obtained by applying the Pythagorean theorem and writing

$$F = \sqrt{F_x^2 + F_y^2} \tag{2.10}$$

or by solving one of the formulas (2.8) for F.

Example 3. A force $\mathbf{F} = (3.5 \text{ kN})\mathbf{i} + (7.5 \text{ kN})\mathbf{j}$ is applied to a bolt A. Determine the magnitude of the force and the angle θ it forms with the horizontal.

First we draw a diagram showing the two rectangular components of the force and the angle θ (Fig. 2.24). From Eq. (2.9), we write

$$\tan \theta = \frac{F_y}{F_x} = \frac{7.5 \text{ kN}}{3.5 \text{ kN}}$$

Using a calculator,† we enter 7.5 kN and divide by 3.5 kN; computing the arc tangent of the quotient, we obtain $\theta = 65.0°$. Solving the second of Eqs. (2.8) for F, we have

$$F = \frac{F_y}{\sin \theta} = \frac{7.5 \text{ kN}}{\sin 65.0°} = 8.28 \text{ kN}$$

The last calculation is facilitated if the value of F_y is stored when originally entered; it may then be recalled to be divided by $\sin \theta$.

Fig. 2.24

2.8. Addition of Forces by Summing x and y Components.
It was seen in Sec. 2.2 that forces should be added according to the parallelogram law. From this law, two other methods, more readily applicable to the *graphical* solution of problems, were derived in Secs. 2.4 and 2.5: the triangle rule for the addition of two forces and the polygon rule for the addition of three or more forces. It was also seen that the force triangle used to define the resultant of two forces could be used to obtain a *trigonometric* solution.

When three or more forces are to be added, no practical trigonometric solution may be obtained from the force polygon which defines the resultant of the forces. In this case, an *analytic* solution of the problem may be obtained by resolving each force into two rectangular components. Con-

---

† It is assumed that the calculator used has keys for the computation of trigonometric and inverse trigonometric functions. Some calculators also have keys for the direct conversion of rectangular coordinates into polar coordinates, and vice versa. Such calculators eliminate the need for the computation of trigonometric functions in Examples 1, 2, and 3 and in problems of the same type.

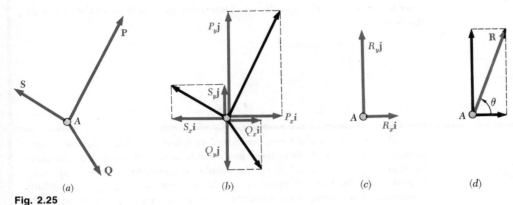

(a) (b) (c) (d)

Fig. 2.25

sider, for instance, three forces $\mathbf{P}$, $\mathbf{Q}$, and $\mathbf{S}$ acting on a particle A (Fig. 2.25a). Their resultant $\mathbf{R}$ is defined by the relation

$$\mathbf{R} = \mathbf{P} + \mathbf{Q} + \mathbf{S} \tag{2.11}$$

Resolving each force into its rectangular components, we write

$$R_x\mathbf{i} + R_y\mathbf{j} = P_x\mathbf{i} + P_y\mathbf{j} + Q_x\mathbf{i} + Q_y\mathbf{j} + S_x\mathbf{i} + S_y\mathbf{j}$$
$$= (P_x + Q_x + S_x)\mathbf{i} + (P_y + Q_y + S_y)\mathbf{j}$$

from which it follows that

$$R_x = P_x + Q_x + S_x \qquad R_y = P_y + Q_y + S_y \tag{2.12}$$

or, for short,

$$R_x = \Sigma F_x \qquad R_y = \Sigma F_y \tag{2.13}$$

We thus conclude that *the scalar components R_x and R_y of the resultant $\mathbf{R}$ of several forces acting on a particle are obtained by adding algebraically the corresponding scalar components of the given forces.*†

In practice, the determination of the resultant $\mathbf{R}$ is carried out in three steps as illustrated in Fig. 2.25. First, the given forces shown in Fig. 2.25a are resolved into their x and y components (Fig. 2.25b). Adding these components, we obtain the x and y components of $\mathbf{R}$ (Fig. 2.25c). Finally, the resultant $\mathbf{R} = R_x\mathbf{i} + R_y\mathbf{j}$ is determined by applying the parallelogram law (Fig. 2.25d). The procedure just described will be carried out most efficiently if the computations are arranged in a table. While it is the only practical analytic method for adding three or more forces, it is also often preferred to the trigonometric solution in the case of the addition of two forces.

---

† Clearly, this result also applies to the addition of other vector quantities, such as velocities, accelerations, or momenta.

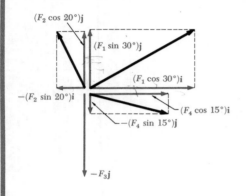

SAMPLE PROBLEM 2.3

Four forces act on bolt A as shown. Determine the resultant of the forces on the bolt.

Solution. The x and y components of each force are determined by trigonometry as shown and are entered in the table below. According to the convention adopted in Sec. 2.7, the scalar number representing a force component is positive if the force component has the same sense as the corresponding coordinate axis. Thus, x components acting to the right and y components acting upward are represented by positive numbers.

Force	Magnitude, N	x Component, N	y Component, N
F_1	150	+129.9	+75.0
F_2	80	−27.4	+75.2
F_3	110	0	−110.0
F_4	100	+96.6	−25.9
		$R_x = +199.1$	$R_y = +14.3$

Thus, the resultant $\mathbf{R}$ of the four forces is

$$\mathbf{R} = R_x\mathbf{i} + R_y\mathbf{j} \qquad \mathbf{R} = (199.1 \text{ N})\mathbf{i} + (14.3 \text{ N})\mathbf{j} \quad \blacktriangleleft$$

The magnitude and direction of the resultant may now be determined. From the triangle shown, we have

$$\tan \alpha = \frac{R_y}{R_x} = \frac{14.3 \text{ N}}{199.1 \text{ N}} \qquad \alpha = 4.1°$$

$$R = \frac{14.3 \text{ N}}{\sin \alpha} = 199.6 \text{ N} \qquad R = 199.6 \text{ N} \angle 4.1° \quad \blacktriangleleft$$

With a calculator, the last computation may be facilitated if the value of R_y is stored when originally entered; it may then be recalled to be divided by $\sin \alpha$. (Also see the footnote on p. 26.)

Problems

Fig. P2.17

Fig. P2.18

(350N) 317, 747.9
Y (800N) 274, 752
(600) -300, 520

Fig. P2.19

2.17 through 2.20   Determine the x and y components of each of the forces shown.

2.21   Cable AC exerts on beam AB a force **P** directed along line AC. Knowing that **P** must have a 1750-N vertical component, determine (*a*) the magnitude of the force **P**, (*b*) its horizontal component.

(725) 500, 525
(1000) 966, -280

Fig. P2.20

Fig. P2.21

2.22   The hydraulic cylinder BD exerts on member ABC a force **P** directed along line BD. Knowing that **P** must have a 750-N component perpendicular to member ABC, determine (*a*) the magnitude of the force **P**, (*b*) its component parallel to ABC.

a) 2140
b) 2060

Fig. P2.22

2.23 The compression member BC exerts on the pin at C a 485-N force directed along line BC. Determine the horizontal and vertical components of that force.

A
C
720 mm
485.
B
650 mm

Fig. P2.23

6 m
A
B
C
2 m 7L.$b

Fig. P2.24

2.24 The tension in the telephone-pole guy wire is 2780 N. Determine the horizontal and vertical components of the force exerted on the anchor at C.

$-879, 2460$

2.25 Using x and y components, solve Prob. 2.1.

2.26 Using x and y components, solve Prob. 2.2.

2.27 Determine the resultant of the three forces of Prob. 2.18.

2.28 Determine the resultant of the three forces of Prob. 2.17.

$1264 N \quad \nearrow 86.7$

2.29 Determine the resultant of the two forces of Prob. 2.19.

2.30 Determine the resultant of the two forces of Prob. 2.20.

$1480. \nearrow 9.53$

2.31 Two cables which have known tensions are attached to the top of pylon AB. A third cable AC is used as a guy wire. Determine the tension in AC, knowing that the resultant of the forces exerted at A by the three cables must be vertical.

2.32 A hoist trolley is subjected to the three forces shown. Knowing that $\alpha = 40°$, determine (a) the magnitude of the force **P** for which the resultant of the three forces is vertical, (b) the corresponding magnitude of the resultant.

$a) 889 \quad b) 2050$

2.33 A hoist trolley is subjected to the three forces shown. Knowing that $P = 1250$ N, determine (a) the value of the angle α for which the resultant of the three forces is vertical, (b) the corresponding magnitude of the resultant.

a)

12°
A
30°
20 kN
45 kN
32 m
B
C
24 m

Fig. P2.31

P
40 α
2000 N
1000 N

Fig. P2.32 and P2.33

2.34 A collar which may slide on a vertical rod is subjected to the three forces shown. Determine (*a*) the value of the angle α tor which the resultant of the three forces is horizontal, (*b*) the corresponding magnitude of the resultant.

26.8
539 N

Fig. P2.34

2.9. Equilibrium of a Particle.

In the preceding sections, we discussed the methods for determining the resultant of several forces acting on a particle. Although it has not occurred in any of the problems considered so far, it is quite possible for the resultant to be zero. In such a case, the net effect of the given forces is zero, and the particle is said to be in equilibrium. We thus have the following definition: *When the resultant of all the forces acting on a particle is zero, the particle is in equilibrium.*

A particle which is acted upon by two forces will be in equilibrium if the two forces have the same magnitude, same line of action, and opposite sense. The resultant of the two forces is then zero. Such a case is shown in Fig. 2.26.

Another case of equilibrium of a particle is represented in Fig. 2.27, where four forces are shown acting on *A*. In Fig. 2.28, the resultant of the given forces is determined by the polygon rule. Starting from point *O* with $\mathbf{F}_1$ and arranging the forces in tip-to-tail fashion, we find that the tip of $\mathbf{F}_4$ coincides with the starting point *O*. Thus the resultant $\mathbf{R}$ of the given system of forces is zero, and the particle is in equilibrium.

Fig. 2.26

Fig. 2.27

Fig. 2.28

The closed polygon drawn in Fig. 2.28 provides a *graphical* expression of the equilibrium of *A*. To express *algebraically* the conditions for the equilibrium of a particle, we write

$$\mathbf{R} = \Sigma\mathbf{F} = 0 \tag{2.14}$$

Resolving each force **F** into rectangular components, we have

$$\Sigma(F_x\mathbf{i} + F_y\mathbf{j}) = 0 \qquad \text{or} \qquad (\Sigma F_x)\mathbf{i} + (\Sigma F_y)\mathbf{j} = 0$$

We conclude that the necessary and sufficient conditions for the equilibrium of a particle are

$$\Sigma F_x = 0 \qquad \Sigma F_y = 0 \tag{2.15}$$

Returning to the particle shown in Fig. 2.27 we check that the equilibrium conditions are satisfied. We write

$$\Sigma F_x = 300 \text{ N} - (200 \text{ N}) \sin 30° - (400 \text{ N}) \sin 30°$$
$$= 300 \text{ N} - 100 \text{ N} - 200 \text{ N} = 0$$

$$\Sigma F_y = -173.2 \text{ N} - (200 \text{ N}) \cos 30° + (400 \text{ N}) \cos 30°$$
$$= -173.2 \text{ N} - 173.2 \text{ N} + 346.4 \text{ N} = 0$$

Fig. 2.27 *(repeated)*

2.10. Newton's First Law of Motion. In the latter part of the seventeenth century, Sir Isaac Newton formulated three fundamental laws upon which the science of mechanics is based. The first of these laws can be stated as follows:

If the resultant force acting on a particle is zero, the particle will remain at rest (if originally at rest) or will move with constant speed in a straight line (if originally in motion).

From this law and from the definition of equilibrium given in Sec. 2.9, it is seen that a particle in equilibrium either is at rest or is moving in a straight line with constant speed. In the following section, various problems concerning the equilibrium of a particle will be considered.

2.11. Problems Involving the Equilibrium of a Particle. Free-Body Diagram. In practice, a problem in engineering mechanics is derived from an actual physical situation. A sketch showing the physical conditions of the problem is known as a *space diagram*.

The methods of analysis discussed in the preceding sections apply to a system of forces acting on a particle. A large number of problems involving actual structures, however, may be reduced to problems concerning the equilibrium of a particle. This is done by choosing a significant particle and drawing a separate diagram showing this particle and all the forces acting on it. Such a diagram is called a *free-body diagram*.

As an example, consider the 75-kg crate shown in the space diagram of Fig. 2.29a. This crate was lying between two buildings, and it is now being lifted onto a truck, which will remove it. The crate is supported by a vertical cable, which is joined at A to two ropes which pass over pulleys attached to the buildings at B and C. It is desired to determine the tension in each of the ropes AB and AC.

In order to solve this problem, a free-body diagram must be drawn, showing a particle in equilibrium. Since we are interested in the rope tensions, the free-body diagram should include at least one of these tensions and, if possible, both tensions. Point A is seen to be a good free body for this problem. The free-body diagram of point A is shown in Fig. 2.29b. It shows point A and the forces exerted on A by the vertical cable and the two ropes. The force exerted by the cable is directed downward and is equal to the weight W of the crate. Recalling Eq. (1.4), we write

$$W = mg = (75 \text{ kg})(9.81 \text{ m/s}^2) = 736 \text{ N}$$

(a) Space diagram

and indicate this value in the free-body diagram. The forces exerted by the two ropes are not known. Since they are respectively equal in magnitude to the tension in rope AB and rope AC, we denote them by $\mathbf{T}_{AB}$ and $\mathbf{T}_{AC}$ and draw them away from A in the directions shown in the space diagram. No other detail is included in the free-body diagram.

Since point A is in equilibrium, the three forces acting on it must form a closed triangle when drawn in tip-to-tail fashion. This *force triangle* has been drawn in Fig. 2.29c. The values T_{AB} and T_{AC} of the tension in the ropes may be found graphically if the triangle is drawn to scale, or they may be found by trigonometry. If the latter method of solution is chosen, we use the law of sines and write

(b) Free-body diagram   (c) Force triangle

Fig. 2.29

$$\frac{T_{AB}}{\sin 60°} = \frac{T_{AC}}{\sin 40°} = \frac{736 \text{ N}}{\sin 80°}$$

$$T_{AB} = 647 \text{ N} \qquad T_{AC} = 480 \text{ N}$$

When a particle is in *equilibrium under three forces*, the problem may always be solved by drawing a force triangle. When a particle is in *equilibrium under more than three forces*, the problem may be solved graphically by drawing a force polygon. If an analytic solution is desired, the *equations of equilibrium* given in Sec. 2.9 should be solved:

$$\Sigma F_x = 0 \qquad \Sigma F_y = 0 \qquad\qquad (2.15)$$

These equations may be solved for no more than *two unknowns;* similarly, the force triangle used in the case of equilibrium under three forces may be solved for two unknowns.

The more common types of problems are those where the two unknowns represent (1) the two components (or the magnitude and direction) of a single force, (2) the magnitude of two forces each of known direction. Problems involving the determination of the maximum or minimum value of the magnitude of a force are also encountered (see Probs. 2.44 and 2.45).

SAMPLE PROBLEM 2.4

In a ship-unloading operation, a 1600-kg automobile is supported by a cable. A rope is tied to the cable at A and pulled in order to center the automobile over its intended position. The angle between the cable and the vertical is 2°, while the angle between the rope and the horizontal is 30°. What is the tension in the rope?

Solution. Point A is chosen as a free body, and the complete free-body diagram is drawn. T_{AB} is the tension in the cable AB, and T_{AC} is the tension in the rope.

Equilibrium Condition. Since only three forces act on the free body, we draw a force triangle to express that it is in equilibrium. Using the law of sines, we write

$$\frac{T_{AB}}{\sin 120°} = \frac{T_{AC}}{\sin 2°} = \frac{15.70 \text{ kN}}{\sin 58°}$$

With a calculator, we first compute and store the value of the last quotient. Multiplying this value successively by sin 120° and sin 2°, we obtain

$$T_{AB} = 16.03 \text{ kN} \qquad T_{AC} = 0.646 \text{ kN} \qquad T_{AC} = 646 \text{ N} \quad \blacktriangleleft$$

SAMPLE PROBLEM 2.5

Determine the magnitude and direction of the smallest force F which will maintain the package shown in equilibrium. Note that the force exerted by the rollers on the package is perpendicular to the incline.

Solution. We choose the package as a free body, assuming that it may be treated as a particle. We draw the corresponding free-body diagram.

Equilibrium Condition. Since only three forces act on the free body, we draw a force triangle to express that it is in equilibrium. Line *1-1* represents the known direction of P. In order to obtain the minimum value of the force F, we choose the direction of F perpendicular to that of P. From the geometry of the triangle obtained, we find

$$F = (294 \text{ N}) \sin 15° = 76.1 \text{ N} \qquad \alpha = 15°$$

$$F = 76.1 \text{ N} \searrow 15° \quad \blacktriangleleft$$

SAMPLE PROBLEM 2.6

As part of the design of a new sailboat, it is desired to determine the drag force which may be expected at a given speed. To do so, a model of the proposed hull is placed in a test channel and three cables are used to keep its bow on the centerline of the channel. Dynamometer readings indicate that for a given speed, the tension is 200 N in cable AB and 300 N in cable AE. Determine the drag force exerted on the hull and the tension in cable AC.

Solution. First, the angles α and β defining the direction of cables AB and AC are determined. We write

$$\tan \alpha = \frac{2.8 \text{ m}}{1.6 \text{ m}} = 1.75 \qquad \tan \beta = \frac{0.6 \text{ m}}{1.6 \text{ m}} = 0.375$$

$$\alpha = 60.26° \qquad\qquad \beta = 20.56°$$

Choosing the hull as a free body, we draw the free-body diagram shown. It includes the forces exerted by the three cables on the hull, as well as the drag force $\mathbf{F}_D$ exerted by the flow.

Equilibrium Condition. We express that the hull is in equilibrium by writing that the resultant of all forces is zero:

$$\mathbf{R} = \mathbf{T}_{AB} + \mathbf{T}_{AC} + \mathbf{T}_{AE} + \mathbf{F}_D = 0 \tag{1}$$

Since more than three forces are involved, we shall resolve the forces into x and y components:

$$\begin{aligned}
\mathbf{T}_{AB} &= -(200 \text{ N}) \sin 60.26°\mathbf{i} + (200 \text{ N}) \cos 60.26°\mathbf{j} \\
&= -(173.6 \text{ N})\mathbf{i} + (99.1 \text{ N})\mathbf{j} \\
\mathbf{T}_{AC} &= T_{AC} \sin 20.56°\mathbf{i} + T_{AC} \cos 20.56°\mathbf{j} \\
&= 0.3512T_{AC}\mathbf{i} + 0.9363T_{AC}\mathbf{j} \\
\mathbf{T}_{AE} &= -(300 \text{ N}) \, \mathbf{j} \\
\mathbf{F}_D &= F_D\mathbf{i}
\end{aligned}$$

Substituting the expressions obtained into Eq. (1) and factoring the unit vectors $\mathbf{i}$ and $\mathbf{j}$, we have

$$(-173.6 \text{ N} + 0.3512T_{AC} + F_D)\mathbf{i} + (99.1 \text{ N} + 0.9363T_{AC} - 300 \text{ N})\mathbf{j} = 0$$

This equation will be satisfied if, and only if, the coefficients of $\mathbf{i}$ and $\mathbf{j}$ are equal to zero. We thus obtain the following two equilibrium equations, which express, respectively, that the sum of the x components and the sum of the y components of the given forces must be zero.

$$(\Sigma F_x = 0:) \qquad\qquad -173.6 \text{ N} + 0.3512T_{AC} + F_D = 0 \tag{2}$$

$$(\Sigma F_y = 0:) \qquad\qquad 99.1 \text{ N} + 0.9363T_{AC} - 300 \text{ N} = 0 \tag{3}$$

From Eq. (3) we find $\qquad\qquad\qquad\qquad\qquad\qquad T_{AC} = +215 \text{ N}$ ◀

and, substituting this value into Eq. (2), $\qquad\qquad\qquad F_D = +98.3 \text{ N}$ ◀

In drawing the free-body diagram, we assumed a sense for each unknown force. A positive sign in the answer indicates that the assumed sense is correct. The complete force polygon may be drawn to check the results.

36

Fig. P2.35

Problems

2.35 through 2.38 Two cables are tied together at C and loaded as shown. Determine the tension in AC and BC.

Fig. P2.36

Fig. P2.37

Fig. P2.38

$T_{AC} = 5186$
$T_{BC} = 6370$
     2190

T_{AC} 12470
T_{BC} 6370

2.39 Two cables are tied together at C and loaded as shown. Knowing that $P = 500$ N and $\alpha = 60°$, determine the tension in AC and BC.

Fig. P2.39

Fig. P2.40

2.40 Two cables are tied together at G and loaded as shown. Knowing that $\alpha = 30°$, determine the tension in AC and BC.

2.41 Two forces of magnitude $T_A = 40$ kN and $T_B = 75$ kN are applied as shown to a welded connection. Knowing that the connection is in equilibrium, determine the magnitudes of the forces T_C and T_D.

Fig. P2.41 and P2.42

2.42 Two forces of magnitude $T_A = 30$ kN and $T_C = 45$ kN are applied as shown to a welded connection. Knowing that the connection is in equilibrium, determine the magnitudes of the forces T_B and T_D.

83.6   72.0

2.43 Two cables are tied together at A and loaded as shown. Knowing that $P = 640$ N, determine the tension in each cable.

2.44 Two cables are tied together at A and loaded as shown. Determine the range of values of P for which both cables remain taut.

$287 \leq P \leq 1600$

2.45 For the cables of Prob. 2.40, find the value of α for which the tension is as small as possible (a) in cable BC, (b) in both cables simultaneously. In each case determine the tension in both cables.

2.46 For the cables of Prob. 2.39, it is known that the maximum allowable tension is 600 N in cable AC and 750 N in cable BC. Determine (a) the maximum force **P** that may be applied at C, (b) the corresponding value of α.

784   70.1

2.47 The 27-kg collar A may slide on a frictionless vertical rod and is connected as shown to a 30-kg counterweight C. Determine the value of h for which the system is in equilibrium.

2.48 A movable bin and its contents have a mass of 300 kg. Determine the shortest chain sling ACB which may be used to lift the loaded bin if the tension in the chain is not to exceed 6250 N.

Fig. P2.43 and P2.44

Fig. P2.47

1235

Fig. P2.48

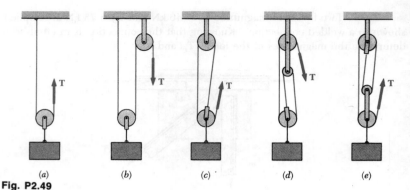

(a) (b) (c) (d) (e)

Fig. P2.49

Fig. P2.51

2.49 A 250-kg crate is supported by several rope-and-pulley arrangements as shown. Determine for each arrangement the tension in the rope. (The tension in the rope is the same on each side of a simple pulley. This can be proved by the methods of Chap. 4.)

2.50 Solve parts *b* and *d* of Prob. 2.49 assuming that the free end of the rope is attached to the crate.

817   613.

2.51 The force **P** is applied to a small wheel which rolls on the cable *ACB*. Knowing that the tension in both parts of the cable is 600 N, determine the magnitude and direction of **P**.

2.52 A 200-kg crate is to be supported by the rope-and-pulley arrangement shown. Determine the magnitude and direction of the force **F** which should be exerted on the free end of the rope.

724 ∆53.4 or 1724 ⩓ 53.4

*2.53 The collar *A* may slide freely on the horizontal frictionless rod. The spring attached to the collar has a constant of 2.5 kN/m and is undeformed when the collar is directly below support *B*. Determine the magnitude of the force **P** required to maintain equilibrium when (*a*) *c* = 180 mm, (*b*) *c* = 320 mm, (*c*) *c* = 450 mm.

Fig. P2.52

Fig. P2.53

Fig. P2.54

2.54 Three forces are applied to a bracket. The directions of the two 150-N forces may vary, but the angle between these forces is always 50°. Determine the range of values of α for which the magnitude of the resultant of the forces applied to the bracket is less than 600 N.

$27.4 \leq \alpha \leq 222.6$

FORCES IN SPACE

2.12. Rectangular Components of a Force in Space.

The problems considered in the first part of this chapter involved only two dimensions; they could be formulated and solved in a single plane. In this section and in the remaining sections of the chapter, we shall discuss problems involving the three dimensions of space.

Consider a force **F** acting at the origin O of the system of rectangular coordinates x, y, z. To define the direction of **F**, we may draw the vertical plane $OBAC$ containing **F** and shown in Fig. 2.30a. This plane passes through the vertical y axis; its orientation is defined by the angle ϕ it forms with the xy plane, while the direction of **F** within the plane is defined by the angle θ_y that **F** forms with the y axis. The force **F** may be resolved into a vertical component $\mathbf{F}_y$ and a horizontal component $\mathbf{F}_h$; this operation, shown in Fig. 2.30b, is carried out in plane $OBAC$ according to the rules developed in the first part of the chapter. The corresponding scalar components are

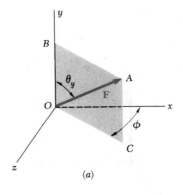

$$F_y = F \cos \theta_y \qquad F_h = F \sin \theta_y \qquad (2.16)$$

But $\mathbf{F}_h$ may be resolved into two rectangular components $\mathbf{F}_x$ and $\mathbf{F}_z$ along the x and z axes, respectively. This operation, shown in Fig. 2.30c, is carried out in the xz plane. We obtain the following expressions for the corresponding scalar components:

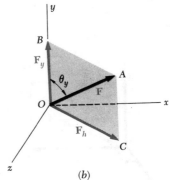

$$F_x = F_h \cos \phi = F \sin \theta_y \cos \phi$$
$$F_z = F_h \sin \phi = F \sin \theta_y \sin \phi \qquad (2.17)$$

The given force **F** has thus been resolved into three rectangular vector components $\mathbf{F}_x$, $\mathbf{F}_y$, $\mathbf{F}_z$, directed along the three coordinate axes.

Applying the Pythagorean theorem to the triangles OAB and OCD of Fig. 2.30, we write

$$F^2 = (OA)^2 = (OB)^2 + (BA)^2 = F_y^2 + F_h^2$$
$$F_h^2 = (OC)^2 = (OD)^2 + (DC)^2 = F_x^2 + F_z^2$$

Eliminating F_h^2 from these two equations and solving for F, we obtain the following relation between the magnitude of **F** and its rectangular scalar components:

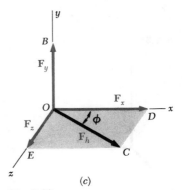

$$F = \sqrt{F_x^2 + F_y^2 + F_z^2} \qquad (2.18)$$

Fig. 2.30

Fig. 2.31

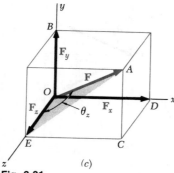

Fig. 2.32

The relationship existing between the force $\mathbf{F}$ and its three components $\mathbf{F}_x$, $\mathbf{F}_y$, $\mathbf{F}_z$ is more easily visualized if a "box" having $\mathbf{F}_x$, $\mathbf{F}_y$, $\mathbf{F}_z$ for edges is drawn as shown in Fig. 2.31. The force $\mathbf{F}$ is then represented by the diagonal OA of this box. Figure 2.31b shows the right triangle OAB used to derive the first of the formulas (2.16): $F_y = F\cos\theta_y$. In Fig. 2.31a and c, two other right triangles have also been drawn: OAD and OAE. These triangles are seen to occupy in the box positions comparable with that of triangle OAB. Denoting by θ_x and θ_z, respectively, the angles that $\mathbf{F}$ forms with the x and z axes, we may derive two formulas similar to $F_y = F\cos\theta_y$. We thus write

$$F_x = F\cos\theta_x \qquad F_y = F\cos\theta_y \qquad F_z = F\cos\theta_z \qquad (2.19)$$

The three angles θ_x, θ_y, θ_z define the direction of the force $\mathbf{F}$; they are more commonly used for this purpose than the angles θ_y and ϕ introduced at the beginning of this section. The cosines of θ_x, θ_y, θ_z are known as the direction cosines of the force $\mathbf{F}$.

Introducing the unit vectors $\mathbf{i}$, $\mathbf{j}$, and $\mathbf{k}$, directed respectively along the x, y, and z axes (Fig. 2.32), we may express $\mathbf{F}$ in the form

$$\mathbf{F} = F_x\mathbf{i} + F_y\mathbf{j} + F_z\mathbf{k} \qquad (2.20)$$

where the scalar components F_x, F_y, F_z are defined by the relations (2.19).

Example 1. A force of 500 N forms angles of 60, 45, and 120°, respectively, with the x, y, and z axes. Find the components F_x, F_y, and F_z of the force.

Substituting $F = 500$ N, $\theta_x = 60°$, $\theta_y = 45°$, $\theta_z = 120°$ into formulas (2.19), we write

$$F_x = (500\text{ N})\cos 60° = +250\text{ N}$$
$$F_y = (500\text{ N})\cos 45° = +354\text{ N}$$
$$F_z = (500\text{ N})\cos 120° = -250\text{ N}$$

Carrying into Eq. (2.20) the values obtained for the scalar components of $\mathbf{F}$, we have

$$\mathbf{F} = (250\text{ N})\mathbf{i} + (354\text{ N})\mathbf{j} - (250\text{ N})\mathbf{k}$$

As in the case of two-dimensional problems, the plus sign indicates that the component has the same sense as the corresponding axis, and the minus sign that it has the opposite sense.

The angle a force $\mathbf{F}$ forms with an axis should be measured from the positive side of the axis and will always be comprised between 0 and 180°. An angle θ_x smaller than 90° (acute) indicates that $\mathbf{F}$ (assumed attached to O) is on the same side of the yz plane as the positive x axis; $\cos\theta_x$ and F_x will then be positive. An angle θ_x larger than 90° (obtuse) would indicate that $\mathbf{F}$ is on the other side of the yz plane; $\cos\theta_x$ and F_x would then be negative. In Example 1 the angles θ_x and θ_y are acute, while θ_z is obtuse: consequently, F_x and F_y are positive, while F_z is negative.

Substituting into (2.20) the expressions obtained for F_x, F_y, F_z in (2.19), we write

$$\mathbf{F} = F(\cos\theta_x\mathbf{i} + \cos\theta_y\mathbf{j} + \cos\theta_z\mathbf{k}) \qquad (2.21)$$

which shows that the force $\mathbf{F}$ may be expressed as the product of the scalar F and of the vector

$$\boldsymbol{\lambda} = \cos\theta_x\mathbf{i} + \cos\theta_y\mathbf{j} + \cos\theta_z\mathbf{k} \qquad (2.22)$$

Clearly, the vector $\boldsymbol{\lambda}$ is a vector of magnitude equal to 1 and of the same direction as $\mathbf{F}$ (Fig. 2.33). We shall refer to $\boldsymbol{\lambda}$ as the *unit vector* along the line of action of $\mathbf{F}$. It follows from (2.22) that the components of the unit vector $\boldsymbol{\lambda}$ are respectively equal to the direction cosines of the line of action of $\mathbf{F}$:

$$\lambda_x = \cos\theta_x \qquad \lambda_y = \cos\theta_y \qquad \lambda_z = \cos\theta_z \qquad (2.23)$$

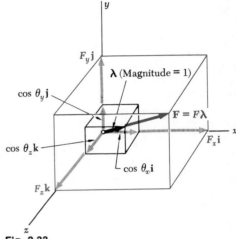

Fig. 2.33

We should observe that the values of the three angles θ_x, θ_y, θ_z are not independent. Expressing that the sum of the squares of the components of $\boldsymbol{\lambda}$ is equal to the square of its magnitude, we write

$$\lambda_x^2 + \lambda_y^2 + \lambda_z^2 = 1$$

or, substituting for λ_x, λ_y, λ_z from (2.23),

$$\cos^2\theta_x + \cos^2\theta_y + \cos^2\theta_z = 1 \qquad (2.24)$$

In Example 1, for instance, once the values $\theta_x = 60°$ and $\theta_y = 45°$ have been selected, the value of θ_z *must* be equal to $60°$ or $120°$ in order to satisfy identity (2.24).

When the components F_x, F_y, F_z of a force $\mathbf{F}$ are given, the magnitude F of the force is obtained from (2.18).† The relations (2.19) may then be solved for the direction cosines,

$$\cos\theta_x = \frac{F_x}{F} \qquad \cos\theta_y = \frac{F_y}{F} \qquad \cos\theta_z = \frac{F_z}{F} \qquad (2.25)$$

and the angles θ_x, θ_y, θ_z characterizing the direction of $\mathbf{F}$ may be found.

Example 2. A force $\mathbf{F}$ has the components $F_x = 200$ N, $F_y = -300$ N, $F_z = 600$ N. Determine its magnitude F and the angle θ_x, θ_y, θ_z it forms with the axes of coordinates.

From formula (2.18) we obtain†

$$F = \sqrt{F_x^2 + F_y^2 + F_z^2}$$
$$= \sqrt{(200\ \text{N})^2 + (-300\ \text{N})^2 + (600\ \text{N})^2}$$
$$= \sqrt{490\ 000\ \text{N}} = 700\ \text{N}$$

---

† With a calculator programmed to convert rectangular coordinates into polar coordinates, the following procedure will be found more expeditious for computing F: First determine F_h from its two rectangular components F_x and F_z (Fig. 2.30c), then determine F from its two rectangular components F_h and F_y (Fig. 2.30b). The actual order in which the three components F_x, F_y, F_z are entered is immaterial.

Substituting the values of the components and magnitude of **F** into Eqs. (2.25), we write

$$\cos \theta_x = \frac{F_x}{F} = \frac{200 \text{ N}}{700 \text{ N}} \qquad \cos \theta_y = \frac{F_y}{F} = \frac{-300 \text{ N}}{700 \text{ N}} \qquad \cos \theta_z = \frac{F_z}{F} = \frac{600 \text{ N}}{700 \text{ N}}$$

Calculating successively each quotient and its arc cosine, we obtain

$$\theta_x = 73.4° \qquad \theta_y = 115.4° \qquad \theta_z = 31.0°$$

The computations indicated may easily be carried out with a calculator.

2.13. Force Defined by Its Magnitude and Two Points on Its Line of Action.

In many applications, the direction of a force **F** is defined by the coordinates of two points, $M(x_1, y_1, z_1)$ and $N(x_2, y_2, z_2)$, located on its line of action (Fig. 2.34). Consider the vector $\overrightarrow{MN}$ joining M

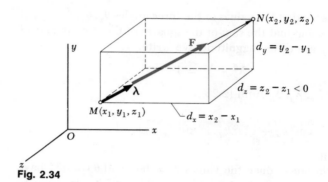

Fig. 2.34

and N and of the same sense as **F**. Denoting its scalar components by d_x, d_y, d_z, respectively, we write

$$\overrightarrow{MN} = d_x\mathbf{i} + d_y\mathbf{j} + d_z\mathbf{k} \tag{2.26}$$

The unit vector $\boldsymbol{\lambda}$ along the line of action of **F** (i.e., along the line MN) may be obtained by dividing the vector $\overrightarrow{MN}$ by its magnitude MN. Substituting for $\overrightarrow{MN}$ from (2.26) and observing that MN is equal to the distance d from M to N, we write

$$\boldsymbol{\lambda} = \frac{\overrightarrow{MN}}{MN} = \frac{1}{d}(d_x\mathbf{i} + d_y\mathbf{j} + d_z\mathbf{k}) \tag{2.27}$$

Recalling that **F** is equal to the product of F and $\boldsymbol{\lambda}$, we have

$$\mathbf{F} = F\boldsymbol{\lambda} = \frac{F}{d}(d_x\mathbf{i} + d_y\mathbf{j} + d_z\mathbf{k}) \tag{2.28}$$

from which it follows that the scalar components of **F** are, respectively,

$$F_x = \frac{Fd_x}{d} \qquad F_y = \frac{Fd_y}{d} \qquad F_z = \frac{Fd_z}{d} \tag{2.29}$$

The relations (2.29) considerably simplify the determination of the components of a force **F** of given magnitude F when the line of action of **F** is defined by two points M and N. Subtracting the coordinates of M from those of N, we first determine the components of the vector $\overrightarrow{MN}$ and the distance d from M to N:

$$d_x = x_2 - x_1 \qquad d_y = y_2 - y_1 \qquad d_z = z_2 - z_1$$
$$d = \sqrt{d_x^2 + d_y^2 + d_z^2}$$

Substituting for F and for d_x, d_y, d_z, and d into the relations (2.29), we obtain the components F_x, F_y, F_z of the force.

The angles θ_x, θ_y, θ_z that **F** forms with the coordinate axes may then be obtained from Eqs. (2.25). Comparing Eqs. (2.22) and (2.27), we may also write

$$\cos \theta_x = \frac{d_x}{d} \qquad \cos \theta_y = \frac{d_y}{d} \qquad \cos \theta_z = \frac{d_z}{d} \qquad (2.30)$$

and determine the angles θ_x, θ_y, θ_z directly from the components and magnitude of the vector MN.

2.14. Addition of Concurrent Forces in Space.

We shall determine the resultant **R** of two or more forces in space by summing their rectangular components. Graphical or trigonometric methods are generally not practical in the case of forces in space.

The method followed here is similar to that used in Sec. 2.8 with coplanar forces. Setting

$$\mathbf{R} = \Sigma \mathbf{F}$$

we resolve each force into its rectangular components and write

$$R_x \mathbf{i} + R_y \mathbf{j} + R_z \mathbf{k} = \Sigma(F_x \mathbf{i} + F_y \mathbf{j} + F_z \mathbf{k})$$
$$= (\Sigma F_x)\mathbf{i} + (\Sigma F_y)\mathbf{j} + (\Sigma F_z)\mathbf{k}$$

from which it follows that

$$R_x = \Sigma F_x \qquad R_y = \Sigma F_y \qquad R_z = \Sigma F_z \qquad (2.31)$$

The magnitude of the resultant and the angles θ_x, θ_y, θ_z it forms with the axes of coordinates are obained by the method of Sec. 2.12. We write

$$R = \sqrt{R_x^2 + R_y^2 + R_z^2} \qquad (2.32)$$

$$\cos \theta_x = \frac{R_x}{R} \qquad \cos \theta_y = \frac{R_y}{R} \qquad \cos \theta_z = \frac{R_z}{R} \qquad (2.33)$$

SAMPLE PROBLEM 2.7

A tower guy wire is anchored by means of a bolt at A. The tension in the wire is 2500 N. Determine (a) the components F_x, F_y, F_z of the force acting on the bolt, (b) the angles θ_x, θ_y, θ_z defining the direction of the force.

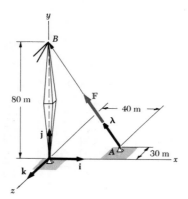

a. Components of the Force. The line of action of the force acting on the bolt passes through A and B, and the force is directed from A to B. The components of the vector $\overrightarrow{AB}$, which has the same direction as the force, are

$$d_x = -40 \text{ m} \qquad d_y = +80 \text{ m} \qquad d_z = +30 \text{ m}$$

The total distance from A to B is

$$AB = d = \sqrt{d_x^2 + d_y^2 + d_z^2} = 94.3 \text{ m}$$

Denoting by $\mathbf{i}$, $\mathbf{j}$, $\mathbf{k}$ the unit vectors along the coordinate axes, we have

$$\overrightarrow{AB} = -(40 \text{ m})\mathbf{i} + (80 \text{ m})\mathbf{j} + (30 \text{ m})\mathbf{k}$$

Introducing the unit vector $\boldsymbol{\lambda} = \overrightarrow{AB}/AB$, we write

$$\mathbf{F} = F\boldsymbol{\lambda} = F\frac{\overrightarrow{AB}}{AB} = \frac{2500 \text{ N}}{94.3 \text{ m}}\overrightarrow{AB}$$

Substituting the expression found for $\overrightarrow{AB}$, we obtain

$$\mathbf{F} = \frac{2500 \text{ N}}{94.3 \text{ m}}[-(40 \text{ m})\mathbf{i} + (80 \text{ m})\mathbf{j} + (30 \text{ m})\mathbf{k}]$$

$$\mathbf{F} = -(1060 \text{ N})\mathbf{i} + (2120 \text{ N})\mathbf{j} + (795 \text{ N})\mathbf{k}$$

The components of $\mathbf{F}$, therefore, are

$$F_x = -1060 \text{ N} \qquad F_y = +2120 \text{ N} \qquad F_z = +795 \text{ N} \quad \blacktriangleleft$$

b. Direction of the Force. Using Eqs. (2.25), we write

$$\cos \theta_x = \frac{F_x}{F} = \frac{-1060 \text{ N}}{2500 \text{ N}} \qquad \cos \theta_y = \frac{F_y}{F} = \frac{+2120 \text{ N}}{2500 \text{ N}}$$

$$\cos \theta_z = \frac{F_z}{F} = \frac{+795 \text{ N}}{2500 \text{ N}}$$

Calculating successively each quotient and its arc cosine, we obtain

$$\theta_x = 115.1° \qquad \theta_y = 32.0° \qquad \theta_z = 71.5° \quad \blacktriangleleft$$

(*Note.* This result could have been obtained by using the components and magnitude of the vector $\overrightarrow{AB}$ rather than those of the force $\mathbf{F}$.)

SAMPLE PROBLEM 2.8

A precast-concrete wall section is temporarily held by the cables shown. Knowing that the tension is 4200 N in cable AB and 6000 N in Cable AC, determine the magnitude and direction of the resultant of the forces exerted by cables AB and AC on stake A.

Solution. The force exerted by each cable on stake A will be resolved into x, y, and z components. We first determine the components and magnitude of the vectors $\overrightarrow{AB}$ and $\overrightarrow{AC}$, measuring them from A toward the wall section. Denoting by $\mathbf{i}$, $\mathbf{j}$, $\mathbf{k}$ the unit vectors along the coordinate axes, we write

$$\overrightarrow{AB} = -(8\text{ m})\mathbf{i} + (4\text{ m})\mathbf{j} + (5.5\text{ m})\mathbf{k} \qquad AB = 10.5\text{ m}$$
$$\overrightarrow{AC} = -(8\text{ m})\mathbf{i} + (4\text{ m})\mathbf{j} - (8\text{ m})\mathbf{k} \qquad AC = 12.0\text{ m}$$

Denoting by λ_{AB} the unit vector along AB, we have

$$\mathbf{T}_{AB} = T_{AB}\lambda_{AB} = T_{AB}\frac{\overrightarrow{AB}}{AB} = \frac{4200\text{ N}}{10.5\text{ m}}\overrightarrow{AB}$$

Substituting the expression found for $\overrightarrow{AB}$, we obtain

$$\mathbf{T}_{AB} = \frac{4200\text{ N}}{10.5\text{ m}}[-(8\text{ m})\mathbf{i} + (4\text{ m})\mathbf{j} + (5.5\text{ m})\mathbf{k}]$$
$$\mathbf{T}_{AB} = -(3200\text{ N})\mathbf{i} + (1600\text{ N})\mathbf{j} + (2200\text{ N})\mathbf{k}$$

Denoting by λ_{AC} the unit vector along AC, we obtain in a similar way

$$\mathbf{T}_{AC} = T_{AC}\lambda_{AC} = T_{AC}\frac{\overrightarrow{AC}}{AC} = \frac{6000\text{ N}}{12\text{ m}}\overrightarrow{AC}$$
$$\mathbf{T}_{AC} = -(4000\text{ N})\mathbf{i} + (2000\text{ N})\mathbf{j} - (4000\text{ N})\mathbf{k}$$

The resultant $\mathbf{R}$ of the forces exerted by the two cables is

$$\mathbf{R} = \mathbf{T}_{AB} + \mathbf{T}_{AC} = -(7200\text{ N})\mathbf{i} + (3600\text{ N})\mathbf{j} - (1800\text{ N})\mathbf{k}$$

The magnitude and direction of the resultant are now determined:

$$R = \sqrt{R_x^2 + R_y^2 + R_z^2} = \sqrt{(-7200)^2 + (3600)^2 + (-1000)^2}$$
$$R = 8250\text{ N} \quad \blacktriangleleft$$

From Eqs. (2.33) we obtain

$$\cos\theta_x = \frac{R_x}{R} = \frac{-7200\text{ N}}{8250\text{ N}} \qquad \cos\theta_y = \frac{R_y}{R} = \frac{+3600\text{ N}}{8250\text{ N}}$$

$$\cos\theta_z = \frac{R_z}{R} = \frac{-1800\text{ N}}{8250\text{ N}}$$

Calculating successively each quotient and its arc cosine, we have

$$\theta_x = 150.8° \qquad \theta_y = 64.1° \qquad \theta_z = 102.6° \quad \blacktriangleleft$$

46

900 N

750 N

35°

65°

O

25°

20°

z

x

y

Fig. P2.55 and P2.56

y

A

z

35°

C

D

B

35°

x

Fig. P2.59 and P2.60

Problems

2.55 Determine (*a*) the *x*, *y*, and *z* components of the 750-N force, (*b*) the angles θ_x, θ_y, and θ_z that the force forms with the coordinate axes.

2.56 Determine (*a*) the *x*, *y*, and *z* components of the 900-N force, (*b*) the angles θ_x, θ_y, and θ_z that the force forms with the coordinate axes.

a) −130.1   b) 816   c) 357
b) 98.3, 25, 66.6

2.57 A gun is aimed at a point *A* located 20° west of north. Knowing that the barrel of the gun forms an angle of 35° with the horizontal and that the maximum recoil force is 800 N, determine (*a*) the *x*, *y*, and *z* components of that force, (*b*) the values of the angles θ_x, θ_y, and θ_z defining the direction of the recoil force. (Assume that the *x*, *y*, and *z* axes are directed, respectively, east, up, and south.)

2.58 Solve Prob. 2.57, assuming that point *A* is located 25° north of west and that the barrel of the gun forms an angle of 30° with the horizontal.

628, −400, 293
38.3, 120, 68.5

2.59 The angle between the spring *AB* and the post *DA* is 30°. Knowing that the tension in the spring is 250 N, determine (*a*) the *x*, *y* and *z* components of the force exerted on the circular plate at *B*, (*b*) the angles θ_x, θ_y, and θ_z defining the direction of the force at *B*.

2.60 The angle between the spring *AC* and the post *DA* is 30°. Knowing that the tension in the spring is 200 N, determine (*a*) the *x*, *y* and *z* components of the force exerted on the circular plate at *C*, (*b*) the angles θ_x, θ_y, and θ_z defining the direction of the force at *C*.

81.9, 173.2, −57.4
65.8, 30.0, 106.7.

2.61 Determine the magnitude and direction of the force $\mathbf{F} = (240 \text{ N})\mathbf{i} - (270 \text{ N})\mathbf{j} + (680 \text{ N})\mathbf{k}$.

2.62 Determine the magnitude and direction of the force $\mathbf{F} = (3450 \text{ N})\mathbf{i} + (1500 \text{ N})\mathbf{j} - (2900 \text{ N})\mathbf{k}$.

2.63 A force acts at the origin in a direction defined by the angles $\theta_x = 70°$ and $\theta_z = 130°$. Knowing that the *y* component of the force is +2000 N, determine (*a*) the other components and the magnitude of the force, (*b*) the value of θ_y.

2.64 A force acts at the origin in a direction defined by the angles $\theta_y = 65°$ and $\theta_z = 40°$. Knowing that the *x* component of the force is −750 N, determine (*a*) the other components and the magnitude of the force, (*b*) the value of θ_x.

2.65   Two cables *BG* and *BH* are attached to frame *ACD* as shown. Knowing that the tension in cable *BG* is 540 N, determine the components of the force exerted by cable *BG* on the frame at *B*.

Fig. P2.65 and P2.66

2.66   Two cables *BG* and *BH* are attached to frame *ACD* as shown. Knowing that the tension in cable *BH* is 750 N, determine the components of the force exerted by cable *BH* on the frame at *B*.

2.67   Knowing that the tension in cable *AB* is 1425 N, determine the components of the force exerted on the plate at *B*.

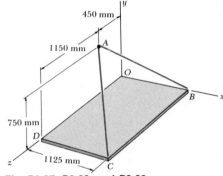

Fig. P2.67, P2.68, and P2.69

2.68   Knowing that the tension in cable *AC* is 2130 N, determine the components of the force exerted on the plate at *C*.

2.69   Knowing that the tension is 1425 N in cable AB and 2130 N in cable *AC*, determine the magnitude and direction of the resultant of the forces exerted at *A* by the two cables.

2.70   Referring to the frame of Prob. 2.65 and knowing that the tension is 540 N in cable *BG* and 750 N in cable *BH*, determine the magnitude and direction of the resultant of the forces exerted by the cables on the frame at *B*.

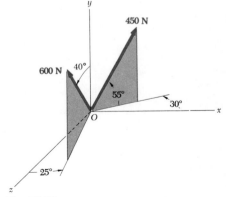

2.71   Determine the resultant of the two forces shown.

Fig. P2.71

2.72 The angle between each of the springs AB and AC and the post DA is 30°. Knowing that the tension is 250 N in spring AB and 200 N in spring AC, determine (a) the magnitude and direction of the resultant of the forces exerted by the springs on the post at A, (b) the point where the resultant intersects the plate.

Fig. P2.72

Fig. P2.73

2.73 The boom OA carries a load $\mathbf{P}$ and is supported by two cables as shown. Knowing that the tension in cable AB is 732 N and that the resultant of the load $\mathbf{P}$ and of the forces exerted at A by the two cables must be directed along OA, determine the tension in cable AC.

2.74 For the boom and loading of Prob. 2.73, determine the magnitude of the load $\mathbf{P}$.

2.15. Equilibrium of a Particle in Space. According to the definition given in Sec. 2.9, a particle A is in equilibrium if the resultant of all the forces acting on A is zero. The components R_x, R_y, R_z of the resultant are given by the relations (2.31); expressing that the components of the resultant are zero, we write

$$\Sigma F_x = 0 \qquad \Sigma F_y = 0 \qquad \Sigma F_z = 0 \qquad (2.34)$$

Equations (2.34) represent the necessary and sufficient conditions for the equilibrium of a particle in space. They may be used to solve problems dealing with the equilibrium of a particle involving no more than three unknowns.

To solve such problems, we first should draw a free-body diagram showing the particle in equilibrium and *all* the forces acting on it. We may then write the equations of equilibrium (2.34) and solve them for three unknowns. In the more common types of problems, these unknowns will represent (1) the three components of a single force or (2) the magnitude of three forces each of known direction.

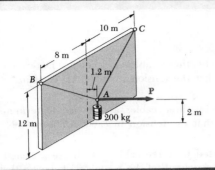

SAMPLE PROBLEM 2.9

A 200-kg cylinder is hung by means of two cables AB and AC, which are attached to the top of a vertical wall. A horizontal force **P** perpendicular to the wall holds the cylinder in the position shown. Determine the magnitude of **P** and the tension in each cable.

Solution. Point A is chosen as a free body; this point is subjected to four forces, three of which are of unknown magnitude.

Introducing the unit vectors **i**, **j**, **k**, we resolve each force into rectangular components.

$$\mathbf{P} = P\mathbf{i}$$
$$\mathbf{W} = -mg\mathbf{j} = -(200 \text{ kg})(9.81 \text{ m/s}^2)\mathbf{j} = -(1962 \text{ N})\mathbf{j} \tag{1}$$

In the case of $\mathbf{T}_{AB}$ and $\mathbf{T}_{AC}$, it is necessary first to determine the components and magnitudes of the vectors $\overrightarrow{AB}$ and $\overrightarrow{AC}$. Denoting by $\boldsymbol{\lambda}_{AB}$ the unit vector along AB, we write

$$\overrightarrow{AB} = -(1.2 \text{ m})\mathbf{i} + (10 \text{ m})\mathbf{j} + (8 \text{ m})\mathbf{k} \qquad AB = 12.86 \text{ m}$$

$$\boldsymbol{\lambda}_{AB} = \frac{\overrightarrow{AB}}{12.86 \text{ m}} = -0.0933\mathbf{i} + 0.778\mathbf{j} + 0.622\mathbf{k}$$

$$\mathbf{T}_{AB} = T_{AB}\boldsymbol{\lambda}_{AB} = -0.0933T_{AB}\mathbf{i} + 0.778T_{AB}\mathbf{j} + 0.622T_{AB}\mathbf{k} \tag{2}$$

Denoting by $\boldsymbol{\lambda}_{AC}$ the unit vector along AC, we write in a similar way

$$\overrightarrow{AC} = -(1.2 \text{ m})\mathbf{i} + (10 \text{ m})\mathbf{j} - (10 \text{ m})\mathbf{k} \qquad AC = 14.19 \text{ m}$$

$$\boldsymbol{\lambda}_{AC} = \frac{\overrightarrow{AC}}{14.19 \text{ m}} = -0.0846\mathbf{i} + 0.705\mathbf{j} - 0.705\mathbf{k}$$

$$\mathbf{T}_{AC} = T_{AC}\boldsymbol{\lambda}_{AC} = -0.0846T_{AC}\mathbf{i} + 0.705T_{AC}\mathbf{j} - 0.705T_{AC}\mathbf{k} \tag{3}$$

Equilibrium Condition. Since A is in equilibrium, we must have

$$\Sigma\mathbf{F} = 0: \qquad \mathbf{T}_{AB} + \mathbf{T}_{AC} + \mathbf{P} + \mathbf{W} = 0$$

or, substituting from (1), (2), (3) for the forces and factoring **i**, **j**, **k**,

$$(-0.0933T_{AB} - 0.0846T_{AC} + P)\mathbf{i}$$
$$+ (0.778T_{AB} + 0.705T_{AC} - 1962 \text{ N})\mathbf{j} + (0.622T_{AB} - 0.705T_{AC})\mathbf{k} = 0$$

Setting the coefficients of **i**, **j**, **k** equal to zero, we write three scalar equations, which express that the sums of the x, y, and z components of the forces are respectively equal to zero.

$$(\Sigma F_x = 0:) \qquad -0.0933T_{AB} - 0.0846T_{AC} + P = 0$$
$$(\Sigma F_y = 0:) \qquad +0.778T_{AB} + 0.705T_{AC} - 1962 \text{ N} = 0$$
$$(\Sigma F_z = 0:) \qquad +0.622T_{AB} - 0.705T_{AC} = 0$$

Solving these equations, we obtain

$$P = 235 \text{ N} \qquad T_{AB} = 1401 \text{ N} \qquad T_{AC} = 1236 \text{ N} \quad \blacktriangleleft$$

50

Fig. P2.75 and P2.76

Problems

2.75 A crate is supported by three cables as shown. Determine the weight W of the crate, knowing that the tension in cable AD is 4620 N.

2.76 A crate is supported by three cables as shown. Determine the weight W of the crate, knowing that the tension in cable AB is 6890 N.

2.77 A container is supported by three cables which are attached to a ceiling as shown. Determine the weight W of the container, knowing that the tension in cable AB is 6 kN.

Fig. P2.77, P2.78, and P2.79

2.78 A container is supported by three cables which are attached to a ceiling as shown. Determine the weight W of the container, knowing that the tension in cable AD is 4.3 kN.

2.79 A container of weight $W = 9.32$ kN is supported by three cables which are attached to a ceiling as shown. Determine the tension in each cable.

2.80 Three cables are connected at A, where the forces P and Q are applied as shown. Determine the tension in each of the cables when $P = 28$ kN and $Q = 0$.

2.81 Three cables are connected at A, where the forces P and Q are applied as shown. Determine the tension in each of the cables when $P = 0$ and $Q = 36.4$ kN.

2.82 Three cables are connected at A, where the forces P and Q are applied as shown. Knowing that $Q = 36.4$ kN and that the tension in cable AD is zero, determine (a) the magnitude and sense of $\mathbf{P}$, (b) the tension in cables AB and AC.

Fig. P2.80, P2.81 and P2.82

2.83 A 16-kg triangular plate is supported by three wires as shown. Determine the tension in each wire, knowing that $a = 150$ mm.

2.84 Solve Prob. 2.83, assuming that $a = 200$ mm.

600 mm

400 mm

200 mm

Fig. P2.83

2 m

4 m

8 m

7.5 m

1 m

3 m

Fig. P2.85

2.85 In trying to move across a slippery icy surface, a 78-kg man uses two ropes AB and AC. Knowing that the force exerted on the man by the icy surface is perpendicular to that surface, determine the tension in each rope.

2.86 Solve Prob. 2.85, assuming that a friend is helping the man at A by pulling on him with a force $\mathbf{P} = -(225 \text{ N})\mathbf{k}$.

2.87 A container of weight $W = 360$ N is supported by cables AB and AC, which are tied to ring A. Knowing that $Q = 0$, determine (a) the magnitude of the force $\mathbf{P}$ which must be applied to the ring to maintain the container in the position shown, (b) the corresponding values of the tension in cables AB and AC.

2.88 Solve Prob. 2.87, knowing that $\mathbf{Q} = (60 \text{ N})\mathbf{k}$.

2.89 A container is supported by a single cable which passes through a frictionless ring A and is attached to fixed points B and C. Two forces $\mathbf{P} = P\mathbf{i}$ and $\mathbf{Q} = Q\mathbf{k}$ are applied to the ring to maintain the container in the position shown. Knowing that the weight of the container is $W = 660$ N, determine the magnitudes of $\mathbf{P}$ and $\mathbf{Q}$. (Hint. The tension must be the same in portions AB and AC of the cable.)

2.90 Determine the weight W of the container of Prob. 2.89, knowing that $P = 478$ N.

2.91 Cable BAC passes through a frictionless ring A and is attached to fixed supports at B and C, while cables AD and AE are both tied to the ring and are attached, respectively, to supports at D and E. Knowing that a 1000-N vertical load $\mathbf{P}$ is applied to ring A, determine the tension in each of the three cables.

2.92 Knowing that the tension in cable AE of Prob. 2.91 is 375N, determine (a) the magnitude of the load $\mathbf{P}$, (b) the tension in cables BAC and AD.

220 mm

160 mm

240 mm

120 mm

480 mm

Fig. P2.87 and P2.89

350 mm   900 mm

500 mm

1200 mm

1600 mm

Fig. P2.91

Fig. P2.93

2.93 A 6-kg circular plate of 200-mm radius is supported as shown by three wires of equal length L. Knowing that $\alpha = 30°$, determine the smallest permissible value of the length L if the tension is not to exceed 35 N in any of the wires.

Fig. P2.94

2.94 Collars A and B are connected by a 440-mm wire and may slide freely on frictionless rods. If a force Q of magnitude 450 N is applied to collar A as shown, determine (a) the tension in the wire when $c = 80$ mm, (b) the corresponding magnitude of the force P required to maintain the equilibrium of the system.

2.95 Solve Prob. 2.94, assuming that $c = 280$ mm.

Review and Summary

In this chapter we have studied the effect of forces on particles, i.e., on bodies of such shape and size that all forces acting on them may be assumed applied at the same point.

Fig. 2.35

Resultant of two forces

Forces are *vector quantities;* they are characterized by a *point of application*, a *magnitude*, and a *direction*, and add according to the *parallelogram law* (Fig. 2.35). The magnitude and direction of the resultant R of two forces P and Q may be determined either graphically or by trigonometry, using successively the law of cosines and the law of sines [Sample Prob. 2.1].

Fig. 2.36

Any given force acting on a particle may be resolved into two or more *components*, i.e., it may be replaced by two or more forces which have the same effect on the particle. A force **F** may be resolved into two components **P** and **Q** by drawing a parallelogram which has **F** for its diagonal; the components **P** and **Q** are then represented by the two adjacent sides of the parallelogram (Fig. 2.36) and may be determined either graphically or by trigonometry [Sec. 2.6].

A force **F** is said to have been resolved into two *rectangular components* if its components F_x and F_y are perpendicular to each other and directed along the coordinates axes (Fig. 2.37). Introducing the *unit vectors* **i** and **j** along the x and y axes, respectively, we write [Sec. 2.7]

$$\mathbf{F}_x = F_x\mathbf{i} \qquad \mathbf{F}_y = F_y\mathbf{j} \tag{2.6}$$

and

$$\mathbf{F} = F_x\mathbf{i} + F_y\mathbf{j} \tag{2.7}$$

where F_x and F_y are the *scalar components* of **F**. These components, which may be positive or negative, are defined by the relations

$$F_x = F\cos\theta \qquad F_y = F\sin\theta \tag{2.8}$$

When the rectangular components F_x and F_y of a force **F** are given, the angle θ defining the direction of the force may be obtained by writing

$$\tan\theta = \frac{F_y}{F_x} \tag{2.9}$$

The magnitude F of the force may then be obtained by solving one of the equations (2.8) for F or by applying the Pythagorean theorem and writing

$$F = \sqrt{F_x^2 + F_y^2} \tag{2.10}$$

When *three or more coplanar forces* act on a particle, the rectangular components of their resultant **R** may be obtained by adding algebraically the corresponding components of the given forces [Sec. 2.8]. We have

$$R_x = \Sigma F_x \qquad R_y = \Sigma F_y \tag{2.13}$$

The magnitude and direction of **R** may then be determined from relations similar to Eqs. (2.9) and (2.10) [Sample Prob. 2.3].

Components of a force

Rectangular components

Unit vectors

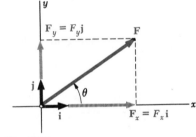

Fig. 2.37

Resultant of several coplanar forces

A force **F** in *three-dimensional space* may be resolved into rectangular components $\mathbf{F}_x$, $\mathbf{F}_y$, and $\mathbf{F}_z$ [Sec. 2.12]. Denoting by θ_x, θ_y, and θ_z, respectively, the angles that **F** forms with the x, y, and z axes (Fig. 2.38), we have

Forces in space

$$F_x = F \cos \theta_x \qquad F_y = F \cos \theta_y \qquad F_z = F \cos \theta_z \qquad (2.19)$$

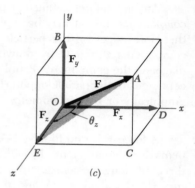

Fig. 2.38

(a) (b) (c)

Direction cosines

The cosines of θ_x, θ_y, θ_z are known as the *direction cosines* of the force **F**. Introducing the unit vectors **i**, **j**, **k** along the coordinate axes, we write

$$\mathbf{F} = F_x\mathbf{i} + F_y\mathbf{j} + F_z\mathbf{k} \qquad (2.20)$$

or

$$\mathbf{F} = F(\cos \theta_x\mathbf{i} + \cos \theta_y\mathbf{j} + \cos \theta_z\mathbf{k}) \qquad (2.21)$$

which shows (Fig. 2.39) that **F** is the product of its magnitude F and of the unit vector

$$\boldsymbol{\lambda} = \cos \theta_x\mathbf{i} + \cos \theta_y\mathbf{j} + \cos \theta_z\mathbf{k} \qquad (2.22)$$

Since the magnitude of $\boldsymbol{\lambda}$ is equal to unity, we must have

$$\cos^2 \theta_x + \cos^2 \theta_y + \cos^2 \theta_z = 1 \qquad (2.24)$$

Fig. 2.39

When the rectangular components F_x, F_y, F_z of a force **F** are given, the magnitude F of the force is found by writing

$$F = \sqrt{F_x^2 + F_y^2 + F_z^2} \qquad (2.18)$$

and the direction cosines of **F** are obtained from Eqs. (2.19). We have

$$\cos \theta_x = \frac{F_x}{F} \qquad \cos \theta_y = \frac{F_y}{F} \qquad \cos \theta_z = \frac{F_z}{F} \qquad (2.25)$$

When a force **F** is defined in three-dimensional space by its magnitude F and two points M and N on its line of action [Sec. 2.13], its rectangular components may by obtained as follows: We first express the vector $\overrightarrow{MN}$ joining points M and N in terms of its components d_x, d_y, and d_z (Fig. 2.40); we write

$$\overrightarrow{MN} = d_x\mathbf{i} + d_y\mathbf{j} + d_z\mathbf{k} \qquad (2.26)$$

We next determine the unit vector **λ** along the line of action of **F** by dividing $\overrightarrow{MN}$ by its magnitude $MN = d$:

$$\boldsymbol{\lambda} = \frac{\overrightarrow{MN}}{MN} = \frac{1}{d}(d_x\mathbf{i} + d_y\mathbf{j} + d_z\mathbf{k}) \qquad (2.27)$$

Recalling that **F** is equal to the product of F and **λ**, we have

$$\mathbf{F} = F\boldsymbol{\lambda} = \frac{F}{d}(d_x\mathbf{i} + d_y\mathbf{j} + d_z\mathbf{k}) \qquad (2.28)$$

from which it follows [Sample Probs. 2.7 and 2.8] that the scalar components of **F** are, respectively,

$$F_x = \frac{Fd_x}{d} \qquad F_y = \frac{Fd_y}{d} \qquad F_z = \frac{Fd_z}{d} \qquad (2.29)$$

When *two or more forces* act on a particle in *three-dimensional space*, the rectangular components of their resultant **R** may be obtained by adding algebraically the corresponding components of the given forces [Sec. 2.14]. We have

$$R_x = \Sigma F_x \qquad R_y = \Sigma F_y \qquad R_z = \Sigma F_z \qquad (2.31)$$

The magnitude and direction of **R** may then be determined from relations similar to Eqs. (2.18) and (2.25) [Sample Prob. 2.8].

A particle is said to be in *equilibrium* when the resultant of all the forces acting on it is zero [Sec. 2.9]. The particle will then remain at rest (if originally at rest) or move with constant speed in a straight line (if originally in motion) [Sec. 2.10].

To solve a problem involving a particle in equilibrium, one first should draw a *free-body diagram* of the particle showing all the forces acting on it [Sec. 2.11]. If *only three coplanar forces* act on the particle, a *force triangle* may be drawn to express that the particle is in equilibrium. This triangle may be solved graphically or by trigonometry for no more than two unknowns [Sample Prob. 2.4]. If *more than three coplanar forces* are involved, the equations of equilibrium

$$\Sigma F_x = 0 \qquad \Sigma F_y = 0 \qquad (2.15)$$

should be used and solved for no more than two unknowns [Sample Prob. 2.6].

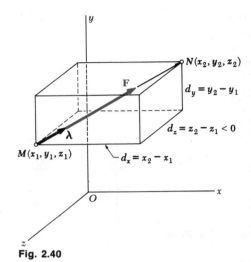

Fig. 2.40

Resultant of forces in space

Equilibrium of a particle

Free-body diagram

Equilibrium in space

When a particle is in *equilibrium in three-dimensional space* [Sec. 2.15), the three equations of equilibrium

$$\Sigma F_x = 0 \qquad \Sigma F_y = 0 \qquad \Sigma F_z = 0 \qquad (2.34)$$

should be used and solved for no more than three unknowns [Sample Prob. 2.9].

Review Problems

2.96 (*a*) Express the weight W required to maintain equilibrium in terms of P, d, and h. (*b*) For $W = 800$ N, $P = 200$ N, and $d = 600$ mm, determine the value of h consistent with equilibrium.

Fig. P2.96

2.97 A cable loop of length 1.5 m is placed around a crate. Knowing that the mass of the crate is 300 kg, determine the tension in the cable for each of the arrangements shown.

(*a*)   (*b*)

Fig. P2.97

Fig. P2.98 and P2.99

2.98 Knowing that the magnitude of the force **P** is 375 N, determine the resultant of the three forces applied at *A*.

2.99 Determine the range of values of P for which the resultant of the three forces applied at A does not exceed 875 N.

2.100 A container is supported by three cables as shown. Determine the weight W of the container, knowing that the tension in cable AB is 500 N.

Fig. P2.100

Fig. P2.102 and P2.103

2.101 In Prob. 2.100, determine the angles θ_x, θ_y, and θ_z for the force exerted at D by cable AD.

2.102 Knowing that $P = 300$ N, determine the tension in cables AC and BC.

2.103 Determine the range of values of **P** for which both cables remain taut.

Fig. P2.104 and P2.105

2.104 The directions of the 300-N forces may vary, but the angle between the forces is always 45°. Determine the value of α for which the resultant of the forces acting at A is directed vertically upward.

2.105 Determine the resultant of the three forces acting at A when (a) $\alpha = 0$, (b) $\alpha = 25°$.

2.106 A 1200-N force acts at the origin in a direction defined by the angles $\theta_x = 65°$ and $\theta_y = 40°$. It is also known that the z component of the force is positive. Determine the value of θ_z and the components of the force.

2.107 Three wires are connected at point D, which is located 450 mm below the T-shaped pipe support ABC. Determine the tension in each wire when a 80-kg cylinder is suspended from point D as shown.

Fig. P2.107

The following problems are designed to be solved with a computer.

2.C1 Write a computer program which can be used to determine the magnitude and direction of the resultant of n forces which act at a fixed point A. Use this program to solve (a) Sample Prob. 2.3, (b) Prob. 2.28.

Fig. P2.C1

Fig. P2.C2

2.C2 A 300-kg crate is supported by the rope-and-pulley arrangement shown. Write a computer program which can be used to determine, for a given value of β, the magnitude and direction of the force $\mathbf{F}$ which should be exerted on the free end of the rope. Use this program to calculate F and α for values of β from 0 to 30° at 5° intervals.

2.C3 A cylinder of weight $W = 650$ N is supported by two cables AC and BC, each 4.6 m long, which are attached to the top of vertical posts. A horizontal force $\mathbf{P}$, perpendicular to the plane containing the posts, holds the cylinder in the position shown. Write a computer program and use it to calculate the elevation h, the magnitude of $\mathbf{P}$, and the tension in each cable for values of a from 0 to 2.8 m at 0.4-m intervals.

Fig. P2.C3

2.C4 Write a computer program which can be used to calculate the magnitude and direction angles of the resultant of n forces which are applied at the origin and act along lines OA_n. For the data given below, use this program to determine the magnitude and direction of (a) $\mathbf{F}_1 + \mathbf{F}_2$, (b) $\mathbf{F}_1 + \mathbf{F}_2 + \mathbf{F}_3$, (c) $\mathbf{F}_1 + \mathbf{F}_2 + \mathbf{F}_3 + \mathbf{F}_4$.

Fig. P2.C4

	F_n, N	x_n, mm	y_n, mm	z_n, mm
$\mathbf{F}_1$	500	400	200	180
$\mathbf{F}_2$	750	500	300	−200
$\mathbf{F}_3$	1000	−180	−60	300
$\mathbf{F}_4$	250	120	280	−400

Rigid Bodies:
Equivalent Systems
of Forces

3.1. Introduction. In the preceding chapter it was assumed that each of the bodies considered could be treated as a single particle. Such a view, however, is not always possible, and a body, in general, should be treated as a combination of a large number of particles. The size of the body will have to be taken into consideration, as well as the fact that forces will act on different particles and thus will have different points of application.

Most of the bodies considered in elementary mechanics are assumed to be *rigid*, a *rigid body* being defined as one which does not deform. Actual structures and machines, however, are never absolutely rigid and deform under the loads to which they are subjected. But these deformations are usually small and do not appreciably affect the conditions of equilibrium or motion of the structure under consideration. They are important, though, as far as the resistance of the structure to failure is concerned, and are considered in the study of mechanics of materials.

In this chapter we shall study the effect of forces exerted on a rigid body and we shall learn how to replace a given system of forces by a simpler equivalent system. Our analysis will rest on the fundamental assumption that the effect of a given force on a rigid body remains unchanged if that force is moved along its line of action (*principle of transmissibility*). It follows that forces acting on a rigid body may be represented by *sliding vectors*, as indicated earlier in Sec. 2.3.

Two important concepts associated with the effect of a force on a rigid body are the *moment of a force about a point* (Sec. 3.6) and the *moment of a force about an axis* (Sec. 3.11). Since the determination of these quantities involves the computation of vector products and scalar products of two vectors, the fundamentals of vector algebra will be introduced in this chapter and applied to the solution of problems involving forces acting on rigid bodies.

Another concept introduced in this chapter is that of a *couple*, i.e., the combination of two forces which have the same magnitude, parallel lines of action, and opposite sense (Sec. 3.12). As we shall see, any system of forces acting on a rigid body may be replaced by an equivalent system consisting of one force attached at a given point and one couple. This basic system is called a *force-couple system*. In the case of concurrent, coplanar, or parallel forces, the equivalent force-couple system may be further reduced to a single force, called the *resultant* of the system, or to a single couple, called the *resultant couple* of the system.

3.2. External and Internal Forces. Forces acting on rigid bodies may be separated into two groups (1) *external forces*, (2) *internal forces*.

1. The *external forces* represent the action of other bodies on the rigid body under consideration. They are entirely responsible for the external behavior of the rigid body. They will either cause it to move or assure that it remains at rest. We shall be concerned only with external forces in this chapter and in Chaps. 4 and 5.
2. The *internal forces* are the forces which hold together the particles forming the rigid body. If the rigid body is structurally composed of several parts, the forces holding the component parts together are also defined as internal forces. Internal forces will be considered in Chaps. 6 and 7.

As an example of external forces, we shall consider the forces acting on a disabled truck that men are pulling forward by means of a rope attached to the front bumper (Fig. 3.1). The external forces acting on the truck are shown in a *free-body diagram* (Fig. 3.2). Let us first consider the *weight* of the truck. Although it embodies the effect of the earth's pull on each of the particles forming the truck, the weight may be represented by the single force **W**. The *point of application* of this force, i.e., the point at which the force acts, is defined as the *center of gravity* of the truck. It will be seen in Chap. 5 how centers of gravity may be determined. The weight **W** tends to make the truck move vertically downward. In fact, it would actually cause the truck to move downward, i.e., to fall, if it were not for the presence of the ground. The ground opposes the downward motion of the truck by means of the reactions R_1 and R_2. These forces are exerted *by* the ground *on* the truck and must therefore be included among the external forces acting on the truck.

The men pulling on the rope exert the force **F**. The point of application of **F** is on the front bumper. The force **F** tends to make the truck move forward in a straight line and does actually make it move, since no external force opposes this motion. (Rolling resistance has been neglected here for simplicity.) This forward motion of the truck, during which all straight lines remain parallel to themselves (the floor of the truck remains horizontal, and its walls remain vertical), is known as a *translation*. Other forces might cause the truck to move differently. For example, the force exerted by a jack placed under the front axle would cause the truck to pivot about its rear axle. Such a motion is a *rotation*. It may be concluded, therefore, that each of the *external forces* acting on a *rigid body* can, if unopposed, impart to the rigid body a motion of translation or rotation, or both.

Fig. 3.1

Fig. 3.2

3.3. Principle of Transmissibility. Equivalent Forces.

The *principle of transmissibility* states that the conditions of equilibrium or of motion of a rigid body will remain unchanged if a force **F** acting at a given point of the rigid body is replaced by a force **F′** of the same magnitude and same direction, but acting at a different point, *provided that the two forces have the same line of action* (Fig. 3.3). The two forces **F** and **F′** have the same effect on the rigid body and are said to be *equivalent*. This principle, which states in fact that the action of a force may be *transmitted* along its line of action, is based on experimental evidence. It *cannot* be derived from the properties established so far in this text and must therefore be accepted as an experimental law. However, as we shall see in Sec. 16.5, the principle of transmissibility may be derived from the study of the dynamics of rigid bodies, but this study requires the introduction of all Newton's three laws and of a number of other concepts as well. We shall therefore base our study of the statics of rigid bodies on the three principles introduced so far, i.e., the parallelogram law of addition, Newton's first law, and the principle of transmissibility.

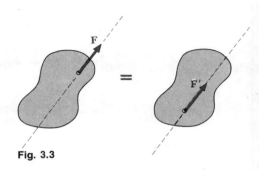

Fig. 3.3

It was indicated in Chap. 2 that the forces acting on a particle could be represented by vectors. These vectors had a well-defined point of application, namely, the particle itself, and were therefore fixed, or bound, vectors. In the case of forces acting on a rigid body, however, the point of application of the force does not matter, as long as the line of action remains unchanged. Thus forces acting on a rigid body must be represented by different kinds of vectors, known as *sliding vectors*, since these vectors may be allowed to slide along their line of action. We should note that all the properties which will be derived in the following sections for the forces acting on a rigid body will be valid more generally for any system of sliding vectors. In order to keep our presentation more intuitive, however, we shall carry it out in terms of physical forces rather than in terms of mathematical sliding vectors.

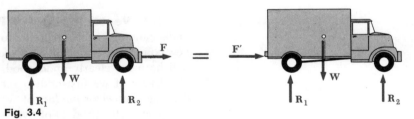

Fig. 3.4

Returning to the example of the truck, we first observe that the line of action of the force **F** is a horizontal line passing through both the front and the rear bumpers of the truck (Fig. 3.4). Using the principle of transmissibility, we may therefore replace **F** by an *equivalent force* **F′** acting on the rear bumper. In other words, the conditions of motion are unaffected, and all the other external forces acting on the truck (**W**, **R**₁, **R**₂) remain unchanged if the men push on the rear bumper instead of pulling on the front bumper.

The principle of transmissibility and the concept of equivalent forces have limitations, however. Consider, for example, a short bar *AB* acted upon by equal and opposite axial forces $\mathbf{P}_1$ and $\mathbf{P}_2$, as shown in Fig. 3.5a. According to the principle of transmissibility, the force $\mathbf{P}_2$ may be replaced by a force $\mathbf{P}_2'$ having the same magnitude, same direction, and same line of action, but acting at A instead of B (Fig. 3.5b). The forces $\mathbf{P}_1$ and $\mathbf{P}_2'$ acting on the same particle may be added according to the rules of Chap. 2, and, being equal and opposite, their sum is found equal to zero. The original system of forces shown in Fig. 3.5a is thus equivalent to no force at all (Fig. 3.5c) from the point of view of the external behavior of the bar.

Fig. 3.5

Consider now the two equal and opposite forces $\mathbf{P}_1$ and $\mathbf{P}_2$ acting on the bar AB as shown in Fig. 3.5d. The force $\mathbf{P}_2$ may be replaced by a force $\mathbf{P}_2'$ having the same magnitude, same direction, and same line of action, but acting at B instead of A (Fig. 3.5e). The forces $\mathbf{P}_1$ and $\mathbf{P}_2'$ may then be added, and their sum is found again to be zero (Fig. 3.5f). From the point of view of the mechanics of rigid bodies, the systems shown in Fig. 3.5a and d are thus equivalent. But the *internal forces* and *deformations* produced by the two systems are clearly different. The bar of Fig. 3.5a is in *tension* and, if not absolutely rigid, will increase in length slightly; the bar of Fig. 3.5d is in *compression* and, if not absolutely rigid, will decrease in length slightly. Thus, while the principle of transmissibility may be used freely to determine the conditions of motion or equilibrium of rigid bodies and to compute the external forces acting on these bodies, it should be avoided, or at least used with care, in determining internal forces and deformations.

3.4. Vector Product of Two Vectors. In order to gain a better understanding of the effect of a force on a rigid body, we shall introduce a new concept, the concept of *moment of a force about a point*. This concept will be more clearly understood, and we shall be able to apply it more effectively, if we first add to the mathematical tools at our disposal by defining the *vector product* of two vectors.

The vector product of two vectors $\mathbf{P}$ and $\mathbf{Q}$ is defined as the vector $\mathbf{V}$ which satisfies the following conditions:

1. The line of action of $\mathbf{V}$ is perpendicular to the plane containing $\mathbf{P}$ and $\mathbf{Q}$ (Fig. 3.6).
2. The magnitude of $\mathbf{V}$ is the product of the magnitudes of $\mathbf{P}$ and $\mathbf{Q}$ and of the sine of the angle θ formed by $\mathbf{P}$ and $\mathbf{Q}$ (the measure of which will always be 180° or less); we thus have

$$V = PQ \sin \theta \qquad (3.1)$$

Fig. 3.6

3. The sense of **V** is such that a person located at the tip of **V** will observe as counterclockwise the rotation through θ which brings the vector **P** in line with the vector **Q**; note that if **P** and **Q** do not have a common point of application, they should first be redrawn from the same point. The three vectors **P**, **Q**, and **V**—taken in that order—are said to form a *right-handed triad.*†

As stated above, the vector **V** satisfying these three conditions (which define it uniquely) is referred to as the vector product of **P** and **Q**; it is represented by the mathematical expression

$$V = P \times Q \tag{3.2}$$

Because of the notation used, the vector product of two vectors **P** and **Q** is also referred to as the *cross product* of **P** and **Q**.

It follows from Eq. (3.1) that, when two vectors **P** and **Q** have either the same direction or opposite directions, their vector product is zero. In the general case when the angle θ formed by the two vectors is neither 0° nor 180°, Eq. (3.1) may be given a simple geometric interpretation: The magnitude V of the vector product of **P** and **Q** measures the area of the parallelogram which has **P** and **Q** for sides (Fig. 3.7). The vector product **P** × **Q** will therefore remain unchanged if we replace **Q** by a vector **Q**′ coplanar with **P** and **Q** and such that the line joining the tips of **Q** and **Q**′ is parallel to **P**. We write

$$V = P \times Q = P \times Q' \tag{3.3}$$

Fig. 3.7

From the third condition used to define the vector product **V** of **P** and **Q**, namely, the condition stating that **P**, **Q**, and **V** must form a right-handed triad, it follows that vector products *are not commutative,* i.e., **Q** × **P** is not equal to **P** × **Q**. Indeed, we may easily check that **Q** × **P** is represented by the vector −**V** equal and opposite to **V**. We thus write

$$Q \times P = -(P \times Q) \tag{3.4}$$

Example. Let us compute the vector product **V** = **P** × **Q** of the vector **P** of magnitude 6 lying in the zx plane at an angle of 30° with the x axis, and of the vector **Q** of magnitude 4 lying along the x axis (Fig. 3.8).

It follows immediately from the definition of the vector product that the vector **V** must lie along the y axis, have the magnitude

$$V = PQ \sin \theta = (6)(4) \sin 30° = 12$$

and be directed upward.

Fig. 3.8

† We should note that the x, y, and z axes used in Chap. 2 form a right-handed system of orthogonal axes and that the unit vectors **i**, **j**, **k** defined in Sec. 2.12 form a right-handed orthogonal triad.

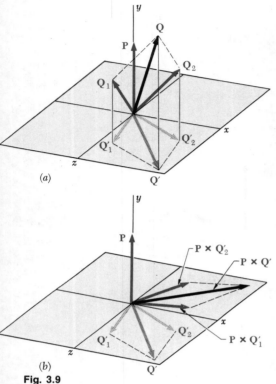

(a)

(b)

Fig. 3.9

We saw that the commutative property does not apply to vector products. We may wonder whether the *distributive* property holds, i.e., whether the relation

$$\mathbf{P} \times (\mathbf{Q}_1 + \mathbf{Q}_2) = \mathbf{P} \times \mathbf{Q}_1 + \mathbf{P} \times \mathbf{Q}_2 \tag{3.5}$$

is valid. The answer is *yes*. Many readers are probably willing to accept without formal proof an answer which they intuitively feel is correct. However, since the entire structure of vector algebra and of statics depends upon the relation (3.5), we shall take time out to derive it.

We may, without any loss of generality, assume that $\mathbf{P}$ is directed along the y axis (Fig. 3.9a). Denoting by $\mathbf{Q}$ the sum of $\mathbf{Q}_1$ and $\mathbf{Q}_2$, we drop perpendiculars from the tips of $\mathbf{Q}$, $\mathbf{Q}_1$, and $\mathbf{Q}_2$ onto the zx plane, defining in this way the vectors $\mathbf{Q}'$, $\mathbf{Q}'_1$, and $\mathbf{Q}'_2$. These vectors will be referred to, respectively, as the *projections* of $\mathbf{Q}$, $\mathbf{Q}_1$, and $\mathbf{Q}_2$ on the zx plane. Recalling the property expressed by Eq. (3.3), we note that the left-hand member of Eq. (3.5) may be replaced by $\mathbf{P} \times \mathbf{Q}'$ and that, similarly, the vector products $\mathbf{P} \times \mathbf{Q}_1$ and $\mathbf{P} \times \mathbf{Q}_2$ may respectively be replaced by $\mathbf{P} \times \mathbf{Q}'_1$ and $\mathbf{P} \times \mathbf{Q}'_2$. Thus, the relation to be proved may be written in the form

$$\mathbf{P} \times \mathbf{Q}' = \mathbf{P} \times \mathbf{Q}'_1 + \mathbf{P} \times \mathbf{Q}'_2 \tag{3.5'}$$

We now observe that $\mathbf{P} \times \mathbf{Q}'$ may be obtained from $\mathbf{Q}'$ by multiplying this vector by the scalar P and rotating it counterclockwise through 90° in the zx plane (Fig. 3.9b); the other two vector products in (3.5') may be obtained in the same manner from $\mathbf{Q}'_1$ and $\mathbf{Q}'_2$, respectively. Now, since the projection of a parallelogram onto an arbitrary plane is a parallelogram, the projection $\mathbf{Q}'$ of the sum $\mathbf{Q}$ of $\mathbf{Q}_1$ and $\mathbf{Q}_2$ must be the sum of the projections $\mathbf{Q}'_1$ and $\mathbf{Q}'_2$ of $\mathbf{Q}_1$ and $\mathbf{Q}_2$ on the same plane (Fig. 3.9a). This relation between the vectors $\mathbf{Q}'$, $\mathbf{Q}'_1$, and $\mathbf{Q}'_2$ will still hold after the three vectors have been multiplied by the scalar P and rotated through 90° (Fig. 3.9b). Thus the relation (3.5') has been proved and we can now be sure that the distributive property holds for vector products.

The third property, the associative property, does not apply to vector products; we have in general

$$(\mathbf{P} \times \mathbf{Q}) \times \mathbf{S} \neq \mathbf{P} \times (\mathbf{Q} \times \mathbf{S}) \tag{3.6}$$

3.5. Vector Products Expressed in Terms of Rectangular Components. We shall now determine the vector product of any two of the unit vectors, $\mathbf{i}$, $\mathbf{j}$, $\mathbf{k}$, defined in Chap. 2. Consider first the product $\mathbf{i} \times \mathbf{j}$ (Fig. 3.10a). Since both vectors have a magnitude equal to 1 and since they are at a right angle to each other, their vector product will also be a unit vector. This unit vector must be $\mathbf{k}$, since the vectors $\mathbf{i}$, $\mathbf{j}$, $\mathbf{k}$ are mutually perpendicular and form a right-handed triad. On the other hand, the product $\mathbf{j} \times \mathbf{i}$ will be equal to $-\mathbf{k}$ since the 90° rotation which brings $\mathbf{j}$ into $\mathbf{i}$ is observed as counterclockwise by a person located at the tip of $-\mathbf{k}$ (Fig. 3.10b). Finally it should be observed that the vector product of a unit vector by itself, such as $\mathbf{i} \times \mathbf{i}$, is equal to zero, since both vectors have the same direction. The vector products of the various possible pairs of unit vectors are

$$
\begin{array}{lll}
\mathbf{i} \times \mathbf{i} = 0 & \mathbf{j} \times \mathbf{i} = -\mathbf{k} & \mathbf{k} \times \mathbf{i} = \mathbf{j} \\
\mathbf{i} \times \mathbf{j} = \mathbf{k} & \mathbf{j} \times \mathbf{j} = 0 & \mathbf{k} \times \mathbf{j} = -\mathbf{i} \\
\mathbf{i} \times \mathbf{k} = -\mathbf{j} & \mathbf{j} \times \mathbf{k} = \mathbf{i} & \mathbf{k} \times \mathbf{k} = 0
\end{array} \tag{3.7}
$$

By arranging in a circle and in counterclockwise order the three letters representing the unit vectors (Fig. 3.11), we may simplify the determination of the sign of the vector product of two unit vectors: The product of two unit vectors will be positive if they follow each other in counterclockwise order, and negative otherwise.

We may now easily express the vector product $\mathbf{V}$ of two given vectors $\mathbf{P}$ and $\mathbf{Q}$ in terms of the rectangular components of these vectors. Resolving $\mathbf{P}$ and $\mathbf{Q}$ into components, we first write

$$
\mathbf{V} = \mathbf{P} \times \mathbf{Q} = (P_x\mathbf{i} + P_y\mathbf{j} + P_z\mathbf{k}) \times (Q_x\mathbf{i} + Q_y\mathbf{j} + Q_z\mathbf{k})
$$

Making use of the distributive property, we express $\mathbf{V}$ as the sum of vector products such as $P_x\mathbf{i} \times Q_y\mathbf{j}$. Observing that each of the expressions obtained is equal to the vector product of two unit vectors, such as $\mathbf{i} \times \mathbf{j}$, multiplied by the product of two scalars, such as P_xQ_y, and recalling the identities (3.7), we obtain, after factoring $\mathbf{i}$, $\mathbf{j}$, and $\mathbf{k}$,

$$
\mathbf{V} = (P_yQ_z - P_zQ_y)\mathbf{i} + (P_zQ_x - P_xQ_z)\mathbf{j} + (P_xQ_y - P_yQ_x)\mathbf{k} \tag{3.8}
$$

The rectangular components of the vector product $\mathbf{V}$ are thus found to be

$$
\begin{aligned}
V_x &= P_yQ_z - P_zQ_y \\
V_y &= P_zQ_x - P_xQ_z \\
V_z &= P_xQ_y - P_yQ_x
\end{aligned} \tag{3.9}
$$

Returning to Eq. (3.8), we observe that its right-hand member represents the expansion of a determinant. The vector product $\mathbf{V}$ may thus be expressed in the following form, more easily memorized:†

$$
\mathbf{V} = \begin{vmatrix} \mathbf{i} & \mathbf{j} & \mathbf{k} \\ P_x & P_y & P_z \\ Q_x & Q_y & Q_z \end{vmatrix} \tag{3.10}
$$

† Any determinant consisting of three rows and three columns may be evaluated by repeating the first and second columns and forming products along each diagonal line. The sum of the products obtained along the colored lines is then subtracted from the sum of the products obtained along the black lines.

(a)

(b)

Fig. 3.10

Fig. 3.11

(a)

(b)

Fig. 3.12

3.6. Moment of a Force about a Point. Let us now consider a force **F** acting on a rigid body (Fig. 3.12). As we know, the force **F** is represented by a vector which defines its magnitude and direction. However, the effect of the force on the rigid body depends also upon its point of application A. The position of A may be conveniently defined by the vector **r** which joins the fixed reference point O with A; this vector is known as the *position vector* of A.† The position vector **r** and the force **F** define the plane shown in Fig. 3.12a.

We shall define the *moment of* **F** *about* O as the vector product of **r** and **F**:

$$\mathbf{M}_O = \mathbf{r} \times \mathbf{F} \qquad (3.11)$$

According to the definition of the vector product given in Sec. 3.4, the moment $\mathbf{M}_O$ must be perpendicular to the plane containing O and the force **F**. The sense of $\mathbf{M}_O$ is defined by the sense of the rotation which would bring the vector **r** in line with the vector **F**; this rotation should be observed as *counterclockwise* by an observer located at the tip of $\mathbf{M}_O$. Another way of defining the sense of $\mathbf{M}_O$ is furnished by the *right-hand rule:* Close your right hand and hold it so that your fingers are curled in the sense of the rotation that **F** would impart to the rigid body about a fixed axis directed along the line of action of $\mathbf{M}_O$; your thumb will indicate the sense of the moment $\mathbf{M}_O$ (Fig. 3.12b).

Finally, denoting by θ the angle between the lines of action of the position vector **r** and the force **F**, we find that the magnitude of the moment of **F** about O is

$$M_O = rF \sin \theta = Fd \qquad (3.12)$$

where d represents the perpendicular distance from O to the line of action of **F**. Since the tendency of a force **F** to make a rigid body rotate about a fixed axis perpendicular to the force depends upon the distance of **F** from that axis, as well as upon the magnitude of **F**, we note that *the magnitude of* $\mathbf{M}_O$ *measures the tendency of the force* **F** *to make the rigid body rotate about a fixed axis directed along* $\mathbf{M}_O$.

In the SI system of units, where a force is expressed in newtons (N) and a distance in metres (m), the moment of a force will be expressed in newton-metres (N·m).

---

† We may easily verify that position vectors obey the law of vector addition and, thus, are truly vectors. Consider, for example, the position vectors **r** and **r**′ of A with respect to two reference points O and O', and the position vector **s** of O with respect to O' (Fig. 3.40a, Sec. 3.16). We check that the position vector $\mathbf{r}' = \overrightarrow{O'A}$ may be obtained from the position vectors $\mathbf{s} = \overrightarrow{O'O}$ and $\mathbf{r} = \overrightarrow{OA}$ by applying the triangle rule for the addition of vectors.

We may observe that the moment $\mathbf{M}_O$ of a force about a point, while it depends upon the magnitude, the line of action, and the sense of the force, does *not* depend upon the actual position of the point of application of the force along its line of action. Conversely, the moment $\mathbf{M}_O$ of a force $\mathbf{F}$ does not characterize the position of the point of application of $\mathbf{F}$.

However, as we shall see presently, the moment $\mathbf{M}_O$ of a force $\mathbf{F}$ of given magnitude and direction *completely defines the line of action of* $\mathbf{F}$. Indeed, the line of action of $\mathbf{F}$ must lie in a plane through O perpendicular to the moment $\mathbf{M}_O$; its distance d from O must be equal to the quotient M_O/F of the magnitudes of $\mathbf{M}_O$ and $\mathbf{F}$; and the sense of $\mathbf{M}_O$ determines whether the line of action of $\mathbf{F}$ is to be drawn on one side or the other of the point O.

We recall from Sec. 3.3 that the principle of transmissibility states that two forces $\mathbf{F}$ and $\mathbf{F}'$ are equivalent (i.e., have the same effect on a rigid body) if they have the same magnitude, same direction, and same line of action. This principle may now be restated as follows: *Two forces $\mathbf{F}$ and $\mathbf{F}'$ are equivalent if, and only if, they are equal* (i.e., have the same magnitude and same direction) *and have equal moments about a given point O.* The necessary and sufficient condition for two forces $\mathbf{F}$ and $\mathbf{F}'$ to be equivalent is thus

$$\mathbf{F} = \mathbf{F}' \quad \text{and} \quad \mathbf{M}_O = \mathbf{M}'_O \tag{3.13}$$

We should observe that it follows from this statement that if the relations (3.13) hold for a given point O, they will hold for any other point.

Problems Involving Only Two Dimensions. Many applications deal with two-dimensional structures, i.e., structures which have length and breadth but only negligible depth, and which are subjected to forces contained in the plane of the structure. Two-dimensional structures and the forces acting on them may be readily represented on a sheet of paper or on a blackboard. Their analysis is therefore considerably simpler than that of three-dimensional structures and forces.

Consider, for example, a rigid slab acted upon by a force $\mathbf{F}$ (Fig. 3.13). The moment of $\mathbf{F}$ about a point O chosen in the plane of the figure is represented by a vector $\mathbf{M}_O$ perpendicular to that plane and of magnitude Fd. In the case of Fig. 3.13a the vector $\mathbf{M}_O$ points *out* of the paper, while in the case of Fig. 3.13b it points *into* the paper. As we look at the figure, we observe the action of $\mathbf{F}$ in the first case as counterclockwise, and in the second case as clockwise. Therefore, it is natural to refer to the sense of the moment of $\mathbf{F}$ about O in Fig. 3.13a as counterclockwise ↰, and in Fig. 3.13b as clockwise ↲.

Since the moment of a force $\mathbf{F}$ acting in the plane of the figure must be perpendicular to that plane, we need only specify the *magnitude* and the *sense* of the moment of $\mathbf{F}$ about O. This may be done by assigning to the magnitude M_O of the moment a positive or negative sign, according to whether the vector $\mathbf{M}_O$ points out of or into the paper.

(a) $M_O = +Fd$

(b) $M_O = -Fd$

Fig. 3.13

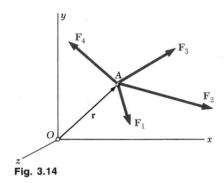

Fig. 3.14

3.7. Varignon's Theorem. The distributive property of vector products may be used to determine the moment of the resultant of several *concurrent forces*. If several forces $\mathbf{F}_1$, $\mathbf{F}_2$, ... are applied at the same point A (Fig. 3.14), and if we denote by $\mathbf{r}$ the position vector of A, it follows immediately from formula (3.5) of Sec. 3.4 that

$$\mathbf{r} \times (\mathbf{F}_1 + \mathbf{F}_2 + \cdots) = \mathbf{r} \times \mathbf{F}_1 + \mathbf{r} \times \mathbf{F}_2 + \cdots \qquad (3.14)$$

In words, *the moment about a given point O of the resultant of several concurrent forces is equal to the sum of the moments of the various forces about the same point O.* This property was originally established by the French mathematician Varignon (1654–1722), long before the introduction of vector algebra, and is known as *Varignon's theorem.*

The relation (3.14) makes it possible to replace the direct determination of the moment of a force $\mathbf{F}$ by the determination of the moments of two or more component forces. As we shall see in the next section, $\mathbf{F}$ will generally be resolved into components parallel to the coordinate axes. However, it may be found more expeditious in some instances to resolve $\mathbf{F}$ into components which are not parallel to the coordinate axes (see Sample Prob. 3.3).

3.8. Rectangular Components of the Moment of a Force. In general, the determination of the moment of a force in space will be considerably simplified if the force and the position vector of its point of application are resolved into rectangular x, y, and z components. Consider, for example, the moment $\mathbf{M}_O$ about O of a force $\mathbf{F}$ of components F_x, F_y, and F_z, applied at a point A of coordinates x, y, and z (Fig. 3.15). Observing that the components of the position vector $\mathbf{r}$ are respectively equal to the coordinates x, y, and z of the point A, we write

$$\mathbf{r} = x\mathbf{i} + y\mathbf{j} + z\mathbf{k} \qquad (3.15)$$
$$\mathbf{F} = F_x\mathbf{i} + F_y\mathbf{j} + F_z\mathbf{k} \qquad (3.16)$$

Substituting for $\mathbf{r}$ and $\mathbf{F}$ from (3.15) and (3.16) into

$$\mathbf{M}_O = \mathbf{r} \times \mathbf{F} \qquad (3.11)$$

and recalling the results obtained in Sec. 3.5, we write the moment $\mathbf{M}_O$ of $\mathbf{F}$ about O in the form

$$\mathbf{M}_O = M_x\mathbf{i} + M_y\mathbf{j} + M_z\mathbf{k} \qquad (3.17)$$

where the components M_x, M_y, and M_z are defined by the relations

$$\begin{aligned} M_x &= yF_z - zF_y \\ M_y &= zF_x - xF_z \\ M_z &= xF_y - yF_x \end{aligned} \qquad (3.18)$$

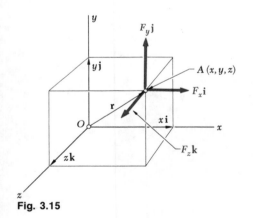

Fig. 3.15

As we shall see in Sec. 3.11, the scalar components M_x, M_y, and M_z of the moment $\mathbf{M}_O$ measure the tendency of the force $\mathbf{F}$ to impart to a rigid body a motion of rotation about the x, y, and z axes, respectively. Substituting from (3.18) into (3.17), we may also write $\mathbf{M}_O$ in the form of the determinant

$$\mathbf{M}_O = \begin{vmatrix} \mathbf{i} & \mathbf{j} & \mathbf{k} \\ x & y & z \\ F_x & F_y & F_z \end{vmatrix} \tag{3.19}$$

To compute the moment $\mathbf{M}_B$ about an arbitrary point B of a force $\mathbf{F}$ applied at A (Fig. 3.16), we must replace the position vector $\mathbf{r}$ in Eq. (3.11) by a vector drawn from B to A. This vector is the *position vector of A relative to B* and will be denoted by $\mathbf{r}_{A/B}$. Observing that $\mathbf{r}_{A/B}$ may be obtained by subtracting $\mathbf{r}_B$ from $\mathbf{r}_A$, we write

$$\mathbf{M}_B = \mathbf{r}_{A/B} \times \mathbf{F} = (\mathbf{r}_A - \mathbf{r}_B) \times \mathbf{F} \tag{3.20}$$

or, using the determinant form,

$$\mathbf{M}_B = \begin{vmatrix} \mathbf{i} & \mathbf{j} & \mathbf{k} \\ x_{A/B} & y_{A/B} & z_{A/B} \\ F_x & F_y & F_z \end{vmatrix} \tag{3.21}$$

where $x_{A/B}$, $y_{A/B}$, and $z_{A/B}$ denote the components of the vector $\mathbf{r}_{A/B}$:

$$x_{A/B} = x_A - x_B \qquad y_{A/B} = y_A - y_B \qquad z_{A/B} = z_A - z_B$$

In the case of *problems involving only two dimensions*, the force $\mathbf{F}$ may be assumed to lie in the xy plane (Fig. 3.17). Carrying $z = 0$ and $F_z = 0$ into the relations (3.19), we obtain

$$\mathbf{M}_O = (xF_y - yF_x)\mathbf{k}$$

We check that the moment of $\mathbf{F}$ about O is perpendicular to the plane of the figure and that it is completely defined by the scalar

$$M_O = M_z = xF_y - yF_x \tag{3.22}$$

As noted earlier, a positive value for M_O indicates that the vector $\mathbf{M}_O$ points out of the paper (the force $\mathbf{F}$ tends to rotate the body counterclockwise about O), and a negative value that the vector $\mathbf{M}_O$ points into the paper (the force $\mathbf{F}$ tends to rotate the body clockwise about O).

To compute the moment about $B(x_B, y_B)$ of a force lying in the xy plane and applied at $A(x_A, y_A)$ (Fig. 3.18), we carry $z_{A/B} = 0$ and $F_z = 0$ in the relations (3.21) and check that the vector $\mathbf{M}_B$ is perpendicular to the xy plane and is defined in magnitude and sense by the scalar

$$M_B = (x_A - x_B)F_y - (y_A - y_B)F_x \tag{3.23}$$

Fig. 3.16

Fig. 3.17

Fig. 3.18

SAMPLE PROBLEM 3.1

A 300-N vertical force is applied to the end of a lever which is attached to a shaft at O. Determine (a) the moment of the 300-N force about O; (b) the magnitude of the horizontal force applied at A which creates the same moment about O; (c) the smallest force applied at A which creates the same moment about O; (d) how far from the shaft a 750-N vertical force must act to create the same moment about O; (e) whether any one of the forces obtained in parts b, c, and d is equivalent to the original force.

a. **Moment about O.** The perpendicular distance from O to the line of action of the 300-N force is

$$d = (0.5 \text{ m}) \cos 60° = 0.25 \text{ m}$$

The magnitude of the moment about O of the 300-N force is

$$M_O = Fd = (300 \text{ N})(0.25 \text{ m}) = 75.0 \text{ N·m}$$

Since the force tends to rotate the lever clockwise about O, the moment will be represented by a vector $\mathbf{M}_O$ perpendicular to the plane of the figure and pointing *into* the paper. We express this fact by writing

$$M_O = 75.0 \text{ N·m} \; \rangle \quad \blacktriangleleft$$

b. **Horizontal Force.** In this case, we have

$$d = (0.5 \text{ m}) \sin 60° = 0.433 \text{ m}$$

Since the moment about O must be 75 N·m, we write

$$M_O = Fd \qquad 75 \text{ N·m} = F(0.433 \text{ m})$$
$$F = 173.2 \text{ N} \qquad\qquad F = 173.2 \text{ N} \rightarrow \quad \blacktriangleleft$$

c. **Smallest Force.** Since $M_O = Fd$, the smallest value of F occurs when d is maximum. We choose the force perpendicular to OA and find $d = 0.5$ m; thus

$$M_O = Fd \qquad 75 \text{ N·m} = F(0.5 \text{ m})$$
$$F = 150 \text{ N} \qquad\qquad F = 150 \text{ N} \; \diagdown 30° \quad \blacktriangleleft$$

d. **750-N Vertical Force.** In this case $M_O = Fd$ yields

$$75 \text{ N·m} = (750 \text{ N})d \qquad\qquad d = 0.1 \text{ m} = 100 \text{ mm}$$

but

$$OB \cos 60° = d \qquad\qquad OB = 200 \text{ mm} \quad \blacktriangleleft$$

e. None of the forces considered in parts b, c, and d is equivalent to the original 300-N force. Although they have the same moment about O, they have different x and y components. In other words, although each force tends to rotate the shaft in the same manner, each causes the lever to pull on the shaft in a different way.

800 N

60°

A

160 mm

B

200 mm

SAMPLE PROBLEM 3.2

A force of 800 N acts on a bracket as shown. Determine the moment of the force about B.

Solution. The moment $\mathbf{M}_B$ of the force $\mathbf{F}$ about B is obtained by forming the vector product

$$\mathbf{M}_B = \mathbf{r}_{A/B} \times \mathbf{F}$$

where $\mathbf{r}_{A/B}$ is the vector drawn from B to A. Resolving $\mathbf{r}_{A/B}$ and $\mathbf{F}$ into rectangular components, we have

$$\mathbf{r}_{A/B} = -(0.2 \text{ m})\mathbf{i} + (0.16 \text{ m})\mathbf{j}$$
$$\mathbf{F} = (800 \text{ N}) \cos 60°\mathbf{i} + (800 \text{ N}) \sin 60°\mathbf{j}$$
$$= (400 \text{ N})\mathbf{i} + (693 \text{ N})\mathbf{j}$$

Recalling the relations (3.7) for the cross products of unit vectors (Sec. 3.5), we obtain

$$\mathbf{M}_B = \mathbf{r}_{A/B} \times \mathbf{F} = [-(0.2 \text{ m})\mathbf{i} + (0.16 \text{ m})\mathbf{j}] \times [(400 \text{ N})\mathbf{i} + (693 \text{ N})\mathbf{j}]$$
$$= -(138.6 \text{ N} \cdot \text{m})\mathbf{k} - (64.0 \text{ N} \cdot \text{m})\mathbf{k}$$
$$= -(202.6 \text{ N} \cdot \text{m})\mathbf{k} \qquad \mathbf{M}_B = 203 \text{ N} \cdot \text{m} \; \downarrow \quad \blacktriangleleft$$

The moment $\mathbf{M}_B$ is a vector perpendicular to the plane of the figure and pointing *into* the paper.

$F_y = (693 \text{ N})\mathbf{j}$

$F = 800 \text{ N}$

60°

A

$F_x = (400 \text{ N})\mathbf{i}$

$+ (0.16 \text{ m})\mathbf{j}$

$\mathbf{r}_{A/B}$

$\mathbf{M}_B$

$-(0.2 \text{ m})\mathbf{i}$

B

20°

A

150 N

900 mm

50°

O

SAMPLE PROBLEM 3.3

A 150-N force acts on the end of the 900-mm lever as shown. Determine the moment of the force about O.

20°

A

Q

900 mm

O

M_O

Solution. The force is replaced by two components, one component $\mathbf{P}$ in the direction of OA and one component $\mathbf{Q}$ perpendicular to OA. Since O is on the line of action of $\mathbf{P}$, the moment of $\mathbf{P}$ about O is zero and the moment of the 150-N force reduces to the moment of $\mathbf{Q}$, which is clockwise and, thus, represented by a negative scalar.

$$Q = (150 \text{ N}) \sin 20° = 51.3 \text{ N}$$
$$M_O = -Q(0.9 \text{ m}) = -(51.3 \text{ N})(0.9 \text{ m}) = -46.2 \text{ N·m}$$

Since the value obtained for the scalar M_O is negative, the moment $\mathbf{M}_O$ points *into* the paper. We write

$$M_O = 46.2 \text{ N·m} \; \downarrow \quad \blacktriangleleft$$

SAMPLE PROBLEM 3.4

A rectangular plate is supported by brackets at A and B and by a wire CD. Knowing that the tension in the wire is 200 N, determine the moment about A of the force exerted by the wire on point C.

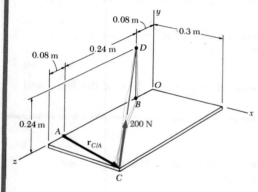

Solution. The moment $\mathbf{M}_A$ about A of the force $\mathbf{F}$ exerted by the wire on point C is obtained by forming the vector product

$$\mathbf{M}_A = \mathbf{r}_{C/A} \times \mathbf{F} \qquad (1)$$

where $\mathbf{r}_{C/A}$ is the vector drawn from A to C,

$$\mathbf{r}_{C/A} = \overrightarrow{AC} = (0.3 \text{ m})\mathbf{i} + (0.08 \text{ m})\mathbf{k} \qquad (2)$$

and where $\mathbf{F}$ is the 200-N force directed along CD. Introducing the unit vector $\boldsymbol{\lambda} = \overrightarrow{CD}/CD$, we write

$$\mathbf{F} = F\boldsymbol{\lambda} = (200 \text{ N})\frac{\overrightarrow{CD}}{CD} \qquad (3)$$

Resolving the vector $\overrightarrow{CD}$ into rectangular components, we have

$$\overrightarrow{CD} = -(0.3 \text{ m})\mathbf{i} + (0.24 \text{ m})\mathbf{j} - (0.32 \text{ m})\mathbf{k} \qquad CD = 0.50 \text{ m}$$

Substituting into (3), we obtain

$$\mathbf{F} = \frac{200 \text{ N}}{0.50 \text{ m}}[-(0.3 \text{ m})\mathbf{i} + (0.24 \text{ m})\mathbf{j} - (0.32 \text{ m})\mathbf{k}]$$
$$= -(120 \text{ N})\mathbf{i} + (96 \text{ N})\mathbf{j} - (128 \text{ N})\mathbf{k} \qquad (4)$$

Substituting for $\mathbf{r}_{C/A}$ and $\mathbf{F}$ from (2) and (4) into (1), and recalling the relations (3.7) of Sec. 3.5, we obtain

$$\mathbf{M}_A = \mathbf{r}_{C/A} \times \mathbf{F} = (0.3\mathbf{i} + 0.08\mathbf{k}) \times (-120\mathbf{i} + 96\mathbf{j} - 128\mathbf{k})$$
$$= (0.3)(96)\mathbf{k} + (0.3)(-128)(-\mathbf{j}) + (0.08)(-120)\mathbf{j} + (0.08)(96)(-\mathbf{i})$$
$$\mathbf{M}_A = -(7.68 \text{ N}\cdot\text{m})\mathbf{i} + (28.8 \text{ N}\cdot\text{m})\mathbf{j} + (28.8 \text{ N}\cdot\text{m})\mathbf{k} \qquad \blacktriangleleft$$

Alternate Solution. As indicated in Sec. 3.8, the moment $\mathbf{M}_A$ may be expressed in the form of a determinant:

$$\mathbf{M}_A = \begin{vmatrix} \mathbf{i} & \mathbf{j} & \mathbf{k} \\ x_C - x_A & y_C - y_A & z_C - z_A \\ F_x & F_y & F_z \end{vmatrix} = \begin{vmatrix} \mathbf{i} & \mathbf{j} & \mathbf{k} \\ 0.3 & 0 & 0.08 \\ -120 & 96 & -128 \end{vmatrix}$$

$$\mathbf{M}_A = -(7.68 \text{ N}\cdot\text{m})\mathbf{i} + (28.8 \text{ N}\cdot\text{m})\mathbf{j} + (28.8 \text{ N}\cdot\text{m})\mathbf{k} \qquad \blacktriangleleft$$

Problems

3.1 A 100-N force is applied to the control rod AB as shown. Knowing that the length of the rod is 225 mm and that $\alpha = 25°$, determine the moment of the force about point B by resolving the force into horizontal and vertical components.

3.2 Solve Prob. 3.1 by resolving the force into components along AB and in a direction perpendicular to AB.

Fig. P3.1 and P3.3

3.3 A 100-N force is applied to the control rod AB as shown. Knowing that the length of the rod is 225 mm and that the moment of the force about B is 12 N·m clockwise, determine the value of α.

3.4 For the brake pedal shown, determine the magnitude and direction of the smallest force $\mathbf{P}$ which has a 104-N·m clockwise moment about B.

3.5 A force $\mathbf{P}$ is applied to the brake pedal at A. Knowing that $P = 450$ N and $\alpha = 30°$, determine the moment of $\mathbf{P}$ about B.

Fig. P3.4 and P3.5

3.6 A 300-N force is applied at A as shown. Determine (*a*) the moment of the 300-N force about D, (*b*) the smallest force applied at B which creates the same moment about D.

Fig. P3.6 and P3.7

3.7 A 300-N force is applied at A as shown. Determine (*a*) the moment of the 300-N force about D, (*b*) the magnitude and sense of the horizontal force applied at C which creates the same moment about D, (*c*) the smallest force applied at C which creates the same moment about D.

Fig. P3.8   **Fig. P3.9**

P3.10 and P3.11

Fig. P3.12

3.8 and 3.9 It is known that the connecting rod AB exerts on the crank BC a 2.5-kN force directed down and to the left along the centerline of AB. Determine the moment of that force about C.

3.10 Rod AB is held in place by the cord AC. Knowing that the tension in the cord is 1500 N and that $c = 360$ mm, determine the moment about B of the force exerted by the cord at point A by resolving that force into horizontal and vertical components applied (*a*) at point A, (*b*) at point C.

3.11 Rod AB is held in place by the cord AC. Knowing that $c = 840$ mm and that the moment about B of the force exerted by the cord at point A is 900 N·m, determine the tension in the cord.

3.12 Form the vector product $\mathbf{P}_1 \times \mathbf{P}_2$ and use the result obtained to prove the identity $\sin (\theta_1 - \theta_2) = \sin \theta_1 \cos \theta_2 - \cos \theta_1 \sin \theta_2$.

3.13 A force $\mathbf{F} = F_x\mathbf{i} + F_y\mathbf{j}$ acts at a point of coordinates x and y. Derive an expression for the perpendicular distance d from the line of action of $\mathbf{F}$ to the origin O of the system of coordinates.

3.14 The line of action of a force $\mathbf{P}$ passes through two points $A(x_1, y_1)$ and $B(x_2, y_2)$. If the force is directed from A to B, determine the moment of the force about the origin.

3.15 Determine the moment about the origin O of the force $\mathbf{F} = 4\mathbf{i} + 5\mathbf{j} - 3\mathbf{k}$ which acts at a point A. Assume that the position vector of A is (*a*) $\mathbf{r} = 2\mathbf{i} - 3\mathbf{j} + 4\mathbf{k}$, (*b*) $\mathbf{r} = 2\mathbf{i} + 2.5\mathbf{j} - 1.5\mathbf{k}$, (*c*) $\mathbf{r} = 2\mathbf{i} + 5\mathbf{j} + 6\mathbf{k}$.

3.16 Determine the moment about the origin O of the force $\mathbf{F} = -2\mathbf{i} + 3\mathbf{j} + 5\mathbf{k}$ which acts at a point A. Assume that the position vector of A is (*a*) $\mathbf{r} = \mathbf{i} + \mathbf{j} + \mathbf{k}$, (*b*) $\mathbf{r} = 2\mathbf{i} + 3\mathbf{j} - 5\mathbf{k}$, (*c*) $\mathbf{r} = -4\mathbf{i} + 6\mathbf{j} + 10\mathbf{k}$.

Fig. P3.17

3.17 A small boat hangs from two davits, one of which is shown in the figure. The tension in line *ABAD* is 410 N. Determine the moment about *C* of the resultant force **R**$_A$ exerted on the davit at *A*.

3.18 A precast concrete wall section is temporarily held by two cables as shown. Knowing that the tension in cable *BD* is 900 N, determine the moment about point *O* of the force exerted by the cable at *B*.

3.19 A 200-N force is applied as shown to the bracket *ABC*. Determine the moment of the force about *A*.

Fig. P3.18

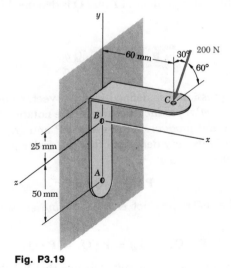

Fig. P3.19

3.20 The 6-m boom *AB* has a fixed end *A*. A steel cable is stretched from the free end *B* of the boom to a point *C* located on the vertical wall. If the tension in the cable is 1900 N, determine the moment about *A* of the force exerted by the cable at *B*.

Fig. P3.20

3.21 In Prob. 3.18, determine the perpendicular distance from point O to cable BD.

3.22 In Prob. 3.18, determine the perpendicular distance from point C to cable BD.

3.23 In Prob. 3.20, determine the perpendicular distance from point A to cable BC.

3.24 In Prob. 3.17, determine the perpendicular distance from point C to portion AD of the line $ABAD$.

3.25 In Sample Prob. 3.4, determine the perpendicular distance from point A to wire CD.

3.26 A single force $\mathbf{F}$ acts at a point A of coordinates $x = y = z = a$. Show that $M_x + M_y + M_z = 0$; that is, show that the *algebraic* sum of the rectangular components of the moment of $\mathbf{F}$ about O is zero.

3.9. Scalar Product of Two Vectors. We shall now expand our knowledge of vector algebra and introduce the *scalar product* of two vectors.

The scalar product of two vectors $\mathbf{P}$ and $\mathbf{Q}$ is defined as the product of the magnitudes of $\mathbf{P}$ and $\mathbf{Q}$ and of the cosine of the angle θ formed by $\mathbf{P}$ and $\mathbf{Q}$ (Fig. 3.19). The scalar product of $\mathbf{P}$ and $\mathbf{Q}$ is denoted by $\mathbf{P} \cdot \mathbf{Q}$. We write therefore

Fig. 3.19

$$\mathbf{P} \cdot \mathbf{Q} = PQ \cos \theta \tag{3.24}$$

Note that the expression just defined is not a vector but a *scalar*, which explains the name *scalar product;* because of the notation used, $\mathbf{P} \cdot \mathbf{Q}$ is also referred to as the *dot product* of the vectors $\mathbf{P}$ and $\mathbf{Q}$.

It follows from its very definition that the scalar product of two vectors is *commutative*, i.e., that

$$\mathbf{P} \cdot \mathbf{Q} = \mathbf{Q} \cdot \mathbf{P} \tag{3.25}$$

To prove that the scalar product is also *distributive*, we must prove the relation

$$\mathbf{P} \cdot (\mathbf{Q}_1 + \mathbf{Q}_2) = \mathbf{P} \cdot \mathbf{Q}_1 + \mathbf{P} \cdot \mathbf{Q}_2 \tag{3.26}$$

We may, without any loss of generality, assume that $\mathbf{P}$ is directed along the y axis (Fig. 3.20). Denoting by $\mathbf{Q}$ the sum of $\mathbf{Q}_1$ and $\mathbf{Q}_2$, and by θ_y the angle $\mathbf{Q}$ forms with the y axis, we express the left-hand member of (3.26) as follows:

$$\mathbf{P} \cdot (\mathbf{Q}_1 + \mathbf{Q}_2) = \mathbf{P} \cdot \mathbf{Q} = PQ \cos \theta_y = PQ_y \tag{3.27}$$

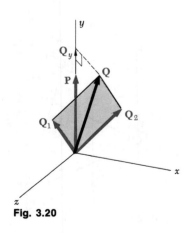

Fig. 3.20

where Q_y is the y component of **Q**. We may, in a similar way, express the right-hand member of (3.26) as

$$\mathbf{P} \cdot \mathbf{Q}_1 + \mathbf{P} \cdot \mathbf{Q}_2 = P(Q_1)_y + P(Q_2)_y \qquad (3.28)$$

Since **Q** is the sum of $\mathbf{Q}_1$ and $\mathbf{Q}_2$, its y component must be equal to the sum of the y components of $\mathbf{Q}_1$ and $\mathbf{Q}_2$. Thus, the expressions obtained in (3.27) and (3.28) are equal and the relation (3.26) has been proved.

As far as the third property—the associative property—is concerned, we note that this property cannot apply to scalar products. Indeed, $(\mathbf{P} \cdot \mathbf{Q}) \cdot \mathbf{S}$ has no meaning, since $\mathbf{P} \cdot \mathbf{Q}$ is not a vector but a scalar.

We shall now express the scalar product of two vectors **P** and **Q** in terms of their rectangular components. Resolving **P** and **Q** into components, we first write

$$\mathbf{P} \cdot \mathbf{Q} = (P_x\mathbf{i} + P_y\mathbf{j} + P_z\mathbf{k}) \cdot (Q_x\mathbf{i} + Q_y\mathbf{j} + Q_z\mathbf{k})$$

Making use of the distributive property, we express $\mathbf{P} \cdot \mathbf{Q}$ as the sum of scalar products such as $P_x\mathbf{i} \cdot Q_x\mathbf{i}$ and $P_x\mathbf{i} \cdot Q_y\mathbf{j}$. But we may easily check from the definition of the scalar product that the scalar products of the unit vectors are either zero or one.

$$\begin{array}{lll} \mathbf{i} \cdot \mathbf{i} = 1 & \mathbf{j} \cdot \mathbf{j} = 1 & \mathbf{k} \cdot \mathbf{k} = 1 \\ \mathbf{i} \cdot \mathbf{j} = 0 & \mathbf{j} \cdot \mathbf{k} = 0 & \mathbf{k} \cdot \mathbf{i} = 0 \end{array} \qquad (3.29)$$

Thus, the expression obtained for $\mathbf{P} \cdot \mathbf{Q}$ reduces to

$$\mathbf{P} \cdot \mathbf{Q} = P_xQ_x + P_yQ_y + P_zQ_z \qquad (3.30)$$

In the particular case when **P** and **Q** are equal, we check that

$$\mathbf{P} \cdot \mathbf{P} = P_x^2 + P_y^2 + P_z^2 = P^2 \qquad (3.31)$$

Applications

1. *Angle formed by two given vectors.* Let two vectors be given in terms of their components:

$$\mathbf{P} = P_x\mathbf{i} + P_y\mathbf{j} + P_z\mathbf{k}$$
$$\mathbf{Q} = Q_x\mathbf{i} + Q_y\mathbf{j} + Q_z\mathbf{k}$$

To determine the angle formed by the two vectors we shall equate the expressions obtained in (3.24) and (3.30) for their scalar product and write:

$$PQ \cos \theta = P_xQ_x + P_yQ_y + P_zQ_z$$

Solving for $\cos \theta$, we have

$$\cos \theta = \frac{P_xQ_x + P_yQ_y + P_zQ_z}{PQ} \qquad (3.32)$$

Fig. 3.21

Fig. 3.22

Fig. 3.23

2. *Projection of a vector on a given axis.* Consider a vector **P** forming an angle θ with an axis, or directed line, *OL* (Fig. 3.21). The *projection of* **P** *on the axis OL* is defined as the scalar

$$P_{OL} = P \cos \theta \qquad (3.33)$$

We note that the projection P_{OL} is equal in absolute value to the length of the segment *OA*; it will be positive if *OA* has the same sense as the axis *OL*, that is, if θ is acute, and negative otherwise. If **P** and *OL* are at a right angle, the projection of **P** on *OL* is zero.

Consider now a vector **Q** directed along *OL* and of the same sense as *OL* (Fig. 3.22). The scalar product of **P** and **Q** may be expressed as

$$\mathbf{P} \cdot \mathbf{Q} = PQ \cos \theta = P_{OL}Q \qquad (3.34)$$

from which it follows that

$$P_{OL} = \frac{\mathbf{P} \cdot \mathbf{Q}}{Q} = \frac{P_x Q_x + P_y Q_y + P_z Q_z}{Q} \qquad (3.35)$$

In the particular case when the vector selected along *OL* is the unit vector $\boldsymbol{\lambda}$ (Fig. 3.23), we write

$$P_{OL} = \mathbf{P} \cdot \boldsymbol{\lambda} \qquad (3.36)$$

Resolving **P** and $\boldsymbol{\lambda}$ into rectangular components, and recalling from Sec. 2.12 that the components of $\boldsymbol{\lambda}$ along the coordinate axes are respectively equal to the direction cosines of *OL*, we express the projection of **P** on *OL* as

$$P_{OL} = P_x \cos \theta_x + P_y \cos \theta_y + P_z \cos \theta_z \qquad (3.37)$$

where θ_x, θ_y, and θ_z denote the angles that the axis *OL* forms with the coordinate axes.

3.10. Mixed Triple Product of Three Vectors. We define the *mixed triple product* of the three vectors **S**, **P**, and **Q** as the scalar expression

$$\mathbf{S} \cdot (\mathbf{P} \times \mathbf{Q}) \qquad (3.38)$$

obtained by forming the scalar product of **S** with the vector product of **P** and **Q**.†

A simple geometrical interpretation may be given for the mixed triple product of **S**, **P**, and **Q** (Fig. 3.24). We first recall from Sec. 3.4 that the vector **P** × **Q** is perpendicular to the plane containing **P** and **Q**, and that its

---

†Another kind of triple product will be introduced later (Chap. 15): the *vector triple product* **S** × (**P** × **Q**).

magnitude is equal to the area of the parallelogram constructed on **P** and **Q**. On the other hand, Eq. (3.34) indicates that the scalar product of **S** and **P** × **Q** may be obtained by multiplying the magnitude of **P** × **Q** (i.e., the area of the parallelogram built on **P** and **Q**) by the projection of **S** on the vector **P** × **Q** (i.e., by the projection of **S** on the normal to the plane containing the parallelogram). The mixed triple product is thus equal, in absolute value, to the volume of the parallelepiped having the vectors **S**, **P**, and **Q** for sides (Fig. 3.25). We may check that the sign of the mixed triple product will be positive if **S**, **P**, and **Q** form a right-handed triad, and negative if they form a left-handed triad [that is, **S** · (**P** × **Q**) will be negative if the rotation which brings **P** into line with **Q** is observed as clockwise from the tip of **S**]. The mixed triple product will be zero if **S**, **P**, and **Q** are coplanar.

Since the parallelepiped defined in the preceding paragraph is independent of the order in which the three vectors are taken, the six mixed triple products which may be formed with **S**, **P**, and **Q** will all have the same absolute value, although not the same sign. We check that

$$\mathbf{S} \cdot (\mathbf{P} \times \mathbf{Q}) = \mathbf{P} \cdot (\mathbf{Q} \times \mathbf{S}) = \mathbf{Q} \cdot (\mathbf{S} \times \mathbf{P})$$
$$= -\mathbf{S} \cdot (\mathbf{Q} \times \mathbf{P}) = -\mathbf{P} \cdot (\mathbf{S} \times \mathbf{Q}) = -\mathbf{Q} \cdot (\mathbf{P} \times \mathbf{S}) \quad (3.39)$$

Arranging in a circle and in counterclockwise order the letters representing the three vectors (Fig. 3.26), we note that the sign of the mixed triple product is conserved if the vectors are permuted in such a way that they are still read in counterclockwise order. Such a permutation is said to be a *circular permutation*. It also follows from (3.39) that the mixed triple product of **S**, **P**, and **Q** may be defined equally well as **S** · (**P** × **Q**) or (**S** × **P**) · **Q**.

We shall now express the mixed triple product of the vectors **S**, **P**, and **Q** in terms of the rectangular components of these vectors. Denoting **P** × **Q** by **V**, and using formula (3.30) to express the scalar product of **S** and **V**, we write

$$\mathbf{S} \cdot (\mathbf{P} \times \mathbf{Q}) = \mathbf{S} \cdot \mathbf{V} = S_x V_x + S_y V_y + S_z V_z$$

Substituting from the relations (3.9) for the components of **V**, we obtain

$$\mathbf{S} \cdot (\mathbf{P} \times \mathbf{Q}) = S_x(P_y Q_z - P_z Q_y) + S_y(P_z Q_x - P_x Q_z) + S_z(P_x Q_y - P_y Q_x) \quad (3.40)$$

This expression may be written in a more compact form if we observe that it represents the expansion of a determinant:

$$\mathbf{S} \cdot (\mathbf{P} \times \mathbf{Q}) = \begin{vmatrix} S_x & S_y & S_z \\ P_x & P_y & P_z \\ Q_x & Q_y & Q_z \end{vmatrix} \quad (3.41)$$

By applying the rules governing the permutation of rows in a determinant, we could easily verify the relations (3.39) which were derived earlier from geometrical considerations.

Fig. 3.24

Fig. 3.25

Fig. 3.26

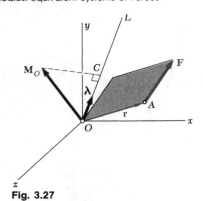

Fig. 3.27

3.11. Moment of a Force about a Given Axis.

Now that we have further increased our knowledge of vector algebra, we shall introduce a new concept, the concept of *moment of a force about an axis*. Consider again a force **F** acting on a rigid body and the moment M_O of that force about O (Fig. 3.27). Let OL be an axis through O; *we define the moment M_{OL} of* **F** *about* OL *as the projection* OC *of the moment* M_O *on the axis* OL. Denoting by λ the unit vector along OL, and recalling from Secs. 3.9 and 3.6, respectively, the expressions (3.36) and (3.11) obtained for the projection of a vector on a given axis and for the moment M_O of a force **F**, we write

$$M_{OL} = \lambda \cdot M_O = \lambda \cdot (r \times F) \qquad (3.42)$$

which shows that the moment M_{OL} of **F** about the axis OL is the scalar obtained by forming the mixed triple product of λ, **r**, and **F**. Expressing M_{OL} in the form of a determinant, we write

$$M_{OL} = \begin{vmatrix} \lambda_x & \lambda_y & \lambda_z \\ x & y & z \\ F_x & F_y & F_z \end{vmatrix} \qquad (3.43)$$

where $\lambda_x, \lambda_y, \lambda_z$ = direction cosines of axis OL
$\qquad x, y, z$ = coordinates of point of application of **F**
$\qquad F_x, F_y, F_z$ = components of force **F**

The physical significance of the moment M_{OL} of a force **F** about a fixed axis OL becomes more apparent if we resolve **F** into two rectangular components F_1 and F_2, with F_1 parallel to OL and F_2 lying in a plane P perpendicular to OL (Fig. 3.28). Resolving **r** similarly into two components r_1 and r_2, and substituting for **F** and **r** into (3.42), we write

$$M_{OL} = \lambda \cdot [(r_1 + r_2) \times (F_1 + F_2)]$$
$$= \lambda \cdot (r_1 \times F_1) + \lambda \cdot (r_1 \times F_2) + \lambda \cdot (r_2 \times F_1) + \lambda \cdot (r_2 \times F_2)$$

Noting that all mixed triple products, except the last one, are equal to zero, since they involve vectors which are coplanar when drawn from a common origin (Sec. 3.10), we have

$$M_{OL} = \lambda \cdot (r_2 \times F_2) \qquad (3.44)$$

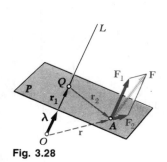

Fig. 3.28

The vector product $r_2 \times F_2$ is perpendicular to the plane P and represents the moment of the component F_2 of **F** about the point Q where OL intersects P. Therefore, the scalar M_{OL}, which will be positive if $r_2 \times F_2$ and OL have the same sense, and negative otherwise, measures the tendency of F_2 to make the rigid body rotate about the fixed axis OL. Since the other component F_1 of **F** does not tend to make the body rotate about OL, we conclude that *the moment M_{OL} of* **F** *about* OL *measures the tendency of the force* **F** *to impart to the rigid body a motion of rotation about the fixed axis* OL.

It follows from the definition of the moment of a force about an axis that the moment of $\mathbf{F}$ about a coordinate axis is equal to the component of $\mathbf{M}_O$ along that axis. Substituting successively each of the unit vectors $\mathbf{i}$, $\mathbf{j}$, and $\mathbf{k}$ for $\boldsymbol{\lambda}$ in (3.42), we check that the expressions thus obtained for the *moments of* $\mathbf{F}$ *about the coordinate axes* are respectively equal to the expressions obtained in Sec. 3.8 for the components of the moment $\mathbf{M}_O$ of $\mathbf{F}$ about O:

$$
\begin{aligned}
M_x &= yF_z - zF_y \\
M_y &= zF_x - xF_z \\
M_z &= xF_y - yF_x
\end{aligned}
\tag{3.18}
$$

We observe that just as the components F_x, F_y, and F_z of a force $\mathbf{F}$ acting on a rigid body measure, respectively, the tendency of $\mathbf{F}$ to move the rigid body in the x, y, and z directions, the moments M_x, M_y, and M_z of $\mathbf{F}$ about the coordinate axes measure the tendency of $\mathbf{F}$ to impart to the rigid body a motion of rotation about the x, y, and z axes, respectively.

More generally, the moment of a force $\mathbf{F}$ applied at A about an axis which does not pass through the origin is obtained by choosing an arbitrary point B on the axis (Fig. 3.29) and determining the projection on the axis BL of the moment $\mathbf{M}_B$ of $\mathbf{F}$ about B. We write

$$
M_{BL} = \boldsymbol{\lambda} \cdot \mathbf{M}_B = \boldsymbol{\lambda} \cdot (\mathbf{r}_{A/B} \times \mathbf{F})
\tag{3.45}
$$

where $\mathbf{r}_{A/B} = \mathbf{r}_A - \mathbf{r}_B$ represents the vector drawn from B to A. Expressing M_{BL} in the form of a determinant, we have

$$
M_{BL} =
\begin{vmatrix}
\lambda_x & \lambda_y & \lambda_z \\
x_{A/B} & y_{A/B} & z_{A/B} \\
F_x & F_y & F_z
\end{vmatrix}
\tag{3.46}
$$

Fig. 3.29

where λ_x, λ_y, λ_z = direction cosines of axis BL

$$
x_{A/B} = x_A - x_B \qquad y_{A/B} = y_A - y_B \qquad z_{A/B} = z_A - z_B
$$

F_x, F_y, F_z = components of force $\mathbf{F}$

It should be noted that the result obtained is independent of the choice of the point B on the given axis. Indeed, denoting by M_{CL} the result obtained with a different point C, we have

$$
\begin{aligned}
M_{CL} &= \boldsymbol{\lambda} \cdot [(\mathbf{r}_A - \mathbf{r}_C) \times \mathbf{F}] \\
&= \boldsymbol{\lambda} \cdot [(\mathbf{r}_A - \mathbf{r}_B) \times \mathbf{F}] + \boldsymbol{\lambda} \cdot [(\mathbf{r}_B - \mathbf{r}_C) \times \mathbf{F}]
\end{aligned}
$$

But, since the vectors $\boldsymbol{\lambda}$ and $\mathbf{r}_B - \mathbf{r}_C$ lie in the same line, the volume of the parallelepiped having the vectors $\boldsymbol{\lambda}$, $\mathbf{r}_B - \mathbf{r}_C$, and $\mathbf{F}$ for sides is zero, as is the mixed triple product of these three vectors (Sec. 3.10). The expression obtained for M_{CL} thus reduces to its first term, which is the expression used earlier to define M_{BL}.

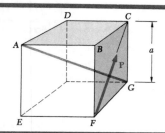

SAMPLE PROBLEM 3.5

A cube of side a is acted upon by a force $\mathbf{P}$ as shown. Determine the moment of $\mathbf{P}$ (a) about A, (b) about the edge AB, (c) about the diagonal AG of the cube. (d) Using the result of part c, determine the perpendicular distance from AG to FC.

a. **Moment about A.** Choosing x, y, and z axes as shown, we resolve into rectangular components the force $\mathbf{P}$ and the vector $\mathbf{r}_{F/A} = \overrightarrow{AF}$ drawn from A to the point of application F of $\mathbf{P}$.

$$\mathbf{r}_{F/A} = a\mathbf{i} - a\mathbf{j} = a(\mathbf{i} - \mathbf{j})$$
$$\mathbf{P} = (P/\sqrt{2})\mathbf{j} - (P/\sqrt{2})\mathbf{k} = (P/\sqrt{2})(\mathbf{j} - \mathbf{k})$$

The moment of $\mathbf{P}$ about A is

$$\mathbf{M}_A = \mathbf{r}_{F/A} \times \mathbf{P} = a(\mathbf{i} - \mathbf{j}) \times (P/\sqrt{2})(\mathbf{j} - \mathbf{k})$$
$$\mathbf{M}_A = (aP/\sqrt{2})(\mathbf{i} + \mathbf{j} + \mathbf{k}) \blacktriangleleft$$

b. **Moment about AB.** Projecting $\mathbf{M}_A$ on AB, we write

$$M_{AB} = \mathbf{i} \cdot \mathbf{M}_A = \mathbf{i} \cdot (aP/\sqrt{2})(\mathbf{i} + \mathbf{j} + \mathbf{k}) \qquad M_{AB} = aP/\sqrt{2} \blacktriangleleft$$

We verify that, since AB is parallel to the x axis, M_{AB} is also the x component of the moment $\mathbf{M}_A$.

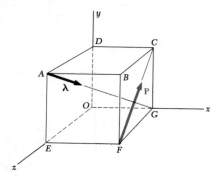

c. **Moment about Diagonal AG.** The moment of $\mathbf{P}$ about AG is obtained by projecting $\mathbf{M}_A$ on AG. Denoting by $\boldsymbol{\lambda}$ the unit vector along AG, we have

$$\boldsymbol{\lambda} = \frac{\overrightarrow{AG}}{AG} = \frac{a\mathbf{i} - a\mathbf{j} - a\mathbf{k}}{a\sqrt{3}} = (1/\sqrt{3})(\mathbf{i} - \mathbf{j} - \mathbf{k})$$

$$M_{AG} = \boldsymbol{\lambda} \cdot \mathbf{M}_A = (1/\sqrt{3})(\mathbf{i} - \mathbf{j} - \mathbf{k}) \cdot (aP/\sqrt{2})(\mathbf{i} + \mathbf{j} + \mathbf{k})$$
$$M_{AG} = (aP/\sqrt{6})(1 - 1 - 1) \qquad M_{AG} = -aP/\sqrt{6} \blacktriangleleft$$

Alternate Method. The moment of $\mathbf{P}$ about AG may also be expressed in the form of a determinant:

$$M_{AG} = \begin{vmatrix} \lambda_x & \lambda_y & \lambda_z \\ x_{F/A} & y_{F/A} & z_{F/A} \\ F_x & F_y & F_z \end{vmatrix} = \begin{vmatrix} 1/\sqrt{3} & -1/\sqrt{3} & -1/\sqrt{3} \\ a & -a & 0 \\ 0 & P/\sqrt{2} & -P/\sqrt{2} \end{vmatrix} = -aP/\sqrt{6}$$

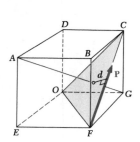

d. **Perpendicular Distance from AG to FC.** We first observe that $\mathbf{P}$ is perpendicular to the diagonal AG. This may be checked by forming the scalar product $\mathbf{P} \cdot \boldsymbol{\lambda}$ and verifying that it is zero:

$$\mathbf{P} \cdot \boldsymbol{\lambda} = (P/\sqrt{2})(\mathbf{j} - \mathbf{k}) \cdot (1/\sqrt{3})(\mathbf{i} - \mathbf{j} - \mathbf{k}) = (P/\sqrt{6})(0 - 1 + 1) = 0$$

The moment M_{AG} may then be expressed as $-Pd$, where d is the perpendicular distance from AG to FC. (The negative sign is used since the rotation imparted to the cube by $\mathbf{P}$ appears as clockwise to an observer at G.) Recalling the value found for M_{AG} in part c,

$$M_{AG} = -Pd = -aP/\sqrt{6} \qquad d = a/\sqrt{6} \blacktriangleleft$$

Problems

3.27 Given the vectors $\mathbf{P} = 2\mathbf{i} + 3\mathbf{j} - \mathbf{k}$, $\mathbf{Q} = 5\mathbf{i} - 4\mathbf{j} + 3\mathbf{k}$, and $\mathbf{S} = -3\mathbf{i} + 2\mathbf{j} - 5\mathbf{k}$, compute the scalar products $\mathbf{P} \cdot \mathbf{Q}$, $\mathbf{P} \cdot \mathbf{S}$, and $\mathbf{Q} \cdot \mathbf{S}$.

3.28 Form the scalar product $\mathbf{P}_1 \cdot \mathbf{P}_2$ and use the result obtained to prove the identity $\cos(\theta_1 - \theta_2) = \cos\theta_1 \cos\theta_2 + \sin\theta_1 \sin\theta_2$.

Fig. P3.28

3.29 Three cables are used to support a container as shown. Determine the angle formed by cables AB and AD.

Fig. P3.29 and P3.30

3.30 Three cables are used to support a container as shown. Determine the angle formed by cables AC and AD.

3.31 Knowing that the tension in cable AC is 945 N, determine (*a*) the angle between cable AC and the boom AB, (*b*) the projection on AB of the force exerted by cable AC at point A.

3.32 Knowing that the tension in cable AD is 540 N, determine (*a*) the angle between cable AD and the boom AB, (*b*) the projection on AB of the force exerted by cable AD at point A.

Fig. P3.31 and P3.32

3.33 The 500-mm tube AB may slide along a horizontal rod. The ends A and B of the tube are connected by elastic cords to the fixed point C. For the position corresponding to $x = 275$ mm, determine the angle formed by the two cords, (*a*) using Eq. (3.32), (*b*) applying the law of cosines to triangle ABC.

3.34 Solve Prob. 3.33 for the position corresponding to $x = 100$ mm.

3.35 Given the vectors $\mathbf{P} = 2\mathbf{i} + 3\mathbf{j} - \mathbf{k}$, $\mathbf{Q} = 5\mathbf{i} - 4\mathbf{j} + 3\mathbf{k}$, and $\mathbf{S} = -3\mathbf{i} + 2\mathbf{j} - 5\mathbf{k}$, compute $\mathbf{P} \cdot (\mathbf{Q} \times \mathbf{S})$, $(\mathbf{P} \times \mathbf{Q}) \cdot \mathbf{S}$, and $(\mathbf{S} \times \mathbf{Q}) \cdot \mathbf{P}$.

3.36 Given the vectors $\mathbf{P} = 4\mathbf{i} - 2\mathbf{j} + 3\mathbf{k}$, $\mathbf{Q} = 2\mathbf{i} + 4\mathbf{j} - 5\mathbf{k}$, and $\mathbf{S} = 7\mathbf{i} - \mathbf{j} + S_z\mathbf{k}$, determine the value of S_z for which the three vectors are coplanar.

Fig. P3.33

3.37 The rectangular platform is hinged at A and B and supported by a cable which passes over a frictionless hook at E. Knowing that the tension in the cable is 1349 N, determine the moment about each of the coordinate axes of the force exerted by the cable at C.

Fig. P3.37

3.38 For the platform of Prob. 3.37, determine the moment about each of the coordinate axes of the force exerted by the cable at D.

3.39 A small boat hangs from two davits, one of which is shown in the figure. It is known that the moment about the z axis of the resultant force $\mathbf{R}_A$ exerted on the davit at A must not exceed 375 N·m in absolute value. Determine the largest allowable tension in line $ABAD$ when $x = 2$ m.

3.40 For the davit of Prob. 3.39, determine the largest allowable distance x when the tension in line $ABAD$ is 300 N.

Fig. P3.39

3.41 A single force $\mathbf{P}$ acts at C in a direction perpendicular to the handle BC of the crank shown. Knowing that $M_x = +20$ N·m, $M_y = -8.75$ N·m, and $M_z = -30$ N·m, determine the magnitude of $\mathbf{P}$ and the values of ϕ and θ.

Fig. P3.41 and P3.42

3.42 A single force $\mathbf{P}$ acts at C in a direction perpendicular to the handle BC of the crank shown. Determine the moment M_x of $\mathbf{P}$ about the x axis when $\theta = 65°$, knowing that $M_y = -15$ N·m and $M_z = -36$ N·m.

3.43 The 575-mm vertical rod *CD* is welded to the midpoint *C* of the 1250-mm rod *AB*. Determine the moment about *AB* of the 1175-N force **P**.

Fig. P3.43 and P3.44

3.44 The 575-mm vertical rod *CD* is welded to the midpoint *C* of the 1250-mm rod *AB*. Determine the moment about *AB* of the 870-N force **Q**.

3.45 The frame *ACD* is hinged at *A* and *D* and supported by a cable which passes through a ring at *B* and is attached to hooks at *G* and *H*. Knowing that the tension in the cable is 1125 N, determine the moment about the diagonal *AD* of the force exerted on the frame by portion *BH* of the cable.

Fig. P3.45

3.46 In Prob. 3.45, determine the moment about the diagonal *AD* of the force exerted on the frame by portion *BG* of the cable.

3.47 Two forces $\mathbf{F}_1$ and $\mathbf{F}_2$ in space have the same magnitude F. Prove that the moment of $\mathbf{F}_1$ about the line of action of $\mathbf{F}_2$ is equal to the moment of $\mathbf{F}_2$ about the line of action of $\mathbf{F}_1$.

3.48 A regular tetrahedron has six edges of length a. A force $\mathbf{P}$ is directed as shown along edge BC. Determine the moment of $\mathbf{P}$ about edge OA.

3.49 A regular tetrahedron has six edges of length a. (a) Show that two opposite edges, such as OA and BC, are perpendicular to each other. (b) Use this property and the result obtained in Prob. 3.48 to determine the perpendicular distance between the edges OA and BC.

Fig. P3.48 and P3.49

***3.50** In Prob. 3.43, determine the perpendicular distance between rod AB and the line of action of $\mathbf{P}$.

***3.51** In Prob. 3.45, determine the perpendicular distance between portion BH of the cable and the diagonal AD.

***3.52** Use the result obtained in Prob. 3.46 to determine the perpendicular distance between portion BG of the cable of Fig. P3.45 and the diagonal AD.

***3.53** Use the result obtained in Prob. 3.44 to determine the perpendicular distance between rod AB and the line of action of $\mathbf{Q}$.

3.12. Moment of a Couple. *Two forces $\mathbf{F}$ and $-\mathbf{F}$ having the same magnitude, parallel lines of action, and opposite sense are said to form a couple* (Fig. 3.30). Clearly, the sum of the components of the two forces in any direction is zero. The sum of the moments of the two forces about a given point, however, is not zero. While the two forces will not translate the body on which they act, they will tend to make it rotate.

Denoting by $\mathbf{r}_A$ and $\mathbf{r}_B$, respectively, the position vectors of the points of application of $\mathbf{F}$ and $-\mathbf{F}$ (Fig. 3.31), we find that the sum of the moments of the two forces about O is

$$\mathbf{r}_A \times \mathbf{F} + \mathbf{r}_B \times (-\mathbf{F}) = (\mathbf{r}_A - \mathbf{r}_B) \times \mathbf{F}$$

Fig. 3.30

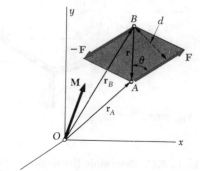

Fig. 3.31

Setting $\mathbf{r}_A - \mathbf{r}_B = \mathbf{r}$, where $\mathbf{r}$ is the vector joining the points of application of the two forces, we conclude that the sum of the moments of $\mathbf{F}$ and $-\mathbf{F}$ about O is represented by the vector

$$M = \mathbf{r} \times \mathbf{F} \qquad (3.47)$$

The vector $\mathbf{M}$ is called the *moment of the couple*; it is a vector perpendicular to the plane containing the two forces and its magnitude is

$$M = rF \sin \theta = Fd \qquad (3.48)$$

where d is the perpendicular distance between the lines of action of $\mathbf{F}$ and $-\mathbf{F}$. The sense of $\mathbf{M}$ is defined by the right-hand rule.

Fig. 3.32

Since the vector $\mathbf{r}$ in (3.47) is independent of the choice of the origin O of the coordinate axes, we note that the same result would have been obtained if the moments of $\mathbf{F}$ and $-\mathbf{F}$ had been computed about a different point O'. Thus, the moment $\mathbf{M}$ of a couple is a *free vector* (Sec. 2.3) which may be applied at any point (Fig. 3.32).

From the definition of the moment of a couple, it also follows that two couples, one consisting of the forces $\mathbf{F}_1$ and $-\mathbf{F}_1$, the other of the forces $\mathbf{F}_2$ and $-\mathbf{F}_2$ (Fig. 3.33), will have equal moments if

$$F_1 d_1 = F_2 d_2 \qquad (3.49)$$

and if the two couples lie in parallel planes (or in the same plane) and have the same sense.

Fig. 3.33

3.13. Equivalent Couples.
Consider the three couples shown in Fig. 3.34, which are made to act successively on the same rectangular box. As seen in the preceding section, the only motion a couple may impart to a rigid body is a rotation. Since each of the three couples shown has the same moment $\mathbf{M}$ (same direction and same magnitude $M = 30$ N·m), we may expect the three couples to have the same effect on the box.

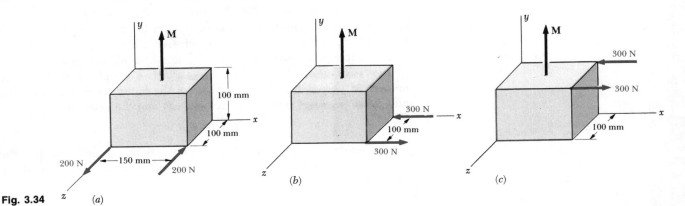

Fig. 3.34

As reasonable as this conclusion may appear, we should not accept it hastily. While intuitive feeling is of great help in the study of mechanics, it should not be accepted as a substitute for logical reasoning. Before stating that two systems (or groups) of forces have the same effect on a rigid body, we should prove that fact on the basis of the experimental evidence introduced so far. This evidence consists of the parallelogram law for the addition of two forces (Sec. 2.2) and of the principle of transmissibility (Sec. 3.3). Therefore, we shall state that *two systems of forces are equivalent* (i.e., they have the same effect on a rigid body) *if we can transform one of them into the other by means of one or several of the following operations:* (1) replacing two forces acting on the same particle by their resultant; (2) resolving a force into two components; (3) canceling two equal and opposite forces acting on the same particle; (4) attaching to the same particle two equal and opposite forces; (5) moving a force along its line of action. Each of these operations is easily justified on the basis of the parallelogram law or the principle of transmissibility.

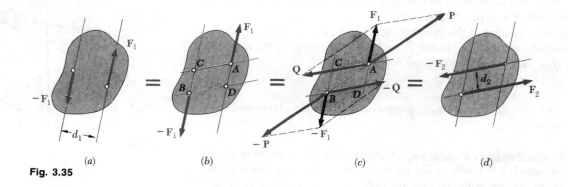

(a) (b) (c) (d)

Fig. 3.35

Let us now prove that *two couples having the same moment* **M** *are equivalent*. First, we shall consider two couples contained in the same plane, and we shall assume that this plane coincides with the plane of the figure (Fig. 3.35). The first couple consists of the forces F_1 and $-F_1$, of magnitude F_1 and at a distance d_1 from each other (Fig. 3.35a), and the second couple of the forces F_2 and $-F_2$, of magnitude F_2 and at a distance d_2 from each other (Fig. 3.35d). Since the two couples have the same moment **M** perpendicular to the plane of the figure, they must have the same sense (assumed here counterclockwise) and the relation

$$F_1 d_1 = F_2 d_2 \qquad (3.49)$$

must be satisfied. To prove that they are equivalent, we shall show that the first couple may be transformed into the second by means of the operations listed above.

Denoting by A, B, C, D the points of intersection of the lines of action of the two couples, we first slide the forces $\mathbf{F}_1$ and $-\mathbf{F}_1$ until they are attached, respectively, at A and B, as shown in Fig. 3.35b. The force $\mathbf{F}_1$ is then resolved into a component $\mathbf{P}$ along line AB and a component $\mathbf{Q}$ along AC (Fig. 3.35c); similarly, the force $-\mathbf{F}_1$ is resolved into $-\mathbf{P}$ along AB and $-\mathbf{Q}$ along BD. The forces $\mathbf{P}$ and $-\mathbf{P}$ have the same magnitude, same line of action, and opposite sense; they may be moved along their common line of action until they are applied at the same point and then canceled. Thus the couple formed by $\mathbf{F}_1$ and $-\mathbf{F}_1$ reduces to a couple consisting of $\mathbf{Q}$ and $-\mathbf{Q}$.

We shall now show that the forces $\mathbf{Q}$ and $-\mathbf{Q}$ are respectively equal to the forces $-\mathbf{F}_2$ and $\mathbf{F}_2$. The moment of the couple formed by $\mathbf{Q}$ and $-\mathbf{Q}$ may be obtained by computing the moment of $\mathbf{Q}$ about B; similarly, the moment of the couple formed by $\mathbf{F}_1$ and $-\mathbf{F}_1$ is the moment of $\mathbf{F}_1$ about B. But, by Varignon's theorem, the moment of $\mathbf{F}_1$ is equal to the sum of the moments of its components $\mathbf{P}$ and $\mathbf{Q}$. Since the moment of $\mathbf{P}$ about B is zero, the moment of the couple formed by $\mathbf{Q}$ and $-\mathbf{Q}$ must be equal to the moment of the couple formed by $\mathbf{F}_1$ and $-\mathbf{F}_1$. Recalling (3.49), we write

$$Qd_2 = F_1d_1 = F_2d_2 \qquad \text{and} \qquad Q = F_2$$

Thus the forces $\mathbf{Q}$ and $-\mathbf{Q}$ are respectively equal to the forces $-\mathbf{F}_2$ and $\mathbf{F}_2$, and the couple of Fig. 3.35a is equivalent to the couple of Fig. 3.35d.

Next we shall consider two couples contained in parallel planes P_1 and P_2 and prove that they are equivalent if they have the same moment. In view of the foregoing we may assume that the couples consist of forces of the same magnitude F acting along parallel lines (Fig. 3.36a and d). We propose to show that the couple contained in plane P_1 may be transformed into the couple contained in plane P_2 by means of the standard operations listed above.

Let us consider the two planes defined respectively by the lines of action of $\mathbf{F}_1$ and $-\mathbf{F}_2$, and of $-\mathbf{F}_1$ and $\mathbf{F}_2$ (Fig. 3.36b). At a point on their line of intersection we attach two forces $\mathbf{F}_3$ and $-\mathbf{F}_3$, respectively equal to $\mathbf{F}_1$ and $-\mathbf{F}_1$. The couple formed by $\mathbf{F}_1$ and $-\mathbf{F}_3$ may be replaced by a couple consisting of $\mathbf{F}_3$ and $-\mathbf{F}_2$ (Fig. 3.36c), since both couples have clearly the same moment and are contained in the same plane. Similarly, the couple formed by $-\mathbf{F}_1$ and $\mathbf{F}_3$ may be replaced by a couple consisting of $-\mathbf{F}_3$ and $\mathbf{F}_2$. Canceling the two equal and opposite forces $\mathbf{F}_3$ and $-\mathbf{F}_3$, we obtain the desired couple in plane P_2 (Fig. 3.36d). Thus, we conclude that two couples having the same moment $\mathbf{M}$ are equivalent, whether they are contained in the same plane or in parallel planes.

The property we have just established is very important for the correct understanding of the mechanics of rigid bodies. It indicates that when a couple acts on a rigid body, it does not matter where the two forces forming the couple act, or what magnitude and direction they have. The only thing which counts is the *moment* of the couple (magnitude and direction). Couples with the same moment will have the same effect on the rigid body.

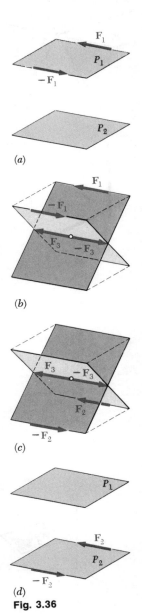

(a)

(b)

(c)

(d)

Fig. 3.36

(a)

(b)

Fig. 3.37

3.14. Addition of Couples. Consider two intersecting planes P_1 and P_2 and two couples acting respectively in P_1 and P_2. We may, without any loss of generality, assume that the couple in P_1 consists of two forces $\mathbf{F}_1$ and $-\mathbf{F}_1$ perpendicular to the line of intersection of the two planes and acting respectively at A and B (Fig. 3.37a). Similarly, we assume that the couple in P_2 consists of two forces $\mathbf{F}_2$ and $-\mathbf{F}_2$ perpendicular to AB and acting respectively at A and B. It is clear that the resultant $\mathbf{R}$ of $\mathbf{F}_1$ and $\mathbf{F}_2$ and the resultant $-\mathbf{R}$ of $-\mathbf{F}_1$ and $-\mathbf{F}_2$ form a couple. Denoting by $\mathbf{r}$ the vector joining B to A, and recalling the definition of the moment of a couple (Sec. 3.12), we express the moment $\mathbf{M}$ of the resulting couple as follows:

$$\mathbf{M} = \mathbf{r} \times \mathbf{R} = \mathbf{r} \times (\mathbf{F}_1 + \mathbf{F}_2)$$

and, by Varignon's theorem,

$$\mathbf{M} = \mathbf{r} \times \mathbf{F}_1 + \mathbf{r} \times \mathbf{F}_2$$

But the first term in the expression obtained represents the moment $\mathbf{M}_1$ of the couple in P_1, and the second term the moment $\mathbf{M}_2$ of the couple in P_2. We have

$$\mathbf{M} = \mathbf{M}_1 + \mathbf{M}_2 \tag{3.50}$$

and we conclude that the sum of two couples of moments $\mathbf{M}_1$ and $\mathbf{M}_2$ is a couple of moment $\mathbf{M}$ equal to the vector sum of $\mathbf{M}_1$ and $\mathbf{M}_2$ (Fig. 3.37b).

3.15. Couples May Be Represented by Vectors. As we saw in Sec. 3.13, couples which have the same moment, whether they act in the same plane or in parallel planes, are equivalent. There is therefore no need to draw the actual forces forming a given couple in order to define its effect on a rigid body (Fig. 3.38a). It is sufficient to draw an arrow equal in magnitude and direction to the moment $\mathbf{M}$ of the couple (Fig. 3.38b). On the other hand, we saw in Sec. 3.14 that the sum of two couples is itself a couple and that the moment $\mathbf{M}$ of the resultant couple may be obtained by forming the vector sum of the moments $\mathbf{M}_1$ and $\mathbf{M}_2$ of the given couples.

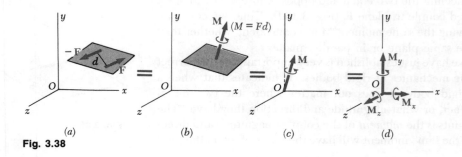

(a)

(b)

(c)

(d)

Fig. 3.38

Thus, couples obey the law of addition of vectors, and the arrow used in Fig. 3.38b to represent the couple defined in Fig. 3.38a may truly be considered a vector.

The vector representing a couple is called a *couple vector*. Note that, in Fig. 3.38, a colored arrow is used to distinguish the couple vector, *which represents the couple itself*, from the vector representing the *moment* of the couple, and that the symbol ⅂ is added to avoid any confusion with vectors representing forces. A couple vector, like the moment of a couple, is a free vector. Its point of application, therefore, may be chosen at the origin of the system of coordinates, if so desired (Fig. 3.38c). Furthermore, the couple vector $\mathbf{M}$ may be resolved into component vectors $\mathbf{M}_x$, $\mathbf{M}_y$, and $\mathbf{M}_z$, directed along the axes of coordinates (Fig. 3.38d) and representing couples acting, respectively, in the yz, zx, and xy planes.

3.16. Resolution of a Given Force into a Force at O and a Couple.

Consider a force $\mathbf{F}$ acting on a rigid body at a point A defined by the position vector $\mathbf{r}$ (Fig. 3.39a). Suppose that for some reason we would rather have the force act at point O. We know that we can move $\mathbf{F}$ along its line of action (principle of transmissibility); but we cannot move it to a point O away from the original line of action without modifying the action of $\mathbf{F}$ on the rigid body.

We may, however, attach two forces at point O, one equal to $\mathbf{F}$ and the other equal to $-\mathbf{F}$, without modifying the action of the original force on the rigid body (Fig. 3.39b). As a result of this tranformation, a force $\mathbf{F}$ is now applied at O; the other two forces form a couple of moment $\mathbf{M}_O = \mathbf{r} \times \mathbf{F}$. Thus, *any force $\mathbf{F}$ acting on a rigid body may be moved to an arbitrary point O, provided that a couple is added, of moment equal to the moment of $\mathbf{F}$ about O.* The couple tends to impart to the rigid body the same motion of rotation about O that the force $\mathbf{F}$ tended to produce before it was transferred to O. The couple is represented by a couple vector $\mathbf{M}_O$ perpendicular to the plane containing $\mathbf{r}$ and $\mathbf{F}$. Since $\mathbf{M}_O$ is a free vector, it may be applied anywhere; for convenience, however, the couple vector is usually attached at O, together with $\mathbf{F}$, and the combination obtained is referred to as a *force-couple system* (Fig. 3.39c).

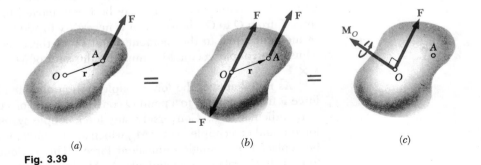

(a) (b) (c)

Fig. 3.39

If the force **F** had been moved from A to a different point O' (Fig. 3.40a and c), the moment $\mathbf{M}_{O'} = \mathbf{r}' \times \mathbf{F}$ of **F** about O' should have been computed, and a new force-couple system, consisting of **F** and of the couple vector $\mathbf{M}_{O'}$, would have been attached at O'. The relation existing between the moments of **F** about O and O' is obtained by writing

$$\mathbf{M}_{O'} = \mathbf{r}' \times \mathbf{F} = (\mathbf{r} + \mathbf{s}) \times \mathbf{F} = \mathbf{r} \times \mathbf{F} + \mathbf{s} \times \mathbf{F}$$

$$\mathbf{M}_{O'} = \mathbf{M}_O + \mathbf{s} \times \mathbf{F} \tag{3.51}$$

where **s** is the vector joining O' to O. Thus, the moment $\mathbf{M}_{O'}$ of **F** about O' is obtained by adding to the moment $\mathbf{M}_O$ of **F** about O the vector product $\mathbf{s} \times \mathbf{F}$ representing the moment about O' of the force **F** applied at O.

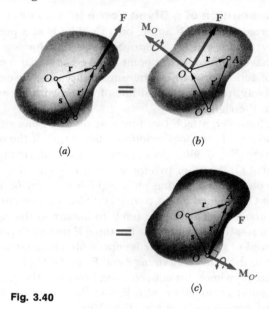

(a)

(b)

(c)

Fig. 3.40

This result could also have been established by observing that, in order to transfer to O' the force-couple system attached at O (Fig. 3.40b and c), the couple vector $\mathbf{M}_O$ may be freely moved to O'; to move the force **F** from O to O', however, it is necessary to add to **F** a couple vector of moment equal to the moment about O' of the force **F** applied at O. Thus, the couple vector $\mathbf{M}_{O'}$ must be the sum of $\mathbf{M}_O$ and of the vector $\mathbf{s} \times \mathbf{F}$.

As noted above, the force-couple system obtained by transferring a force **F** from a point A to a point O consists of **F** and of a couple vector $\mathbf{M}_O$ perpendicular to **F**. Conversely, any force-couple system consisting of a force **F** and of a couple vector $\mathbf{M}_O$ which are *mutually perpendicular* may be replaced by a single equivalent force. This is done by moving the force **F** in the plane perpendicular to $\mathbf{M}_O$ until its moment about O becomes equal to the moment of the couple to be eliminated.

Determine the components of the single couple equivalent to the two couples shown.

Solution. Our computations will be simplified if we attach two equal and opposite 100-N forces at A. This enables us to replace the original 100-N force couple by two new 100-N force couples, one of which lies in the xz plane and the other in a plane parallel to the xy plane. The three couples shown in the adjoining sketch may be represented by three couple vectors $\mathbf{M}_x$, $\mathbf{M}_y$, and $\mathbf{M}_z$ directed along the coordinate axes. The corresponding moments are

$$M_x = -(150\text{ N})(0.360\text{ m}) = -54.0\text{ N·m}$$
$$M_y = +(100\text{ N})(0.240\text{ m}) = +24.0\text{ N·m}$$
$$M_z = +(100\text{ N})(0.180\text{ m}) = +18.0\text{ N·m}$$

These three moments represent the components of the single couple $\mathbf{M}$ equivalent to the two given couples. We write

$$\mathbf{M} = -(54.0\text{ N·m})\mathbf{i} + (24.0\text{ N·m})\mathbf{j} + (18.0\text{ N·m})\mathbf{k} \quad \blacktriangleleft$$

Alternate Solution. The components of the equivalent single couple $\mathbf{M}$ may also be obtained by computing the sum of the moments of the four given forces about an arbitrary point. Selecting point D, we write

$$\mathbf{M} = \mathbf{M}_D = (0.360\text{ m})\mathbf{j} \times (-150\text{ N})\mathbf{k} + [(0.180\text{ m})\mathbf{j} - (0.240\text{ m})\mathbf{k}] \times (-100\text{ N})\mathbf{i}$$

and, after computing the various cross products,

$$\mathbf{M} = -(54.0\text{ N · m})\mathbf{i} + (24.0\text{ N·m})\mathbf{j} + (18.0\text{ N·m})\mathbf{k} \quad \blacktriangleleft$$

SAMPLE PROBLEM 3.7

Replace the couple and force shown by an equivalent single force applied to the lever. Determine the distance from the shaft to the point of application of this equivalent force.

Solution. First the given force and couple are replaced by an equivalent force-couple system at O. We move the force $\mathbf{F} = -(400 \text{ N})\mathbf{j}$ to O and at the same time add a couple of moment $\mathbf{M}_O$ equal to the moment about O of the force in its original position.

$$\mathbf{M}_O = \overrightarrow{OB} \times \mathbf{F} = [(0.150 \text{ m})\mathbf{i} + (0.260 \text{ m})\mathbf{j}] \times (-400 \text{ N})\mathbf{j}$$
$$= -(60 \text{ N} \cdot \text{m})\mathbf{k}$$

This couple is added to the couple of moment $-(24 \text{ N} \cdot \text{m})\mathbf{k}$ formed by the two 200-N forces, and a couple of moment $-(84 \text{ N} \cdot \text{m})\mathbf{k}$ is obtained. This last couple may be eliminated by applying $\mathbf{F}$ at a point C chosen in such a way that

$$-(84 \text{ N} \cdot \text{m})\mathbf{k} = \overrightarrow{OC} \times \mathbf{F}$$
$$= [(OC) \cos 60°\mathbf{i} + (OC) \sin 60°\mathbf{j}] \times (-400 \text{ N})\mathbf{j}$$
$$= -(OC) \cos 60°(400 \text{ N})\mathbf{k}$$

We conclude that

$$(OC) \cos 60° = 0.210 \text{ m} = 210 \text{ mm} \qquad OC = 420 \text{ mm} \quad \blacktriangleleft$$

Alternate Solution. Since the effect of a couple does not depend on its location, the couple of moment $-(24 \text{ N} \cdot \text{m})\mathbf{k}$ may be moved to B; we thus obtain a force-couple system at B. The couple may now be eliminated by applying $\mathbf{F}$ at a point C chosen in such a way that

$$-(24 \text{ N} \cdot \text{m})\mathbf{k} = \overrightarrow{BC} \times \mathbf{F}$$
$$= -(BC) \cos 60°(400 \text{ N})\mathbf{k}$$

We conclude that

$$(BC) \cos 60° = 0.060 \text{ m} = 60 \text{ mm} \qquad BC = 120 \text{ mm}$$
$$OC = OB + BC = 300 \text{ mm} + 120 \text{ mm} \qquad OC = 420 \text{ mm} \quad \blacktriangleleft$$

Problems

3.54 Two 80-N forces are applied as shown to the corners B and D of a rectangular plate. (*a*) Determine the moment of the couple formed by the two forces by resolving each force into horizontal and vertical components and adding the moments of the two resulting couples. (*b*) Use the result obtained to determine the perpendicular distance between lines BE and DF.

Fig. P3.54

3.55 A piece of plywood in which several holes are being drilled successively has been secured to a workbench by means of two nails. Knowing that the drill exerts a 12-N·m couple on the piece of plywood, determine the magnitude of the resulting forces applied to the nails if they are located (*a*) at A and B, (*b*) at B and C, (*c*) at A and C.

Fig. P3.55

Fig. P3.56 and P3.57

3.56 Four 38 mm-diameter pegs are attached to a board as shown. Two strings are passed around the pegs and pulled with the forces indicated. (*a*) Determine the resultant couple acting on the board. (*b*) If only one string is used, around which pegs should it pass and in what directions should it be pulled to create the same couple with the minimum tension in the string? (*c*) What is the value of that minimum tension?

3.57 Four pegs of the same diameter are attached to a board as shown. Two strings are passed around the pegs and pulled with the forces indicated. Determine the diameter of the pegs, knowing that the resultant couple applied to the board is 128.0 N·m counterclockwise.

3.58 The two shafts of a speed-reducer unit are subjected to couples of magnitude $M_1 = 12$ N·m and $M_2 = 5$ N·m respectively. Replace the two couples by a single equivalent couple, specifying its magnitude and the direction of its axis.

Fig. P3.58

3.59 Replace the two couples shown by a single equivalent couple, specifying its magnitude and the direction of its axis.

Fig. P3.59

3.60 Solve Prob. 3.59, assuming that two 10-N vertical forces have been added, one acting upward at C and the other downward at B.

3.61 Shafts A and B connect the gear box to the wheel assemblies of a tractor, and shaft C connects it to the engine. Shafts A and B lie in the vertical yz plane, while shaft C is directed along the x axis. Replace the couples applied to the shafts by a single equivalent couple, specifying its magnitude and the direction of its axis.

Fig. P3.61

3.62 A 300-N vertical force $\mathbf{P}$ is applied at A to the bracket shown, which is held by screws at B and C. (*a*) Replace $\mathbf{P}$ by an equivalent force-couple system at B. (*b*) Find the two horizontal forces at B and C which are equivalent to the couple obtained in part *a*.

Fig. P3.62

Fig. P3.63

3.63 A 1300-N force is applied at A to the rolled-steel section shown. Replace that force by an equivalent force-couple system at the center C of the section.

3.64 Force **P** has a magnitude of 300 N and is applied at A in a direction perpendicular to the handle ($\alpha = 0$). Assuming $\beta = 30°$, replace force **P** by (a) an equivalent force-couple system at B, (b) an equivalent system formed by two parallel forces applied at B and C.

3.65 Solve Prob. 3.64, assuming that force **P** is horizontal ($\alpha = \beta = 30°$).

3.66 Force **P** is applied to the handle at A. Replace **P** by an equivalent system formed by two parallel forces applied at B and C and show that (a) these forces are parallel to **P**, (b) their magnitudes are independent of both α and β.

3.67 The shearing forces exerted on the cross section of a steel channel may be represented by a 900-N vertical force and two 250-N horizontal forces as shown. Replace this force and couple by a single force **F** applied at point C and determine the distance x from C to line BD. (Point C is defined as the *shear center* of the section.)

Fig. P3.64 and P3.66

Fig. P3.67

3.68 A force and couple act as shown on a square plate of side $a = 625$ mm. Knowing that $P = 300$ N, $Q = 200$ N, and $\alpha = 50°$, replace the given force and couple by a single force applied at a point located (a) on line AB, (b) on line AC. In each case determine the distance from A to the point of application of the force.

Fig. P3.68 and P3.69

3.69 The force and couple shown are to be replaced by an equivalent single force. Knowing that $P = 2Q$, determine the required value of α if the line of action of the single equivalent force is to pass through (a) point A, (b) point C.

3.70 Replace the 250-kN force **P** by an equivalent force-couple system at G.

Fig. P3.70

3.71 The 3-m boom AB has a fixed end A and the tension in cable BC is 2850 N. Replace the force that the cable exerts at B by an equivalent force-couple system at A.

Fig. P3.71

Fig. P3.72

3.72 The jib crane shown is oriented so that its boom AD is parallel to the x axis and is used to move a heavy crate. Knowing that the tension in cable AB is 13 kN, replace the force exerted by the cable at A by an equivalent force-couple system at the center O of the base of the crane.

3.73 Replace the 150-N force by an equivalent force-couple system at A.

Fig. P3.73

Fig. P3.74

3.74 The speed-reducer unit shown has a mass of 33.5 kg and its center of gravity is located on the y axis. Show that the weight of the unit and the two couples acting on it, of magnitude $M_1 = 27.1$ N·m and $M_2 = 5.42$ N·m, respectively, may be replaced by a single equivalent force and determine (a) the magnitude and direction of that force, (b) the point where its line of action intersects the floor.

3.75 Five separate force-couple systems act at the corners of a bent plate as shown. Find two force-couple systems which are equivalent.

Fig. P3.75 and P3.76

3.76 Five separate force-couple systems act at the corners of a bent plate as shown. Determine which of these systems is equivalent to a force $\mathbf{F} = (60\ \text{N})\mathbf{j}$ and a couple $\mathbf{M} = (9\ \text{N}\cdot\text{m})\mathbf{i} - (6\ \text{N}\cdot\text{m})\mathbf{j}$ located at the origin O.

3.17. Reduction of a System of Forces to One Force and One Couple.

Consider a system of forces $\mathbf{F}_1$, $\mathbf{F}_2$, $\mathbf{F}_3$, etc., acting on a rigid body at the points A_1, A_2, A_3, etc., defined by the position vectors $\mathbf{r}_1$, $\mathbf{r}_2$, $\mathbf{r}_3$, etc. (Fig. 3.41a). As seen in the preceding section, $\mathbf{F}_1$ may be moved from A_1 to a given point O if a couple of moment $\mathbf{M}_1$ equal to the moment $\mathbf{r}_1 \times \mathbf{F}_1$ of $\mathbf{F}_1$ about O is added to the original system of forces. Repeating this procedure with $\mathbf{F}_2$, $\mathbf{F}_3$, etc., we obtain the system shown in Fig. 3.41b, consisting of forces acting at O and of couples. Since the forces are now concurrent, they may be added vectorially and replaced by their resultant $\mathbf{R}$. Similarly, the couple vectors $\mathbf{M}_1$, $\mathbf{M}_2$, $\mathbf{M}_3$, etc., may be added vectorially and replaced by a single couple vector $\mathbf{M}_O^R$. Any system of forces, however complex, may thus be reduced to an *equivalent force-couple system acting at a given point O* (Fig. 3.41c). We should note that while each of the couple vectors $\mathbf{M}_1$, $\mathbf{M}_2$, $\mathbf{M}_3$, etc., in Fig. 3.41b is perpendicular to the corresponding force, the resultant force $\mathbf{R}$ and the resultant couple vector $\mathbf{M}_O^R$ in Fig. 3.41c will not, in general, be perpendicular to each other.

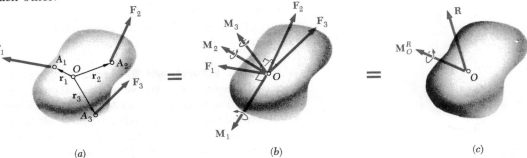

(a)   (b)   (c)

Fig. 3.41

The equivalent force-couple system is defined by the equations

$$\mathbf{R} = \Sigma\mathbf{F} \qquad \mathbf{M}_O^R = \Sigma\mathbf{M}_O = \Sigma(\mathbf{r} \times \mathbf{F}) \tag{3.52}$$

which express that the force $\mathbf{R}$ is obtained by adding all the forces of the system, while the moment $\mathbf{M}_O^R$ of the couple, called *moment resultant* of the system, is obtained by adding the moments about O of all the forces of the system.

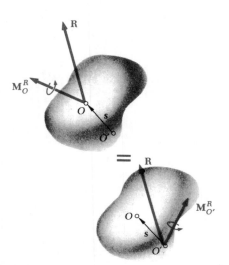

Fig. 3.42

Once a given system of forces has been reduced to a force and a couple at a point O, it may easily be reduced to a force and a couple at another point O'. While the resultant force $\mathbf{R}$ will remain unchanged, the new moment resultant $\mathbf{M}_{O'}^R$ will be equal to the sum of $\mathbf{M}_O^R$ and of the moment about O' of the force $\mathbf{R}$ attached at O (Fig. 3.42). We have

$$\mathbf{M}_{O'}^R = \mathbf{M}_O^R + \mathbf{s} \times \mathbf{R} \tag{3.53}$$

In practice, the reduction of a given system of forces to a single force $\mathbf{R}$ at O and a couple vector $\mathbf{M}_O^R$ will be carried out in terms of components. Resolving each position vector $\mathbf{r}$ and each force $\mathbf{F}$ of the system into rectangular components, we write

$$\mathbf{r} = x\mathbf{i} + y\mathbf{j} + z\mathbf{k} \tag{3.54}$$
$$\mathbf{F} = F_x\mathbf{i} + F_y\mathbf{j} + F_z\mathbf{k} \tag{3.55}$$

Substituting for $\mathbf{r}$ and $\mathbf{F}$ into (3.52) and factoring the unit vectors $\mathbf{i}$, $\mathbf{j}$, $\mathbf{k}$, we obtain $\mathbf{R}$ and $\mathbf{M}_O^R$ in the form

$$\mathbf{R} = R_x\mathbf{i} + R_y\mathbf{j} + R_z\mathbf{k} \qquad \mathbf{M}_O^R = M_x^R\mathbf{i} + M_y^R\mathbf{j} + M_z^R\mathbf{k} \tag{3.56}$$

The components R_x, R_y, R_z represent, respectively, the sums of the x, y, and z components of the given forces and measure the tendency of the system to impart to the rigid body a motion of translation in the x, y, or z direction. Similarly, the components M_x^R, M_y^R, M_z^R represent, respectively, the sums of the moments of the given forces about the x, y, and z axes and measure the tendency of the system to impart to the rigid body a motion of rotation about the x, y, or z axis.

If the magnitude and direction of the force $\mathbf{R}$ are desired, they may be obtained from the components R_x, R_y, R_z by means of the relations (2.18) and (2.19) of Sec. 2.12; similar computations will yield the magnitude and direction of the couple vector $\mathbf{M}_O^R$.

3.18. Equivalent Systems of Forces. We have seen in the preceding section that any system of forces acting on a rigid body may be reduced to a force-couple system at a given point O. This equivalent force-couple system characterizes completely the effect of the given system on the rigid body. *Two systems of forces are equivalent, therefore, if they may be reduced to the same force-couple system at a given point O.* Recalling that the force-couple system at O is defined by the relations (3.52), we state: *Two systems of forces* $\mathbf{F}_1, \mathbf{F}_2, \mathbf{F}_3$, *etc., and* $\mathbf{F}'_1, \mathbf{F}'_2, \mathbf{F}'_3$, *etc., are equivalent if, and only if, the sums of the forces and the sums of the moments about a given point O of the forces of the two systems are, respectively, equal.* Expressed mathematically, the necessary and sufficient conditions for the two systems of forces to be equivalent are

$$\Sigma \mathbf{F} = \Sigma \mathbf{F}' \quad \text{and} \quad \Sigma \mathbf{M}_O = \Sigma \mathbf{M}'_O \tag{3.57}$$

Note that to prove that two systems of forces are equivalent, the second of the relations (3.57) must be established with respect to *only one point O*. It will hold, however, with respect to *any point* if the two systems are equivalent.

Resolving the forces and moments in (3.57) into their rectangular components, we may express the necessary and sufficient conditions for the equivalence of two systems of forces acting on a rigid body as follows:

$$\begin{array}{ccc} \Sigma F_x = \Sigma F'_x & \Sigma F_y = \Sigma F'_y & \Sigma F_z = \Sigma F'_z \\ \Sigma M_x = \Sigma M'_x & \Sigma M_y = \Sigma M'_y & \Sigma M_z = \Sigma M'_z \end{array} \tag{3.58}$$

These equations have a simple physical significance. They express that two systems of forces are equivalent if they tend to impart to the rigid body (1) the same translation in the x, y, and z directions, respectively, and (2) the same rotation about the x, y, and z axes, respectively.

3.19. Equipollent Systems of Vectors. When two systems of vectors satisfy Eqs. (3.57) or (3.58), i.e., when their resultants and their moment resultants about an arbitrary point O are respectively equal, the two systems are said to be *equipollent*. The result established in the preceding section may thus be restated as follows: *If two systems of forces acting on a rigid body are equipollent, they are also equivalent.*

It is important to note that this statement does not apply to *any* system of vectors. Consider for example a system of forces acting on a set of independent particles which do *not* form a rigid body. A different system of forces acting on the same particles may happen to be equipollent to the first one, i.e., it may have the same resultant and the same moment resultant. Yet, since different forces will now act on the various particles, their effects on these particles will be different; the two systems of forces, while equipollent, are *not equivalent.*

3.20. Further Reduction of a System of Forces. We saw in Sec. 3.17 that any given system of forces acting on a rigid body may be reduced to an equivalent force-couple system at O, consisting of a force $\mathbf{R}$ equal to the sum of the forces of the system, and of a couple vector $\mathbf{M}^R_O$ of moment equal to the moment resultant of the system.

When $\mathbf{R} = 0$, the force-couple system reduces to the couple vector $\mathbf{M}^R_O$. The given system of forces may then be reduced to a single couple, called the *resultant couple* of the system.

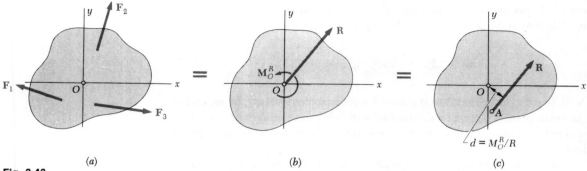

(a)   (b)   (c)

Fig. 3.43

We shall now investigate the conditions under which a given system of forces may be reduced to a single force. It follows from Sec. 3.16 that the force-couple system at O may be replaced by a single force $\mathbf{R}$ acting along a new line of action if $\mathbf{R}$ and $\mathbf{M}_O^R$ are mutually perpendicular. The systems of forces which may be reduced to a single force, or *resultant*, are therefore the systems for which the force $\mathbf{R}$ and the couple vector $\mathbf{M}_O^R$ are mutually perpendicular. While this condition *is generally not satisfied* by systems of forces in space, it *will be satisfied* by systems consisting of (1) concurrent forces, (2) coplanar forces, or (3) parallel forces. We shall discuss these cases separately.

1. *Concurrent forces* are applied at the same point and may therefore be added directly into their resultant $\mathbf{R}$. Thus, they always reduce to a single force. Concurrent forces have been discussed in detail in Chap. 2.

2. *Coplanar forces* act in the same plane, which we shall assume here to be the plane of the figure (Fig. 3.43a). The sum $\mathbf{R}$ of the forces of the system will also lie in the plane of the figure, while the moment of each force about O, and thus the moment resultant $\mathbf{M}_O^R$, will be perpendicular to that plane. The force-couple system at O consists therefore of a force $\mathbf{R}$ and a couple vector $\mathbf{M}_O^R$ which are mutually perpendicular (Fig. 3.43b).† They may be reduced to a single force $\mathbf{R}$ by moving $\mathbf{R}$ in the plane of the figure until its moment about O becomes equal to $\mathbf{M}_O^R$. The distance from O to the line of action of $\mathbf{R}$ is $d = M_O^R/R$ (Fig. 3.43c).

As noted in Sec. 3.17, the reduction of a system of forces is considerably simplified if the forces are resolved into rectangular components. The force-couple system at O is then characterized by the components (Fig. 3.44a)

$$R_x = \Sigma F_x \qquad R_y = \Sigma F_y \qquad M_z^R = M_O^R = \Sigma M_O \qquad (3.59)$$

---

† Since the couple vector $\mathbf{M}_O^R$ is perpendicular to the plane of the figure, it has been represented by the symbol $\uparrow$. A counterclockwise couple $\uparrow$ corresponds to a vector pointing out of the paper, and a clockwise couple $\downarrow$ to a vector pointing into the paper.

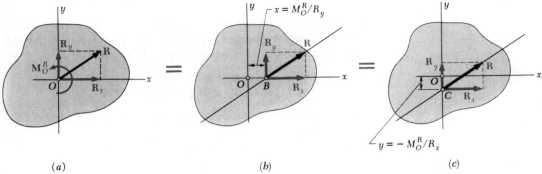

Fig. 3.44

To reduce the system to a single force **R** we shall express that the moment of **R** about O must be equal to $\mathbf{M}_O^R$. Denoting by x and y the coordinates of the point of application A of the resultant, and recalling formula (3.22) of Sec. 3.8, we write

$$xR_y - yR_x = M_O^R$$

which represents the equation of the line of action of **R**. We may also determine directly the x and y intercepts of the line of action of the resultant by noting that $\mathbf{M}_O^R$ must be equal to the moment about O of the y component of **R** when **R** is attached at B (Fig. 3.44b), and to the moment of its x component when **R** is attached at C (Fig. 3.44c).

3. *Parallel forces* have parallel lines of action and may or may not have the same sense. Assuming here that the forces are parallel to the y axis (Fig. 3.45a), we note that their sum **R** will also be parallel to the y axis. On the other hand, since the moment of a given force must be perpendicular to that force, the moment about O of each force of the system, and thus the moment resultant $\mathbf{M}_O^R$, will lie in the zx plane. The force-couple system at O consists therefore of a force **R** and a couple vector $\mathbf{M}_O^R$ which are mutually perpendicular (Fig. 3.45b). They may be reduced to a single force **R** (Fig. 3.45c) or, if $\mathbf{R} = 0$, to a single couple of moment $\mathbf{M}_O^R$.

Fig. 3.45

In practice, the force-couple system at O will be characterized by the components

$$R_y = \Sigma F_y \qquad M_x^R = \Sigma M_x \qquad M_z^R = \Sigma M_z \qquad (3.60)$$

The reduction of the system to a single force may be carried out by moving $\mathbf{R}$ to a new point of application $A(x, 0, z)$ chosen so that the moment of $\mathbf{R}$ about O is equal to $\mathbf{M}_O^R$. We write

$$\mathbf{r} \times \mathbf{R} = \mathbf{M}_O^R$$
$$(x\mathbf{i} + z\mathbf{k}) \times R_y\mathbf{j} = M_x^R\mathbf{i} + M_z^R\mathbf{k}$$

Computing the vector products and equating the coefficients of the corresponding unit vectors in both members of the equation, we obtain two scalar equations which define the coordinates of A:

$$-zR_y = M_x^R \qquad xR_y = M_z^R$$

These equations express that the moments of $\mathbf{R}$ about the x and z axes must, respectively, be equal to M_x^R and M_z^R.

* 3.21. Reduction of a System of Forces to a Wrench.

In the general case of a system of forces in space, the equivalent force-couple system at O consists of a force $\mathbf{R}$ and a couple vector $\mathbf{M}_O^R$ which are not perpendicular, and neither of which is zero (Fig. 3.46a). Thus, the system of forces *cannot* be reduced to a single force or a single couple. The couple vector, however, may be replaced by two other couple vectors obtained by resolving $\mathbf{M}_O^R$ into a component $\mathbf{M}_1$ along $\mathbf{R}$ and a component $\mathbf{M}_2$ in a plane perpendicular to $\mathbf{R}$ (Fig. 3.46b). The couple vector $\mathbf{M}_2$ and the force $\mathbf{R}$ may then be replaced by a single force $\mathbf{R}$ acting along a new line of action.

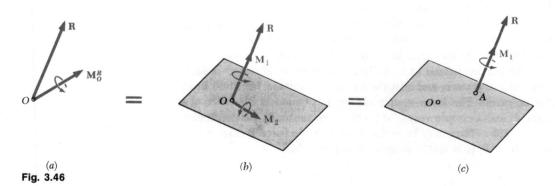

(a)

(b)

(c)

Fig. 3.46

The original system of forces thus reduces to $\mathbf{R}$ and to the couple vector $\mathbf{M}_1$ (Fig. 3.46c), i.e., to $\mathbf{R}$ and a couple acting in the plane perpendicular to $\mathbf{R}$. This particular force-couple system is called a *wrench* because the resulting combination of push and twist is the same that would be caused by an actual wrench. The line of action of $\mathbf{R}$ is known as the *axis of the wrench*, and the ratio $p = M_1/R$ is called the *pitch* of the wrench. A wrench, therefore, consists of two collinear vectors, namely, a force $\mathbf{R}$ and a couple vector

$$\mathbf{M}_1 = p\mathbf{R} \qquad (3.61)$$

Recalling the expression (3.35) obtained in Sec. 3.9 for the projection of a vector on the line of action of another vector, we note that the projection of $\mathbf{M}_O^R$ on the line of action of $\mathbf{R}$ is

$$M_1 = \frac{\mathbf{R} \cdot \mathbf{M}_O^R}{R}$$

Thus, the pitch of the wrench may be expressed as†

$$p = \frac{M_1}{R} = \frac{\mathbf{R} \cdot \mathbf{M}_O^R}{R^2} \qquad (3.62)$$

To define the axis of the wrench we may write a relation involving the position vector $\mathbf{r}$ of an arbitrary point P located on that axis. Attaching the resultant force $\mathbf{R}$ and couple vector $\mathbf{M}_1$ at P (Fig. 3.47), and expressing that the moment about O of this force-couple system is equal to the moment resultant $\mathbf{M}_O^R$ of the original force system, we write

$$\mathbf{M}_1 + \mathbf{r} \times \mathbf{R} = \mathbf{M}_O^R \qquad (3.63)$$

or, recalling Eq. (3.61),

$$p\mathbf{R} + \mathbf{r} \times \mathbf{R} = \mathbf{M}_O^R \qquad (3.64)$$

Fig. 3.47

---

† The expressions obtained for the projection of the couple vector on the line of action of $\mathbf{R}$ and for the pitch of the wrench are independent of the choice of point O. Using the relation (3.53) of Sec. 3.17, we check that if a different point O' had been used, the numerator in (3.62) would be

$$\mathbf{R} \cdot \mathbf{M}_{O'}^R = \mathbf{R} \cdot (\mathbf{M}_O^R + \mathbf{s} \times \mathbf{R}) = \mathbf{R} \cdot \mathbf{M}_O^R + \mathbf{R} \cdot (\mathbf{s} \times \mathbf{R})$$

Since the mixed triple product $\mathbf{R} \cdot (\mathbf{s} \times \mathbf{R})$ is identically equal to zero, we have

$$\mathbf{R} \cdot \mathbf{M}_{O'}^R = \mathbf{R} \cdot \mathbf{M}_O^R$$

Thus, the scalar product $\mathbf{R} \cdot \mathbf{M}_O^R$ is independent of the choice of point O.

SAMPLE PROBLEM 3.8

A 4.80-m beam is subjected to the forces shown. Reduce the given system of forces to (a) an equivalent force-couple system at A, (b) an equivalent force-couple system at B, (c) a single force or resultant.

Note. Since the reactions at the supports are not included in the given system of forces, the given system will not maintain the beam in equilibrium.

a. **Force-Couple System at A.** The force-couple system at A equivalent to the given system of forces consists of a force **R** and a couple M_A^R defined as follows:

$$\mathbf{R} = \Sigma\mathbf{F}$$
$$= (150\text{ N})\mathbf{j} - (600\text{ N})\mathbf{j} + (100\text{ N})\mathbf{j} - (250\text{ N})\mathbf{j} = -(600\text{ N})\mathbf{j}$$
$$\mathbf{M}_A^R = \Sigma(\mathbf{r} \times \mathbf{F})$$
$$= (1.6\mathbf{i}) \times (-600\mathbf{j}) + (2.8\mathbf{i}) \times (100\mathbf{j}) + (4.8\mathbf{i}) \times (-250\mathbf{j})$$
$$= -(1880\text{ N·m})\mathbf{k}$$

The equivalent force-couple system at A is thus

$$\mathbf{R} = 600\text{ N} \downarrow \qquad \mathbf{M}_A^R = 1880\text{ N·m} \downarrow \quad \blacktriangleleft$$

b. **Force-Couple System at B.** We shall find a force-couple system at B equivalent to the force-couple system at A determined in part *a*. The force **R** is unchanged, but a new couple $\mathbf{M}_B^R$ must be determined, the moment of which is equal to the moment about B of the force-couple system determined in part *a*. Thus, we have

$$\mathbf{M}_B^R = \mathbf{M}_A^R + \overrightarrow{BA} \times \mathbf{R}$$
$$= -(1880\text{ N·m})\mathbf{k} + (-4.8\text{ m})\mathbf{i} \times (-600\text{ N})\mathbf{j}$$
$$= -(1880\text{ N·m})\mathbf{k} + (2880\text{ N·m})\mathbf{k} = +(1000\text{ N·m})\mathbf{k}$$

The equivalent force-couple system at B is thus

$$\mathbf{R} = 600\text{ N} \downarrow \qquad \mathbf{M}_B^R = 1000\text{ N·m} \uparrow \quad \blacktriangleleft$$

c. **Single Force or Resultant.** The resultant of the given system of forces is equal to **R** and its point of application must be such that the moment of **R** about A is equal to $\mathbf{M}_A^R$. We write

$$\mathbf{r} \times \mathbf{R} = \mathbf{M}_A^R$$
$$x\mathbf{i} \times (-600\text{ N})\mathbf{j} = -(1880\text{ N·m})\mathbf{k}$$
$$-x(600\text{ N})\mathbf{k} = -(1880\text{ N·m})\mathbf{k}$$

and conclude that $x = 3.13$ m. Thus, the single force equivalent to the given system is defined as

$$\mathbf{R} = 600\text{ N} \downarrow \qquad x = 3.13\text{ m} \quad \blacktriangleleft$$

SAMPLE PROBLEM 3.9

Four tugboats are used to bring an ocean liner to its pier. Each tugboat exerts a 30-kN force in the direction shown. Determine (a) the equivalent force-couple system at the foremast O, (b) the point on the hull where a single, more powerful tugboat should push to produce the same effect as the original four tugboats.

a. Force-couple System at O. Each of the given forces is resolved into components in the diagram shown (kilonewtons are used). The force-couple system at O equivalent to the given system of forces consists of a force **R** and a couple M_O^R defined as follows:

$$\mathbf{R} = \Sigma \mathbf{F}$$
$$= (15\mathbf{i} - 26\mathbf{j}) + (18\mathbf{i} - 24\mathbf{j}) + (-30\mathbf{j}) + (21.2\mathbf{i} + 21.2\mathbf{j})$$
$$= 54.2\mathbf{i} - 58.8\mathbf{j}$$

$$\mathbf{M}_O^R = \Sigma(\mathbf{r} \times \mathbf{F})$$
$$= (-27\mathbf{i} + 15\mathbf{j}) \times (15\mathbf{i} - 26\mathbf{j})$$
$$+ (30\mathbf{i} + 21\mathbf{j}) \times (18\mathbf{i} - 24\mathbf{j})$$
$$+ (120\mathbf{i} + 21\mathbf{j}) \times (-30\mathbf{j})$$
$$+ (90\mathbf{i} - 21\mathbf{j}) \times (21.2\mathbf{i} + 21.2\mathbf{j})$$
$$= (702 - 225 - 720 - 378 - 3600 + 1908 + 445)\mathbf{k}$$
$$= -1868\mathbf{k}$$

The equivalent force-couple system at O is thus

$$\mathbf{R} = (54.2 \text{ kN})\mathbf{i} - (58.8 \text{ kN})\mathbf{j} \qquad \mathbf{M}_O^R = -(1868 \text{ kN·m})\mathbf{k}$$
or $\quad \mathbf{R} = 80.0 \text{ kN} \quad \measuredangle 47.3° \qquad \mathbf{M}_O^R = 1868 \text{ kN·m} \downarrow \quad$ ◄

Remark. Since all the forces are contained in the plane of the figure, we could have expected the sum of their moments to be perpendicular to that plane. Note that the moment of each force component could have been obtained directly from the diagram by forming the product of its magnitude and its perpendicular distance to O, and assigning to this product a positive or a negative sign, depending upon the sense of the moment.

b. Single Tugboat. The force exerted by a single tugboat must be equal to **R** and its point of application A must be such that the moment of **R** about O is equal to M_O^R. Observing that the position vector of A is

$$\mathbf{r} = x\mathbf{i} + 21\mathbf{j}$$

we write

$$\mathbf{r} \times \mathbf{R} = \mathbf{M}_O^R$$
$$(x\mathbf{i} + 21\mathbf{j}) \times (54.2\mathbf{i} - 58.8\mathbf{j}) = -1868\mathbf{k}$$
$$- x(58.8)\mathbf{k} - 1138\mathbf{k} = -1868\mathbf{k}$$

$$x = 12.41 \text{ m} \quad ◄$$

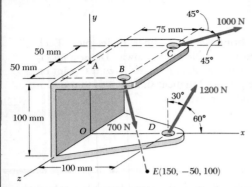

SAMPLE PROBLEM 3.10

Three cables are attached to a bracket as shown. Replace the forces exerted by the cables by an equivalent force-couple system at A.

Solution. We first determine the relative position vectors drawn from point A to the points of application of the various forces and resolve the forces into rectangular components. Observing that $\mathbf{F}_B = (700 \text{ N})\boldsymbol{\lambda}_{BE}$ where

$$\boldsymbol{\lambda}_{BE} = \frac{\overrightarrow{BE}}{BE} = \frac{75\mathbf{i} - 150\mathbf{j} + 50\mathbf{k}}{175}$$

we have, using metres and newtons,

$$\mathbf{r}_{B/A} = \overrightarrow{AB} = 0.075\mathbf{i} + 0.050\mathbf{k} \qquad \mathbf{F}_B = 300\mathbf{i} - 600\mathbf{j} + 200\mathbf{k}$$
$$\mathbf{r}_{C/A} = \overrightarrow{AC} = 0.075\mathbf{i} - 0.050\mathbf{k} \qquad \mathbf{F}_C = 707\mathbf{i} \qquad\quad - 707\mathbf{k}$$
$$\mathbf{r}_{D/A} = \overrightarrow{AD} = 0.100\mathbf{i} - 0.100\mathbf{j} \qquad \mathbf{F}_D = 600\mathbf{i} + 1039\mathbf{j}$$

The force-couple system at A equivalent to the given forces consists of a force $\mathbf{R} = \Sigma\mathbf{F}$ and a couple $\mathbf{M}_A^R = \Sigma(\mathbf{r} \times \mathbf{F})$. The force $\mathbf{R}$ is readily obtained by adding respectively the x, y, and z components of the forces:

$$\mathbf{R} = \Sigma\mathbf{F} \doteq (1607 \text{ N})\mathbf{i} + (439 \text{ N})\mathbf{j} - (507 \text{ N})\mathbf{k} \qquad \blacktriangleleft$$

The computation of $\mathbf{M}_A^R$ will be facilitated if we express the moments of the forces in the form of determinants (Sec. 3.8):

$$\mathbf{r}_{B/A} \times \mathbf{F}_B = \begin{vmatrix} \mathbf{i} & \mathbf{j} & \mathbf{k} \\ 0.075 & 0 & 0.050 \\ 300 & -600 & 200 \end{vmatrix} = 30\mathbf{i} \qquad\quad -45\mathbf{k}$$

$$\mathbf{r}_{C/A} \times \mathbf{F}_C = \begin{vmatrix} \mathbf{i} & \mathbf{j} & \mathbf{k} \\ 0.075 & 0 & -0.050 \\ 707 & 0 & -707 \end{vmatrix} = \qquad 17.68\mathbf{j}$$

$$\mathbf{r}_{D/A} \times \mathbf{F}_D = \begin{vmatrix} \mathbf{i} & \mathbf{j} & \mathbf{k} \\ 0.100 & -0.100 & 0 \\ 600 & 1039 & 0 \end{vmatrix} = \qquad\qquad 163.9\mathbf{k}$$

Adding the expressions obtained, we have

$$\mathbf{M}_A^R = \Sigma(\mathbf{r} \times \mathbf{F}) = (30 \text{ N·m})\mathbf{i} + (17.68 \text{ N·m})\mathbf{j} + (118.9 \text{ N·m})\mathbf{k} \qquad \blacktriangleleft$$

The rectangular components of the force $\mathbf{R}$ and the couple $\mathbf{M}_A^R$ are shown in the adjoining sketch.

A square foundation mat supports the four columns shown. [ ] magnitude and point of application of the resultant of the fo [ ]

Solution. We shall first reduce the given system of forces to a force-couple system at the origin O of the coordinates. This force-couple system consists of a force $\mathbf{R}$ and a couple $\mathbf{M}_O^R$ defined as follows:

$$\mathbf{R} = \Sigma\mathbf{F} \qquad \mathbf{M}_O^R = \Sigma(\mathbf{r} \times \mathbf{F})$$

The position vectors of the points of application of the various forces are determined and the computations are arranged in tabular form.

r, m	F, kN	r × F, kN·m
0	$-200\mathbf{j}$	0
$5\mathbf{i}$	$-60\mathbf{j}$	$-300\mathbf{k}$
$5\mathbf{i} + 2.5\mathbf{k}$	$-40\mathbf{j}$	$100\mathbf{i} - 200\mathbf{k}$
$2\mathbf{i} + 5\mathbf{k}$	$-100\mathbf{j}$	$500\mathbf{i} - 200\mathbf{k}$
	$\mathbf{R} = -400\mathbf{j}$	$\mathbf{M}_O^R = 600\mathbf{i} - 700\mathbf{k}$

Since the force $\mathbf{R}$ and the couple vector $\mathbf{M}_O^R$ are mutually perpendicular, the force-couple system obtained may be reduced further to a single force $\mathbf{R}$. The new point of application of $\mathbf{R}$ will be selected in the plane of the mat and in such a way that the moment of $\mathbf{R}$ about O will be equal to $\mathbf{M}_O^R$. Denoting by $\mathbf{r}$ the position vector of the desired point of application, and by x and z its coordinates, we write

$$\mathbf{r} \times \mathbf{R} = \mathbf{M}_O^R$$
$$(x\mathbf{i} + z\mathbf{k}) \times (-400\mathbf{j}) = 600\mathbf{i} - 700\mathbf{k}$$
$$-400x\mathbf{k} + 400z\mathbf{i} = 600\mathbf{i} - 700\mathbf{k}$$

from which it follows that

$$-400x = -700 \qquad 400z = 600$$
$$x = 1.75\text{m} \qquad z = 1.50 \text{ m}$$

We conclude that the resultant of the given system of forces is

$$\mathbf{R} = 400 \text{ kN} \downarrow \qquad \text{at } x = 1.75 \text{ m}, z = 1.50 \text{ m} \quad \blacktriangleleft$$

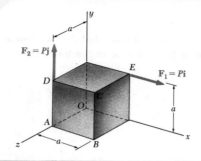

Two forces of the same magnitude P act on a cube of side a as shown. Replace the two forces by an equivalent wrench and determine (a) the magnitude and direction of the resultant force $\mathbf{R}$, (b) the pitch of the wrench, (c) the point where the axis of the wrench intersects the yz plane.

Solution. We first determine the equivalent force-couple system at the origin O. We observe that the position vectors of the points of application E and D of the two given forces are $\mathbf{r}_E = a\mathbf{i} + a\mathbf{j}$ and $\mathbf{r}_D = a\mathbf{j} + a\mathbf{k}$. The resultant $\mathbf{R}$ of the two forces and their moment resultant $\mathbf{M}_O^R$ about O are

$$\mathbf{R} = \mathbf{F}_1 + \mathbf{F}_2 = P\mathbf{i} + P\mathbf{j} = P(\mathbf{i} + \mathbf{j}) \tag{1}$$
$$\mathbf{M}_O^R = \mathbf{r}_E \times \mathbf{F}_1 + \mathbf{r}_D \times \mathbf{F}_2 = (a\mathbf{i} + a\mathbf{j}) \times P\mathbf{i} + (a\mathbf{j} + a\mathbf{k}) \times P\mathbf{j}$$
$$= -Pa\mathbf{k} - Pa\mathbf{i} = -Pa(\mathbf{i} + \mathbf{k}) \tag{2}$$

(a) **Resultant Force R.** It follows from Eq. (1) and the adjoining sketch that the resultant force $\mathbf{R}$ has the magnitude $R = P\sqrt{2}$, lies in the xy plane, and forms angles of $45°$ with the x and y axes. Thus

$$R = P\sqrt{2} \qquad \theta_x = \theta_y = 45° \qquad \theta_z = 90° \quad \blacktriangleleft$$

(b) **Pitch of Wrench.** Recalling formula (3.62) of Sec. 3.21 and Eqs. (1) and (2) above, we write

$$p = \frac{\mathbf{R} \cdot \mathbf{M}_O^R}{R^2} = \frac{P(\mathbf{i} + \mathbf{j}) \cdot (-Pa)(\mathbf{i} + \mathbf{k})}{(P\sqrt{2})^2} = \frac{-P^2 a(1 + 0 + 0)}{2P^2} \qquad p = -\frac{a}{2} \quad \blacktriangleleft$$

(c) **Axis of Wrench.** It follows from the above and from Eq. (3.61) of Sec. 3.21 that the wrench consists of the force $\mathbf{R}$ found in (1) and of the couple vector

$$\mathbf{M}_1 = p\mathbf{R} = -\frac{a}{2}P(\mathbf{i} + \mathbf{j}) = -\frac{Pa}{2}(\mathbf{i} + \mathbf{j}) \tag{3}$$

To find the point where the axis of the wrench intersects the yz plane, we shall express that the moment of the wrench about O is equal to the moment resultant $\mathbf{M}_O^R$ of the original system:

$$\mathbf{M}_1 + \mathbf{r} \times \mathbf{R} = \mathbf{M}_O^R$$

or, noting that $\mathbf{r} = y\mathbf{j} + z\mathbf{k}$ and substituting for $\mathbf{R}$, $\mathbf{M}_O^R$, and $\mathbf{M}_1$ from Eqs. (1), (2), and (3),

$$-\frac{Pa}{2}(\mathbf{i} + \mathbf{j}) + (y\mathbf{j} + z\mathbf{k}) \times P(\mathbf{i} + \mathbf{j}) = -Pa(\mathbf{i} + \mathbf{k})$$

$$-\frac{Pa}{2}\mathbf{i} - \frac{Pa}{2}\mathbf{j} - Py\mathbf{k} + Pz\mathbf{j} - Pz\mathbf{i} = -Pa\mathbf{i} - Pa\mathbf{k}$$

Equating the coefficients of $\mathbf{k}$, and then the coefficients of $\mathbf{j}$, we find

$$y = a \qquad z = a/2 \quad \blacktriangleleft$$

Problems

3.77 A 3-m beam is loaded in the various ways represented in the figure. Find two loadings which are equivalent.

Fig. P3.77

3.78 A 3-m beam is loaded as shown. Determine the loading of Prob. 3.77 which is equivalent to this loading.

3.79 Determine the resultant of the loads and the distance from point A to its line of action for the beam and loading of (a) Prob. 3.77a, (b) Prob. 3.77b, (c) Prob. 3.78.

Fig. P3.78

Fig. P3.80

3.80 By driving the truck shown over a scale, it was determined that the loads on the front and rear axles are, respectively, 18 kN and 12 kN when the truck is empty. Determine (a) the location of the center of gravity of the truck, (b) the weight and location of the center of gravity of the heaviest load which may be carried by the truck if the load on each axle is not to exceed 40 kN.

3.81 Determine the distance from point A to the line of action of the resultant of the three loads shown when (a) $x = 0.5$ m, (b) $x = 1.5$ m, (c) $x = 2.5$ m.

3.82 Express as a function of x the distance d from point A to the line of action of the resultant of the three loads shown.

Fig. P3.81 and P3.82

3.83 Four forces act on a 700 × 375 mm plate as shown. (*a*) Find the resultant of these forces. (*b*) Locate the two points where the line of action of the resultant intersects the edge of the plate.

Fig. P3.83

3.84 Solve Prob. 3.83, assuming that the 760-N force is directed to the right.

3.85 The three forces shown and a couple of magnitude $M = 8$ N·m are applied to an angle bracket. (*a*) Find the resultant of this system of forces. (*b*) Locate the points where the line of action of the resultant intersects line AB and line BC.

Fig. P3.85 and P3.86

3.86 The three forces shown and a couple **M** are applied to an angle bracket. Find the moment of the couple if the line of action of the resultant of the force system is to pass through (*a*) point A, (*b*) point B, (*c*) point C.

3.87 Two cables exert forces of 90 kN each on a truss of weight $W = 200$ kN. Find the resultant force acting on the truss and the point of intersection of its line of action with line AB.

Fig. P3.87

Fig. P3.88

3.88 A force **P** of given magnitude P is applied to the edge of a semicircular plate of radius a as shown. (*a*) Replace **P** by an equivalent force-couple system at the point D obtained by drawing the perpendicular from B to the x axis. (*b*) Determine the value of θ for which the moment of the equivalent force-couple system at D is maximum.

3.89 A blade held in a brace is used to tighten a screw at A. (*a*) Determine the forces exerted at B and C, knowing that these forces are equivalent to a force-couple system at A consisting of $\mathbf{R} = -(25\ \text{N})\mathbf{i} + R_y\mathbf{j} + R_z\mathbf{k}$ and $\mathbf{M}_A^R = -(13.5\ \text{N}\cdot\text{m})\mathbf{i}$. (*b*) Find the corresponding values of R_y and R_z. (*c*) What is the orientation of the slot in the head of the screw for which the blade is least likely to slip when the brace is in the position shown?

Fig. P3.89

Fig. P3.90

3.90 A machine component is subjected to the forces shown, each of which is parallel to one of the coordinate axes. Replace these forces by an equivalent force-couple system at A.

3.91 In order to unscrew the tapped faucet A, a plumber uses two pipe wrenches as shown. By exerting a 200-N force on each wrench, at a distance of 240 mm from the axis of the pipe and in a direction perpendicular to the pipe and to the wrench, he prevents the pipe from rotating, and thus avoids loosening or further tightening the joint between the pipe and the tapped elbow C. Determine (*a*) the angle θ that the wrench at A should form with the vertical if elbow C is not to rotate about the vertical, (*b*) the force-couple system at C equivalent to the two 200-N forces when this condition is satisfied.

3.92 Assuming $\theta = 60°$ in Prob. 3.91, replace the two 200-N forces by an equivalent force-couple system at D and determine whether the plumber's action tends to tighten or loosen the joint between (*a*) pipe CD and elbow D, (*b*) elbow D and pipe DE. Assume all threads to be right-handed.

3.93 Assuming $\theta = 60°$ in Prob. 3.91, replace the two 200-N forces by an equivalent force-couple system at E and determine whether the plumber's action tends to tighten or loosen the joint between (*a*) pipe DE and elbow E, (*b*) elbow E and pipe EF. Assume all threads to be right-handed.

Fig. P3.91

3.94 A rectangular concrete foundation mat supports four column loads as shown. Determine the magnitude and point of application of the resultant of the four loads.

Fig. P3.94

3.95 A concrete foundation mat in the shape of a regular hexagon of side 3 m supports four column loads as shown. Determine the magnitude and point of application of the resultant of the four loads.

3.96 Determine the magnitudes of the additional loads which must be applied at B and F if the resultant of all six loads is to pass through the center of the mat.

3.97 In Prob. 3.94, determine the magnitude and point of application of the smallest additional load which must be applied to the foundation mat if the resultant of the five loads is to pass through the center of the mat.

Fig. P3.95 and P3.96

Fig. P3.98

*3.98 Three forces of the same magnitude P act on a cube of side a as shown. Replace the three forces by an equivalent wrench and determine (a) the magnitude and direction of the resultant force $\mathbf{R}$, (b) the pitch of the wrench, (c) the axis of the wrench.

*3.99 The two shafts of a speed-reducer unit are subjected to couples of magnitude $M_1 = 12$ N·m and $M_2 = 5$ N·m, respectively. The unit has a mass of 36 kg and its center of gravity is located on the z axis at $z = 216$ mm. Replace the weight and the two couples by an equivalent wrench and determine (a) the resultant force $\mathbf{R}$, (b) the pitch of the wrench, (c) the point where the axis of the wrench intersects the xz plane.

Fig. P3.99

*3.100 Two forces of magnitude P act as shown along the diagonals GC and AE of the horizontal faces of a rectangular parallelepiped. Replace the two forces by an equivalent system consisting of (a) a force and couple at O, (b) a wrench. (Specify the pitch and axis of the wrench.)

Fig. P3.100

*3.101 In an automated manufacturing process three holes are drilled simultaneously as shown in an aluminum block. Each drill exerts a 50-N force and a 0.100-N · m couple on the block. Knowing that drill A rotates counterclockwise, and drills B and C clockwise (as observed from each drill), reduce the forces and couples exerted by the drills on the block to an equivalent wrench and determine (a) the resultant force $\mathbf{R}$, (b) the pitch of the wrench, (c) the point where the axis of the wrench intersects the xz plane.

Fig. P3.101

*3.102 If only drills A and B are used in the manufacturing process of Prob. 3.101, show that the forces and couples exerted by the two drills on the aluminum block may be reduced to a single force $\mathbf{R}$ and determine (a) the magnitude and direction of $\mathbf{R}$, (b) the line of action of $\mathbf{R}$.

*3.103 In Sample Prob. 3.12 an additional force $\mathbf{Q} = Q\mathbf{k}$ is applied at the corner B of the cube. Knowing that the three forces acting on the cube may be reduced to a single force $\mathbf{R}$, determine (a) the force $\mathbf{Q}$, (b) the magnitude and direction of $\mathbf{R}$, (c) the point where the line of action of $\mathbf{R}$ intersects the yz plane.

Fig. P3.104

*3.104 A rectangular block is acted upon by the three forces shown, which are directed along its edges. Replace these forces by an equivalent wrench and determine (a) the magnitude and direction of the resultant force $\mathbf{R}$, (b) the pitch of the wrench, (c) the point where the axis of the wrench intersects the yz plane.

*3.105 Replace the two wrenches shown by a single equivalent wrench and determine (a) the resultant force $\mathbf{R}$, (b) the pitch of the single equivalent wrench, (c) the point where its axis intersects the xz plane.

*3.106 Assuming $\theta = 60°$ in Prob. 3.91, replace the two 200-N forces by an equivalent wrench. Determine (a) the magnitude and direction of the resultant force $\mathbf{R}$, (b) the pitch of the wrench, (c) the point where the axis of the wrench intersects the yz plane.

Fig. P3.105

Fig. P3.108

*3.107 In Prob. 3.90, replace the forces applied to the machine component by an equivalent wrench. Determine (a) the magnitude and direction of the resultant force **R**, (b) the pitch of the wrench, (c) the point where the axis of the wrench intersects the xz plane.

*3.108 (a) Replace the wrench shown by an equivalent system consisting of two forces perpendicular to the x axis and applied respectively at A and B. (b) Solve part a assuming R = 150 N, M = 20 N·m, a = 125 mm, and b = 50 mm.

*3.109 Show that, in general, a wrench may be replaced by two forces chosen in such a way that one force passes through a given point while the other force lies in a given plane.

*3.110 Show that a wrench may be replaced by two perpendicular forces, one of which is applied at a given point.

*3.111 Show that a wrench may be replaced by two forces, one of which has a prescribed line of action.

Review and Summary

In this chapter we studied the effect of forces exerted on a rigid body. We first learned to distinguish between *external* and *internal* forces [Sec. 3.2] and saw that, according to the *principle of transmissibility*, the effect of an external force on a rigid body remains unchanged if that force is moved along its line of action [Sec. 3.3]. In other words, two forces **F** and **F′** acting on a rigid body at two different points have the same effect on that body if they have the same magnitude, same direction, and same line of action (Fig. 3.48). Two such forces are said to be *equivalent*.

Principle of transmissibility

Fig. 3.48

Fig. 3.49

Before proceeding with the discussion of *equivalent systems of forces*, we introduced the concept of *vector product of two vectors* [Sec. 3.4]. The vector product

$$\mathbf{V} = \mathbf{P} \times \mathbf{Q}$$

of the vectors **P** and **Q** was defined as a vector perpendicular to the plane containing **P** and **Q** (Fig. 3.49), of magnitude

$$V = PQ \sin \theta \qquad (3.1)$$

and directed in such a way that a person located at the tip of **V** will observe as counterclockwise the rotation through θ which brings the vector **P** in line with the vector **Q**. The three vectors **P**, **Q**, and **V**—taken in that order—are said to form a *right-handed triad*. It follows that the vector products **Q** × **P** and **P** × **Q** are represented by equal and opposite vectors. We have

$$\mathbf{Q} \times \mathbf{P} = -(\mathbf{P} \times \mathbf{Q}) \qquad (3.4)$$

It also follows from the definition of the vector product of two vectors that the vector products of the unit vectors **i**, **j**, and **k** are

$$\mathbf{i} \times \mathbf{i} = 0 \qquad \mathbf{i} \times \mathbf{j} = \mathbf{k} \qquad \mathbf{j} \times \mathbf{i} = -\mathbf{k}$$

and so on. The sign of the vector product of two unit vectors may be obtained by arranging in a circle and in counterclockwise order the three letters representing the unit vectors (Fig. 3.50): The product of two unit vectors will be positive if they follow each other in counterclockwise order, and negative otherwise.

The *rectangular components of the vector product* **V** of two vectors **P** and **Q** were expressed [Sec. 3.5] as

$$\begin{aligned} V_x &= P_y Q_z - P_z Q_y \\ V_y &= P_z Q_x - P_x Q_z \\ V_z &= P_x Q_y - P_y Q_x \end{aligned} \qquad (3.9)$$

Using a determinant form, we also wrote

$$\mathbf{V} = \begin{vmatrix} \mathbf{i} & \mathbf{j} & \mathbf{k} \\ P_x & P_y & P_z \\ Q_x & Q_y & Q_z \end{vmatrix} \qquad (3.10)$$

Vector product of two vectors

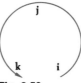

Fig. 3.50

Rectangular components of vector product

Rigid Bodies: Equivalent Systems of Forces

Moment of a force about a point

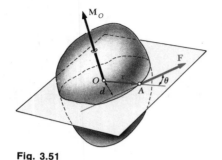

Fig. 3.51

Rectangular components of moment

Fig. 3.52

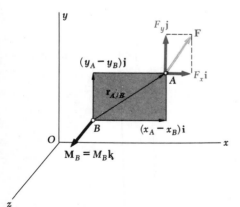

Fig. 3.53

The *moment of a force* **F** *about a point* O was defined [Sec. 3.6] as the vector product

$$\mathbf{M}_O = \mathbf{r} \times \mathbf{F} \tag{3.11}$$

where **r** is the *position vector* drawn from O to the point of application A of the force **F** (Fig. 3.51). Denoting by θ the angle between the lines of action of **r** and **F**, we found that the magnitude of the moment of **F** about O may be expressed as

$$M_O = rF \sin \theta = Fd \tag{3.12}$$

where d represents the perpendicular distance from O to the line of action of **F**.

The *rectangular components of the moment* $\mathbf{M}_O$ *of a force* **F** were expressed [Sec. 3.8] as

$$
\begin{aligned}
M_x &= yF_z - zF_y \\
M_y &= zF_x - xF_z \\
M_z &= xF_y - yF_x
\end{aligned}
\tag{3.18}
$$

where x, y, z are the components of the position vector **r** (Fig. 3.52). Using a determinant form, we also wrote

$$
\mathbf{M}_O = \begin{vmatrix} \mathbf{i} & \mathbf{j} & \mathbf{k} \\ x & y & z \\ F_x & F_y & F_z \end{vmatrix}
\tag{3.19}
$$

In the more general case of the moment about an arbitrary point B of a force **F** applied at A, we had

$$
\mathbf{M}_B = \begin{vmatrix} \mathbf{i} & \mathbf{j} & \mathbf{k} \\ x_{A/B} & y_{A/B} & z_{A/B} \\ F_x & F_y & F_z \end{vmatrix}
\tag{3.21}
$$

where $x_{A/B}$, $y_{A/B}$, and $z_{A/B}$ denote the components of the vector $\mathbf{r}_{A/B}$:

$$x_{A/B} = x_A - x_B \qquad y_{A/B} = y_A - y_B \qquad z_{A/B} = z_A - z_B$$

In the case of *problems involving only two dimensions*, the force **F** may be assumed to lie in the xy plane. Its moment $\mathbf{M}_B$ about a point B in the same plane is perpendicular to that plane (Fig. 3.53) and is completely defined by the scalar

$$M_B = (x_A - x_B)F_y - (y_A - y_B)F_x \tag{3.23}$$

Various methods for the computation of the moment of a force about a point were illustrated in Sample Probs. 3.1 through 3.4.

The *scalar product* of two vectors **P** and **Q** [Sec. 3.9] was denoted by **P·Q** and defined as the scalar quantity

$$\mathbf{P}\cdot\mathbf{Q} = PQ \cos\theta \qquad (3.24)$$

where θ is the angle between P and Q (Fig. 3.54). Expressing the scalar product of **P** and **Q** in terms of the rectangular components of the two vectors, we had

$$\mathbf{P}\cdot\mathbf{Q} = P_x Q_x + P_y Q_y + P_z Q_z \qquad (3.30)$$

Fig. 3.54

The *projection of a vector* **P** *on an axis OL* (Fig. 3.55) may be obtained by forming the scalar product of **P** and the unit vector **λ** along *OL*. We have

$$P_{OL} = \mathbf{P}\cdot\boldsymbol{\lambda} \qquad (3.36)$$

or, using rectangular components,

$$P_{OL} = P_x \cos\theta_x + P_y \cos\theta_y + P_z \cos\theta_z \qquad (3.37)$$

where θ_x, θ_y, and θ_z denote the angles that the axis *OL* forms with the coordinate axes.

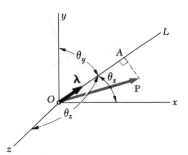

Fig. 3.55

The *mixed triple product* of the three vectors **S**, **P**, and **Q** was defined as the scalar expression

$$\mathbf{S}\cdot(\mathbf{P}\times\mathbf{Q}) \qquad (3.38)$$

obtained by forming the scalar product of **S** with the vector product of **P** and **Q** [Sec. 3.10]. It was shown that

$$\mathbf{S}\cdot(\mathbf{P}\times\mathbf{Q}) = \begin{vmatrix} S_x & S_y & S_z \\ P_x & P_y & P_z \\ Q_x & Q_y & Q_z \end{vmatrix}$$

where the elements of the determinant are the rectangular components of the three vectors.

Moment of a force about an axis

Fig. 3.56

Couples

Fig. 3.57

The *moment of a force* **F** *about an axis OL* [Sec. 3.11] was defined as the projection OC on OL of the moment $\mathbf{M}_O$ of the force **F** (Fig. 3.56), i.e., as the mixed triple product of the unit vector $\boldsymbol{\lambda}$, the position vector **r**, and the force **F**:

$$M_{OL} = \boldsymbol{\lambda} \cdot \mathbf{M}_O = \boldsymbol{\lambda} \cdot (\mathbf{r} \times \mathbf{F}) \qquad (3.42)$$

Using the determinant form for the mixed triple product, we have

$$M_{OL} = \begin{vmatrix} \lambda_x & \lambda_y & \lambda_z \\ x & y & z \\ F_x & F_y & F_z \end{vmatrix} \qquad (3.43)$$

where λ_x, λ_y, λ_z = direction cosines of axis OL
$\quad\quad x$, y, z = components of **r**
$\quad\quad F_x$, F_y, F_z = components of **F**

An example of the determination of the moment of a force about a skew axis was given in Sample Prob. 3.5.

Two forces **F** *and* $-$**F** *having the same magnitude, parallel lines of action, and opposite sense are said to form a couple* [Sec. 3.12]. It was shown that the moment of a couple is independent of the point about which it is computed; it is a vector **M** perpendicular to the plane of the couple and equal in magnitude to the product of the common magnitude F of the forces and the perpendicular distance d between their lines of action (Fig. 3.57).

Two couples having the same moment **M** are *equivalent*, i.e., they have the same effect on a given rigid body [Sec. 3.13]. The sum of two couples is itself a couple [Sec. 3.14] and the moment **M** of the resultant couple may be obtained by adding vectorially the moments $\mathbf{M}_1$ and $\mathbf{M}_2$ of the original couples [Sample Prob. 3.6]. It follows that a couple may be represented by a vector, called a *couple vector*, equal in magnitude and direction to the moment **M** of the couple [Sec. 3.15]. A couple vector is a *free vector* which may be attached to the origin O if so desired and resolved into components (Fig. 3.58).

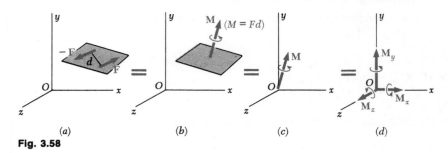

(a) (b) (c) (d)

Fig. 3.58

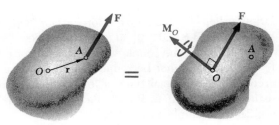

Fig. 3.59

Any force **F** acting at a point A of a rigid body may be replaced by a *force-couple system* at an arbitrary point O, consisting of the force **F** applied at O and a couple of moment $\mathbf{M}_O$ equal to the moment about O of the force **F** in its original position [Sec. 3.16]; it should be noted that the force **F** and the couple vector $\mathbf{M}_O$ are always perpendicular to each other (Fig. 3.59).

Reduction of a system of forces to a force-couple system

It follows [Sec. 3.17] that *any system of forces may be reduced to a force-couple system at a given point O* by replacing each of the forces of the system by an equivalent force-couple system at O (Fig. 3.60) and adding all the forces and all the couples obtained in this manner into a resultant force **R** and a resultant couple $\mathbf{M}_O^R$ [Sample Probs. 3.8 through 3.11]. Note that, in general, the resultant **R** and the couple vector $\mathbf{M}_O^R$ will not be perpendicular to each other.

 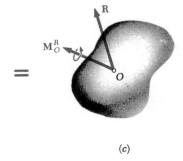

(a) $\qquad\qquad$ (b) $\qquad\qquad$ (c)

Fig. 3.60

Equivalent systems of forces

We concluded from the above [Sec. 3.18] that, as far as rigid bodies are concerned, *two systems of forces* $\mathbf{F}_1$, $\mathbf{F}_2$, $\mathbf{F}_3$, *etc., and* $\mathbf{F}_1'$, $\mathbf{F}_2'$, $\mathbf{F}_3'$, *etc., are equivalent if, and only if,*

$$\Sigma\mathbf{F} = \Sigma\mathbf{F}' \quad \text{and} \quad \Sigma\mathbf{M}_O = \Sigma\mathbf{M}_O' \qquad (3.57)$$

Further reduction of a system of forces

If the resultant force **R** and the resultant couple vector $\mathbf{M}_O^R$ are perpendicular to each other, the force-couple system at O may be further reduced to a single resultant force [Sec. 3.20]. This will be the case for systems consisting either of (*a*) concurrent forces (cf. Chap. 2), (*b*) copla-nar forces [Sample Probs. 3.8 and 3.9], or (*c*) parallel forces [Sample Prob. 3.11]. If the resultant **R** and the couple vector $\mathbf{M}_O^R$ are *not* perpendicular to each other, the system *cannot* be reduced to a single force. It may, however, be reduced to a special type of force-couple system called a *wrench*, consisting of the resultant **R** and of a couple vector $\mathbf{M}_1$ directed along **R** [Sec. 3.21 and Sample Prob. 3.12].

Review Problems

3.112 A crane is oriented so that the end of the 25-m boom AO lies in the yz plane. At the instant shown the tension in cable AB is 4 kN. Determine the moment about each of the coordinate axes of the force exerted on A by cable AB.

3.113 The 25-m crane boom AO lies in the yz plane. Determine the maximum permissible tension in cable AB if the absolute value of the moments about the coordinate axes of the force exerted on A by cable AB must be as follows: $|M_x| \leq 60$ kN · m, $|M_y| \leq 12$ kN · m, $|M_z| \leq 8$ kN · m.

3.114 A force **P** of magnitude 2600 N acts on the frame shown at point E. Determine the moment of **P** (*a*) about point D, (*b*) about a line joining points O and D.

Fig. P3.112 and P3.113

Fig. P3.114 and P3.115

3.115 A force **P** acts on the frame shown at point E. Knowing that the absolute value of the moment of **P** about a line joining points F and B is 400 N·m, determine the magnitude of the force **P**.

3.116 and 3.117 It is known that the slide B exerts on rod AB a 800-N force perpendicular to rod BC and directed down and to the right. Determine the moment of that force about A.

Fig. P3.116   Fig. P3.117

Fig. P3.118

3.118 A 500-N force is applied to a bent plate as shown. Determine (*a*) an equivalent force-couple system at B, (*b*) an equivalent system formed by a vertical force at A and a force at B.

3.119 A 150×300 mm plate is subjected to four loads. Find the resultant of the four loads and the two points at which the line of action of the resultant intersects the edge of the plate.

Fig. P3.119

3.120 A concrete foundation mat of 5-m radius supports four equally spaced columns, each of which is located 4 m from the center of the mat. Determine the magnitude and the point of application of the resultant of the four loads.

3.121 Determine the magnitude and point of application of the smallest additional load which must be applied to the foundation mat of Prob. 3.120 if the resultant of the five loads is to pass through the center of the mat.

Fig. P3.120

Fig. P3.122

Fig. P3.123

3.122 Replace the three forces shown by (*a*) a force-couple system at *A*, (*b*) a wrench. (Specify the pitch and axis of the wrench.)

3.123 Three horizontal forces are applied as shown to a vertical cast-iron arm. Determine the resultant of the forces and the distance from the ground to its line of action when (*a*) $P = 160$ N, (*b*) $P = 1000$ N, (*c*) $P = 5200$ N.

The following problems are designed to be solved with a computer.

3.C1 A beam *AB* is subjected to several vertical forces as shown. Write a computer program which can be used to determine the magnitude of the resultant and point *C* where its line of action intersects *AB*. Use this program to solve (*a*) Sample Prob. 3.8*c*, (*b*) Prob. 3.81.

3.C2 Two forces **P** and **Q** of magnitude $P = 50$ N and $Q = 120$ N are applied as shown to corners *A* and *B* of a square plate of side $a = 500$ mm. Write a computer program which can be used to calculate the equivalent force-couple system at *D*. Use this program to determine the magnitude and the direction of **R** and the couple $\mathbf{M}_D$ for values of β from 0 to 360° at 30° intervals.

Fig. P3.C1

Fig. P3.C2

Fig. P3.C3

3.C3   A force **P** of magnitude 2600 N acts on the frame shown at point E. Several comparative designs are to be made, using various lengths z for portions AC and BD of the frame. Write a computer program and use it to calculate, for values of z from 0 to 500 mm at 25-mm intervals, (a) the rectangular components and magnitude of the moment of **P** about point O, (b) the moment of **P** about a line joining points O and D.

3.C4   Write a computer program which can be used to determine the magnitude and point of application of the resultant of the vertical forces P_1, $P_2, \ldots, P_n$ which act at points $A_1, A_2, \ldots, A_n$ located in the xz plane. Use this program to solve (a) Sample Prob. 3.11, (b) Prob. 3.94, (c) Prob. 3.95.

Fig. P3.C4

Equilibrium of Rigid Bodies

4.1. Introduction. We saw in the preceding chapter that the external forces acting on a rigid body may be reduced to a force-couple system at some arbitrary point O. When the force and the couple are both equal to zero, the external forces form a system equivalent to zero and the rigid body is said to be in *equilibrium*.

The necessary and sufficient conditions for the equilibrium of a rigid body, therefore, may be obtained by setting $\mathbf{R}$ and $\mathbf{M}_O^R$ equal to zero in the relations (3.52) of Sec. 3.17:

$$\Sigma \mathbf{F} = 0 \qquad \Sigma \mathbf{M}_O = \Sigma(\mathbf{r} \times \mathbf{F}) = 0 \qquad (4.1)$$

Resolving each force and each moment into its rectangular components, we may express the necessary and sufficient conditions for the equilibrium of a rigid body by the following six scalar equations:

$$\Sigma F_x = 0 \qquad \Sigma F_y = 0 \qquad \Sigma F_z = 0 \qquad (4.2)$$
$$\Sigma M_x = 0 \qquad \Sigma M_y = 0 \qquad \Sigma M_z = 0 \qquad (4.3)$$

The equations obtained may be used to determine unknown forces applied to the rigid body or unknown reactions exerted on it by its supports. We note that Eqs. (4.2) express the fact that the components of the external forces in the x, y, and z directions are balanced; Eqs. (4.3) express the fact that the moments of the external forces about the x, y, and z axes are balanced. The system of the external forces, therefore, will impart no motion of translation or rotation to the rigid body considered.

In order to write the equations of equilibrium for a rigid body, it is essential to first identify correctly all the forces acting on that body and draw the corresponding *free-body diagram*. In this chapter we shall first consider the equilibrium of *two-dimensional structures* subjected to forces contained in their plane and learn to draw their free-body diagram. In addition to the forces *applied* to the structure, we shall consider the *reactions* exerted on the structure by its supports. We shall learn to associate a specific reaction with each type of support and determine whether the structure is properly supported, so that we may know in advance whether the equations of equilibrium may actually be solved for the unknown forces and reactions. Later in the chapter, we shall consider the equilibrium of three-dimensional structures and subject them and their supports to the same kind of analysis.

4.2. Free-Body Diagram. In solving a problem concerning the equilibrium of a rigid body, it is essential to consider *all* the forces acting on the body; it is equally important to exclude any force which is not directly applied on the body. Omitting a force or adding an extraneous one would destroy the conditions of equilibrium. Therefore, the first step in the solution of the problem should consist in drawing a *free-body diagram* of the rigid body under consideration. Free-body diagrams have already been used on many occasions in Chap. 2. However, in view of their importance to the solution of equilibrium problems, we shall summarize here the various steps which must be followed in drawing a free-body diagram.

First, a clear decision is made regarding the choice of the free body to be used. This body is then detached from the ground and separated from any other body. The contour of the body thus isolated is sketched.

All external forces are then indicated. These forces represent the action exerted *on* the free body *by* the ground and the bodies which have been detached; they should be applied at the various points where the free body was supported by the ground or connected to the other bodies. The *weight* of the free body should also be included among the external forces, since it represents the attraction exerted by the earth on the various particles forming the free body. As will be seen in Chap. 5, the weight should be applied at the center of gravity of the body. When the free body is made of several parts, the forces the various parts exert on each other should *not* be included among the external forces. These forces are internal forces as far as the free body is concerned.

The magnitude and direction of the *known external forces* should be clearly marked on the free-body diagram. Care should be taken to indicate the sense of the force exerted *on* the free body, not that of the force exerted *by* the free body. Known external forces generally include the *weight* of the free body and *forces applied* for a given purpose.

Unknown external forces usually consist of the *reactions*—sometimes called *constraining forces*—through which the ground and other bodies oppose a possible motion of the free body and thus constrain it to remain in the same position. Reactions are exerted at the points where the free body is *supported* or *connected* to other bodies. They will be discussed in detail in Secs. 4.3 and 4.8.

The free-body diagram should also include dimensions, since these may be needed in the computation of moments of forces. Any other detail, however, should be omitted.

4.3. Reactions at Supports and Connections for a Two-Dimensional Structure. In the first part of this chapter we shall consider the equilibrium of a two-dimensional structure; i.e., we shall assume that the structure considered and the forces applied to it are contained in the plane of the figure. Clearly, the reactions needed to maintain the structure in the same position will also be contained in the plane of the figure.

The reactions exerted on a two-dimensional structure may be divided into three groups, corresponding to three types of *supports,* or *connections:*

1. *Reactions Equivalent to a Force with Known Line of Action.* Supports and connections causing reactions of this group include *rollers, rockers, frictionless surfaces, short links and cables, collars on frictionless rods,* and *frictionless pins in slots.* Each of these supports and connections can prevent motion in one direction only. They are shown in Fig. 4.1, together with the reaction they produce. Reactions of this group involve *one unknown,* namely, the magnitude of the reaction; this magnitude should be denoted by an appropriate letter. The line of action of the reaction is known and should be indicated clearly in the free-body diagram. The sense of the reaction must be as shown in Fig. 4.1 in the case of a frictionless surface (away from the surface) or of a cable (tension in the direction of the cable). The reaction may be directed either way in the case of double-track rollers, links, collars on rods, and pins in slots. Single-track rollers and rockers are generally assumed to be reversible, and thus the corresponding reactions may also be directed either way.

2. *Reactions Equivalent to a Force of Unknown Direction.* Supports and connections causing reactions of this group include *frictionless pins in fitted holes, hinges,* and *rough surfaces.* They can prevent translation of the free body in all directions, but they cannot prevent the body from rotating about the connection. Reactions of this group involve *two unknowns* and are usually represented by their x and y components. In the case of a rough surface, the component normal to the surface must be directed away from the surface.

3. *Reactions Equivalent to a Force and a·Couple.* These reactions are caused by *fixed supports* which oppose any motion of the free body and thus constrain it completely. Fixed supports actually produce forces over the entire surface of contact; these forces, however, form a system which may be reduced to a force and a couple. Reactions of this group involve *three unknowns,* consisting usually of the two components of the force and the moment of the couple.

Support or Connection	Reaction	Number of Unknowns
Rollers — Rocker — Frictionless surface	Force with known line of action	1
Short cable — Short link	Force with known line of action	1
Collar on frictionless rod — Frictionless pin in slot	90° Force with known line of action	1
Frictionless pin or hinge — Rough surface	or α Force of unknown direction	2
Fixed support	or α Force and couple	3

Fig. 4.1 Reactions at supports and connections.

When the sense of an unknown force or couple is not clearly apparent, no attempt should be made to determine it. Instead, the sense of the force or couple should be arbitrarily assumed; the sign of the answer obtained will indicate whether the assumption is correct or not.

4.4. Equilibrium of a Rigid Body in Two Dimensions. The conditions stated in Sec. 4.1 for the equilibrium of a rigid body become considerably simpler in the case of a two-dimensional structure. Choosing the x and y axes in the plane of the structure, we have

$$F_z = 0 \qquad M_x = M_y = 0 \qquad M_z = M_O$$

for each of the forces applied to the structure. Thus, the six equations of equilibrium derived in Sec. 4.1 reduce to

$$\Sigma F_x = 0 \qquad \Sigma F_y = 0 \qquad \Sigma M_O = 0 \qquad (4.4)$$

and to three trivial identities $0 = 0$. Since the third of the equations (4.4) must be satisfied regardless of the choice of the origin O, we may write the equations of equilibrium for a two-dimensional structure in the more general form

$$\Sigma F_x = 0 \qquad \Sigma F_y = 0 \qquad \Sigma M_A = 0 \qquad (4.5)$$

where A is any point in the plane of the structure. The three equations obtained may be solved for no more than *three unknowns*.

We saw in the preceding section that unknown forces usually consist of reactions, and that the number of unknowns corresponding to a given reaction depends upon the type of support or connection causing that reaction. Referring to Sec. 4.3, we check that the equilibrium equations (4.5) may be used to determine the reactions of two rollers and one cable, or of one fixed support, or of one roller and one pin in a fitted hole, etc.

Consider, for instance, the truss shown in Fig. 4.2a, which is subjected to the given forces **P**, **Q**, and **S**. The truss is held in place by a pin at A and a roller at B. The pin prevents point A from moving by exerting on the truss a force which may be resolved into the components $\mathbf{A}_x$ and $\mathbf{A}_y$; the roller keeps the truss from rotating about A by exerting the vertical force **B**. The free-body diagram of the truss is shown in Fig. 4.2b; it includes the reactions $\mathbf{A}_x$, $\mathbf{A}_y$, and **B** as well as the applied forces **P**, **Q**, **S**, and the weight **W** of the truss. Expressing that the sum of the moments about A of all the forces shown in Fig. 4.2b is zero, we write the equation $\Sigma M_A = 0$, which may be solved for the magnitude B since it does not contain A_x or A_y. Expressing, then, that the sum of the x components and the sum of the y components of the forces are zero, we write the equations $\Sigma F_x = 0$ and $\Sigma F_y = 0$, which may be solved for the components A_x and A_y, respectively.

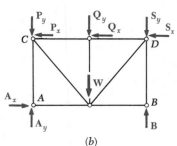

(a)

(b)

Fig. 4.2

Additional equations could be obtained by expressing that the sum of the moments of the external forces about points other than A is zero. We could write, for instance, $\Sigma M_B = 0$. Such a statement, however, does not contain any new information, since it has already been established that the system of the forces shown in Fig. 4.2b is equivalent to zero. The additional equation *is not independent* and cannot be used to determine a fourth unknown. It will be useful, however, for checking the solution obtained from the original three equations of equilibrium.

While the three equations of equilibrium cannot be *augmented* by additional equations, any of them may be *replaced* by another equation. Therefore, an alternate system of equations of equilibrium is

$$\Sigma F_x = 0 \qquad \Sigma M_A = 0 \qquad \Sigma M_B = 0 \qquad (4.6)$$

where the line AB is chosen in a direction different from the y direction (Fig. 4.2b). These equations are sufficient conditions for the equilibrium of the truss. The first two equations indicate that the external forces must reduce to a single vertical force at A. Since the third equation requires that the moment of this force be zero about a point B which is not on its line of action, the force must be zero and the rigid body is in equilibrium.

A third possible set of equations of equilibrium is

$$\Sigma M_A = 0 \qquad \Sigma M_B = 0 \qquad \Sigma M_C = 0 \qquad (4.7)$$

where the points A, B, and C are not in a straight line (Fig. 4.2b). The first equation requires that the external forces reduce to a single force at A; the second equation requires that this force pass through B; the third, that it pass through C. Since the points A, B, C are not in a straight line, the force must be zero, and the rigid body is in equilibrium.

The equation $\Sigma M_A = 0$, which expresses that the sum of the moments of the forces about pin A is zero, possesses a more definite physical meaning than either of the other two equations (4.7). These two equations express a similar idea of balance, but with respect to points about which the rigid body is not actually hinged. They are, however, as useful as the first equation, and our choice of equilibrium equations should not be unduly influenced by the physical meaning of these equations. Indeed, it will be desirable in practice to choose equations of equilibrium containing only one unknown, since this eliminates the necessity of solving simultaneous equations. Equations containing only one unknown may be obtained by summing moments about the point of intersection of the lines of action of two unknown forces or, if these forces are parallel, by summing components in a direction perpendicular to their common direction. In the case of the truss of Fig. 4.3, for example, which is held by rollers at A and B and a short link at D, the reactions at A and B may be eliminated by summing x components. The reactions at A and D will be eliminated by summing moments about C and the reactions at B and D by summing moments about D. The equations obtained are

Fig. 4.3

$$\Sigma F_x = 0 \qquad \Sigma M_C = 0 \qquad \Sigma M_D = 0$$

Each of these equations contains only one unknown.

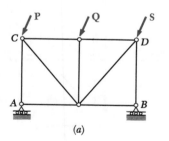

Fig. 4.4 Statically indeterminate reactions.

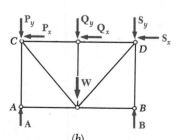

Fig. 4.5 Partial constraints.

4.5. Statically Indeterminate Reactions. Partial Constraints.

In each of the two examples considered in the preceding section (Figs. 4.2 and 4.3), the types of supports used were such that the rigid body could not possibly move under the given loads or under any other loading conditions. In such cases, the rigid body is said to be *completely constrained*. We also recall that the reactions corresponding to these supports involved *three unknowns* and could be determined by solving the three equations of equilibrium. When such a situation exists, the reactions are said to be *statically determinate*.

Consider now the truss shown in Fig. 4.4a, which is held by pins at A and B. These supports provide more constraints than are necessary to keep the truss from moving under the given loads or under any other loading conditions. We also note from the free-body diagram of Fig. 4.4b that the corresponding reactions involve *four unknowns*. Since, as was pointed out in Sec. 4.4, only three independent equilibrium equations are available, there are *more unknowns than equations*, and all the unknowns cannot be determined. While the equations $\Sigma M_A = 0$ and $\Sigma M_B = 0$ yield the vertical components B_y and A_y, respectively, the equation $\Sigma F_x = 0$ gives only the sum $A_x + B_x$ of the horizontal components of the reactions at A and B. The components A_x and B_x are said to be *statically indeterminate*. They could be determined by considering the deformations produced in the truss by the given loading, but this method is beyond the scope of statics and belongs to the study of mechanics of materials.

The supports used to hold the truss shown in Fig. 4.5a consist of rollers at A and B. Clearly, the constraints provided by these supports are not sufficient to keep the truss from moving. While any vertical motion is prevented, the truss is free to move horizontally. The truss is said to be *partially constrained*.† Turning our attention to Fig. 4.5b, we note that the reactions at A and B involve only *two unknowns*. Since three equations of equilibrium must still be satisfied, there are *fewer unknowns than equations*, and one of the equilibrium equations will not be satisfied. While the equations $\Sigma M_A = 0$ and $\Sigma M_B = 0$ can be satisfied by a proper choice of reactions at A and B, the equation $\Sigma F_x = 0$ will not be satisfied unless the sum of the horizontal components of the applied forces happens to be zero. We thus check that the equilibrium of the truss of Fig. 4.5 cannot be maintained under general loading conditions.

It appears from the above that if a rigid body is to be completely constrained and if the reactions at its supports are to be statically determinate, *there must be as many unknowns as there are equations of equilibrium*. When this condition is *not* satisfied, we may be sure that the rigid body is not completely constrained, or that the reactions at its supports are not statically determinate, or both.

We should note, however, that, while *necessary*, the above condition is *not sufficient*. In other words, the fact that the number of unknowns is equal to the number of equations is no guarantee that the body is completely constrained or that the reactions at its supports are statically deter-

---

† Partially constrained bodies are often referred to as *unstable*. However, to avoid confusion between this type of instability, due to insufficient constraints, and the type of instability considered in Chap. 10, which relates to the behavior of a rigid body when its equilibrium is disturbed, we shall restrict the use of the words *stable* and *unstable* to the latter case.

minate. Consider the truss shown in Fig. 4.6a, which is held by rollers at A, B, and E. While there are three unknown reactions, $\mathbf{A}$, $\mathbf{B}$, and $\mathbf{E}$ (Fig. 4.6b), the equation $\Sigma F_x = 0$ will not be satisfied unless the sum of the horizontal components of the applied forces happens to be zero. There is a sufficient number of constraints, but these constraints are not properly arranged, and the truss is free to move horizontally. We say that the truss is *improperly constrained*. Since only two equilibrium equations are left for determining three unknowns, the reactions will be statically indeterminate. Thus, improper constraints also produce static indeterminacy.

Another example of improper constraints—and of static indeterminacy—is provided by the truss shown in Fig. 4.7. This truss is held by a pin at A and by rollers at B and C, which altogether involve four unknowns. Since only three independent equilibrium equations are available, the reactions at the supports are statically indeterminate. On the other hand, we note that the equation $\Sigma M_A = 0$ cannot be satisfied under general loading conditions, since the lines of action of the reactions $\mathbf{B}$ and $\mathbf{C}$ are required to pass through A. We conclude that the truss can rotate about A and that it is improperly constrained.†

The examples of Figs. 4.6 and 4.7 lead us to conclude that *a rigid body is improperly constrained whenever the supports, even though they may provide a sufficient number of reactions, are arranged in such a way that the reactions must be either concurrent or parallel.*‡

In summary, to be sure that a two-dimensional rigid body is completely constrained and that the reactions at its supports are statically determinate, we should check that the reactions involve three—and only three—unknowns, and that the supports are arranged in such a way that they do not require the reactions to be either concurrent or parallel.

Supports involving statically indeterminate reactions should be used with care in the *design* of structures, and only with a full knowledge of the problems they may cause. On the other hand, the *analysis* of structures possessing statically indeterminate reactions often may be partially carried out by the methods of statics. In the case of the truss of Fig. 4.4, for example, the vertical components of the reactions at A and B were obtained from the equilibrium equations.

For obvious reasons, supports producing partial or improper constraints should be avoided in the design of stationary structures. However, a partially or improperly constrained structure will not necessarily collapse; under particular loading conditions, equilibrium may be maintained. For example, the trusses of Figs. 4.5 and 4.6 will be in equilibrium if the applied forces $\mathbf{P}$, $\mathbf{Q}$, and $\mathbf{S}$ are vertical. Besides, structures which are designed to move *should* be only partially constrained. A railroad car, for instance, would be of little use if it were completely constrained by having its brakes applied permanently.

† Rotation of the truss about A requires some "play" in the supports at B and C. In practice such play will always exist. Besides, we may note that if the play is kept small, the displacements of the rollers B and C and, thus, the distances from A to the lines of action of the reactions $\mathbf{B}$ and $\mathbf{C}$, will also be small. The equation $\Sigma M_A = 0$ will then require that $\mathbf{B}$ and $\mathbf{C}$ be very large, a situation which may well result in the failure of the supports at B and C.

‡ Because this situation arises from an inadequate arrangement or *geometry* of the supports, it is often referred to as *geometric instability*.

(a)

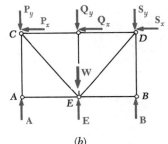

(b)

Fig. 4.6 Improper constraints.

(a)

(b)

Fig. 4.7 Improper constraints.

SAMPLE PROBLEM 4.1

A fixed crane has a mass of 1000 kg and is used to lift a 2400-kg crate. It is held in place by a pin at A and a rocker at B. The center of gravity of the crane is located at G. Determine the components of the reactions at A and B.

Solution. A free-body diagram of the crane is drawn. Multiplying the masses of the crane and of the crate by $g = 9.81$ m/s^2, we obtain the corresponding weights, that is, 9810 N or 9.81 kN, and 23 500 N or 23.5 kN. The reaction at pin A is a force of unknown direction, represented by its components A_x and A_y. The reaction at the rocker B is perpendicular to the rocker surface; thus it is horizontal. We assume that A_x, A_y, and B act in the directions shown.

Determination of B. We express that the sum of the moments of all external forces about point A is zero. The equation obtained will contain neither A_x nor A_y since the moments of A_x and A_y about A are zero. Multiplying the magnitude of each force by its perpendicular distance from B, we write

$$+\uparrow \Sigma M_A = 0: \qquad +B(1.5 \text{ m}) - (9.81 \text{ kN})(2 \text{ m}) - (23.5 \text{ kN})(6 \text{ m}) = 0$$
$$B = +107.1 \text{ kN} \qquad\qquad \mathbf{B} = 107.1 \text{ kN} \rightarrow \blacktriangleleft$$

Since the result is positive, the reaction is directed as assumed.

Determination of A_x. The magnitude A_x is determined by expressing that the sum of the horizontal components of all external forces is zero.

$$\xrightarrow{+} \Sigma F_x = 0: \qquad A_x + B = 0$$
$$A_x + 107.1 \text{ kN} = 0$$
$$A_x = -107.1 \text{ kN} \qquad\qquad \mathbf{A}_x = 107.1 \text{ kN} \leftarrow \blacktriangleleft$$

Since the result is negative, the sense of A_x is opposite to that assumed originally.

Determination of A_y. The sum of the vertical components must also equal zero.

$$+\uparrow \Sigma F_y = 0: \qquad A_y - 9.81 \text{ kN} - 23.5 \text{ kN} = 0$$
$$A_y = +33.3 \text{ kN} \qquad\qquad \mathbf{A}_y = 33.3 \text{ kN} \uparrow \blacktriangleleft$$

Adding vectorially the components $\mathbf{A}_x$ and $\mathbf{A}_y$, we find that the reaction at A is 112.2 kN ⦨17.3°.

Check. The values obtained for the reactions may be checked by recalling that the sum of the moments of all external forces about any point must be zero. For example, considering point B, we write

$$+\uparrow \Sigma M_B = -(9.81 \text{ kN})(2 \text{ m}) - (23.5 \text{ kN})(6 \text{ m}) + (107.1 \text{ kN})(1.5 \text{ m}) = 0$$

SAMPLE PROBLEM 4.2

Three loads are applied to a beam as shown. The beam is supported by a roller at A and by a pin at B. Neglecting the weight of the beam, determine the reaction at A and B when P = 75 kN.

Solution. A free-body diagram of the beam is drawn. The reaction at A is vertical and is denoted by **A**. The reaction at B is represented by components **B**$_x$ and **B**$_y$. Each component is assumed to act in the direction shown.

Equilibrium Equations. We write the following three equilibrium equations and solve for the reactions indicated:

$$\xrightarrow{+}\Sigma F_x = 0: \qquad\qquad B_x = 0 \qquad\qquad \mathbf{B}_x = 0 \blacktriangleleft$$

$$+\uparrow \Sigma M_A = 0:$$
$$-(75 \text{ kN})(1.5 \text{ m}) + B_y(4.5 \text{ m}) - (30 \text{ kN})(5.5 \text{ m}) - (30 \text{ kN})(6.5 \text{ m}) = 0$$
$$B_y = +105.0 \text{ kN} \qquad \mathbf{B}_y = 105.0 \text{ kN} \uparrow \blacktriangleleft$$

$$+\uparrow \Sigma M_B = 0:$$
$$-A(4.5 \text{ m}) + (75 \text{ kN})(3 \text{ m}) - (30 \text{ kN})(1 \text{ m}) - (30 \text{ kN})(2 \text{ m}) = 0$$
$$A = +30.0 \text{ kN} \qquad \mathbf{A} = 30.0 \text{ kN} \uparrow \blacktriangleleft$$

Check. The results are checked by adding the vertical components of all the external forces:

$$+\uparrow \Sigma F_y = +30.0 \text{ kN} - 75 \text{ kN} + 105.0 \text{ kN} - 30 \text{ kN} - 30 \text{ kN} = 0$$

Remark. In this problem the reactions at both A and B are vertical; however, these reactions are vertical for different reasons. At A, the beam is supported by a roller; hence the reaction cannot have any horizontal component. At B, the horizontal component of the reaction is zero because it must satisfy the equilibrium equation $\Sigma F_x = 0$ and because none of the other forces acting on the beam has a horizontal component.

We could have noticed at first glance that the reaction at B was vertical and dispensed with the horizontal component **B**$_x$. This, however, is a bad practice. In following it, we would run the risk of forgetting the component **B**$_x$ when the loading conditions require such a component (i.e., when a horizontal load is included). Also, the component **B**$_x$ was found to be zero by using and solving an equilibrium equation, $\Sigma F_x = 0$. By setting **B**$_x$ equal to zero immediately, we might not realize that we actually make use of this equation and thus might lose track of the number of equations available for solving the problem.

SAMPLE PROBLEM 4.3

A loading car is at rest on a track forming an angle of 25° with the vertical. The combined mass of the car and of its load is 2500 kg, and their center of gravity G is located halfway between the two axles and 750 mm from the track. The car is held by a cable attached 600 mm from the track. Determine the tension in the cable and the reaction at each pair of wheels.

Solution. A free-body diagram of the car is drawn. The reaction at each wheel is perpendicular to the track, and the tension force **T** is parallel to the track. For convenience, we choose the x axis parallel to the track and the y axis perpendicular to the track. The weight of the loaded car is

$$W = mg = (2500 \text{ kg})(9.81 \text{ m/s}^2) = 24.5 \text{ kN}$$

Resolving the weight into x and y components, we have

$$W_x = +(24.5 \text{ kN}) \cos 25° = 22.2 \text{ kN}$$
$$W_y = -(24.5 \text{ kN}) \sin 25° = -10.35 \text{ kN}$$

Equilibrium Equations. We take moments about A to eliminate **T** and $\mathbf{R_1}$ from the computation.

$+\gamma\Sigma M_A = 0$:
$$-(10.35 \text{ kN})(0.625 \text{ m}) - (22.2 \text{ kN})(0.15 \text{ m}) + R_2(1.25 \text{ m}) = 0$$
$$R_2 = +7.84 \text{ kN} \qquad\qquad \mathbf{R_2} = 7.84 \text{ kN} \nearrow \;\blacktriangleleft$$

Now, taking moments about B to eliminate **T** and $\mathbf{R_2}$ from the computation, we write

$+\gamma\Sigma M_B = 0$: $(10.35 \text{ kN})(0.625 \text{ m}) - (22.2 \text{ kN})(0.15 \text{ m}) - R_1(1.25 \text{ m}) = 0$
$$R_1 = +2.51 \text{ kN} \qquad\qquad \mathbf{R_1} = 2.51 \text{ kN} \nearrow \;\blacktriangleleft$$

The value of T is found by writing

$\searrow +\Sigma F_x = 0$: $\qquad +22.2 \text{ kN} - T = 0$
$$T = +22.2 \text{ kN} \qquad\qquad \mathbf{T} = 22.2 \text{ kN} \nwarrow \;\blacktriangleleft$$

The computed values of the reactions are shown in the adjacent sketch.

Check. The computations are verified by writing

$$\nearrow +\Sigma F_y = +2.51 \text{ kN} + 7.84 \text{ kN} - 10.35 \text{ kN} = 0$$

A check could also have been obtained by computing moments about any point except A or B.

136

SAMPLE PROBLEM 4.4

The frame shown supports part of the roof of a small building. Knowing that the tension in the cable is 150 kN, determine the reaction at the fixed end E.

Solution. A free-body diagram of the frame and of the cable BDF is drawn. The reaction at the fixed end E is represented by the force components E_x and E_y and the couple M_E. The other forces acting on the free body are the four 20-kN loads and the 150-kN force exerted at end F of the cable.

Equilibrium Equations. Noting that $DF = \sqrt{(4.5 \text{ m})^2 + (6 \text{ m})^2} = 7.5$ m, we write

$$\xrightarrow{+} \Sigma F_x = 0: \qquad E_x + \frac{4.5}{7.5}(150 \text{ kN}) = 0$$

$$E_x = -90.0 \text{ kN} \qquad \mathbf{E}_x = 90.0 \text{ kN} \leftarrow \qquad \blacktriangleleft$$

$$+\uparrow \Sigma F_y = 0: \qquad E_y - 4(20 \text{ kN}) - \frac{6}{7.5}(150 \text{ kN}) = 0$$

$$E_y = +200 \text{ kN} \qquad \mathbf{E}_y = 200 \text{ kN} \uparrow \qquad \blacktriangleleft$$

$$+\uparrow \Sigma M_E = 0: \quad (20 \text{ kN})(7.2 \text{ m}) + (20 \text{ kN})(5.4 \text{ m}) + (20 \text{ kN})(3.6 \text{ m})$$

$$+ (20 \text{ kN})(1.8 \text{ m}) - \frac{6}{7.5}(150 \text{ kN})(4.5 \text{ m}) + M_E = 0$$

$$M_E = +180.0 \text{ kN} \cdot \text{m} \qquad \mathbf{M}_E = 180.0 \text{ kN} \cdot \text{m} \uparrow \qquad \blacktriangleleft$$

SAMPLE PROBLEM 4.5

A 200-kg block is attached to the lever AO as shown. The constant of the spring BC is $k = 50$ kN/m, and the spring is unstretched when $\theta = 0$. Determine the position of equilibrium.

Solution. *Force Exerted by Spring.* Denoting by s the deflection of the spring from its undeformed position, and noting that $s = r\theta$, we write

$$F = ks = kr\theta$$

Equilibrium Equation. Summing the moments of $\mathbf{W}$ and $\mathbf{F}$ about O,

$$+\uparrow \Sigma M_O = 0: \quad mgl \sin \theta - r(kr\theta) = 0 \qquad \sin \theta = \frac{kr^2}{mgl}\theta$$

Substituting the given data, we obtain

$$\sin \theta = \frac{(50 \times 10^3 \text{ N/m})(0.075 \text{ m})^2}{(200 \text{ kg})(9.81 \text{ m/s}^2)(0.200 \text{ m})}\theta \qquad \sin \theta = 0.71670$$

Solving by trial and error, we find $\qquad \theta = 0 \qquad \theta = 78.3° \qquad \blacktriangleleft$

Fig. P4.1

Fig. P4.4 and P4.5

Fig. P4.6

Problems

4.1 A 2800-kg forklift truck is used to lift a 1500-kg crate. Determine the reaction at each of the two (*a*) front wheels *A*, (*b*) rear wheels *B*.

Fig. P4.2

4.2 A gardener uses a 50-N wheelbarrow to transport a 220-N bag of fertilizer. What force must she exert on each handle?

4.3 The gardener of Prob. 4.2 wishes to transport a second 220-N bag of fertilizer at the same time as the first one. Determine the maximum allowable horizontal distance from the axle *A* of the wheelbarrow to the center of gravity of the second bag if she can hold only 65 N with each arm.

4.4 A load of lumber of weight $W = 25$ kN is being raised by a mobile crane. The weight of the boom *ABC* and the combined weight of the truck and driver are as shown. Determine the reaction at each of the two (*a*) front wheels *H*, (*b*) rear wheels *K*.

4.5 A load of lumber of weight $W = 25$ kN is being raised as shown by a mobile crane. Knowing that the tension is 25 kN in all portions of cable *AEF* and that the weight of boom *ABC* is 3 kN, determine (*a*) the tension in rod *CD*, (*b*) the reaction at pin *B*.

4.6 A truck-mounted crane is used to lift a 3-kN compressor. The weights of the boom *AB* and of the truck are as shown, and the angle the boom forms with the horizontal is $\alpha = 40°$. Determine the reaction at each of the two (*a*) rear wheels *C*, (*b*) front wheels *D*.

4.7 For the truck-mounted crane of Prob. 4.6, determine the smallest allowable value of α if the truck is not to tip over when a 13-kN load is lifted.

4.8 For the beam of Sample Prob. 4.2, determine the range of values of **P** for which the beam will be safe, knowing that the maximum allowable value for each of the reactions is 125 kN and that the reaction at A must be directed upward.

4.9 Three loads are applied as shown to a light beam supported by cables attached at B and D. Neglecting the weight of the beam, determine the range of values of Q for which neither cable becomes slack when P = 0.

4.10 Three loads are applied as shown to a light beam supported by cables attached at B and D. Knowing that the maximum allowable tension in each cable is 12 kN and neglecting the weight of the beam, determine the range of values of Q for which the loading is safe when P = 0.

4.11 For the beam of Prob. 4.10, determine the range of values of Q for which the loading is safe when P = 5 kN.

4.12 Determine the maximum load which may be raised by the mobile crane of Prob. 4.4 without tipping over, knowing that the largest force which can be exerted by the hydraulic cylinder D is 100 kN, and that the maximum allowable tension in cable AEF is 35 kN.

4.13 Determine the tension in cable ABD and the reaction at the support C.

4.14 Two links AB and DE are connected by a bell crank as shown. Knowing that the tension in link AB is 900 N, determine (a) the tension in link DE, (b) the reaction at C.

Fig. P4.9 and P4.10

Fig. P4.13

Fig. P4.14 and P4.15

4.15 Two links AB and DE are connected by a bell crank as shown. Determine the maximum force which may be safely exerted by link AB on the bell crank if the maximum allowable value for the reaction at C is 2 kN.

4.16 The lever AB is hinged at C and attached to a control cable at A. If the lever is subjected at B to a 500-N horizontal force, determine (a) the tension in the cable, (b) the reaction at C.

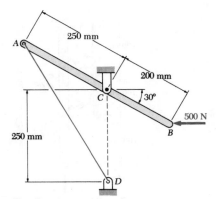

Fig. P4.16

4.17 A truss may be supported in three different ways as shown. In each case, determine the reactions at the supports.

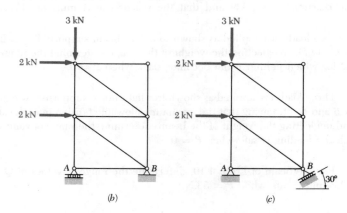

Fig. P4.17   (a)   (b)   (c)

4.18 Determine the reactions at A and B when (a) $\alpha = 0$, (b) $\alpha = 90°$, (c) $\alpha = 30°$.

4.19 Solve Prob. 4.18, assuming that the 375-N force has been replaced by a 75-N·m clockwise couple.

4.20 The mechanism shown is designed to measure the tension in a heavy paper tape used in a manufacturing process. Determine (a) the force exerted at E by the spring when the tension in the tape is 150 N, (b) the corresponding reaction at D.

Fig. P4.18

Fig. P4.20

Fig. P4.21

4.21 A light rod AD supports a 150-N vertical load and is attached to collars B and C which may slide freely on the rods shown. Knowing that the wire attached at A forms an angle $\alpha = 30°$ with the horizontal, determine (a) the tension in the wire, (b) the reactions at B and C.

4.22 Solve Prob. 4.21, assuming that $\alpha = 0$.

4.23 A light bar *AD* is suspended from a cable *BE* and supports a 20-kg block at *C*. The extremities *A* and *D* of the bar are in contact with frictionless, vertical walls. Determine the tension in cable *BE* and the reactions at *A* and *D*.

Fig. P4.23

4.24 A movable bracket is held at rest by a cable attached at *C* and by frictionless rollers at *A* and *B*. For the loading shown, determine (*a*) the tension in the cable, (*b*) the reactions at *A* and *B*.

Fig. P4.24

4.25 The spanner shown is used to rotate a shaft. A pin fits in a hole at *A*, while a flat, frictionless surface rests against the shaft at *B*. If a 300-N force **P** is exerted on the spanner at *D*, find (*a*) the reaction at *B*, (*b*) the component of the reaction at *A* in a direction perpendicular to *AC*.

4.26 The spanner shown is used to rotate a shaft. A pin fits in a hole at *A*, while a flat, frictionless surface rests against the shaft at *B*. If the moment about *C* of the force exerted on the shaft at *A* is to be 90 N · m, find (*a*) the force **P** which should be exerted on the spanner at *D*, (*b*) the corresponding value of the force exerted on the spanner at *B*.

Fig. P4.25 and P4.26

4.27 A 70 kg overhead garage door consists of a uniform rectangular panel *AC*, 2100 mm high, supported by the cable *AE* attached at the middle of the upper edge of the door and by two sets of frictionless rollers at *A* and *B*. Each set consists of two rollers located on either side of the door. The rollers *A* are free to move in horizontal channels, while the rollers *B* are guided by vertical channels. If the door is held in the position for which *BD* = 1050 mm, determine (*a*) the tension in cable *AE*, (*b*) the reaction at each of the four rollers.

4.28 In Prob. 4.27, determine the distance *BD* for which the tension in cable *AE* is equal to 3 kN.

Fig. P4.27

4.29 The tensioner shown is used to maintain a given tension in the transmission belt *CDE*. The triangular receptacle contains a helical spring which exerts a couple **M** on arm *AB*, causing the 50-mm-radius idler pulley at *B* to press against the belt. Knowing that, in the position shown, the tension in the belt is *T* = 200 N, determine (*a*) the couple **M** exerted on arm *AB*, (*b*) the horizontal and vertical components of the force exerted at *A* on arm *AB*.

Fig. P4.29

4.30 The rig shown consists of a 500-kg horizontal member *ABC* and a vertical member *DBE* welded together at *B*. The rig is being used to raise a 1500 kg crate at a distance *x* = 3.6 m from the vertical member *DBE*. If the tension in the cable is 20 kN, determine the reaction at *E*, assuming that the cable is (*a*) anchored at *F* as shown in the figure, (*b*) attached to the vertical member at a point located 0.3 m above *E*.

4.31 For the rig and crate of Prob. 4.30, and assuming that the cable is anchored at *F* as shown, determine (*a*) the required tension in cable *ADCF* if the maximum value of the couple at *E* as *x* varies from 0.5 to 5.2 m is to be as small as possible, (*b*) the corresponding maximum value of the couple.

4.32 For the frame of Sample Prob. 4.4, determine the range of allowable values of the tension in cable *BDF* if the magnitude of the couple at the fixed end *E* is not to exceed 150 kN · m.

4.33 Rod *AD* is acted upon by a vertical force **P** at end *A* and by two equal and opposite horizontal forces of magnitude *Q* at points *B* and *C*. Neglecting the weight of the rod, express the angle θ corresponding to the equilibrium position in terms of *P* and *Q*.

Fig. P4.30

Fig. P4.33

Fig. P4.34

4.34 A uniform rod *AB* of length *l* and weight *W* is suspended from two cords *AC* and *BC* of equal length. Determine the angle θ corresponding to the equilibrium position when a couple **M** is applied to the rod.

4.35 and 4.36 A vertical load **P** is applied at end B of rod BC. (a) Neglecting the weight of the rod, express the angle θ corresponding to the equilibrium position in terms of P, l, and the counterweight W. (b) Determine the value of θ corresponding to equilibrium if $P = 2W$.

Fig. P4.35

Fig. P4.36

Fig. P4.37

4.37 A vertical load **P** is applied at end B of rod BC. The constant of the spring is k and the spring is unstretched when $\theta = 0$. (a) Neglecting the weight of the rod, express the angle θ corresponding to the equilibrium position in terms of P, k, and l. (b) Determine the value of θ corresponding to equilibrium if $P = 2kl$.

4.38 A force **P** of magnitude 400 N is applied to end E of cable CDE which passes under pulley D and is attached to the mechanism at C. Neglecting the weight of the mechanism and the radius of the pulley, determine the value of θ corresponding to equilibrium. The constant of the spring is $k = 4$ kN/m, and the spring is unstretched when $\theta = 90°$. (*Hint.* Solve by trial and error.)

4.39 A slender rod AB, of weight W, is attached to blocks A and B which may move freely in the guides shown. The constant of the spring is k and the spring is unstretched when AB is horizontal. (a) Neglecting the weight of the blocks, derive an equation in θ, W, l, and k which must be satisfied when the rod is in equilibrium. (b) Find the value of k, knowing that $W = 40$ N, $l = 0.8$ m, and that the rod is in equilibrium when $\theta = 36°$.

Fig. P4.38

Fig. P4.39

4.40 The internal spring AC is of constant k and is undeformed when $\theta = 60°$ (a) Derive an equation in θ, W, a, and k which must be satisfied when the system is in equilibrium. (b) Find the value of k, knowing that $W = 80$ N, $a = 300$ mm, and that the system is in equilibrium when $\theta = 25°$.

Fig. P4.40

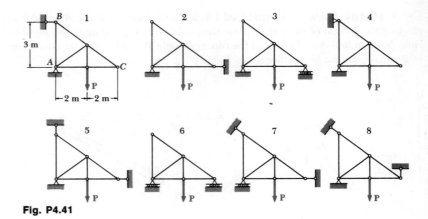

Fig. P4.41

4.41 A truss may be supported in eight different ways as shown. All connections consist of frictionless pins, rollers, and short links. In each case, determine whether (*a*) the truss is completely, partially, or improperly constrained, (*b*) the reactions are statically determinate or indeterminate, (*c*) the equilibrium of the truss is maintained in the position shown. Also, wherever possible, compute the reactions, assuming that the magnitude of the force **P** is 60 kN.

4.42 Nine identical rectangular plates, 500 × 750 mm, and each of mass $m = 40$ kg, are held in a vertical plane as shown. All connections consist of frictionless pins, rollers, or short links. For each case, answer the questions listed in Prob. 4.41, and, wherever possible, compute the reactions.

Fig. P4.42

4.6. Equilibrium of a Two-Force Body.

A particular case of equilibrium which is of considerable interest is that of a rigid body subjected to two forces. Such a body is commonly called a *two-force body*. We shall show that *if a two-force body is in equilibrium, the two forces must have the same magnitude, same line of action, and opposite sense*.

Consider a corner plate subjected to two forces $\mathbf{F}_1$ and $\mathbf{F}_2$ acting at A and B, respectively (Fig. 4.8*a*). If the plate is to be in equilibrium, the sum of the moments of $\mathbf{F}_1$ and $\mathbf{F}_2$ about any axis must be zero. First, we sum moments about A: Since the moment of $\mathbf{F}_1$ is obviously zero, the moment of $\mathbf{F}_2$ must also be zero and the line of action of $\mathbf{F}_2$ must pass through A (Fig. 4.8*b*). Summing moments about B, we prove similarly that the line of

Fig. 4.8

action of $\mathbf{F}_1$ must pass through B (Fig. 4.8c). Both forces have the same line of action (line AB). From the equation $\Sigma F_x = 0$ or $\Sigma F_y = 0$, it is seen that they must have also the same magnitude but opposite sense.

If several forces act at two points A and B, the forces acting at A may be replaced by their resultant $\mathbf{F}_1$ and those acting at B by their resultant $\mathbf{F}_2$. Thus a two-force body may be more generally defined as *a rigid body subjected to forces acting at only two points*. The resultants $\mathbf{F}_1$ and $\mathbf{F}_2$ then must have the same line of action, same magnitude, and opposite sense.

In our study of structures, frames, and machines, we shall see that the recognition of two-force bodies will enable us to simplify the solution of certain problems.

4.7. Equilibrium of a Three-Force Body.
Another case of equilibrium that is of great interest is that of a *three-force body*, i.e., a rigid body subjected to three forces or, more generally, *a rigid body subjected to forces acting at only three points*. Consider a rigid body subjected to a system of forces which may be reduced to three forces $\mathbf{F}_1$, $\mathbf{F}_2$, and $\mathbf{F}_3$ acting at A, B, and C, respectively (Fig. 4.9a). We shall show that if the body is in equilibrium, *the lines of action of the three forces must be either concurrent or parallel*.

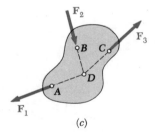

Fig. 4.9

Since the rigid body is in equilibrium, the sum of the moments of $\mathbf{F}_1$, $\mathbf{F}_2$, and $\mathbf{F}_3$ about any axis must be zero. Assuming that the lines of action of $\mathbf{F}_1$ and $\mathbf{F}_2$ intersect, and denoting their point of intersection by D, we sum moments about D (Fig. 4.9b); since the moments of $\mathbf{F}_1$ and $\mathbf{F}_2$ about D are zero, the moment of $\mathbf{F}_3$ about D must also be zero and the line of action of $\mathbf{F}_3$ must pass through D (Fig. 4.9c). The three lines of action are concurrent. The only exception occurs when none of the lines intersect; the lines of action are then parallel.

Although problems concerning three-force bodies may be solved by the general methods of Secs. 4.3 to 4.5, the property just established may be used to solve them either graphically, or mathematically from simple trigonometric or geometric relations.

A man raises a 10-kg joist, of length 4 m, by pulling on a rope. Find the tension T in the rope and the reaction at A.

Solution. The joist is a three-force body since it is acted upon by three forces: its weight **W**, the force **T** exerted by the rope, and the reaction **R** of the ground at A. We note that

$$W = mg = (10 \text{ kg})(9.81 \text{ m/s}^2) = 98.1 \text{ N}$$

Three-Force Body. Since the joist is a three-force body, the forces acting on it must be concurrent. The reaction **R**, therefore, will pass through the point of intersection C of the lines of action of the weight **W** and of the tension force **T**. This fact will be used to determine the angle α that **R** forms with the horizontal.

Drawing the vertical BF through B and the horizontal CD through C, we note that

$$AF = BF = (AB) \cos 45° = (4 \text{ m}) \cos 45° = 2.828 \text{ m}$$
$$CD = EF = AE = \tfrac{1}{2}(AF) = 1.414 \text{ m}$$
$$BD = (CD) \cot (45° + 25°) = (1.414 \text{ m}) \tan 20° = 0.515 \text{ m}$$
$$CE = DF = BF - BD = 2.828 \text{ m} - 0.515 \text{ m} = 2.313 \text{ m}$$

We write

$$\tan \alpha = \frac{CE}{AE} = \frac{2.313 \text{ m}}{1.414 \text{ m}} = 1.636$$

$$\alpha = 58.6° \blacktriangleleft$$

We now know the direction of all the forces acting on the joist.

Force Triangle. A force triangle is drawn as shown, and its interior angles are computed from the known directions of the forces. Using the law of sines, we write

$$\frac{T}{\sin 31.4°} = \frac{R}{\sin 110°} = \frac{98.1 \text{ N}}{\sin 38.6°}$$

$$T = 81.9 \text{ N} \blacktriangleleft$$
$$R = 147.8 \text{ N} \measuredangle 58.6° \blacktriangleleft$$

Problems

4.43 The spanner shown is used to rotate a shaft. A pin fits in a hole at A, while a flat, frictionless surface rests against the shaft at B. If a 300-N force $\mathbf{P}$ is exerted on the spanner at D, find the reactions at A and B.

Fig. P4.43

Fig. P4.44

4.44 Determine the reactions at B and C when $a = 30$ mm.

4.45 Using the method of Sec. 4.7, solve Prob. 4.18b.

4.46 Using the method of Sec. 4.7, solve Prob. 4.18c.

4.47 A T-shaped bracket supports a 300-N load as shown. Determine the reactions at A and C when (a) $\alpha = 90°$, (b) $\alpha = 45°$.

4.48 One end of rod AB rests in the corner A and the other is attached to cord BD. If the rod supports at 200-N load at its midpoint C, find the reaction at A and the tension in the cord.

Fig. P4.47

Fig. P4.48

Fig. P4.49

4.49 A 300-mm wooden beam weighing 54 kg is supported by a pin and bracket at A and by cable BC. Find the reaction at A and the tension in the table.

Fig. P4.52

Fig. P4.53

Fig. P4.57

4.50 Using the method of Sec. 4.7, solve Prob. 4.14.

4.51 Using the method of Sec. 4.7, solve Prob. 4.16.

4.52 A uniform 2500-kg plate girder is held in a horizontal position by two crane cables. Determine the angle α and the tension in each cable.

4.53 Rod AB is supported by a pin and bracket at A and rests against a frictionless peg at C. Determine the reactions at A and C when a 170-N vertical force is applied at B.

4.54 Solve Prob. 4.53, assuming that the 170-N force applied at B is horizontal and directed to the left.

Fig. P4.55

4.55 The L-shaped member ACB is supported by a pin and bracket at C and by an inextensible cord attached at A and B and passing over a frictionless pulley at D. The tension may be assumed to be the same in portions AD and BD of the cord. If the magnitudes of the forces applied at A and B are, respectively, $P = 125$ N and $Q = 0$, determine (a) the tension in the cord, (b) the reaction at C.

4.56 For the L-shaped member of Prob. 4.55, (a) express the tension T in the cord in terms of the magnitudes P and Q of the forces applied at A and B, (b) assuming $Q = 200$ N, find the smallest allowable value of P if the equilibrium is to be maintained.

4.57 The uniform rod AB lies in a vertical plane with its ends resting against the frictionless surfaces AC and BC. Determine the relation between the angles θ and α when the rod is in equilibrium.

4.58 A slender rod of length L is lodged between peg C and the vertical wall. It supports a load $\mathbf{P}$ at end A. Neglecting friction and the weight of the rod, determine the angle θ corresponding to equilibrium.

Fig. P4.58

Fig. P4.59

4.59 A 1.2-m rod, of uniform cross section, is held in equilibrium as shown, with one end against a frictionless vertical wall and the other end attached to a cord. Determine the length of the cord.

4.60 A worker pushes a 50-kg wheelbarrow at a constant speed up an 18° incline. Determine the magnitude and direction of (a) the force he exerts on each handle, (b) the reaction at C. (*Hint.* The wheel is a two-force body.)

Fig. P4.60

Fig. P4.61

*4.61 A slender rod of length $2r$ and weight W is attached to a collar at B and rests on a circular cylinder of radius r. Knowing that the collar may slide freely along a vertical guide and neglecting friction, determine the value of θ corresponding to equilibrium.

*4.62 A uniform rod AB of length $3R$ and weight W rests inside a hemispherical bowl of radius R as shown. Neglecting friction, determine the angle θ corresponding to equilibrium.

Fig. P4.62

4.8. Reactions at Supports and Connections for a Three-Dimensional Structure. The reactions on a three-dimensional structure range from the single force of known direction exerted by a frictionless surface to the force-couple system exerted by a fixed support. Consequently, the number of unknowns associated with the reaction at a support or connection may vary from one to six in problems involving the equilibrium of a three-dimensional structure. Various types of supports and connections are shown in Fig. 4.10 with the corresponding reactions. A simple way of determining the type of reaction corresponding to a given support or connection and the number of unknowns involved is to find which of the six fundamental motions (translation in x, y, and z directions, rotation about the x, y, and z axes) are allowed and which motions are prevented.

Ball supports, frictionless surfaces, and cables, for example, prevent translation in one direction only and thus exert a single force of known line of action; they each involve one unknown, namely, the magnitude of the reaction. Rollers on rough surfaces and wheels on rails prevent translation in two directions; the corresponding reactions consist of two unknown force components. Rough surfaces in direct contact and ball-and-socket supports prevent translation in three directions; these supports involve three unknown force components.

Some supports and connections may prevent rotation as well as translation; the corresponding reactions include, then, couples as well as forces. The reaction at a fixed support, for example, which prevents any motion (rotation as well as translation), consists of three unknown forces and three unknown couples. A universal joint, which is designed to allow rotation about two axes, will exert a reaction consisting of three unknown force components and one unknown couple.

Other supports and connections are primarily intended to prevent translation; their design, however, is such that they also prevent some rotations. The corresponding reactions consist essentially of force components but *may* also include couples. One group of supports of this type includes hinges and bearings designed to support radial loads only (for example, journal bearings, roller bearings). The corresponding reactions consist of two force components but may also include two couples. Another group includes pin-and-bracket supports, hinges, and bearings designed to support an axial thrust as well as a radial load (for example, ball bearings). The corresponding reactions consist of three force components but may include two couples. However, these supports will not exert any appreciable couples under normal conditions of use. Therefore, *only* force components should be included in their analysis, *unless* it is found that couples are necessary to maintain the equilibrium of the rigid body, or unless the support is known to have been specifically designed to exert a couple (see Probs. 4.87 through 4.90).

Fig. 4.10 Reactions at supports and connections.

Ball

Frictionless surface

Force with known
line of action
(one unknown)

Cable

Force with known
line of action
(one unknown)

Roller on
rough surface

Wheel on rail

Two force components

Rough surface

Ball and socket

Three force components

Universal
joint

Three force components
and one couple

Fixed support

Three force components
and three couples

Hinge and bearing supporting radial load only

Two force components
(and two couples)

Pin and bracket

Hinge and bearing supporting
axial thrust and radial load

Three force components
(and two couples)

4.9. Equilibrium of a Rigid Body in Three Dimensions.

We saw in Sec. 4.1 that six scalar equations are required to express the conditions for the equilibrium of a rigid body in the general three-dimensional case:

$$\Sigma F_x = 0 \qquad \Sigma F_y = 0 \qquad \Sigma F_z = 0 \qquad (4.2)$$
$$\Sigma M_x = 0 \qquad \Sigma M_y = 0 \qquad \Sigma M_z = 0 \qquad (4.3)$$

These equations may be solved for no more than *six unknowns*, which generally will represent reactions at supports or connections.

In most problems the scalar equations (4.2) and (4.3) will be more conveniently obtained if we first express in vector form the conditions for the equilibrium of the rigid body considered. We write

$$\Sigma \mathbf{F} = 0 \qquad \Sigma \mathbf{M}_O = \Sigma(\mathbf{r} \times \mathbf{F}) = 0 \qquad (4.1)$$

and express the forces **F** and position vectors **r** in terms of scalar components and unit vectors. Next we compute all vector products, either by direct calculation or by means of determinants (see Sec. 3.8), observing that as many as three unknown reaction components may be eliminated from these computations through a judicious choice of point O. Equating to zero the coefficients of the unit vectors in each of the two relations (4.1), we obtain the desired scalar equations.†

If the reactions involve more than six unknowns, there are more unknowns than equations, and some of the reactions are *statically indeterminate*. If the reactions involve less than six unknowns, there are more equations than unknowns, and some of the equations of equilibrium cannot be satisfied under general loading conditions; the rigid body is only *partially constrained*. Under the particular loading conditions corresponding to a given problem, however, the extra equations often reduce to trivial identities such as $0 = 0$ and may be disregarded; although only partially constrained, the rigid body remains in equilibrium (see Sample Probs. 4.7 and 4.8). Even with six or more unknowns, it is possible that some equations of equilibrium will not be satisfied. This may occur when the supports are such that the reactions are forces which must either be parallel or intersect the same line; the rigid body is then *improperly constrained*.

---

† In some problems, it will be found convenient to eliminate the reactions at two points A and B from the solution by writing the equilibrium equation $\Sigma M_{AB} = 0$, which involves the determination of the moments of the forces about the axis AB joining points A and B (see Sample Prob. 4.10).

SAMPLE PROBLEM 4.7

A 20-kg ladder used to reach high shelves in a storeroom is supported by two flanged wheels A and B mounted on a rail and by an unflanged wheel C resting against a rail fixed to the wall. An 80-kg man stands on the ladder and leans to the right. The line of action of the combined weight $\mathbf{W}$ of the man and ladder intersects the floor at point D. Determine the reactions at A, B, and C.

Solution. A free-body diagram of the ladder is drawn. The forces involved are the combined weight of the man and ladder,

$$\mathbf{W} = -mg\mathbf{j} = -(80 \text{ kg} + 20 \text{ kg})(9.81 \text{ m/s}^2)\mathbf{j} = -(981 \text{ N})\mathbf{j}$$

and five unknown reaction components, two at each flanged wheel and one at the unflanged wheel. The ladder is thus only partially constrained; it is free to roll along the rails. It is, however, in equilibrium under the given load since the equation $\Sigma F_x = 0$ is satisfied.

Equilibrium Equations. We express that the forces acting on the ladder form a system equivalent to zero:

$$\Sigma \mathbf{F} = 0: \qquad A_y\mathbf{j} + A_z\mathbf{k} + B_y\mathbf{j} + B_z\mathbf{k} - (981 \text{ N})\mathbf{j} + C\mathbf{k} = 0$$
$$(A_y + B_y - 981 \text{ N})\mathbf{j} + (A_z + B_z + C)\mathbf{k} = 0 \qquad (1)$$

$$\Sigma \mathbf{M}_A = \Sigma(\mathbf{r} \times \mathbf{F}) = 0: \qquad 1.2\mathbf{i} \times (B_y\mathbf{j} + B_z\mathbf{k}) + (0.9\mathbf{i} - 0.6\mathbf{k}) \times (-981\mathbf{j})$$
$$+ (0.6\mathbf{i} + 3\mathbf{j} - 1.2\mathbf{k}) \times C\mathbf{k} = 0$$

Computing the vector products, we have†

$$1.2B_y\mathbf{k} - 1.2B_z\mathbf{j} - 882.9\mathbf{k} - 588.6\mathbf{i} - 0.6C\mathbf{j} + 3C\mathbf{i} = 0$$
$$(3C - 588.6)\mathbf{i} - (1.2B_z + 0.6C)\mathbf{j} + (1.2B_y - 882.9)\mathbf{k} = 0 \qquad (2)$$

Setting the coefficients of $\mathbf{i}$, $\mathbf{j}$, $\mathbf{k}$ equal to zero in Eq. (2), we obtain the following three scalar equations, which express that the sum of the moments about each coordinate axis must be zero:

$$3C - 588.6 = 0 \qquad C = +196.2 \text{ N}$$
$$1.2B_z + 0.6C = 0 \qquad B_z = -98.1 \text{ N}$$
$$1.2B_y - 882.9 = 0 \qquad B_y = +736 \text{ N}$$

The reactions at B and C are therefore

$$\mathbf{B} = +(736 \text{ N})\mathbf{j} - (98.1 \text{ N})\mathbf{k} \qquad \mathbf{C} = +(196.2 \text{ N})\mathbf{k} \quad \blacktriangleleft$$

Setting the coefficients of $\mathbf{j}$ and $\mathbf{k}$ equal to zero in Eq. (1), we obtain two scalar equations expressing that the sums of the components in the y and z directions are zero. Substituting for B_y, B_z, and C the values obtained above, we write

$$A_y + B_y - 981 = 0 \qquad A_y + 736 - 981 = 0 \qquad A_y = +245 \text{ N}$$
$$A_z + B_z + C = 0 \qquad A_z - 98.1 + 196.2 = 0 \qquad A_z = -98.1 \text{ N}$$

We conclude that the reaction at A is $\qquad \mathbf{A} = +(245 \text{ N})\mathbf{j} - (98.1 \text{ N})\mathbf{k} \quad \blacktriangleleft$

†The moments in this Sample Problem and in Sample Probs. 4.8 and 4.9 could also be expressed in the form of determinants (see Sample Prob. 3.10).

SAMPLE PROBLEM 4.8

A 120 kg sign of uniform density measures 1.5 by 2.4 m and is supported by a ball and socket at A and by two cables. Determine the tension in each cable and the reaction at A.

Solution. A free-body diagram of the sign is drawn. The forces acting on the free body are the weight $\mathbf{W} = -(120 \text{ kg})(9.81 \text{ m/s}^2)\mathbf{j} = -(1177 \text{ N})\mathbf{j}$ and the reaction at A, B, and E. The reaction at A is a force of unknown direction and is represented by three unknown components. Since the directions of the forces exerted by the cables are known, these forces involve only one unknown each, namely the magnitudes T_{BD} and T_{EC}. Since there are only five unknowns, the sign is partially constrained. It may rotate freely about the x axis; it is, however, in equilibrium under the given loading since the equation $\Sigma M_x = 0$ is satisfied.

The components of the forces $\mathbf{T}_{BD}$ and $\mathbf{T}_{EC}$ may be expressed in terms of the unknown magnitudes T_{BD} and T_{EC} by writing.

$$\overrightarrow{BD} = -(2.4 \text{ m})\mathbf{i} + (1.2 \text{ m})\mathbf{j} - (2.4 \text{ m})\mathbf{k} \qquad BD = 3.60 \text{ m}$$
$$\overrightarrow{EC} = -(1.8 \text{ m})\mathbf{i} + (0.9 \text{ m})\mathbf{j} + (0.6 \text{ m})\mathbf{k} \qquad EC = 2.10 \text{ m}$$

$$\mathbf{T}_{BD} = T_{BD}\left(\frac{\overrightarrow{BD}}{BD}\right) = T_{BD}(-\tfrac{2}{3}\mathbf{i} + \tfrac{1}{3}\mathbf{j} - \tfrac{2}{3}\mathbf{k})$$

$$\mathbf{T}_{EC} = T_{EC}\left(\frac{\overrightarrow{EC}}{EC}\right) = T_{EC}(-\tfrac{6}{7}\mathbf{i} + \tfrac{3}{7}\mathbf{j} + \tfrac{2}{7}\mathbf{k})$$

Equilibrium Equations. We express that the forces acting on the sign form a system equivalent to zero:

$$\Sigma \mathbf{F} = 0: \quad A_x\mathbf{i} + A_y\mathbf{j} + A_z\mathbf{k} + \mathbf{T}_{BD} + \mathbf{T}_{EC} - (1177 \text{ N}) = 0$$
$$(A_x - \tfrac{2}{3}T_{BD} - \tfrac{6}{7}T_{EC})\mathbf{i} + (A_y + \tfrac{1}{3}T_{BD} + \tfrac{3}{7}T_{EC} - 1177 \text{ N})\mathbf{j}$$
$$+ (A_z - \tfrac{2}{3}T_{BD} + \tfrac{2}{7}T_{EC})\mathbf{k} = 0 \qquad (1)$$

$$\Sigma \mathbf{M}_A = \Sigma(\mathbf{r} \times \mathbf{F}) = 0:$$
$$(2.4 \text{ m})\mathbf{i} \times T_{BD}(-\tfrac{2}{3}\mathbf{i} + \tfrac{1}{3}\mathbf{j} - \tfrac{2}{3}\mathbf{k})$$
$$+ (1.8 \text{ m})\mathbf{i} \times T_{EC}(-\tfrac{6}{7}\mathbf{i} + \tfrac{3}{7}\mathbf{j} + \tfrac{2}{7}\mathbf{k})$$
$$+ (1.2 \text{ m})\mathbf{i} \times (-1177 \text{ N})\mathbf{j} = 0$$
$$(0.8T_{BD} + 0.7714T_{EC} - 1412)\mathbf{k} + (1.6T_{BD} - 0.5143T_{EC})\mathbf{j} = 0 \qquad (2)$$

Setting the coefficients of $\mathbf{j}$ and $\mathbf{k}$ equal to zero in Eq. (2), we obtain two scalar equations which may be solved for T_{BD} and T_{EC}:

$$T_{BD} = 441 \text{ N} \qquad T_{EC} = 1373 \text{ N} \quad \blacktriangleleft$$

Setting the coefficients of $\mathbf{i}, \mathbf{j}$, and $\mathbf{k}$ equal to zero in Eq. (1), we obtain three more equations which yield the components of $\mathbf{A}$. We have

$$\mathbf{A} = +(1471 \text{ N})\mathbf{i} + (441 \text{ N})\mathbf{j} - (98.1 \text{ N})\mathbf{k} \quad \blacktriangleleft$$

160 mm

C

240 mm

240 mm B

240 mm

A

$r = 240$ mm

D

SAMPLE PROBLEM 4.9

A uniform pipe cover of radius $r = 240$ mm and mass 30 kg is held in a horizontal position by the cable CD. Assuming that the bearing at B does not exert any axial thrust, determine the tension in the cable and the reactions at A and B.

80 mm
160 mm

$r = 240$ mm C 240 mm

$B_y\mathbf{j}$

$B_x\mathbf{i}$

B

$A_y\mathbf{j}$

$A_x\mathbf{i}$

A $r = 240$ mm G T

$A_z\mathbf{k}$

z

D

$W = -(294\text{ N})\mathbf{j}$ $r = 240$ mm

Solution. A free-body diagram is drawn with the coordinate axes shown. The forces acting on the free body are the weight of the cover,

$$\mathbf{W} = -mg\mathbf{j} = -(30\text{ kg})(9.81\text{ m/s}^2)\mathbf{j} = -(294\text{ N})\mathbf{j}$$

and reactions involving six unknowns, namely, the magnitude of the force $\mathbf{T}$ exerted by the cable, three force components at hinge A, and two at hinge B. The components of $\mathbf{T}$ are expressed in terms of the unknown magnitude T by resolving the vector $\overrightarrow{DC}$ into rectangular components and writing

$$\overrightarrow{DC} = -(480\text{ mm})\mathbf{i} + (240\text{ mm})\mathbf{j} - (160\text{ mm})\mathbf{k} \qquad DC = 560\text{ mm}$$

$$\mathbf{T} = T\frac{\overrightarrow{DC}}{DC} = -\tfrac{6}{7}T\mathbf{i} + \tfrac{3}{7}T\mathbf{j} - \tfrac{2}{7}T\mathbf{k}$$

Equilibrium Equations. We express that the forces acting on the pipe cover form a system equivalent to zero:

$$\Sigma\mathbf{F} = 0: \qquad A_x\mathbf{i} + A_y\mathbf{j} + A_z\mathbf{k} + B_x\mathbf{i} + B_y\mathbf{j} + \mathbf{T} - (294\text{ N})\mathbf{j} = 0$$
$$(A_x + B_x - \tfrac{6}{7}T)\mathbf{i} + (A_y + B_y + \tfrac{3}{7}T - 294\text{ N})\mathbf{j} + (A_z - \tfrac{2}{7}T)\mathbf{k} = 0 \qquad (1)$$

$$\Sigma\mathbf{M}_B = \Sigma(\mathbf{r} \times \mathbf{F}) = 0:$$
$$2r\mathbf{k} \times (A_x\mathbf{i} + A_y\mathbf{j} + A_z\mathbf{k})$$
$$+ (2r\mathbf{i} + r\mathbf{k}) \times (-\tfrac{6}{7}T\mathbf{i} + \tfrac{3}{7}T\mathbf{j} - \tfrac{2}{7}T\mathbf{k})$$
$$+ (r\mathbf{i} + r\mathbf{k}) \times (-294\text{ N})\mathbf{j} = 0$$
$$(-2A_y - \tfrac{3}{7}T + 294\text{ N})r\mathbf{i} + (2A_x - \tfrac{2}{7}T)r\mathbf{j} + (\tfrac{6}{7}T - 294\text{ N})r\mathbf{k} = 0 \qquad (2)$$

Setting the coefficients of the unit vectors equal to zero in Eq. (2), we write three scalar equations, which yield

$$A_x = +49.0\text{ N} \qquad A_y = +73.5\text{ N} \qquad T = 343\text{ N} \quad \blacktriangleleft$$

Setting the coefficients of the unit vectors equal to zero in Eq. (1), we obtain three more scalar equations. After substituting the values of T, A_x, and A_y into these equations, we obtain

$$A_z = +98.0\text{ N} \qquad B_x = +245\text{ N} \qquad B_y = +73.5\text{ N}$$

The reactions at A and B are therefore

$$\mathbf{A} = +(49.0\text{ N})\mathbf{i} + (73.5\text{ N})\mathbf{j} + (98.0\text{ N})\mathbf{k} \qquad \mathbf{B} = +(245\text{ N})\mathbf{i} + (73.5\text{ N})\mathbf{j} \quad \blacktriangleleft$$

A 450-N load **P** is applied at the corner C of a rigid pipe $ABCD$ which has been bent as shown. The pipe is supported by the ball-and-socket joints A and D fastened, respectively, to the floor and to a vertical wall, and by a cable attached at the midpoint E of the portion BC of the pipe and at a point G on the wall. Determine (a) where G should be located if the tension in the cable is to be minimum, (b) the corresponding minimum value of the tension.

Solution. The free-body diagram of the pipe includes the load $\mathbf{P} = -450\mathbf{j}$, the reactions at A and D, and the force **T** exerted by the cable. To eliminate the reactions at A and D from the computations, we express that the sum of the moments of the forces about AD is zero. Denoting by $\boldsymbol{\lambda}$ the unit vector along AD, we write

$$\Sigma M_{AD} = 0: \qquad \boldsymbol{\lambda} \cdot (\overrightarrow{AE} \times \mathbf{T}) + \boldsymbol{\lambda} \cdot (\overrightarrow{AC} \times \mathbf{P}) = 0 \qquad (1)$$

The second term in Eq. (1) may be computed as follows:

$$\overrightarrow{AC} \times \mathbf{P} = (4\mathbf{i} + 4\mathbf{j}) \times (-450\mathbf{j}) = -1800\mathbf{k}$$

$$\boldsymbol{\lambda} = \frac{\overrightarrow{AD}}{AD} = \frac{4\mathbf{i} + 4\mathbf{j} - 2\mathbf{k}}{6} = \tfrac{2}{3}\mathbf{i} + \tfrac{2}{3}\mathbf{j} - \tfrac{1}{3}\mathbf{k}$$

$$\boldsymbol{\lambda} \cdot (\overrightarrow{AC} \times \mathbf{P}) = (\tfrac{2}{3}\mathbf{i} + \tfrac{2}{3}\mathbf{j} - \tfrac{1}{3}\mathbf{k}) \cdot (-1800\mathbf{k}) = +600$$

Substituting the value obtained into Eq. (1), we write

$$\boldsymbol{\lambda} \cdot (\overrightarrow{AE} \times \mathbf{T}) = -600 \text{ N·m} \qquad (2)$$

Minimum Value of Tension. Recalling the commutative property for mixed triple products, we rewrite Eq. (2) in the form

$$\mathbf{T} \cdot (\boldsymbol{\lambda} \times \overrightarrow{AE}) = -600 \text{ N·m} \qquad (3)$$

which shows that the projection of **T** on the vector $\boldsymbol{\lambda} \times \overrightarrow{AE}$ is a constant. It follows that **T** is minimum when parallel to the vector

$$\boldsymbol{\lambda} \times \overrightarrow{AE} = (\tfrac{2}{3}\mathbf{i} + \tfrac{2}{3}\mathbf{j} - \tfrac{1}{3}\mathbf{k}) \times (2\mathbf{i} + 4\mathbf{j}) = \frac{4\mathbf{i} - 2\mathbf{j} + 4\mathbf{k}}{3}$$

The corresponding unit vector being $\tfrac{2}{3}\mathbf{i} - \tfrac{1}{3}\mathbf{j} + \tfrac{2}{3}\mathbf{k}$, we write

$$\mathbf{T}_{\min} = T(\tfrac{2}{3}\mathbf{i} - \tfrac{1}{3}\mathbf{j} + \tfrac{2}{3}\mathbf{k}) \qquad (4)$$

Substituting for **T** and $\boldsymbol{\lambda} \times \overrightarrow{AE}$ in Eq. (3), we find $T = -300$. Carrying this value into (4), we obtain

$$\mathbf{T}_{\min} = -200\mathbf{i} + 100\mathbf{j} - 200\mathbf{k} \qquad T_{\min} = 300 \text{ N} \blacktriangleleft$$

Location of G. Since the vector $\overrightarrow{EG}$ and the force $\mathbf{T}_{\min}$ have the same direction, their components must be proportional. Denoting by $x, y, 0$ the coordinates of G, we write

$$\frac{x - 2}{-200} = \frac{y - 4}{+100} = \frac{0 - 2}{-200} \qquad x = 0 \qquad y = 5 \text{ m} \blacktriangleleft$$

Problems

4.63 A 1.2×2.4 m sheet of plywood with a mass of 18 kg has been temporarily propped against column CD. It rests at A and B on small wooden blocks and against protruding nails. Neglecting friction at all surfaces of contact, determine the reactions at A, B, and C.

Fig. P4.63

4.64 Two transmission belts pass over a double-sheaved pulley which is attached to an axle supported by bearings at A and D. The radius of the inner sheave is 125 mm and the radius of the outer sheave is 250 mm. Knowing that when the system is at rest, the tension is 90 N in both portions of belt B and 150 N in both portions of belt C, determine the reactions at A and D. Assume that the bearing at D does not exert any axial thrust.

4.65 Solve Prob. 4.64, assuming that the pulley rotates at a constant rate and that $T_B = 104$ N, $T'_B = 84$ N, and $T_C = 175$ N.

4.66 A small winch is used to raise a 600-N load. Find (a) the magnitude of the vertical force $\mathbf{P}$ which should be applied at C to maintain equilibrium in the position shown, (b) the reactions at A and B, assuming that the bearing at B does not exert any axial thrust.

Fig. P4.64

Fig. P4.66

4.67 A 200-mm lever and a 240-mm-diameter pulley are welded to the axle *BE* which is supported by bearings at *C* and *D*. If a 720-N vertical load is applied at *A* when the lever is horizontal, determine (*a*) the tension in the cord, (*b*) the reactions at *C* and *D*. Assume that the bearing at *D* does not exert any axial thrust.

Fig. P4.67

4.68 Solve Prob. 4.67, assuming that the axle has been rotated clockwise in its bearings by 30° and that the 720-N load remains vertical.

4.69 The 20-kg square plate shown is supported by three wires. Determine the tension in each wire.

4.70 The 35-kg rectangular plate shown is supported by three wires. Determine the tension in each wire.

Fig. P4.69

Fig. P4.70

4.71 A load *W* is to be placed on the 35-kg plate of Prob. 4.70. Determine the magnitude of *W* and the point where it should be placed if the tension is to be 300 N in each of the three wires.

4.72 Determine the mass and location of the smallest block which should be placed on the 20-kg plate of Prob. 4.69 if the tensions in the three wires are to be equal.

4.73 A 12-m pole supports a horizontal cable *CD* and is held by a ball and socket at *A* and two cables *BE* and *BF*. Knowing that the tension in cable *CD* is 14 kN and assuming that *CD* is parallel to the *x* axis ($\phi = 0$), determine the tension in cables *BE* and *BF* and the reaction at *A*.

4.74 Solve Prob. 4.73, assuming that cable *CD* forms an angle $\phi = 25°$ with the vertical *xy* plane.

4.75 The 4-m boom *AB* is acted upon by the 5-kN force shown. Determine (*a*) the tension in each cable, (*b*) the reaction at the ball and socket at *A*.

Fig. P4.75

4.76 Solve Prob. 4.75, assuming that the 5-kN load is applied at point *B*.

4.77 A 300-kg crate hangs from a cable which passes over a pulley *B* and is attached to a support at *H*. The 100-kg boom *AB* is supported by a ball and socket at *A* and by two cables *DE* and *DF*. The center of gravity of the boom is located at *G*. Determine (*a*) the tension in cables *DE* and *DF*, (*b*) the reaction at *A*.

4.78 In Prob. 4.73, determine the angle ϕ for which the tension in *BF* is maximum (*a*) if cable *BE* is not to become slack, (*b*) if cable *BE* is replaced by a rod which can withstand either a tension or a compression force.

4.79 The lid of a roof scuttle has a mass of 30 kg. It is hinged at corners *A* and *B* and maintained in the desired position by a rod *CD* pivoted at *C*; a pin at end *D* of the rod fits into one of several holes drilled in the edge of the lid. For $\alpha = 50°$, determine (*a*) the magnitude of the force exerted by rod *CD*, (*b*) the reactions at the hinges. Assume that the hinge at *B* does not exert any axial thrust.

4.80 Solve Prob. 4.79, assuming $\alpha = 30°$.

Fig. P4.73

Fig. P4.77

Fig. P4.79

Fig. P4.81

Fig. P4.82

Fig. P4.83

4.81 The 26-kg horizontal platform *ABCD* supports a 1500-N load at its center. The platform is normally held in position by hinges at *A* and *B* and by braces *CE* and *DE*. If brace *DE* is removed, determine the reactions at the hinges and the force exerted by the remaining brace *CE*. The hinge at *A* does not exert any axial thrust.

4.82 A 1.2 × 2.4 m sheet of plywood is temporarily held by nails at *D* and *E* and by two wooden braces nailed at *A*, *B*, and *C*. Wind is blowing on the hidden face of the plywood sheet and it is assumed that its effect may be represented by a force *P***k** applied at the center of the sheet. Knowing that each brace becomes unsafe with respect to buckling when subjected to a 1.8-kN axial force, determine (*a*) the maximum allowable value of the magnitude *P* of the wind force, (*b*) the corresponding value of the *z* component of the reaction at *E*. Assume that the nails are loose and do not exert any couple.

4.83 A 250-kg uniform rectangular platform, 3.20 m long and 2.25 m wide, is supported by hinges at *A* and *B* and by a cable attached to corners *C* and *D* of the platform and passing over a frictionless hook *E*. Assuming that the tension is the same in both parts of the cable and that the hinge at *A* does not exert any axial thrust, determine (*a*) the tension in the cable, (*b*) the reactions at *A* and *B*.

4.84 Solve Prob. 4.83, assuming that cable *CED* is replaced by a cable attached to corner *C* and to hook *E*.

4.85 Solve Prob. 4.83, assuming that cable *CED* is replaced by a cable attached to corner *D* and to hook *E*.

4.86 Solve Prob. 4.83, assuming that cable *CED* is replaced by two cables, *CE* and *DE*, attached, respectively, to corners *C* and *D* and tied to hook *E*, and that the hinge at *A* is replaced by a roller exerting on the platform a force parallel to the *z* axis.

4.87 Solve Prob. 4.81, assuming that the hinge at *A* has been removed and that the hinge at *B* can exert couples about axes parallel to the *x* and *y* axes, respectively.

4.88 Solve Prob. 4.81, assuming that the hinge at *B* has been removed and that the hinge at *A* can exert an axial thrust, as well as couples about axes parallel to the *x* and *y* axes, respectively.

4.89 Solve Prob. 4.83, assuming that the hinge at *A* has been removed and that the hinge at *B* can exert couples about axes parallel to the *y* and *z* axes, respectively.

4.90 Solve Prob. 4.83, assuming that the hinge at *B* has been removed and that the hinge at *A* can exert an axial thrust, as well as couples about axes parallel to the *y* and *z* axes, respectively.

4.91 The uniform rod *AB* has a mass of 8 kg. It is supported by a ball and socket at *A* and by cord *CD* which is attached to the midpoint *C* of the rod. Knowing that the rod leans against a frictionless vertical wall at *B*, determine (*a*) the tension in the cord, (*b*) the reactions at *A* and *B*.

Fig. P4.91

4.92 The rigid L-shaped member *ABC* is supported by a ball and socket at *A* and by three cables. Determine the tension in each cable and the reaction at *A* caused by the 2.5 kN load applied at *G*.

Fig. P4.92

4.93 A 180-kg catamaran is sailing in a straight course and at a constant speed. The effect of the wind on the sail may be represented by the force $\mathbf{F} = (420\ \mathrm{N})\mathbf{i} - (560\ \mathrm{N})\mathbf{k}$ applied at the point of coordinates $x = -0.48$ m, $y = 3$ m, $z = -0.36$ m. Due to the efforts of the crew, the mast is maintained in a vertical position and the twin hulls are subjected to equal forces, consisting of buoyant forces $\mathbf{B} = B\mathbf{j}$ along the lines of action $x = -0.6$ m, $z = \pm 1.2$ m, drag forces $\mathbf{D} = -D\mathbf{i}$ along the lines of action $y = -0.6$ m, $z = \pm 1.2$ m, and side forces $\mathbf{S} = S\mathbf{k}$ along the common line of action $x = -d$, $y = -0.6$ m. Determine (*a*) the magnitude *D* of the drag on each of the hulls, (*b*) the magnitude *S* of each of the side forces, and the distance *d* defining their line of action.

4.94 The catamaran of Prob. 4.93 is manned by two sailors, one of mass 75 kg and the other 60 kg. The center of gravity of the boat is located at $x = -0.9$ m, $z = 0$, and the 75-kg sailor is sitting at $x = -1.5$ m, $z = +1.2$ m, while the 60-kg sailor leans overboard to maintain the mast in a vertical position. Determine the *x* and *z* coordinates of the center of gravity of the second sailor.

Fig. P4.93

Fig. P4.95

4.95 In order to clean the clogged drainpipe *AE*, a plumber has discon-nected both ends of the pipe and introduced a power snake through the opening at *A*. The cutting head of the snake is connected by a heavy cable to an electric motor which keeps it rotating at a constant speed while the plumber forces the cable into the pipe. The forces exerted by the plumber and the motor on the end of the cable may be represented by the wrench $\mathbf{F} = -(32 \text{ N})\mathbf{j}$, $\mathbf{M} = -(130 \text{ N·m})\mathbf{j}$. Determine the additional reactions at *B*, *C*, and *D* caused by the cleaning operation. Assume that the reaction at each support consists of two force components perpendicular to the pipe.

4.96 Solve Prob. 4.95, assuming that the plumber exerts no force on the end of the cable and that the motor exerts a couple $\mathbf{M} = -(130 \text{ N·m})\mathbf{j}$.

Dimensions in mm

Fig. P4.97

4.97 The rigid L-shaped member *ABC* is supported by a ball and a socket at *A* and by three cables. If a 1.8-kN load is applied at *F*, determine the tension in each cable.

4.98 Solve Prob. 4.97, assuming that the 1.8-kN load is applied at C.

4.99 The 650 × 700 mm plate *ABCD* is supported by hinges along edge *AB* and by wire *CE*. Knowing that the 40-kg plate is uniform, determine the tension in the wire.

4.100 Solve Prob. 4.99, assuming that the wire *CE* is replaced by a wire connecting *E* and *D*.

Fig. P4.99

4.101 The bent rod *ABC* is hinged to a vertical wall by means of two brackets and bears at *C* against another vertical wall. The upper bracket fits in a groove in the rod to prevent the rod from sliding down. Neglecting friction, determine the reaction at *C* when a 150-N load is applied at *D* as shown.

Fig. P4.101

4.102 The frame *ACD* is supported by ball-and-socket joints at *A* and *D* and by a cable which passes through a ring at *B* and is attached to hooks at *G* and *H*. Knowing that the frame supports at point *C* a load of magnitude $P = 335$ N, determine the tension in the cable.

4.103 Solve Prob. 4.102, assuming that the cable *GBH* is replaced by a cable *GB* attached at *G* and *B*.

Fig. P4.102

Dimensions in mm
Fig. P4.104

4.104 Two rods are welded together to form a T-shaped lever which leans against a frictionless vertical wall at *D* and is supported by bearings at *A* and *B*. A vertical force **P** of magnitude 600 N is applied at the midpoint *E* of rod *DC*. Determine the reaction at *D*.

Review and Summary

This chapter was devoted to the study of the *equilibrium of rigid bodies*, i.e., to the situation when the external forces acting on a rigid body *form a system equivalent to zero* [Sec. 4.1]. We then have

$$\Sigma \mathbf{F} = 0 \qquad \Sigma \mathbf{M}_O = \Sigma (\mathbf{r} \times \mathbf{F}) = 0 \tag{4.1}$$

Resolving each force and each moment into its rectangular components, we may express the necessary and sufficient conditions for the equilibrium of a rigid body by the following six scalar equations:

$$\Sigma F_x = 0 \qquad \Sigma F_y = 0 \qquad \Sigma F_z = 0 \tag{4.2}$$
$$\Sigma M_x = 0 \qquad \Sigma M_y = 0 \qquad \Sigma M_z = 0 \tag{4.3}$$

These equations may be used to determine unknown forces applied to the rigid body or unknown reactions exerted by its supports.

It is essential, when solving a problem involving the equilibrium of a rigid body, to consider *all* the forces acting on the body. Therefore, the first step in the solution of the problem should be to draw a *free-body diagram* showing the body under consideration and all the forces acting on it, unknown as well as known [Sec. 4.2].

In the first part of the chapter, we considered the *equilibrium of a two-dimensional structure*, i.e., we assumed that the structure considered and the forces applied to it were contained in the plane of the figure. We saw that each of the reactions exerted on the structure by its supports could involve one, two, or three unknowns, depending upon the type of support [Sec. 4.3].

In the case of a two-dimensional structure, Eqs. (4.1), or Eqs. (4.2) and (4.3), reduce to *three equilibrium equations*, namely

$$\Sigma F_x = 0 \qquad \Sigma F_y = 0 \qquad \Sigma M_A = 0 \tag{4.5}$$

where A is an arbitrary point in the plane of the structure [Sec. 4.4]. These equations may be solved for three unknowns. While the three equilibrium equations (4.5) cannot be *augmented* by additional equations, any of them may be *replaced* by another equation. Therefore, we may write alternative sets of equilibrium equations, such as

$$\Sigma F_x = 0 \qquad \Sigma M_A = 0 \qquad \Sigma M_B = 0 \tag{4.6}$$

where the line AB is chosen in a direction different from the y direction, or

$$\Sigma M_A = 0 \qquad \Sigma M_B = 0 \qquad \Sigma M_C = 0 \tag{4.7}$$

where the points A, B, and C are not in a straight line.

Since any set of equilibrium equations may be solved for only three unknowns, the reactions at the supports of a rigid two-dimensional structure may not be completely determined if they involve *more than three unknowns*; they are said to be *statically indeterminate* [Sec. 4.5]. On the other hand, if the reactions involve *fewer than three unknowns*, equilibrium will not be maintained under general loading conditions; the structure is said to be *partially constrained*. The fact that the reactions involve exactly three unknowns is no guarantee that the equilibrium equations can be solved for all three unknowns. If the supports are arranged in such a way that the reactions *must be either concurrent or parallel*, the reactions are statically indeterminate and the structure is said to be *improperly constrained*.

Statical indeterminacy

Partial constraints

Improper constraints

Two particular cases of equilibrium of a rigid body were given special attention. In Sec. 4.6, a *two-force body* was defined as a rigid body subjected to forces at only two points, and it was shown that the resultants $\mathbf{F}_1$ and $\mathbf{F}_2$ of these forces must have the *same magnitude, same line of action, and opposite sense* (Fig. 4.11), a property which will simplify the solution of certain problems in later chapters. In Sec. 4.7, a *three-force body* was defined as a rigid body subjected to forces at only three points, and it was shown that the resultants $\mathbf{F}_1$, $\mathbf{F}_2$, and $\mathbf{F}_3$ of these forces must be *either concurrent* (Fig. 4.12) *or parallel*. This property provides us with an alternative approach to the solution of problems involving a three-force body [Sample Prob. 4.6].

Two-force body

Three-force body

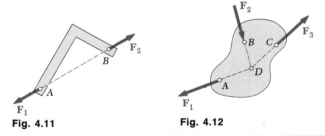

Fig. 4.11   **Fig. 4.12**

In the second part of the chapter, we considered the *equilibrium of a three-dimensional body* and saw that each of the reactions exerted on the body by its supports could involve from one to six unknowns, depending upon the type of support [Sec. 4.8].

Equilibrium of a three-dimensional body

In the general case of the equilibrium of a three-dimensional body, all of the six scalar equilibrium equations (4.2) and (4.3) listed at the beginning of this review should be used and solved for *six unknowns* [Sec. 4.9]. In most problems, however, these equations will be more conveniently obtained if we first write

$$\Sigma\mathbf{F} = 0 \qquad \Sigma\mathbf{M}_O = \Sigma(\mathbf{r} \times \mathbf{F}) = 0 \qquad (4.1)$$

and express the forces $\mathbf{F}$ and position vectors $\mathbf{r}$ in terms of scalar components and unit vectors. The vector products may then be computed either directly or by means of determinants, and the desired scalar equations obtained by equating to zero the coefficients of the unit vectors [Sample Probs. 4.7 through 4.9].

We noted that as many as three unknown reaction components may be eliminated from the computation of $\Sigma\mathbf{M}_O$ in the second of the relations (4.1) through a judicious choice of point O. Also, the reactions at two points A and B may be eliminated from the solution of some problems by writing the equation $\Sigma M_{AB} = 0$, which involves the computation of the moments of the forces about an axis AB joining points A and B [Sample Prob. 4.10].

If the reactions involve more than six unknowns, some of the reactions are *statically indeterminate;* if they involve less than six unknowns, the rigid body is only *partially constrained.* Even with six or more unknowns, the rigid body will be *improperly constrained* if the supports are such that the reactions must either be parallel or intersect the same line.

Review Problems

4.105 A 150-kg cylindrical tank, 1.6 m in diameter, is to be raised over a 0.4-m obstruction. A cable is wrapped around the tank and pulled horizontally as shown. Knowing that the corner of the obstruction at A is rough, find the required tension in the cable and the reaction at A.

Fig. P4.105

Fig. P4.106

4.106 A force **P** of magnitude 450 N is applied to member ABC which is supported by a frictionless pin at A and by cable BDC. Since the cable passes over a pulley at D, the tension may be assumed to be the same in portions BD and CD of the cable. Determine (*a*) the tension in the cable, (*b*) the reaction at A when $a = 60$ mm.

4.107 Knowing that the tension in all portions of the belt is 600 N, determine the reactions at supports A and B of the plate when (a) $\alpha = 0$, (b) $\alpha = 90°$, (c) $\alpha = 30°$.

Fig. P4.107

4.108 A 0.9×1.5 m storm window with a mass of 7 kg is supported by hinges at A and B. In the position shown, it is held away from the side of the house by a 0.6-m stick CD. Assuming that the hinge at A does not exert any axial thrust, determine (a) the magnitude of the force exerted by the stick, (b) the reactions at A and B.

4.109 Solve Prob. 4.108, assuming that the hinge at B has been removed and that the hinge at A can exert an axial thrust, as well as couples about axes parallel to the x and y axes, respectively.

Fig. P4.108

4.110 A worker is pushing a 50-kg wheelbarrow up an 18° incline when he encounters a 35-mm obstruction at D. Determine the magnitude and direction of (a) the force he must apply to each handle to start the wheel over the obstruction, (b) the corresponding reaction at D. (*Hint.* As it starts rotating about D, the wheel is a two-force body.)

Fig. P4.110

Fig. P4.111

4.111 A vertical load $\mathbf{P}$ is applied at end B of rod BC. The constant of the spring is k and the spring is unstretched when $\theta = 60°$. (a) Neglecting the weight of the rod, express the angle θ corresponding to the equilibrium position in terms of P, k, and l. (b) Determine the values of θ corresponding to equilibrium if $P = \frac{1}{4}kl$.

4.112 A slender rod BC of length L and weight W is held by two cables as shown. Knowing that cable AB is horizontal and that the rod forms an angle of 40° with the horizontal, determine (a) the angle θ that cable CD forms with the horizontal, (b) the tension in each cable.

Fig. P4.112

Fig. P4.113

4.113 The uniforms rod AB weighs has a mass of 10 kg. It is supported by a ball and socket at A and leans against both rod CD and the vertical wall. Assuming the wall and the rods to be frictionless, determine (a) the force which rod CD exerts on AB, (b) the reactions at A and B. (*Hint.* The force exerted by CD on AB must be perpendicular to both rods.)

4.114 A force $\mathbf{P}$ is applied to a bent rod AD which may be supported in four different ways as shown. In each case determine the reactions at the supports.

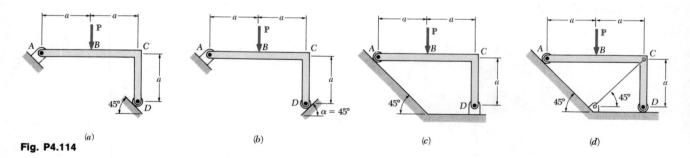

(a)   (b)   (c)   (d)

Fig. P4.114

Fig. P4.115

4.115 Determine the reactions at A and B for the truss and loading shown.

*4.116 In the problems listed below, the rigid bodies considered were completely constrained, and the reactions were statically determinate. For each of these rigid bodies it is possible to create an improper set of constraints by changing either a dimension of the body or the direction of a reaction. In each problem determine the value of α or of a which results in improper constraints. (a) Prob. 4.21, (b) Prob. 4.44, (c) Prob. 4.106, (d) Prob. 4.114b, (e) Prob. 4.115.

The following problems are designed to be solved with a computer.

4.C1 Two wheels A and B, of weight W_A and W_B, respectively, are connected by a rod of negligible weight and are free to roll on the surface shown.
Write a computer program which can be used to determine the angle α that the
rod forms with the horizontal in its equilibrium position. Use this program to
calculate α for values of θ from 0 to 90° at 5° intervals. Consider the cases when
(a) $W_A = W_B$, (b) $W_A = 2W_B$.

Fig. P4.C1

Fig. P4.C2

4.C2 A vertical load **P** is applied to the end of rod BC. Write a computer
program which can be used to calculate the magnitude P of the load required for
the equilibrium of the system. For $M = 4$ kg and $l = 625$ mm, use this program to
calculate P for values of θ from 0 to 90° at 5° intervals.

4.C3 The derrick shown supports a 2000-kg crate. It is held by a ball and
socket at A and by two cables attached at D and E. Knowing that the derrick
stands in a vertical plane forming the angle ϕ with the xy plane, write a computer
program and use it to calculate the tension in each cable for values of ϕ from 0 to
40° at 4° intervals.

Fig. P4.C3

Fig. P4.C4

4.C4 The frame ACD is supported by ball-and-socket joints at A and D and
by a cable which passes through a ring at B and is attached to hooks at G and H.
Knowing that the frame supports at point C a load of magnitude $P = 335$ N, write
a computer program and use it to calculate the tension in the cable for values of y
from 0 to 1.5 m at 100-mm intervals.

Distributed Forces: Centroids and Centers of Gravity

CHAPTER

5

5.1. Introduction. We have assumed so far that the attraction exerted by the earth on a rigid body could be represented by a single force **W**. This force, called the force of gravity, or the weight of the body, was to be applied at the *center of gravity* of the body (Sec. 3.2). Actually, the earth exerts a force on each of the particles forming the body. The action of the earth on a rigid body should thus be represented by a large number of small forces distributed over the entire body. We shall see in this chapter, however, that all these small forces may be replaced by a single equivalent force **W**. We shall also learn to determine the center of gravity, i.e., the point of application of the resultant **W**, for various shapes of bodies.

In the first part of the chapter, we shall consider two-dimensional bodies, such as flat plates and wires contained in a given plane. We shall introduce two concepts closely associated with the determination of the center of gravity of a plate or wire, namely, the concept of *centroid* of an area or line, and the concept of *first moment* of an area or line with respect to a given axis.

We shall also find that the computation of the area of a surface of revolution or of the volume of a body of revolution is directly related to the determination of the centroid of the line or area used to generate that surface or body of revolution (Theorems of Pappus-Guldinus). And, as we shall see in Secs. 5.8 and 5.9, the determination of the centroid of an area simplifies the analysis of beams subjected to distributed loads and the computation of the forces exerted on submerged rectangular surfaces such as hydraulic gates and portions of dams.

In the last part of the chapter, we shall learn to determine the center of gravity of a three-dimensional body, as well as the centroid of a volume and the first moments of that volume with respect to the coordinate planes.

5.2. Center of Gravity of a Two-Dimensional Body. Let

us first consider a flat horizontal plate (Fig. 5.1). We may divide the plate into n small elements. The coordinates of the first element are denoted by x_1 and y_1, those of the second element by x_2 and y_2, etc. The forces exerted by the earth on the elements of plate will be denoted, respectively, by ΔW_1, ΔW_2, . . . , ΔW_n. These forces or weights are directed toward the center of the earth; however, for all practical purposes they may be assumed parallel. Their resultant is therefore a single force in the same direction. The magnitude W of this force is obtained by adding the magnitudes of the elementary weights.

$$\Sigma F_z: \qquad W = \Delta W_1 + \Delta W_2 + \cdots + \Delta W_n$$

To obtain the coordinates $\bar{x}$ and $\bar{y}$ of the point G where the resultant $\mathbf{W}$ should be applied, we write that the moments of $\mathbf{W}$ about the y and x axes are equal to the sum of the corresponding moments of the elementary weights,

$$\Sigma M_y: \qquad \bar{x}W = x_1\,\Delta W_1 + x_2\,\Delta W_2 + \cdots + x_n\,\Delta W_n$$
$$\Sigma M_x: \qquad \bar{y}W = y_1\,\Delta W_1 + y_2\,\Delta W_2 + \cdots + y_n\,\Delta W_n \qquad (5.1)$$

If we now increase the number of elements into which the plate is divided and simultaneously decrease the size of each element, we obtain at the limit the following expressions:

$$W = \int dW \qquad \bar{x}W = \int x\,dW \qquad \bar{y}W = \int y\,dW \qquad (5.2)$$

These equations define the weight $\mathbf{W}$ and the coordinates $\bar{x}$ and $\bar{y}$ of the center of gravity G of a flat plate. The same equations may be derived for a wire lying in the xy plane (Fig. 5.2). We shall observe, in the latter case, that the center of gravity G will generally not be located on the wire.

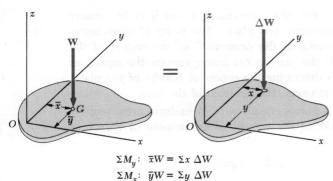

$$\Sigma M_y: \quad \bar{x}W = \Sigma x\,\Delta W$$
$$\Sigma M_x: \quad \bar{y}W = \Sigma y\,\Delta W$$

Fig. 5.1 Center of gravity of a plate.

$$\Sigma M_y: \quad \bar{x}W = \Sigma x\,\Delta W$$
$$\Sigma M_x: \quad \bar{y}W = \Sigma y\,\Delta W$$

Fig. 5.2 Center of gravity of a wire.

5.3. Centroids of Areas and Lines.

In the case of a homogeneous plate of uniform thickness, the magnitude ΔW of the weight of an element of plate may be expressed as

$$\Delta W = \rho g t\, \Delta A$$

where ρ = density (mass per unit volume) of material
$\quad g$ = acceleration of gravity (g = 9.81 m/s²)
$\quad t$ = thickness of plate
$\quad \Delta A$ = area of element

Similarly, we may express the magnitude W of the weight of the entire plate in the form

$$W = \rho g t A$$

where A is the total area of the plate. We check that since ρ is expressed in kg/m³, g in m/s², t in s, and A in m², the weight W is expressed in kg·m/s², that is, in newtons.

Substituting for ΔW and W in the moment equations (5.1) and dividing throughout by $\rho g t$, we write

$$\Sigma M_y: \quad \bar{x} A = x_1\, \Delta A_1 + x_2\, \Delta A_2 + \cdots + x_n\, \Delta A_n$$
$$\Sigma M_x: \quad \bar{y} A = y_1\, \Delta A_1 + y_2\, \Delta A_2 + \cdots + y_n\, \Delta A_n$$

If we increase the number of elements into which the area A is divided and simultaneously decrease the size of each element, we obtain at the limit

$$\bar{x} A = \int x\, dA \qquad \bar{y} A = \int y\, dA \tag{5.3}$$

These equations define the coordinates $\bar{x}$ and $\bar{y}$ of the center of gravity of a homogeneous plate. The point of coordinates $\bar{x}$ and $\bar{y}$ is also known as the *centroid C of the area A* of the plate (Fig. 5.3). If the plate is not homogeneous, the equations cannot be used to determine the center of gravity of the plate; they still define, however, the centroid of the area.

In the case of a homogeneous wire of uniform cross section, the magnitude ΔW of the weight of an element of wire may be expressed as

$$\Delta W = \rho g a\, \Delta L$$

where ρ = density of material
$\quad a$ = cross-sectional area of wire
$\quad \Delta L$ = length of element

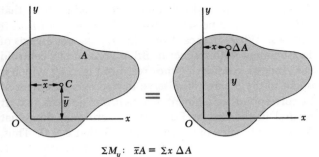

$$\Sigma M_y: \quad \bar{x}A = \Sigma x\, \Delta A$$
$$\Sigma M_x: \quad \bar{y}A = \Sigma y\, \Delta A$$

Fig. 5.3 Centroid of an area.

$$\Sigma M_y: \quad \bar{x}L = \Sigma x\, \Delta L$$
$$\Sigma M_x: \quad \bar{y}L = \Sigma y\, \Delta L$$

Fig. 5.4 Centroid of a line.

The center of gravity of the wire then coincides with the *centroid C of the line L* defining the shape of the wire (Fig. 5.4). The coordinates $\bar{x}$ and $\bar{y}$ of the centroid of the line L are obtained from the equations

$$\bar{x}L = \int x\, dL \qquad \bar{y}L = \int y\, dL \tag{5.4}$$

5.4. First Moments of Areas and Lines. The integral $\int x\, dA$ in Eqs. (5.3) of the preceding section is known as the *first moment of the area A with respect to the y axis* and is denoted by Q_y. Similarly, the integral $\int y\, dA$ defines the *first moment of A with respect to the x axis* and is denoted by Q_x. We write

$$Q_y = \int x\, dA \qquad Q_x = \int y\, dA \tag{5.5}$$

Comparing Eqs. (5.3) with Eqs. (5.5), we note that the first moments of the area A may be expressed as the products of the area and of the coordinates of its centroid:

$$Q_y = \bar{x}A \qquad Q_x = \bar{y}A \tag{5.6}$$

It follows from Eqs. (5.6) that the coordinates of the centroid of an area may be obtained by dividing the first moments of that area by the area itself. The computation of the first moments of an area is also useful in the determination of shearing stresses under transverse loadings in mechanics of materials. Finally, we observe from Eqs. (5.6) that if the centroid of an area is located on a coordinate axis, the first moment of the area with respect to that axis is zero, and the converse is also true.

Relations similar to Eqs. (5.5) and (5.6) may be used to define the first moments of a line with respect to the coordinate axes and to express these moments as the products of the length L of the line and of the coordinates $\bar{x}$ and $\bar{y}$ of its centroid.

Fig. 5.5

Fig. 5.7

An area A is said to be *symmetric with respect to an axis BB'* if to every point P of the area corresponds a point P' of the same area such that the line PP' is perpendicular to BB' and is divided into two equal parts by that axis (Fig. 5.5a). A line L is said to be symmetric with respect to BB' if it satisfies similar conditions. When an area A or a line L possesses an axis of symmetry BB', its first moment with respect to BB' is zero and its centroid is located on that axis. Indeed, considering the area A of Fig. 5.5b, which is symmetric with respect to the y axis, we observe that to every element of area dA of abscissa x corresponds an element of area dA' of abscissa $-x$. It follows that the integral in the first of Eqs. (5.5) is zero and, thus, that $Q_y = 0$. It also follows from the first of the relations (5.3) that $\bar{x} = 0$. Thus, if an area A or a line L possesses an axis of symmetry, its centroid C is located on that axis.

We further note that if an area or line possesses two axes of symmetry, its centroid C must be located at the intersection of the two axes of symmetry (Fig. 5.6). This property enables us to determine immediately the centroid of areas such as circles, ellipses, squares, rectangles, equilateral triangles, or other symmetric figures, as well as the centroid of lines in the shape of the circumference of a circle, the perimeter of a square, etc.

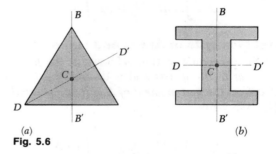

Fig. 5.6

An area A is said to be *symmetric with respect to a center O* if to every element of area dA of coordinates x and y corresponds an element of area dA' of coordinates $-x$ and $-y$ (Fig. 5.7). It then follows that the integrals in Eqs. (5.5) are both zero, and that $Q_x = Q_y = 0$. It also follows from Eqs. (5.3) that $\bar{x} = \bar{y} = 0$, that is, the centroid of the area coincides with its center of symmetry O. It may be shown in a similar way that the centroid of a line symmetric with respect to a center O coincides with O.

It should be noted that a figure possessing a center of symmetry does not necessarily possess an axis of symmetry (Fig. 5.7), while a figure possessing two axes of symmetry does not necessarily possess a center of symmetry (Fig. 5.6a). However, if a figure possesses two axes of symmetry at a right angle to each other, the point of intersection of these axes will be a center of symmetry (Fig. 5.6b).

Centroids of unsymmetrical areas and lines and of areas and lines possessing only one axis of symmetry will be determined by the methods of Secs. 5.6 and 5.7. Centroids of common shapes of areas and lines are shown in Fig. 5.8A and B. The formulas defining these centroids will be derived in the Sample Problems and Problems following Secs. 5.6 and 5.7.

Shape		$\bar{x}$	$\bar{y}$	Area
Triangular area			$\dfrac{h}{3}$	$\dfrac{bh}{2}$
Quarter-circular area		$\dfrac{4r}{3\pi}$	$\dfrac{4r}{3\pi}$	$\dfrac{\pi r^2}{4}$
Semicircular area		0	$\dfrac{4r}{3\pi}$	$\dfrac{\pi r^2}{2}$
Quarter-elliptical area		$\dfrac{4a}{3\pi}$	$\dfrac{4b}{3\pi}$	$\dfrac{\pi ab}{4}$
Semielliptical area		0	$\dfrac{4b}{3\pi}$	$\dfrac{\pi ab}{2}$
Semiparabolic area		$\dfrac{3a}{8}$	$\dfrac{3h}{5}$	$\dfrac{2ah}{3}$
Parabolic area		0	$\dfrac{3h}{5}$	$\dfrac{4ah}{3}$
Parabolic spandrel		$\dfrac{3a}{4}$	$\dfrac{3h}{10}$	$\dfrac{ah}{3}$
General spandrel		$\dfrac{n+1}{n+2}a$	$\dfrac{n+1}{4n+2}h$	$\dfrac{ah}{n+1}$
Circular sector		$\dfrac{2r\sin\alpha}{3\alpha}$	0	αr^2

Fig. 5.8A Centroids of common shapes of areas.

Shape		$\bar{x}$	$\bar{y}$	Length
Quarter-circular arc	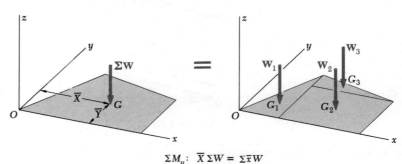	$\dfrac{2r}{\pi}$	$\dfrac{2r}{\pi}$	$\dfrac{\pi r}{2}$
Semicircular arc		0	$\dfrac{2r}{\pi}$	πr
Arc of circle		$\dfrac{r \sin \alpha}{\alpha}$	0	$2\alpha r$

Fig. 5.8B Centroids of common shapes of lines.

5.5. Composite Plates and Wires. In many instances, a flat plate may be divided into rectangles, triangles, or other common shapes shown in Fig. 5.8A. The abscissa $\bar{X}$ of its center of gravity G may be determined from the abscissas $\bar{x}_1$, $\bar{x}_2$, . . . of the centers of gravity of the various parts by expressing that the moment of the weight of the whole plate about the y axis is equal to the sum of the moments of the weights of the various parts about the same axis (Fig. 5.9). The ordinate $\bar{Y}$ of the center of gravity of the plate is found in a similar way by equating moments about the x axis. We write

ΣM_y: $\bar{X}(W_1 + W_2 + \cdots + W_n) = \bar{x}_1 W_1 + \bar{x}_2 W_2 + \cdots + \bar{x}_n W_n$

ΣM_x: $\bar{Y}(W_1 + W_2 + \cdots + W_n) = \bar{y}_1 W_1 + \bar{y}_2 W_2 + \cdots + \bar{y}_n W_n$

$$\Sigma M_y:\ \ \bar{X}\Sigma W = \Sigma \bar{x} W$$
$$\Sigma M_x:\ \ \bar{Y}\Sigma W = \Sigma \bar{y} W$$

Fig. 5.9 Center of gravity of a composite plate.

or, for short,

$$\bar{X}\Sigma W = \Sigma \bar{x}W \qquad \bar{Y}\Sigma W = \Sigma \bar{y}W \qquad (5.7)$$

These equations may be solved for the coordinates $\bar{X}$ and $\bar{Y}$ of the center of gravity of the plate.

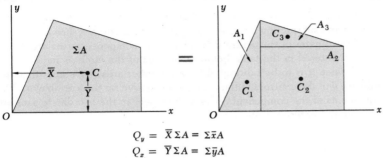

$$Q_y = \bar{X}\Sigma A = \Sigma \bar{x}A$$
$$Q_x = \bar{Y}\Sigma A = \Sigma \bar{y}A$$

Fig. 5.10 Centroid of a composite area.

If the plate is homogeneous and of uniform thickness, the center of gravity coincides with the centroid C of its area. The abscissa $\bar{X}$ of the centroid of the area may be determined by noting that the first moment Q_y of the composite area with respect to the y axis may be expressed both as the product of $\bar{X}$ and the total area and as the sum of the first moments of the elementary areas with respect to the y axis (Fig. 5.10). The ordinate $\bar{Y}$ of the centroid is found in a similar way by considering the first moment Q_x of the composite area. We have

$$Q_y = \bar{X}(A_1 + A_2 + \cdots + A_n) = \bar{x}_1 A_1 + \bar{x}_2 A_2 + \cdots + \bar{x}_n A_n$$
$$Q_x = \bar{Y}(A_1 + A_2 + \cdots + A_n) = \bar{y}_1 A_1 + \bar{y}_2 A_2 + \cdots + \bar{y}_n A_n$$

or, for short,

$$Q_y = \bar{X}\Sigma A = \Sigma \bar{x}A \qquad Q_x = \bar{Y}\Sigma A = \Sigma \bar{y}A \qquad (5.8)$$

These equations yield the first moments of the composite area, or they may be solved for the coordinates $\bar{X}$ and $\bar{Y}$ of its centroid.

Care should be taken to record the moment of each area with the appropriate sign. First moments of areas, just like moments of forces, may be positive or negative. For example, an area whose centroid is located to the left of the y axis will have a negative first moment with respect to that axis. Also, the area of a hole should be recorded with a negative sign (Fig. 5.11).

Similarly, it is possible in many cases to determine the center of gravity of a composite wire or the centroid of a composite line by dividing the wire or line into simpler elements (see Sample Prob. 5.2).

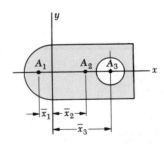

	$\bar{x}$	A	$\bar{x}A$
A_1 Semicircle	$-$	$+$	$-$
A_2 Full rectangle	$+$	$+$	$+$
A_3 Circular hole	$+$	$-$	$-$

Fig. 5.11

SAMPLE PROBLEM 5.1

For the plane area shown, determine (a) the first moments with respect to the x and y axes, (b) the location of the centroid.

Solution. The area is obtained by adding a rectangle, a triangle, and a semicircle and subtracting a circle. Using the coordinate axes shown, the area and the coordinates of the centroid of each of the component areas are determined and entered in the table below. The area of the circle is indicated as negative, since it is to be subtracted from the other areas. We note that the coordinate $\bar{y}$ of the centroid of the triangle is negative for the axes shown. The first moments of the component areas with respect to the coordinate axes are computed and entered in the table.

Component	A, mm²	$\bar{x}$, mm	$\bar{y}$, mm	$\bar{x}A$, mm³	$\bar{y}A$, mm³
Rectangle	$(120)(80) = 9.6 \times 10^3$	60	40	$+576 \times 10^3$	$+384 \times 10^3$
Triangle	$\frac{1}{2}(120)(60) = 3.6 \times 10^3$	40	-20	$+144 \times 10^3$	-72×10^3
Semicircle	$\frac{1}{2}\pi(60)^2 = 5.655 \times 10^3$	60	105.46	$+339.3 \times 10^3$	$+596.4 \times 10^3$
Circle	$-\pi(40)^2 = -5.027 \times 10^3$	60	80	-301.6×10^3	-402.2×10^3
	$\Sigma A = 13.828 \times 10^3$			$\Sigma\bar{x}A = +757.7 \times 10^3$	$\Sigma\bar{y}A = +506.2 \times 10^3$

a. First Moments of Area. Using Eqs. (5.8), we write

$$Q_x = \Sigma\bar{y}A = 506.2 \times 10^3 \text{ mm}^3$$
$$Q_x = 506 \times 10^3 \text{ mm}^3 \quad \blacktriangleleft$$
$$Q_y = \Sigma\bar{x}A = 757.7 \times 10^3 \text{ mm}^3$$
$$Q_y = 758 \times 10^3 \text{ mm}^3 \quad \blacktriangleleft$$

b. Location of Centroid. Substituting the values obtained from the table into the equations defining the centroid of a composite area, we obtain

$$\bar{X}\Sigma A = \Sigma\bar{x}A: \quad \bar{X}(13.828 \times 10^3 \text{ mm}^2) = 757.7 \times 10^3 \text{ mm}^3$$
$$\bar{X} = 54.8 \text{ mm} \quad \blacktriangleleft$$
$$\bar{Y}\Sigma A = \Sigma\bar{y}A: \quad \bar{Y}(13.828 \times 10^3 \text{ mm}^2) = 506.2 \times 10^3 \text{ mm}^3$$
$$\bar{Y} = 36.6 \text{ mm} \quad \blacktriangleleft$$

The figure shown is made of a thin homogeneous wire. Determine its center of gravity.

Solution. Since the figure is formed of homogeneous wire, its center of gravity may be located by determining the centroid of the corresponding line. Choosing the coordinate axes shown, with origin at A, we determine the coordinates of the centroid of each segment of line and compute its moments with respect to the coordinate axes.

Segment	L, mm	$\bar{x}$, mm	$\bar{y}$, mm	$\bar{x}L$, mm²	$\bar{y}L$, mm²
AB	480	240	0	115.2×10^3	0
BC	520	240	100	124.8×10^3	52×10^3
CA	200	0	100	0	20×10^3
	$\Sigma L = 1200$			$\Sigma \bar{x}L =$ 240×10^3	$\Sigma \bar{y}L =$ 72×10^3

Substituting the values obtained from the table into the equations defining the centroid of a composite line, we obtain

$$\bar{X} \Sigma L = \Sigma \bar{x}L: \qquad \bar{X}(1200 \text{ mm}) = 240 \times 10^3 \text{ mm}^2 \qquad \bar{X} = 200 \text{ mm} \blacktriangleleft$$

$$\bar{Y} \Sigma L = \Sigma \bar{y}L: \qquad \bar{Y}(1200 \text{ mm}) = 72 \times 10^3 \text{ mm}^2 \qquad \bar{Y} = 60 \text{ mm} \blacktriangleleft$$

SAMPLE PROBLEM 5.3

A uniform semicircular rod of weight W and radius r is attached to a pin at A and bears against a frictionless surface at B. Determine the reactions at A and B.

Solution. A free-body diagram of the rod is drawn. The forces acting on the rod consist of its weight $\mathbf{W}$ applied at the center of gravity G, whose position is obtained from Fig. 5.8B, of a reaction at A represented by its components $\mathbf{A}_x$ and $\mathbf{A}_y$, and of a horizontal reaction at B.

$$+\!\uparrow \Sigma M_A = 0: \qquad B(2r) - W\left(\frac{2r}{\pi}\right) = 0$$

$$B = +\frac{W}{\pi} \qquad\qquad \mathbf{B} = \frac{W}{\pi}\!\rightarrow \quad \blacktriangleleft$$

$$\xrightarrow{+} \Sigma F_x = 0: \qquad A_x + B = 0$$

$$A_x = -B = -\frac{W}{\pi} \qquad \mathbf{A}_x = \frac{W}{\pi}\!\leftarrow$$

$$+\!\uparrow \Sigma F_y = 0: \qquad A_y - W = 0 \qquad \mathbf{A}_y = W\!\uparrow$$

Adding the two components of the reaction at A:

$$A = \left[W^2 + \left(\frac{W}{\pi}\right)^2\right]^{1/2} \qquad\qquad A = W\left(1 + \frac{1}{\pi^2}\right)^{1/2} \quad \blacktriangleleft$$

$$\tan\alpha = \frac{W}{W/\pi} = \pi \qquad\qquad \alpha = \tan^{-1}\pi \quad \blacktriangleleft$$

The answers may also be expressed as follows:

$$\mathbf{A} = 1.049W \,\angle\, 72.3° \qquad \mathbf{B} = 0.318W\!\rightarrow \quad \blacktriangleleft$$

Problems

5.1 through 5.11   Locate the centroid of the plane area shown.

Fig. P5.1

Fig. P5.2

Fig. P5.3

Fig. P5.4

Fig. P5.5

Fig. P5.6

Fig. P5.7

Fig. P5.8

Fig. P5.9

Fig. P5.10

Fig. P5.11

5.12 through 5.15 Locate the centroid of the plane area shown.

Fig. P5.12

Fig. P5.13

Fig. P5.14

Fig. P5.15

5.16 Determine the abscissa of the centroid of the circular segment in terms of r and α.

Fig. P5.16

Fig. P5.17

5.17 Determine the abscissa of the centroid of the trapezoid shown in terms of h_1, h_2, and a.

5.18 Locate the centroid C in Prob. 5.10 in terms of r_1 and r_2 and show that as r_1 approaches r_2, the location of C approaches that for a semicircular arc of radius $\frac{1}{2}(r_1 + r_2)$.

5.19 For the semiannular area of Prob. 5.10, determine the ratio of r_1 to r_2 for which the centroid of the area is located at $x = -\frac{1}{2}r_2$ and $y = 0$.

5.20 For the plane area of Prob. 5.9, determine the ratio of a to r for which the centroid of the area is located at point B.

5.21 For the semiannular area of Prob. 5.10, determine the ratio of r_1 to r_2 for which the centroid of the area is located at point B.

5.22 A built-up beam has been constructed by nailing together seven planks as shown. The nails are equally spaced along the beam and the beam supports a vertical load. As proved in mechanics of materials, the shearing forces exerted on the nails at A and B are proportional to the first moments with respect to the centroidal x axis of the shaded areas shown, respectively, in parts a and b of the figure. Knowing that the force exerted on the nail at A is 120 N, determine the force exerted on the nail at B.

Dimensions in mm

Fig. P5.22

5.23 and 5.24 The horizontal x axis is drawn through the centroid C of the area shown and divides it into two component areas A_1 and A_2. Determine the first moment of each component area with respect to the x axis and explain the result obtained.

Dimensions in mm
Fig. P5.23

Fig. P5.24

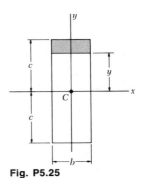

Fig. P5.25

5.25 The first moment of the shaded area with respect to the x axis is denoted by Q_x. (a) Express Q_x in terms of b, c, and the distance y from the base of the shaded area to the x axis. (b) For what value of y is Q_x maximum and what is that maximum value?

5.26 through 5.29   A thin homogeneous wire is bent to form the perimeter of the figure indicated. Locate the center of gravity of the wire figure thus formed.

5.26   Fig. P5.2
5.27   Fig. P5.3
5.28   Fig. P5.4
5.29   Fig. P5.5

5.30   A 4-kg uniform circular rod has a radius of 250 mm and is attached to a pin at C and to the cable AB. Determine (a) the tension in the cable, (b) the reaction at C.

Fig. P5.30

Fig. P5.31 and P5.32

5.31   The homogeneous wire $ABCD$ is bent as shown and is attached to a hinge at C. Determine the length L for which portion BCD of the wire is horizontal.

5.32   The homogeneous wire $ABCD$ is bent as shown and is attached to a hinge at C. Determine the length L for which portion AB of the wire is horizontal.

Fig. P5.33

5.33   Knowing that the figure shown is formed of a thin homogeneous wire, determine the length l of portion CE of the wire for which the center of gravity of the figure is located at point C, when (a) $\theta = 15°$, (b) $\theta = 60°$.

5.34 Determine the distance h for which the centroid of the shaded area is as high above line BB' as possible when (a) $k = 0.10$, (b) $k = 0.80$.

Fig. P5.34 and P5.35

5.35 Show that when the distance h is selected to maximize the distance $\bar{y}$ from line BB' to the centroid of the shaded area, we also have $\bar{y} = h$.

Fig. P5.36 and P5.37

5.36 Determine by approximate means the x coordinate of the centroid of the area shown.

5.37 Determine by approximate means the y coordinate of the centroid of the area shown.

5.38 Divide the parabolic spandrel shown into five vertical sections and determine by approximate means the x coordinate of its centroid; approximate the spandrel by rectangles of the form $bcc'b'$. What is the percentage error in the answer obtained? (See Fig. 5.8A for exact answer.)

Fig. P5.38

5.39 Solve Prob. 5.38, using rectangles of the form $bdd'b'$.

5.6. Determination of Centroids by Integration. The centroid of an area bounded by analytical curves (i.e., curves defined by algebraic equations) is usually determined by computing the integrals in Eqs. (5.3) of Sec. 5.3:

$$\bar{x}A = \int x \, dA \qquad \bar{y}A = \int y \, dA \qquad (5.3)$$

If the element of area dA is chosen equal to a small square of sides dx and dy, the determination of each of these integrals requires a *double integration* in x and y. A double integration is also necessary if polar coordinates are used and if dA is chosen equal to a small square of sides dr and $r \, d\theta$.

In most cases, however, it is possible to determine the coordinates of the centroid of an area by performing a single integration. This is achieved by choosing for dA a thin rectangle or strip, or a thin sector or pie-shaped element (Fig. 5.12); the centroid of the thin rectangle is located at its center, and the centroid of the thin sector at a distance $\frac{2}{3}r$ from its vertex (as for a triangle). The coordinates of the centroid of the area under consideration are then obtained by expressing that the first moment of the entire area with respect to each of the coordinate axes is equal to the sum (or integral) of the corresponding moments of the elements of area. Denoting by $\bar{x}_{el}$ and $\bar{y}_{el}$ the coordinates of the centroid of the element dA, we write

$$\begin{aligned} Q_y = \bar{x}A = \int \bar{x}_{el} \, dA \\ Q_x = \bar{y}A = \int \bar{y}_{el} \, dA \end{aligned} \qquad (5.9)$$

If the area itself is not already known, it may also be computed from these elements.

The coordinates $\bar{x}_{el}$ and $\bar{y}_{el}$ of the centroid of the element of area should be expressed in terms of the coordinates of a point located on the curve bounding the area under consideration. Also, the element of area dA should be expressed in terms of the coordinates of the point and their differentials. This has been done in Fig. 5.12 for three common types of elements; the pie-shaped element of part c should be used when the equation of the curve bounding the area is given in polar coordinates. The appropriate expressions should be substituted in formulas (5.9), and the equation of the curve should be used to express one of the coordinates in terms of the other. The integration is thus reduced to a single integration which may be performed according to the usual rules of calculus. Once the area and the integrals in Eqs. (5.9) have been determined, these equations may be solved for the coordinates $\bar{x}$ and $\bar{y}$ of the centroid of the area.

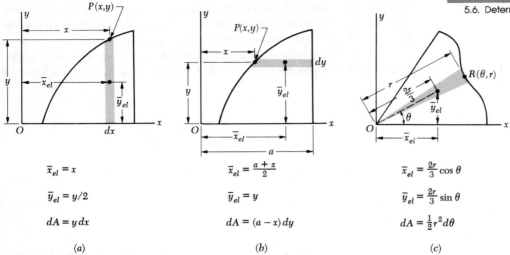

$$\bar{x}_{el} = x$$

$$\bar{y}_{el} = y/2$$

$$dA = y\,dx$$

(a)

$$\bar{x}_{el} = \frac{a+x}{2}$$

$$\bar{y}_{el} = y$$

$$dA = (a-x)\,dy$$

(b)

$$\bar{x}_{el} = \frac{2r}{3}\cos\theta$$

$$\bar{y}_{el} = \frac{2r}{3}\sin\theta$$

$$dA = \tfrac{1}{2}r^2\,d\theta$$

(c)

Fig. 5.12 Centroids and areas of differential elements.

The centroid of a line defined by an algebraic equation may be determined by computing the integrals in Eqs. (5.4) of Sec. 5.3:

$$\bar{x}L = \int x\,dL \qquad \bar{y}L = \int y\,dL \qquad (5.4)$$

The element dL should be replaced by one of the following expressions, depending upon the type of equation used to define the line (these expressions may be derived by using the Pythagorean theorem):

$$dL = \sqrt{1 + \left(\frac{dy}{dx}\right)^2}\,dx$$

$$dL = \sqrt{1 + \left(\frac{dx}{dy}\right)^2}\,dy$$

$$dL = \sqrt{r^2 + \left(\frac{dr}{d\theta}\right)^2}\,d\theta$$

The equation of the line is then used to express one of the coordinates in terms of the other, the integration may be performed by the methods of calculus, and Eqs. (5.4) may be solved for the coordinates $\bar{x}$ and $\bar{y}$ of the centroid of the line.

5.7. Theorems of Pappus-Guldinus. These theorems, which were first formulated by the Greek geometer Pappus during the third century A.D. and later restated by the Swiss mathematician Guldinus, or Guldin (1577–1643), deal with surfaces and bodies of revolution.

A *surface of revolution* is a surface which may be generated by rotating a plane curve about a fixed axis. For example (Fig. 5.13), the surface of

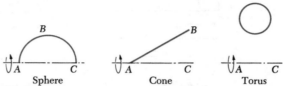

Fig. 5.13 Generating a surface of revolution.

a sphere may be obtained by rotating a semicircular arc *ABC* about the diameter *AC*; the surface of a cone by rotating a straight line *AB* about an axis *AC*; the surface of a torus or ring by rotating the circumference of a circle about a nonintersecting axis. A *body of revolution* is a body which may be generated by rotating a plane area about a fixed axis. A solid sphere may be obtained by rotating a semicircular area, a cone by rotating a triangular area, and a solid torus by rotating a full circular area (Fig. 5.14).

Fig. 5.14 Generating a body of revolution.

THEOREM I. *The area of a surface of revolution is equal to the length of the generating curve times the distance traveled by the centroid of the curve while the surface is being generated.*

Proof. Consider an element dL of the line L (Fig. 5.15) which is revolved about the x axis. The area dA generated by the element dL is equal to $2\pi y\, dL$. Thus, the entire area generated by L is $A = \int 2\pi y\, dL$. But we saw in Sec. 5.3 that the integral $\int y\, dL$ is equal to $\bar{y}L$. We have therefore

$$A = 2\pi\bar{y}L \tag{5.10}$$

where $2\pi\bar{y}$ is the distance traveled by the centroid of L. It should be noted

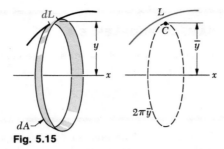

Fig. 5.15

that the generating curve should not cross the axis about which it is rotated; if it did, the two sections on either side of the axis would generate areas of opposite signs and the theorem would not apply.

THEOREM II. *The volume of a body of revolution is equal to the generating area times the distance traveled by the centroid of the area while the body is being generated.*

Proof. Consider an element dA of the area A which is revolved about the x axis (Fig. 5.16). The volume dV generated by the element dA is equal

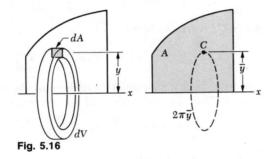

Fig. 5.16

to $2\pi y\, dA$. Thus, the entire volume generated by A is $V = \int 2\pi y\, dA$. But since the integral $\int y\, dA$ is equal to $\bar{y}A$ (Sec. 5.3), we have

$$V = 2\pi\bar{y}A \tag{5.11}$$

where $2\pi\bar{y}$ is the distance traveled by the centroid of A. Again, it should be noted that the theorem does not apply if the axis of rotation intersects the generating area.

The theorems of Pappus-Guldinus offer a simple way for computing the area of surfaces of revolution and the volume of bodies of revolution. They may also be used conversely to determine the centroid of a plane curve when the area of the surface generated by the curve is known or to determine the centroid of a plane area when the volume of the body generated by the area is known (see Sample Prob. 5.8).

Determine by direct integration the centroid of a parabolic spandrel.

Solution. The value of k is determined by substituting $x = a$ and $y = b$ in the given equation. We have $b = ka^2$ and $k = b/a^2$. The equation of the curve is thus

$$y = \frac{b}{a^2} x^2 \qquad \text{or} \qquad x = \frac{a}{b^{1/2}} y^{1/2}$$

Vertical Differential Element. We choose the differential element shown and find the total area of the figure.

$$A = \int dA = \int y\, dx = \int_0^a \frac{b}{a^2} x^2\, dx = \left[\frac{b}{a^2} \frac{x^3}{3} \right]_0^a = \frac{ab}{3}$$

The first moment of the differential element with respect to the y axis is $\bar{x}_{el}\, dA$; hence, the first moment of the entire area with respect to this axis is

$$Q_y = \int \bar{x}_{el}\, dA = \int xy\, dx = \int_0^a x \left(\frac{b}{a^2} x^2 \right) dx = \left[\frac{b}{a^2} \frac{x^4}{4} \right]_0^a = \frac{a^2 b}{4}$$

Since $Q_y = \bar{x}A$, we have

$$\bar{x}A = \int \bar{x}_{el}\, dA \qquad \bar{x}\frac{ab}{3} = \frac{a^2 b}{4} \qquad \bar{x} = \tfrac{3}{4}a \quad \blacktriangleleft$$

Likewise, the first moment of the differential element with respect to the x axis is $\bar{y}_{el}\, dA$, and the first moment of the entire area is

$$Q_x = \int \bar{y}_{el}\, dA = \int \frac{y}{2} y\, dx = \int_0^a \frac{1}{2} \left(\frac{b}{a^2} x^2 \right)^2 dx = \left[\frac{b^2}{2a^4} \frac{x^5}{5} \right]_0^a = \frac{ab^2}{10}$$

Since $Q_x = \bar{y}A$, we have

$$\bar{y}A = \int \bar{y}_{el}\, dA \qquad \bar{y}\frac{ab}{3} = \frac{ab^2}{10} \qquad \bar{y} = \tfrac{3}{10}b \quad \blacktriangleleft$$

Horizontal Differential Element. The same result may be obtained by considering a horizontal element. The first moments of the area are

$$Q_y = \int \bar{x}_{el}\, dA = \int \frac{a + x}{2}(a - x)\, dy = \int_0^b \frac{a^2 - x^2}{2}\, dy$$

$$= \frac{1}{2} \int_0^b \left(a^2 - \frac{a^2}{b}y \right) dy = \frac{a^2 b}{4}$$

$$Q_x = \int \bar{y}_{el}\, dA = \int y(a - x)\, dy = \int y \left(a - \frac{a}{b^{1/2}} y^{1/2} \right) dy$$

$$= \int_0^b \left(ay - \frac{a}{b^{1/2}} y^{3/2} \right) dy = \frac{ab^2}{10}$$

The expressions obtained are again substituted in the equations defining the centroid of the area to obtain $\bar{x}$ and $\bar{y}$.

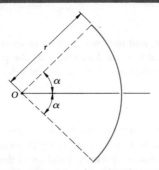

SAMPLE PROBLEM 5.5

Determine the centroid of the arc of circle shown.

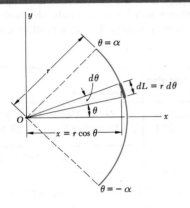

Solution. Since the arc is symmetrical with respect to the x axis, we have $\bar{y} = 0$. A differential element is chosen as shown, and the length of the arc is determined by integration.

$$L = \int dL = \int_{-\alpha}^{\alpha} r \, d\theta = r \int_{-\alpha}^{\alpha} d\theta = 2r\alpha$$

The first moment of the arc with respect to the y axis is

$$Q_y = \int x \, dL = \int_{-\alpha}^{\alpha} (r \cos \theta)(r \, d\theta) = r^2 \int_{-\alpha}^{\alpha} \cos \theta \, d\theta$$

$$= r^2 [\sin \theta]_{-\alpha}^{\alpha} = 2r^2 \sin \alpha$$

Since $Q_y = \bar{x}L$, we write

$$\bar{x}(2r\alpha) = 2r^2 \sin \alpha \qquad\qquad \bar{x} = \frac{r \sin \alpha}{\alpha} \quad \blacktriangleleft$$

SAMPLE PROBLEM 5.6

Determine the area of the surface of revolution shown, obtained by rotating a quarter-circular arc about a vertical axis.

Solution. According to Theorem I of Pappus-Guldinus, the area generated is equal to the product of the length of the arc and the distance traveled by its centroid. Referring to Fig. 5.8B, we have

$$\bar{x} = 2r - \frac{2r}{\pi} = 2r\left(1 - \frac{1}{\pi}\right)$$

$$A = 2\pi\bar{x}L = 2\pi 2r\left(1 - \frac{1}{\pi}\right)\frac{\pi r}{2}$$

$$A = 2\pi r^2(\pi - 1) \quad \blacktriangleleft$$

The outside diameter of a pulley is 0.8 m, and the cross section of its rim is as shown. Determine the mass and weight of the rim, knowing that the pulley is made of steel and that the density of steel is $\rho = 7.85 \times 10^3 \text{ kg/m}^3$.

Solution. The volume of the rim may be found by applying Theorem II of Pappus-Guldinus, which states that the volume equals the product of the given cross-sectional area and of the distance traveled by its centroid in one complete revolution. However, the volume will be more easily obtained if we observe that the cross section consists of rectangle (I) with a positive area and rectangle (II) with a negative area.

	Area, mm²	$\bar{y}$, mm	Distance Traveled by C, mm	Volume, mm³
I	+5000	375	$2\pi(375) = 2356$	$(5000)(2356) = 11.78 \times 10^6$
II	−1800	365	$2\pi(365) = 2293$	$(-1800)(2293) = -4.13 \times 10^6$
				Volume of rim = 7.65×10^6

Since 1 mm = 10^{-3} m, we have 1 mm³ = $(10^{-3}$ m$)^3 = 10^{-9}$ m³, and we obtain $V = 7.65 \times 10^6$ mm³ = $(7.65 \times 10^6)(10^{-9}$ m³) = 7.65×10^{-3} m³.

$$m = \rho V = (7.85 \times 10^3 \text{ kg/m}^3)(7.65 \times 10^{-3} \text{ m}^3) \qquad m = 60.0 \text{ kg} \blacktriangleleft$$
$$W = mg = (60.0 \text{ kg})(9.81 \text{ m/s}^2) = 589 \text{ kg·m/s}^2 \qquad W = 589 \text{ N} \blacktriangleleft$$

SAMPLE PROBLEM 5.8

Using the theorems of Pappus-Guldinus, determine (a) the centroid of a semicircular area, (b) the centroid of a semicircular arc. We recall that the volume of a sphere is $\frac{4}{3}\pi r^3$ and that its surface area is $4\pi r^2$.

Solution. The volume of a sphere is equal to the product of the area of a semicircle and of the distance traveled by the centroid of the semicircle in one revolution about the x axis.

$$V = 2\pi\bar{y}A \qquad \tfrac{4}{3}\pi r^3 = 2\pi\bar{y}(\tfrac{1}{2}\pi r^2) \qquad \bar{y} = \frac{4r}{3\pi} \blacktriangleleft$$

Likewise, the area of a sphere is equal to the product of the length of the generating semicircle and of the distance traveled by its centroid in one revolution.

$$A = 2\pi\bar{y}L \qquad 4\pi r^2 = 2\pi\bar{y}(\pi r) \qquad \bar{y} = \frac{2r}{\pi} \blacktriangleleft$$

Problems

5.40 through 5.43 Determine by direct integration the centroid of the area shown.

Fig. P5.40

Fig. P5.41

Fig. P5.42

Fig. P5.43

5.44 through 5.49 Derive by direct integration the expressions for $\bar{x}$ and $\bar{y}$ given in Fig. 5.8 for:

    5.44 A general spandrel $(y = kx^n)$
    5.45 A quarter-elliptical area
    5.46 A semicircular area
    5.47 A semiparabolic area
    5.48 A circular sector
    5.49 A quarter-circular arc

5.50 Determine by direct integration the x coordinate of the centroid of the area shown.

5.51 Determine by direct integration the y coordinate of the centroid of the area shown.

*5.52 and *5.53 Determine by direct integration the centroid of the area shown.

Fig. P5.50 and P5.51

Fig. P5.52

Fig. P5.53

5.54 Determine the centroid of the area shown when $a = 100$ mm.

Fig. P5.54 and P5.55

5.55 Determine the centroid of the area shown in terms of a.

5.56 Determine the volume of the solid obtained by rotating the area of Prob. 5.7 about (a) the x axis, (b) the y axis.

5.57 Determine the volume of the solid obtained by rotating the trapezoid of Prob. 5.3 about (a) the x axis, (b) the y axis.

5.58 Determine the volume of the solid generated by rotating the parabolic spandrel shown about (a) the x axis, (b) the axis AA'.

Fig. P5.58

Fig. P5.59

5.59 Determine the surface area and the volume of the torus obtained by rotating the circular area shown about the axis AA'.

5.60 A spherical dish is formed by passing a horizontal plane through a spherical shell of radius R. Knowing that $R = 250$ mm and $\phi = 60°$, determine the area of the inside surface of the dish.

Fig. 5.60

5.61 Determine the volume and mass of water required to completely fill the spherical dish of Prob. 5.60.

5.62 A spherical pressure vessel has an inside diameter of 0.8 m. Determine (a) the volume of liquefied propane required to fill the vessel to a depth of 0.6 m, (b) the corresponding mass of the liquefied propane. (Density of liquefied propane $= 580$ kg/m³.)

5.63 For the pressure vessel of Prob. 5.62, determine the area of the surface in contact with the liquefied propane.

5.64 Determine the volume and total surface area of the body shown.

52 mm 42 mm

60 mm

20 mm

Fig. P5.64

32 mm

12 mm

8 mm

9 mm

6 mm

A

A'

Fig. P5.65

5.65 Determine the volume and mass of the cast-iron pipe collar obtained by rotating the shaded area about the centerline of the 12-mm-diameter pipe. (Density of cast iron = 7200 kg/m³.)

5.66 Determine the volume and mass of the solid brass knob shown. (Density of brass = 8470 kg/m³.)

5.67 Determine the total surface area of the solid brass knob shown.

30 mm

r = 18 mm

r = 18 mm

Fig. P5.66 and P5.67

5.68 The rim of a 2-kg double-groove V-belt sheave of 250-mm outside diameter is made of cast iron. Knowing that the cross-sectional area of the rim is 368 mm², determine the distance $\bar{y}$ from the axis of rotation AA' to the centroid of the cross section of the rim. (Density of cast iron = 7200 kg/m³.)

$\bar{y}$

A

A'

Fig. P5.68

5.69 An oil-storage tank in the form of a shell of constant strength has the cross section shown. (This is also the cross section of a drop of water on an unwetted surface.) Determine by approximate means (*a*) the volume of the tank, (*b*) the surface area of the tank.

Fig. P5.69

5.70 A 60-W standard light bulb has the cross section shown. For the portion of the bulb above the base and neglecting the thickness of the glass, determine (*a*) the volume of inert gas inside the bulb, (*b*) the outside surface area of the bulb.

Fig. P5.70

5.71 Determine the volume of the solid of revolution formed by revolving each of the plane areas shown about its vertical edge *AB*. Show that the volumes of the solids formed are in the ratio 6:4:3:2:1.

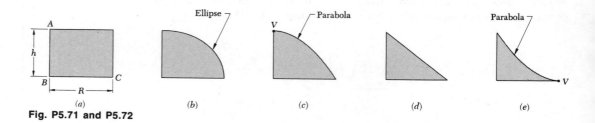

Fig. P5.71 and P5.72

5.72 Determine the volume of the solid formed by revolving each of the plane areas shown about its base *BC*. Show that the volumes of the solids formed are in the ratio 15:10:8:5:3.

* 5.8. Distributed Loads on Beams.

The concept of centroid of an area may be used to solve other problems besides those dealing with the weight of flat plates. Consider, for example, a beam supporting a *distributed load*; this load may consist of the weight of materials supported directly or indirectly by the beam, or it may be caused by wind or hydrostatic pressure. The distributed load may be represented by plotting the load w supported per unit length (Fig. 5.17); this load will be expressed in N/m. The magnitude of the force exerted on an element of beam of length dx is $dW = w\,dx$, and the total load supported by the beam is

$$W = \int_0^L w\,dx$$

But the product $w\,dx$ is equal in magnitude to the element of area dA shown in Fig. 5.17a, and W is thus equal in magnitude to the total area A under the load curve,

$$W = \int dA = A$$

We shall now determine where a *single concentrated load* $\mathbf{W}$, of the same magnitude W as the total distributed load, should be applied on the beam if it is to produce the same reactions at the supports (Fig. 5.17b). This concentrated load $\mathbf{W}$, which represents the resultant of the given distributed loading, should be equivalent to this loading as far as the free-body diagram of the entire beam is concerned. The point of application P of the equivalent concentrated load $\mathbf{W}$ will therefore be obtained by expressing that the moment of $\mathbf{W}$ about point O is equal to the sum of the moments of the elementary loads $d\mathbf{W}$ about O:

$$(OP)W = \int x\,dW$$

or, since $dW = w\,dx = dA$ and $W = A$,

$$(OP)A = \int_0^L x\,dA \qquad (5.12)$$

Since the integral represents the first moment with respect to the w axis of the area under the load curve, it may be replaced by the product $\bar{x}A$. We have therefore $OP = \bar{x}$, where $\bar{x}$ is the distance from the w axis to the centroid C of the area A (this is *not* the centroid of the beam).

A *distributed load on a beam may thus be replaced by a concentrated load; the magnitude of this single load is equal to the area under the load curve, and its line of action passes through the centroid of that area.* It should be noted, however, that the concentrated load is equivalent to the given loading only as far as external forces are concerned. It may be used to determine reactions but should not be used to compute internal forces and deflections.

(a)

(b)

Fig. 5.17

Fig. 5.18

(a)

(b)

Fig. 5.19

*5.9 Forces on Submerged Surfaces. The approach used in the preceding section may be used to determine the resultant of the hydrostatic pressure forces exerted on a *rectangular surface* submerged in a liquid. Consider the rectangular plate shown in Fig. 5.18, of length L and width b perpendicular to the plane of the figure. As noted in Sec. 5.8, the load exerted on an element of plate of length dx is $w\,dx$, where w is the load per unit length. But this load may also be expressed as $p\,dA = pb\,dx$, where p is the gage pressure in the liquid† and b is the width of the plate; thus, $w = bp$. Since, on the other hand, the gage pressure in a liquid is $p = \rho gh$, where ρ is the density of the liquid and h is the vertical distance from the free surface, it follows that

$$w = bp = b\rho gh \qquad (5.13)$$

which shows that the load per unit length w is proportional to h and, thus, varies linearly with x.

Recalling the results of Sec. 5.8, we observe that the resultant **R** of the hydrostatic forces exerted on one side of the plate is equal in magnitude to the trapezoidal area under the load curve and that its line of action passes through the centroid C of that area. The point P of the plate where **R** is applied is known as the *center of pressure*.‡

We shall consider next the forces exerted by a liquid on a curved surface of constant width (Fig. 5.19a). Since the determination of the resultant **R** of these forces by direct integration would not be easy, we shall consider the free body obtained by detaching the volume of liquid ABD bounded by the curved surface AB and by the two plane surfaces AD and DB shown in Fig. 5.19b. The forces acting on the free body ABD consist of the weight **W** of the volume of liquid detached, the resultant $\mathbf{R}_1$ of the forces exerted on AD, the resultant $\mathbf{R}_2$ of the forces exerted on BD, and the resultant $-\mathbf{R}$ of the forces exerted *by the curved surface on the liquid*. The resultant $-\mathbf{R}$ is equal and opposite to, and has the same line of action as the resultant **R** of the forces exerted *by the liquid on the curved surface*. The forces **W**, $\mathbf{R}_1$, and $\mathbf{R}_2$ may be determined by standard methods; after their values have been found, the force $-\mathbf{R}$ will be obtained by solving the equations of equilibrium for the free body of Fig. 5.19b. The resultant **R** of the hydrostatic forces exerted on the curved surface will then be obtained by reversing the sense of $-\mathbf{R}$.

The methods outlined in this section may be used to determine the resultant of the hydrostatic forces exerted on the surface of dams or on rectangular gates and vanes. Resultants of forces on submerged surfaces of variable width should be determined by the methods of Chap. 9.

---

†The pressure p, which represents a load per unit area, is expressed in N/m². The derived SI unit N/m² is called a *pascal* (Pa).

‡ Noting that the area under the load curve is equal to $w_E L$ and recalling Eq. (5.13), we may write

$$R = w_E L = (bp_E)L = p_E(bL) = p_E A$$

where A denotes the area of the *plate*. Thus, the magnitude of **R** may be obtained by multiplying the area of the plate by the pressure at its center E. The resultant **R**, however, *should be applied at P, not at E.*

$w_B = 4500\ \text{N/m}$ **SAMPLE PROBLEM 5.9**

A beam supports a distributed load as shown. (*a*) Determine the equivalent concentrated load. (*b*) Determine the reactions at the supports.

a. **Equivalent Concentrated Load.** The magnitude of the resultant of the load is equal to the area under the load curve, and the line of action of the resultant passes through the centroid of the same area. We divide the area under the load curve into two triangles and construct the table below. To simplify the computations and tabulation, the given loads per unit length have been converted into kN/m.

Component	A, kN	$\bar{x}$, m	$\bar{x}A$, kN·m
Triangle I	4.5	2	9
Triangle II	13.5	4	54
	$\Sigma A = 18.0$	...	$\Sigma \bar{x}A = 63$

18 kN

Thus, $\bar{X}\Sigma A = \Sigma \bar{x}A$: $\bar{X}(18\ \text{kN}) = 63\ \text{kN·m}$ $\bar{X} = 3.5\ \text{m}$

The equivalent concentrated load is

$$W = 18\ \text{kN} \downarrow \blacktriangleleft$$

and its line of action is located at a distance

$$\bar{X} = 3.5\ \text{m to the right of } A \blacktriangleleft$$

b. **Reactions.** The reaction at A is vertical and is denoted by **A**; the reaction at B is represented by its components $\mathbf{B}_x$ and $\mathbf{B}_y$. The given load may be considered as the sum of two triangular loads as shown. The resultant of each triangular load is equal to the area of the triangle and acts at its centroid. We write the following equilibrium equations for the free body shown:

$\xrightarrow{+}\Sigma F_x = 0$: $\quad\quad\quad\quad\quad\quad\quad\quad\quad\quad\quad\quad\quad\quad\quad\quad \mathbf{B}_x = 0 \blacktriangleleft$

$+\uparrow\Sigma M_A = 0$: $-(4.5\ \text{kN})(2\ \text{m}) - (13.5\ \text{kN})(4\ \text{m}) + B_y(6\ \text{m}) = 0$

$$\mathbf{B}_y = 10.5\ \text{kN} \uparrow \blacktriangleleft$$

$+\uparrow\Sigma M_B = 0$: $+(4.5\ \text{kN})(4\ \text{m}) + (13.5\ \text{kN})(2\ \text{m}) - A(6\ \text{m}) = 0$

$$\mathbf{A} = 7.5\ \text{kN} \uparrow \blacktriangleleft$$

Alternate Solution. The given distributed load may be replaced by its resultant, which was found in part *a*. The reactions may be determined by writing the equilibrium equations $\Sigma F_x = 0$, $\Sigma M_A = 0$, and $\Sigma M_B = 0$. We again obtain

$$\mathbf{B}_x = 0 \quad\quad \mathbf{B}_y = 10.5\ \text{kN} \uparrow \quad\quad \mathbf{A} = 7.5\ \text{kN} \uparrow \blacktriangleleft$$

SAMPLE PROBLEM 5.10

The cross section of a concrete dam is as shown. Consider a section of the dam 1 m thick, and determine (a) the resultant of the reaction forces exerted by the ground on the base of the dam AB, (b) the resultant of the pressure forces exerted by the water on the face BC of the dam. Density of concrete = 2.40×10^3 kg/m^3; of water = 10^3 kg/m^3.

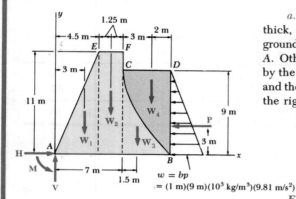

a. **Ground Reaction.** As a free body we choose a section $AEFCDB$, 1 m thick, of the dam and water as shown. The reaction forces exerted by the ground on the base AB are represented by an equivalent force-couple system at A. Other forces acting on the free body are the weight of the dam, represented by the weights of its components $\mathbf{W}_1$, $\mathbf{W}_2$, and $\mathbf{W}_3$, the weight of the water $\mathbf{W}_4$, and the resultant $\mathbf{P}$ of the pressure forces exerted on section BD by the water to the right of section BD. We have

$$W_1 = \tfrac{1}{2}(4.5 \text{ m})(11 \text{ m})(1 \text{ m})(2.40 \times 10^3 \text{ kg/m}^3)(9.81 \text{ m/s}^2) = 583 \text{ kN}$$
$$W_2 = (2.5 \text{ m})(11 \text{ m})(1 \text{ m})(2.40 \times 10^3 \text{ kg/m}^3)(9.81 \text{ m/s}^2) = 647 \text{ kN}$$
$$W_3 = \tfrac{1}{3}(5 \text{ m})(9 \text{ m})(1 \text{ m})(2.40 \times 10^3 \text{ kg/m}^3)(9.81 \text{ m/s}^2) = 353 \text{ kN}$$
$$W_4 = \tfrac{2}{3}(5 \text{ m})(9 \text{ m})(1 \text{ m})(10^3 \text{ kg/m}^3)(9.81 \text{ m/s}^2) = 294 \text{ kN}$$
$$P = \tfrac{1}{2}(9 \text{ m})(1 \text{ m})(9 \text{ m})(10^3 \text{ kg/m}^3)(9.81 \text{ m/s}^2) = 397 \text{ kN}$$

Equilibrium Equations

$\xrightarrow{+} \Sigma F_x = 0:$ $\qquad H - 397 \text{ kN} = 0$ $\qquad\qquad\qquad$ $\mathbf{H} = 397 \text{ kN} \rightarrow$ ◀

$+\uparrow \Sigma F_y = 0:$ $\qquad V - 583 \text{ kN} - 647 \text{ kN} - 353 \text{ kN} - 294 \text{ kN} = 0$
$$\mathbf{V} = 1877 \text{ kN} \uparrow \quad ◀$$

$+\uparrow \Sigma M_A = 0:$ $\quad -(583 \text{ kN})(3 \text{ m}) - (647 \text{ kN})(5.75 \text{ m}) - (353 \text{ kN})(8.5 \text{ m})$
$$-(294 \text{ kN})(10 \text{ m}) + (397 \text{ kN})(3 \text{ m}) + M = 0$$
$$\mathbf{M} = 10219 \text{ kN·m} \uparrow \quad ◀$$

We may replace the force-couple system obtained by a single force acting at a distance d to the right of A, where

$$d = \frac{10219 \text{ kN·m}}{1877 \text{ kN}} = 5.44 \text{ m}$$

b. **Resultant R of Water Forces.** The parabolic section of water BCD is chosen as a free body. The forces involved are the resultant $-\mathbf{R}$ of the forces exerted by the dam on the water, the weight $\mathbf{W}_4$, and the force $\mathbf{P}$. Since these forces must be concurrent, $-\mathbf{R}$ passes through the point of intersection G of $\mathbf{W}_4$ and $\mathbf{P}$. A force triangle is drawn from which the magnitude and direction of $-\mathbf{R}$ are determined. The resultant $\mathbf{R}$ of the forces exerted by the water on the face BC is equal and opposite:

$$\mathbf{R} = 494 \text{ kN} \; \measuredangle 36.5° \quad ◀$$

Problems

5.73 and 5.74 Determine the magnitude and location of the resultant of the distributed load shown. Also calculate the reactions at A and B.

Fig. P5.73

Fig. P5.74

5.75 through 5.80 Determine the reactions at the beam supports for the given loading condition.

Fig. P5.75

Fig. P5.76

Fig. P5.77

Fig. P5.78

Fig. P5.79

Fig. P5.80

5.81 Determine the reactions at the beam supports for the given loading condition when $w_0 = $ **7 kN/m**

5.82 Determine (a) the distributed load w_0 at the end C of the beam ABC for which the reaction at C is zero, (b) the corresponding reaction at B.

Fig. P5.81 and P5.82

Fig. P5.83

5.83 The beam AB supports two concentrated loads and rests on soil which exerts a linearly distributed upward load as shown. Determine the values of w_A and w_B corresponding to equilibrium.

5.84 For the beam and loading of Prob. 5.83, determine (*a*) the distance a for which $w_A = 18$ kN/m, (*b*) the corresponding value of w_B.

In the following problems, use $\rho = 10^3$ kg/m³ for the density of fresh water and $\rho_c = 2.40 \times 10^3$ kg/m³ for the density of concrete.

5.85 and 5.86 The cross section of a concrete dam is as shown. Consider a section of the dam 1 m thick, and determine (*a*) the resultant of the reaction forces exerted by the ground on the base AB of the dam, (*b*) the resultant of the pressure forces exerted by the water on the face BC of the dam.

Fig. P5.85

Fig. P5.86

Fig. P5.87

5.87 A freshwater marsh is drained to the ocean through an automatic tide gate which is 1.2 m wide and 0.9 m high. The gate is held by hinges located along its top edge at A and bears on a sill at B. At a given time, the water level in the marsh is $h = 1.8$ m and in the ocean $d = 2.7$ m. Determine the force exerted by the sill on the gate at B and the hinge reaction at A. (Density of salt water $= 1.03 \times 10^3$ kg/m³.)

5.88 The automatic tide gate described in Prob. 5.87 is used to drain a freshwater marsh into the ocean. If the water level in the marsh is $h = 1.8$ m determine the ocean level d for which the gate will open.

5.89 An automatic valve consists of a 225×225 mm square plate which is pivoted about a horizontal axis through A located at a distance $h = 90$ mm above the lower edge. Determine the depth of water d for which the valve will open.

5.90 An automatic valve consists of a 225×225 mm square plate which is pivoted about a horizontal axis through A. If the valve is to open when the depth of water $d = 450$ mm, determine the distance h from the bottom of the valve to the pivot A.

Fig. P5.89 and P5.90

5.91 The gate AB is located at the end of a 2-m-wide water channel and is supported by hinges along its top edge A. Knowing that the floor of the channel is frictionless, determine the reactions at A and B when $d = 3$ m.

5.92 Solve Prob. 5.91 when $d = 2.1$ m.

Fig. P5.91

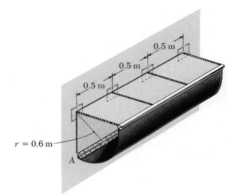

Fig. P5.95

Fig. P5.93

5.93 The quick-acting gate AB is 525 mm wide and is held in its closed position by a vertical cable and by hinges located along its top edge B. For a depth of water $d = 1.8$ m, determine the minimum tension required in cable AC to prevent the gate from opening.

5.94 For the gate of Prob. 5.93 determine the depth d for which the gate will open when $T = 3600$ N.

5.95 A long trough is supported by a continuous hinge along its lower edge and by a series of horizontal cables attached to its upper edge. Determine the tension in each of the cables, at a time when the trough is completely full of water.

5.96 Determine the minimum allowable value of the width a of the rectangular concrete dam if the dam is not to overturn about point A when $d = 4$ m. Assume that a seal exists at B and that no water pressure is present under the dam.

5.97 Solve Prob. 5.96, assuming that a seal exists only at A and that the full hydrostatic pressure at B is present under the dam from A to B.

Fig. P5.96 and P5.98

5.98 Knowing that the width of the rectangular concrete dam is $a = 1.2$ m, determine the maximum allowable value of the depth d of water if the dam is not to overturn about A. Assume that a seal exists at B and that no water pressure is present under the dam.

5.99 The end of a freshwater channel consists of a plate $ABCD$ which is hinged at B and is 0.5 m wide. Knowing that $a = 0.6$ m, determine the reactions at A and B.

5.100 The end of a freshwater channel consists of a plate $ABCD$ which is hinged at B and is 0.5 m wide. Determine the length a for which the reaction at A is zero.

Fig. P5.99 and P5.100

VOLUMES

5.10. Center of Gravity of a Three-Dimensional Body. Centroid of a Volume. The *center of gravity* G of a three-dimensional body is obtained by dividing the body into small elements and expressing that the weight $\mathbf{W}$ of the body attached at G is equivalent to the system of distributed forces $\Delta\mathbf{W}$ representing the weights of the small elements. Choosing the y axis vertical with positive sense upward (Fig. 5.20), and denoting by $\bar{\mathbf{r}}$ the position vector of G, we write that $\mathbf{W}$ is equal

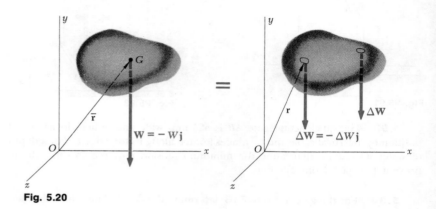

Fig. 5.20

to the sum of the elementary weights $\Delta\mathbf{W}$ and that its moment about O is equal to the sum of the moments about O of the elementary weights:

$$\Sigma\mathbf{F}: \qquad -W\mathbf{j} = \Sigma(-\Delta W\mathbf{j}) \tag{5.13}$$
$$\Delta\mathbf{M}_O: \qquad \bar{\mathbf{r}} \times (-W\mathbf{j}) = \Sigma[\mathbf{r} \times (-\Delta W\mathbf{j})]$$

Rewriting the last equation in the form

$$\bar{\mathbf{r}}W \times (-\mathbf{j}) = (\Sigma\mathbf{r}\,\Delta W) \times (-\mathbf{j}) \tag{5.14}$$

we observe that the weight $\mathbf{W}$ of the body will be equivalent to the system of the elementary weights $\Delta\mathbf{W}$ if the following conditions are satisfied:

$$W = \Sigma\,\Delta W \qquad \bar{\mathbf{r}}W = \Sigma\mathbf{r}\,\Delta W$$

Increasing the number of elements and simultaneously decreasing the size of each element, we obtain at the limit

$$W = \int dW \qquad \bar{\mathbf{r}}W = \int \mathbf{r}\,dW \tag{5.15}$$

We note that the relations obtained are independent of the orientation of the body. For example, if the body and the axes of coordinates were rotated so that the z axis pointed upward, the unit vector $-\mathbf{j}$ would be replaced by $-\mathbf{k}$ in Eqs. (5.13) and (5.14), but the relations (5.15) would remain unchanged. Resolving the vectors $\bar{\mathbf{r}}$ and $\mathbf{r}$ into rectangular components, we verify that the second of the relations (5.15) is equivalent to the three scalar equations

$$\bar{x}W = \int x\,dW \qquad \bar{y}W = \int y\,dW \qquad \bar{z}W = \int z\,dW \qquad (5.16)$$

If the body is made of a homogeneous material of density ρ, the magnitude dW of the weight of an infinitesimal element may be expressed in terms of the volume dV of the element, and the magnitude W of the total weight in terms of the total volume V. We write

$$dW = \rho g dV \qquad W = \rho g V$$

Substituting for dW and W in the second of the relations (5.15), we write

$$\bar{\mathbf{r}}V = \int \mathbf{r}\,dV \qquad (5.17)$$

or, in scalar form,

$$\bar{x}V = \int x\,dV \qquad \bar{y}V = \int y\,dV \qquad \bar{z}V = \int z\,dV \qquad (5.18)$$

The point of coordinates $\bar{x}$, $\bar{y}$, $\bar{z}$ is also known as the *centroid C of the volume V of the body*. If the body is not homogeneous, Eqs. (5.18) cannot be used to determine the center of gravity of the body; they still define, however, the centroid of the volume.

The integral $\int x\,dV$ is known as the *first moment of the volume with respect to the yz plane*. Similarly, the integrals $\int y\,dV$ and $\int z\,dV$ define the first moments of the volume with respect to the zx plane and the xy plane, respectively. It is seen from Eqs. (5.18) that if the centroid of a volume is located in a coordinate plane, the first moment of the volume with respect to that plane is zero.

A volume is said to be symmetrical with respect to a given plane if to every point P of the volume corresponds a point P' of the same volume, such that the line PP' is perpendicular to the given plane and divided into two equal parts by that plane. The plane is said to be a *plane of symmetry* for the given volume. When a volume V possesses a plane of symmetry, the first moment of V with respect to that plane is zero and the centroid of the volume must be located in the plane of symmetry. When a volume possesses two planes of symmetry, the centroid of the volume must be located on the line of intersection of the two planes. Finally, when a volume possesses three planes of symmetry which intersect in a well-defined point (i.e., not along a common line), the point of intersection of the three planes must coincide with the centroid of the volume. This property enables us to determine immediately the centroid of the volume of spheres, ellipsoids, cubes, rectangular parallelepipeds, etc.

Centroids of unsymmetrical volumes or of volumes possessing only one or two planes of symmetry should be determined by integration (Sec. 5.12). Centroids of common shapes of volumes are shown in Fig. 5.21. It should be observed that the centroid of a volume of revolution in general *does not coincide* with the centroid of its cross section. Thus, the centroid of a hemisphere is different from that of a semicircular area, and the centroid of a cone is different from that of a triangle.

Shape		$\bar{x}$	Volume
Hemisphere		$\dfrac{3a}{8}$	$\frac{2}{3}\pi a^3$
Semiellipsoid of revolution		$\dfrac{3h}{8}$	$\frac{2}{3}\pi a^2 h$
Paraboloid of revolution		$\dfrac{h}{3}$	$\frac{1}{2}\pi a^2 h$
Cone		$\dfrac{h}{4}$	$\frac{1}{3}\pi a^2 h$
Pyramid		$\dfrac{h}{4}$	$\frac{1}{3}abh$

Fig. 5.21 Centroids of common shapes of volumes.

5.11. Composite Bodies.

If a body can be divided into several of the common shapes shown in Fig. 5.21, its center of gravity G may be determined by expressing that the moment about O of its total weight is equal to the sum of the moments about O of the weights of the various component parts. Proceeding as in Sec. 5.10, we obtain the following equations defining the coordinates, $\overline{X}$, $\overline{Y}$, $\overline{Z}$ of the center of gravity G.

$$\overline{X}\Sigma W = \Sigma \overline{x}W \qquad \overline{Y}\Sigma W = \Sigma \overline{y}W \qquad \overline{Z}\Sigma W = \Sigma \overline{z}W \qquad (5.19)$$

If the body is made of a homogeneous material, its center of gravity coincides with the centroid of its volume and the following equations may be used:

$$\overline{X}\Sigma V = \Sigma \overline{x}V \qquad \overline{Y}\Sigma V = \Sigma \overline{y}V \qquad \overline{Z}\Sigma V = \Sigma \overline{z}V \qquad (5.20)$$

5.12. Determination of Centroids of Volumes by Integration.

The centroid of a volume bounded by analytical surfaces may be determined by computing the integrals given in Sec. 5.10:

$$\overline{x}V = \int x\,dV \qquad \overline{y}V = \int y\,dV \qquad \overline{z}V = \int z\,dV \qquad (5.21)$$

If the element of volume dV is chosen equal to a small cube of sides dx, dy, and dz, the determination of each of these integrals requires a *triple integration* in x, y, and z. However, it is possible to determine the coordinates of the centroid of most volumes by *double integration* if dV is chosen equal to the volume of a thin filament as shown in Fig. 5.22. The coordinates of the centroid of the volume are then obtained by writing

$$\overline{x}V = \int \overline{x}_{el}\,dV \qquad \overline{y}V = \int \overline{y}_{el}\,dV \qquad \overline{z}V = \int \overline{z}_{el}\,dV \qquad (5.22)$$

and substituting for the volume dV and the coordinates $\overline{x}_{el}$, $\overline{y}_{el}$, $\overline{z}_{el}$ the expressions given in Fig. 5.22. Using the equation of the surface to express z in terms of x and y, the integration is reduced to a double integration in x and y.

If the volume under consideration possesses *two planes of symmetry*, its centroid must be located on their line of intersection. Choosing the x axis along this line, we have

$$\overline{y} = \overline{z} = 0$$

and the only coordinate to determine is $\overline{x}$. This will be done most conveniently by dividing the given volume into thin slabs parallel to the yz plane. In the particular case of a body of revolution, these slabs are circular; their volume dV is given in Fig. 5.23. Substituting for $\overline{x}_{el}$ and dV into the equation

$$\overline{x}V = \int \overline{x}_{el}\,dV \qquad (5.23)$$

and expressing the radius r of the slab in terms of x, we may determine $\overline{x}$ by a single integration.

$$\overline{x}_{el} = x, \ \overline{y}_{el} = y, \ \overline{z}_{el} = \frac{z}{2}$$

$$dV = z\,dx\,dy$$

Fig. 5.22 Determination of the centroid of a volume by double integration.

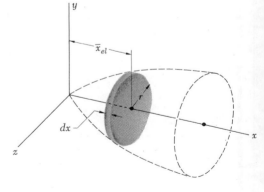

$$\overline{x}_{el} = x$$

$$dV = \pi r^2\,dx$$

Fig. 5.23 Determination of the centroid of a body of revolution.

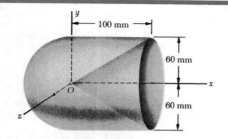

Determine the center of gravity of the homogeneous body of revolution shown.

Solution. Because of symmetry, the center of gravity lies on the x axis. The body is seen to consist of a hemisphere, plus a cylinder, minus a cone, as shown. The volume and the abscissa of the centroid of each of these components are obtained from Fig. 5.21 and entered in the table below. The total volume of the body and the first moment of its volume with respect to the yz plane are then determined.

Component	Volume, mm³		$\bar{x}$, mm	$\bar{x}V$, mm⁴
Hemisphere	$\dfrac{1}{2}\dfrac{4\pi}{3}(60)^3$	$=\quad 0.452 \times 10^6$	-22.5	-10.17×10^6
Cylinder	$\pi(60)^2(100)$	$=\quad 1.131 \times 10^6$	$+50$	$+56.55 \times 10^6$
Cone	$-\dfrac{\pi}{3}(60)^2(100)$	$= -0.377 \times 10^6$	$+75$	-28.28×10^6
	$\Sigma V =$	1.206×10^6	$\cdots$	$\Sigma \bar{x}V = +18.10 \times 10^6$

Thus,

$$\bar{X}\Sigma V = \Sigma \bar{x}V: \qquad \bar{X}(1.206 \times 10^6 \text{ mm}^3) = 18.10 \times 10^6 \text{ mm}^4$$

$$\bar{X} = 15 \text{ mm} \quad \blacktriangleleft$$

Locate the center of gravity of the steel machine element shown. Both holes are of 25-mm diameter.

Solution. The machine element is seen to consist of a rectangular parallelepiped (I) plus a quarter cylinder (II) minus two 25-mm-diameter cylinder (III and IV). The volume and the coordinates of the centroid of each component are determined and entered in the table below. Using the data accumulated in the table, we then determine the total volume and the moments of the volume about each of the coordinate planes.

	V, mm^3	$\bar{x}$, mm	$\bar{y}$, mm	$\bar{z}$, mm	$\bar{x}V$, mm^4	$\bar{y}V$, mm^4	$\bar{z}V$, mm^4
I	$(112)(50)(12) = 67\ 200$	6	-25	56	403 200	$-1\ 680\ 000$	3 763 200
II	$\frac{1}{4}\pi(50)^2(12) = 23\ 562$	33.22	-21.22	6	782 730	$-499\ 990$	141 370
III	$-\pi(12.5)^2(12) = -5\ 890$	6	-25	37	$-35\ 340$	147 250	$-217\ 930$
IV	$-\pi(12.5)^2(12) = -5\ 890$	6	-25	87	$-35\ 340$	147 250	$-512\ 430$
	$\Sigma V = 78\ 982$				$\Sigma\bar{x}V = 1\ 115\ 250$	$\Sigma\bar{y}V = -1\ 885\ 490$	$\Sigma\bar{z}V = 3\ 174\ 210$

Thus,

$$\bar{X}\Sigma V = \Sigma\bar{x}V: \quad \bar{X}(78\ 982\ \text{mm}^3) = 1\ 115\ 250\ \text{mm}^4 \qquad \bar{X} = 14.12\ \text{mm} \blacktriangleleft$$
$$\bar{Y}\Sigma V = \Sigma\bar{y}V: \quad \bar{Y}(78\ 982\ \text{mm}^3) = -1\ 885\ 490\ \text{mm}^4 \qquad \bar{Y} = -23.9\ \text{mm} \blacktriangleleft$$
$$\bar{Z}\Sigma V = \Sigma\bar{z}V: \quad \bar{Z}(78\ 982\ \text{mm}^3) = 3\ 174\ 210\ \text{mm}^4 \qquad \bar{Z} = 40.2\ \text{mm} \blacktriangleleft$$

SAMPLE PROBLEM 5.13

Determine the location of the centroid of the half right circular cone shown.

Solution. Since the xy plane is a plane of symmetry, the centroid lies in this plane and $\bar{z} = 0$. A slab of thickness dx is chosen as a differential element. The volume of this element is

$$dV = \tfrac{1}{2}\pi r^2\, dx$$

The coordinates $\bar{x}_{el}$ and $\bar{y}_{el}$ of the centroid of the element are obtained from Fig. 5.8 (semicircular area).

$$\bar{x}_{el} = x \qquad \bar{y}_{el} = \frac{4r}{3\pi}$$

We observe that r is proportional to x and write

$$\frac{r}{x} = \frac{a}{h} \qquad r = \frac{a}{h}x$$

The volume of the body is

$$V = \int dV = \int_0^h \tfrac{1}{2}\pi r^2\, dx = \int_0^h \tfrac{1}{2}\pi \left(\frac{a}{h}x\right)^2 dx = \frac{\pi a^2 h}{6}$$

The moment of the differential element with respect to the yz plane is $\bar{x}_{el}\, dV$; and the total moment of the body with respect to this plane is

$$\int \bar{x}_{el}\, dV = \int_0^h x(\tfrac{1}{2}\pi r^2)\, dx = \int_0^h x(\tfrac{1}{2}\pi)\left(\frac{a}{h}x\right)^2 dx = \frac{\pi a^2 h^2}{8}$$

Thus,

$$\bar{x} V = \int \bar{x}_{el}\, dV \qquad \bar{x}\frac{\pi a^2 h}{6} = \frac{\pi a^2 h^2}{8} \qquad \bar{x} = \tfrac{3}{4}h \quad \blacktriangleleft$$

Likewise, the moment of the differential element with respect to the zx plane is $\bar{y}_{el}\, dV$; and the total moment is

$$\int \bar{y}_{el}\, dV = \int_0^h \frac{4r}{3\pi}(\tfrac{1}{2}\pi r^2)\, dx = \frac{2}{3}\int_0^h \left(\frac{a}{h}x\right)^3 dx = \frac{a^3 h}{6}$$

Thus,

$$\bar{y} V = \int \bar{y}_{el}\, dV \qquad \bar{y}\frac{\pi a^2 h}{6} = \frac{a^3 h}{6} \qquad \bar{y} = \frac{a}{\pi} \quad \blacktriangleleft$$

Problems

5.101 Determine the location of the centroid of the composite body shown when (*a*) $h = 2b$, (*b*) $h = 2.5b$.

Fig. P5.101

5.102 Determine the *y* coordinate of the centroid of the body shown when (*a*) $b = \frac{1}{3}h$, (*b*) $b = \frac{1}{2}h$.

Fig. P5.102

Fig. P5.103 and P5.104

5.103 Determine the *y* coordinate of the centroid of the body shown.

5.104 Determine the *z* coordinate of the centroid of the body shown. (*Hint.* Use the result of Sample Prob. 5.13.)

5.105 Determine the location of the center of gravity of the parabolic reflector shown, which is formed by machining a rectangular block so that the curved surface is a paraboloid of revolution of base radius *a* and height *h*.

Fig. P5.105

5.106 For the machine element shown, locate the *x* coordinate of the center of gravity.

Dimensions in mm

Fig. P5.106

5.107 and 5.108 For the machine element shown, locate the y coordinate of the center of gravity.

Fig. P5.107 and P5.110

Fig. P5.108 and P5.109

5.109 For the machine element shown, locate the z coordinate of the center of gravity.

5.110 For the machine element shown, locate the x coordinate of the center of gravity.

5.111 For the machine element shown, locate the y coordinate of the center of gravity.

Fig. P5.111

Fig. P5.112

5.112 A wastebasket, designed to fit in the corner of a room, is 400 mm high and has a base in the shape of a quarter circle of radius 250 mm. Locate the center of gravity of the wastebasket, knowing that it is made of sheet metal of uniform thickness.

5.113 and 5.114 Locate the center of gravity of the sheet-metal form shown.

Fig. P5.113

Fig. P5.114

5.115 A corner reflector for tracking by radar has two sides in the shape of a quarter circle of radius 375 mm and one side in the shape of a triangle. Locate the center of gravity of the reflector, knowing that it is made of sheet metal of uniform thickness.

Fig. P5.115

Fig. P5.116

Fig. P5.117

5.116 and 5.117 Locate the center of gravity of the figure shown, knowing that it is made of thin brass rods of uniform diameter.

5.118 Three brass plates are brazed to a steel pipe to form the flagpole base shown. Knowing that the pipe has a wall thickness of 6 mm and that each plate is 5 mm thick, determine the location of the center of gravity of the base (Density: brass = 8470 kg/m³; steel = 7850 kg/m³.)

Fig. P5.118

5.119 A brass collar, of length 50 mm, is mounted on an aluminum rod of length 80 mm. Locate the center of gravity of the composite body. (Densities: brass = 8470 kg/m³; aluminum = 2800 kg/m³.)

Fig. P5.119

5.120 Solve Prob. 5.119, assuming that the collar is made of aluminum and the rod is made of brass.

5.121 through 5.123 Derive by direct integration the expression given for $\bar{x}$ in Fig. 5.21 for:

    5.121 A hemisphere
    5.122 A semiellipsoid of revolution
    5.123 A paraboloid of revolution

5.124 and 5.125 Locate the centroid of the volume obtained by rotating the shaded area about the x axis.

Fig. P5.124

Fig. P5.125

Fig. P5.126

5.126 Locate the centroid of the volume obtained by rotating the shaded area about the y axis.

*5.127 Locate the centroid of the volume generated by revolving the portion shown of the cosine curve about the x axis.

Fig. P5.127 and P5.128

*5.128 Locate the centroid of the volume generated by revolving the portion shown of the cosine curve about the y axis. (*Hint.* Use as an element of volume a thin cylindrical shell of radius r and thickness dr.)

5.129 Locate the centroid of the volume of the irregular pyramid shown.

Fig. P5.129

Fig. P5.130

*5.130 A thin spherical cup has a radius R and a uniform thickness t. Show by direct integration that the center of gravity of the cup is located at a distance $\frac{1}{2}h$ above the base of the cup.

5.131 Determine by direct integration the z coordinate of the centroid of the volume shown, which was cut from a rectangular prism by an oblique plane.

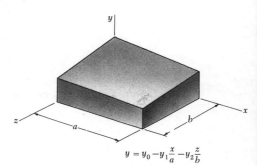

$$y = y_0 - y_1\frac{x}{a} - y_2\frac{z}{b}$$

Fig. P5.131

5.132 Solve Prob. 5.131, when $a = 250$ mm, $b = 200$ mm, $y_0 = 180$ mm, $y_1 = 80$ mm, and $y_2 = 40$ mm.

5.133 Locate the centroid of the section shown, which was cut from a thin circular pipe by an oblique plane.

Fig. P5.133

Fig. P5.134

5.134 Locate the centroid of the section shown, which was cut from a circular cylinder by an oblique plane.

Review and Summary

This chapter was devoted chiefly to the determination of the *center of gravity* of a rigid body, i.e., to the determination of the point G where a single force $\mathbf{W}$, called the *weight* of the body, may be applied to represent the effect of the earth's attraction on the body.

Center of gravity
of a two-dimensional body

In the first part of the chapter, we considered *two-dimensional bodies*, such as flat plates and wires contained in the xy plane. By adding components in the vertical z direction and moments about the horizontal y and x axes [Sec. 5.2], we derived the relations

$$W = \int dW \qquad \bar{x}W = \int x \, dW \qquad \bar{y}W = \int y \, dW \qquad (5.2)$$

which define the weight of the body and the coordinates $\bar{x}$ and $\bar{y}$ of its center of gravity.

Centroid of an area or line

In the case of a *homogeneous flat plate of uniform thickness* [Sec. 5.3], the center of gravity G of the plate coincides with the *centroid C of the area A* of the plate, the coordinates of which are defined by the relations

$$\bar{x}A = \int x \, dA \qquad \bar{y}A = \int y \, dA \qquad (5.3)$$

Similarly, the determination of the center of gravity of a *homogeneous flat wire of uniform cross section* reduces to that of the *centroid C of the line L* representing the wire; we have

$$\bar{x}L = \int x \, dL \qquad \bar{y}L = \int y \, dL \qquad (5.4)$$

First moments

The integrals in Eqs. (5.3) are referred to as the *first moments* of the area A with respect to the y and x axes and denoted by Q_y and Q_x, respectively [Sec. 5.4]. We have

$$Q_y = \bar{x}A \qquad Q_x = \bar{y}A \qquad (5.6)$$

The first moments of a line may be defined in a similar way.

Properties of symmetry

The determination of the centroid C of an area or line is simplified when the area or line possesses certain *properties of symmetry*. If the area or line is symmetric with respect to an axis, its centroid C will lie on that axis; if it is symmetric with respect to two axes, C will be located at the intersection of the two axes; if it is symmetric with respect to a center O, C will coincide with O.

Center of gravity
of a composite body

The *areas and centroids of various common shapes* have been tabulated in Fig. 5.8. When a flat plate may be divided into several of these shapes, the coordinates $\bar{X}$ and $\bar{Y}$ of its center of gravity G may be determined from the coordinates $\bar{x}_1, \bar{x}_2, \ldots$ and $\bar{y}_1, \bar{y}_2, \ldots$ of the centers of

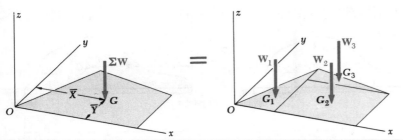

Fig. 5.24

gravity G_1, G_2, . . . of the various parts [Sec. 5.5]. Equating moments about the y and x axes, respectively (Fig. 5.24), we have

$$\overline{X}\Sigma W = \Sigma \overline{x}W \qquad \overline{Y}\Sigma W = \Sigma \overline{y}W \qquad (5.7)$$

If the plate is homogeneous and of uniform thickness, the center of gravity coincides with the centroid C of the area of the plate and Eqs. (5.7) reduce to

$$Q_y = \overline{X}\Sigma A = \Sigma \overline{x}A \qquad Q_x = \overline{Y}\Sigma A = \Sigma \overline{y}A \qquad (5.8)$$

These equations yield the first moments of the composite area, or they may be solved for the coordinates $\overline{X}$ and $\overline{Y}$ of its centroid [Sample Prob. 5.1]. The determination of the center of gravity of a composite wire is carried out in a similar fashion [Sample Prob. 5.2].

When an area is bounded by analytical curves, the coordinates of its centroid may be determined *by integration* [Sec. 5.6]. This may be done by computing the double integrals in Eqs. (5.3), or through a *single integration,* using one of the thin rectangular or pie-shaped elements of area shown in Fig. 5.12. Denoting by $\overline{x}_{el}$ and $\overline{y}_{el}$ the coordinates of the centroid of the element dA, we have

Determination of centroid by integration

$$Q_y = \overline{x}A = \int \overline{x}_{el} \, dA \qquad Q_x = \overline{y}A = \int \overline{y}_{el} \, dA \qquad (5.9)$$

It is advantageous to use the same element of area to compute both of the first moments Q_y and Q_x; the same element may also be used to determine the area A [Sample Prob. 5.4].

The *theorems of Pappus-Guldinus* relate the determination of the area of a surface of revolution or the volume of a body of revolution to the determination of the centroid of the generating curve or area [Sec. 5.7]. The area A of the surface generated by rotating a curve of length L about a fixed axis (Fig. 5.25a) is

Theorems of Pappus-Guldinus

$$A = 2\pi \overline{y}L \qquad (5.10)$$

where $\overline{y}$ represents the distance from the centroid C of the curve to the fixed axis. Similarly, the volume V of the body generated by rotating an area A about a fixed axis (Fig. 5.25b) is

$$V = 2\pi \overline{y}A \qquad (5.11)$$

where $\overline{y}$ represents the distance from the centroid C of the area to the fixed axis.

Fig. 5.25

Fig. 5.26

The concept of centroid of an area may be used to solve problems
other than those dealing with the weight of flat plates. For example, to
determine the reactions at the supports of a beam [Sec. 5.8], we may
replace a *distributed load w* by a concentrated load W equal in magnitude
to the area A under the load curve and passing through the centroid C of
that area (Fig. 5.26). The same approach may be used to determine the
resultant of the hydrostatic forces exerted on a *rectangular plate submerged in a liquid* [Sec. 5.9].

The last part of the chapter was devoted to the determination of the
center of gravity G of a three-dimensional body. The coordinates $\bar{x}$, $\bar{y}$, $\bar{z}$
of G were defined by the relations

$$\bar{x}W = \int x \, dW \qquad \bar{y}W = \int y \, dW \qquad \bar{z}W = \int z \, dW \quad (5.16)$$

In the case of a *homogeneous body*, the center of gravity G coincides with

the *centroid C of the volume V* of the body, the coordinates of which are
defined by the relations

$$\bar{x}V = \int x \, dV \qquad \bar{y}V = \int y \, dV \qquad \bar{z}V = \int z \, dV \quad (5.18)$$

If the volume possesses a *plane of symmetry*, its centroid C will lie in that
plane; if it possesses two planes of symmetry, C will be located on the line
of intersection of the two planes; if it possesses three planes of symmetry
intersecting at one point only, C will coincide with that point [Sec. 5.10].

The *volumes and centroids of various common three-dimensional
shapes* have been tabulated in Fig. 5.21. When a body may be divided
into several of these shapes, the coordinates $\overline{X}$, $\overline{Y}$, $\overline{Z}$ of its center of gravity
G may be determined from the corresponding coordinates of the centers
of gravity of its various parts [Sec. 5.11]. We have

$$\overline{X}\Sigma W = \Sigma \bar{x}W \qquad \overline{Y}\Sigma W = \Sigma \bar{y}W \qquad \overline{Z}\Sigma W = \Sigma \bar{z}W \quad (5.19)$$

If the body is made of a homogeneous material, its center of gravity coincides with the centroid C of its volume and we write [Sample Probs. 5.11
and 5.12]

$$\overline{X}\Sigma V = \Sigma \bar{x}V \qquad \overline{Y}\Sigma V = \Sigma \bar{y}V \qquad \overline{Z}\Sigma V = \Sigma \bar{z}V \quad (5.20)$$

When a volume is bounded by analytical surfaces, the coordinates of its centroid may be determined by *integration* [Sec. 5.12]. To avoid the computation of the triple integrals in Eqs. (5.18), we may use elements of volume in the shape of thin filaments, as shown in Fig. 5.22. Denoting by $\bar{x}_{el}$, $\bar{y}_{el}$, and $\bar{z}_{el}$ the coordinates of the centroid of the element dV, we write the relations

$$\bar{x}V = \int \bar{x}_{el} \, dV \qquad \bar{y}V = \int \bar{y}_{el} \, dV \qquad \bar{z}V = \int \bar{z}_{el} \, dV \quad (5.22)$$

which involve only double integrals. If the volume possesses *two planes of symmetry*, its centroid C is located on their line of intersection. Choosing the x axis along that line and dividing the volume into thin slabs parallel to the yz plane, we determine C from the relation

$$\bar{x}V = \int \bar{x}_{el} \, dV \qquad (5.23)$$

through a *single integration* [Sample Prob. 5.13].

Determination of centroid by integration

Review Problems

5.135 Determine by approximate means the x and y coordinates of the centroid of the area shown.

Fig. P5.135

5.136 Determine the center of gravity of the machine element shown.

Fig. P5.136

Fig. P5.137 and P5.138

5.137 Determine the volume of the body shown.

5.138 Determine the total surface area of the body shown.

5.139 A curved slot is cut in a uniform disk of radius r. The disk is mounted on a frictionless shaft at O and is in equilibrium in the position shown. After a weight W_1 has been attached to the rim of the disk at A, the disk takes a new position of equilibrium in which line BOC is vertical. At what point on the rim should a second weight W_2 be attached, and how large should W_2 be, if the center of gravity of the disk and the two weights is to be located at O?

Fig. 5.139

Fig. P5.140

Fig. P5.141

5.140 Locate the centroid of the irregular pyramid shown. (*Hint.* See Fig. 5.21.)

5.141 Locate the center of gravity of the sheet-metal form shown.

Fig. P5.142

5.142 Locate the center of gravity of a thin hemispherical shell of radius r and thickness t. (*Hint.* Consider the shell as formed by removing a hemisphere of radius r from a hemisphere of radius $r + t$; then neglect the terms containing t^2 and t^3, and keep those terms containing t.)

5.143 The bin shown is made of sheet metal of uniform thickness. Determine (*a*) the center of gravity of the bin when $a = 125$ mm and $b = 375$ mm, (*b*) the ratio a/b for which the y coordinate of the center of gravity is $\bar{y} = -\frac{1}{2}a$.

Fig. P5.143

Fig. P5.144

5.144 Locate the centroid of the plane area shown.

5.145 A 1.5 × 1.5 m gate is located in a wall below water level. (*a*) Determine the magnitude and location of the resultant of the forces exerted by the water on the gate. (*b*) If the gate is hinged along its top edge A, determine the force exerted on the gate by the brace BC.

Fig. P5.145

Fig. P5.146 |←——— 3 m ———→|←— 1 m —→|

5.146 Determine the reactions at the beam supports for the given loading condition.

The following problems are designed to be solved with a computer.

5.C1 Approximate the plane area shown by a series of rectangles of the form $bb'd'd$ and write a computer program which can be used to calculate the coordinates $\overline{X}$ and $\overline{Y}$ of the centroid of the area shown in part a of the figure. Use this program to calculate $\overline{X}$ and $\overline{Y}$ for the areas shown in parts b and c of the figure.

Fig. P5.C1 (a)

(b)

(c)

5.C2 The area of the parabolic reflector of Prob. 5.105 may be obtained by rotating the parabola shown about the y axis. Approximate the parabola by 10 straight-line segments and write a computer program which can be used to calculate the area of the parabolic reflector. Use this program to determine the area of the reflector when (a) $a = 250$ mm, $h = 75$ mm, (b) $a = 300$ mm, $h = 200$ mm, (c) $a = 375$ mm, $h = 450$ mm.

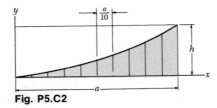

Fig. P5.C2

5.C3 Write a computer program and use it to solve Prob. 5.91 for values of d from 0 to 3 m at 0.3-m intervals.

5.C4 Sheet metal of uniform thickness is used to form the bin shown which has a base in the shape of a quarter circle and three sides. Write a computer program which can be used to calculate the coordinates of the center of gravity of the bin. Use this program to locate the center of gravity for (a) $a = 400$ mm, $b = c = d = 200$ mm, (b) $a = 400$ mm, $b = d = 600$ mm, $c = 300$ mm, (c) $a = 400$ mm, $b = 500$ mm, $c = 200$ mm, $d = 300$ mm.

Fig. P5.C4

Analysis of Structures

6.1. Introduction. The problems considered in the preceding chapters concerned the equilibrium of a single rigid body, and all forces involved were external to the rigid body. We shall now consider problems dealing with the equilibrium of structures made of several connected parts. These problems call for the determination not only of the external forces acting on the structure but also of the forces which hold together the various parts of the structure. From the point of view of the structure as a whole, these forces are *internal forces*.

Consider, for example, the crane shown in Fig. 6.1a, which carries a load W. The crane consists of three beams AD, CF, and BE connected by frictionless pins; it is supported by a pin at A and by a cable DG. The free-body diagram of the crane has been drawn in Fig. 6.1b. The external

Fig. 6.1   (a)   (b)   (c)

forces are shown in the diagram and include the weight $\mathbf{W}$, the two components $\mathbf{A}_x$ and $\mathbf{A}_y$ of the reaction at A, and the force $\mathbf{T}$ exerted by the cable at D. The internal forces holding the various parts of the crane together do not appear in the diagram. If, however, the crane is dismembered and if a free-body diagram is drawn for each of its component parts, the forces holding the three beams together must also be represented, since these forces are external forces from the point of view of each component part (Fig. 6.1c).

It will be noted that the force exerted at B by member BE on member AD has been represented as equal and opposite to the force exerted at the same point by member AD on member BE; similarly, the force exerted at E by BE on CF is shown equal and opposite to the force exerted by CF on BE; and the components of the force exerted at C by CF on AD are shown equal and opposite to the components of the force exerted by AD on CF. This is in conformity with Newton's third law, which states that *the forces of action and reaction between bodies in contact have the same magnitude, same line of action, and opposite sense.* As pointed out in Chap. 1, this law is one of the six fundamental principles of elementary mechanics and is based on experimental evidence. Its application is essential to the solution of problems involving connected bodies.

In this chapter, we shall consider three broad categories of engineering structures:

1. *Trusses,* which are designed to support loads and are usually stationary, fully constrained structures. Trusses consist exclusively of straight members connected at joints located at the ends of each member. Members of a truss, therefore, are *two-force members,* i.e., members acted upon by two equal and opposite forces directed along the member.

2. *Frames,* which are also designed to support loads and are also usually stationary, fully constrained structures. However, like the crane of Fig. 6.1, frames always contain at least one *multiforce member,* i.e., a member acted upon by three or more forces which, in general, are not directed along the member.

3. *Machines,* which are designed to transmit and modify forces and are structures containing moving parts. Machines, like frames, always contain at least one multiforce member.

TRUSSES

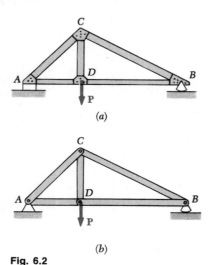

Fig. 6.2

6.2. Definition of a Truss. The truss is one of the major types of engineering structures. It provides both a practical and an economical solution to many engineering situations, especially in the design of bridges and buildings. A truss consists of straight members connected at joints; a typical truss is shown in Fig. 6.2a. Truss members are connected at their extremities only; thus no member is continuous through a joint. In Fig. 6.2a, for example, there is no member *AB*; there are instead two distinct members *AD* and *DB*. Most actual structures are made of several trusses joined together to form a space framework. Each truss is designed to carry those loads which act in its plane and thus may be treated as a two-dimensional structure.

In general, the members of a truss are slender and can support little lateral load; all loads, therefore, must be applied to the various joints, and not to the members themselves. When a concentrated load is to be applied between two joints, or when a distributed load is to be supported by the truss, as in the case of a bridge truss, a floor system must be provided which, through the use of stringers and floor beams, transmits the load to the joints (Fig. 6.3).

Fig. 6.3

The weights of the members of the truss are also assumed to be applied to the joints, half of the weight of each member being applied to each of the two joints the member connects. Although the members are actually joined together by means of riveted or welded connections, it is customary to assume that the members are pinned together; therefore, the forces acting at each end of a member reduce to a single force and no couple. Thus, the only forces assumed to be applied to a truss member are a single force at each end of the member. Each member may then be treated as a two-force member, and the entire truss may be considered as a group of pins and two-force members (Fig. 6.2b). An individual member may be acted upon as shown in either of the two sketches of Fig. 6.4. In the first sketch, the forces tend to pull the member apart, and the member is in tension, while in the second sketch, the forces tend to compress the member, and the member is in compression. Several typical trusses are shown in Fig. 6.5.

(a)   (b)

Fig. 6.4

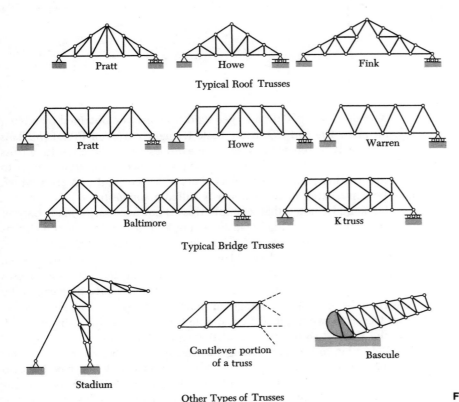

Pratt   Howe   Fink

Typical Roof Trusses

Pratt   Howe   Warren

Baltimore   K truss

Typical Bridge Trusses

Stadium   Cantilever portion of a truss   Bascule

Other Types of Trusses

Fig. 6.5

6.3. Simple Trusses. Consider the truss of Fig. 6.6a, which is made of four members connected by pins at A, B, C, and D. If a load is applied at B, the truss will greatly deform and lose completely its original shape. On the other hand, the truss of Fig. 6.6b, which is made of three members connected by pins at A, B, and C, will deform only slightly under a load applied at B. The only possible deformation for this truss is one involving small changes in the length of its members. The truss of Fig. 6.6b is said to be a *rigid truss*, the term rigid being used here to indicate that the truss *will not collapse*.

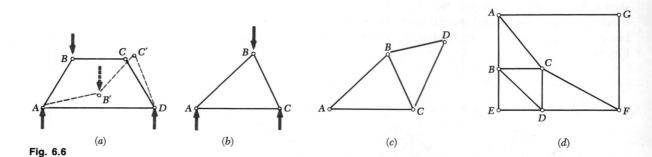

Fig. 6.6

(a) (b) (c) (d)

As shown in Fig. 6.6c, a larger rigid truss may be obtained by adding two members BD and CD to the basic triangular truss of Fig. 6.6b. This procedure may be repeated as many times as desired, and the resulting truss will be rigid if each time we add two new members, we attach them to separate existing joints and connect them at a new joint.† A truss which may be constructed in this manner is called a *simple truss*.

It should be noted that a simple truss is not necessarily made only of triangles. The truss of Fig. 6.6d, for example, is a simple truss which was constructed from triangle ABC by adding successively the joints D, E, F, and G. On the other hand, rigid trusses are not always simple trusses, even when they appear to be made of triangles. The Fink and Baltimore trusses shown in Fig. 6.5, for instance, are not simple trusses, since they cannot be constructed from a single triangle in the manner described above. All the other trusses shown in Fig. 6.5 are simple trusses, as may be easily checked. (For the K truss, start with one of the central triangles.)

Returning to the basic triangular truss of Fig. 6.6b, we note that this truss has three members and three joints. The truss of Fig. 6.6c has two more members and one more joint, i.e., altogether five members and four joints. Observing that every time two new members are added, the number of joints is increased by one, we find that in a simple truss the total number of members is $\underline{m = 2n - 3}$, where n is the total number of joints.

† The three joints must not be in a straight line.

6.4. Analysis of Trusses by the Method of Joints.

We saw in Sec. 6.2 that a truss may be considered as a group of pins and two-force members. The truss of Fig. 6.2, whose free-body diagram is shown in Fig. 6.7a, may thus be dismembered, and a free-body diagram can be drawn for each pin and each member (Fig. 6.7b). Each member is acted upon by two forces, one at each end; these forces have the same magnitude, same line of action, and opposite sense (Sec. 4.6). Besides, Newton's third law indicates that the forces of action and reaction between a member and a pin are equal and opposite. Therefore, the forces exerted by a member on the two pins it connects must be directed along that member and be equal and opposite. The common magnitude of the forces exerted by a member on the two pins it connects is commonly referred to as the *force in the member* considered, even though this quantity is actually a scalar. Since the lines of action of all the internal forces in a truss are known, the analysis of a truss reduces to computing the forces in its various members and to determining whether each of its members is in tension or in compression.

Since the entire truss is in equilibrium, each pin must be in equilibrium. The fact that a pin is in equilibrium may be expressed by drawing its free-body diagram and writing two equilibrium equations (Sec. 2.9). If the truss contains n pins, there will be therefore $2n$ equations available, which may be solved for $2n$ unknowns. In the case of a simple truss, we have $m = 2n - 3$, that is, $2n = m + 3$, and the number of unknowns which may be determined from the free-body diagrams of the pins is thus $m + 3$. This means that the forces in all the members, as well as the two components of the reaction $\mathbf{R}_A$, and the reaction $\mathbf{R}_B$ may be found by considering the free-body diagrams of the pins.

The fact that the entire truss is a rigid body in equilibrium may be used to write three more equations involving the forces shown in the free-body diagram of Fig. 6.7a. Since they do not contain any new information, these equations are not independent from the equations associated with the free-body diagrams of the pins. Nevertheless, they may be used to determine immediately the components of the reactions at the supports. The arrangement of pins and members in a simple truss is such that it will then always be possible to find a joint involving only two unknown forces. These forces may be determined by the methods of Sec. 2.11 and their values transferred to the adjacent joints and treated as known quantities at these joints. This procedure may be repeated until all unknown forces have been determined.

As an example, we shall analyze the truss of Fig. 6.7 by considering successively the equilibrium of each pin, starting with a joint at which only two forces are unknown. In the truss considered, all pins are subjected to at least three unknown forces. Therefore, the reactions at the supports must first be determined by considering the entire truss as a free body and using the equations of equilibrium of a rigid body. We find in this way that $\mathbf{R}_A$ is vertical and determine the magnitudes of $\mathbf{R}_A$ and $\mathbf{R}_B$.

The number of unknown forces at joint A is thus reduced to two, and these forces may be determined by considering the equilibrium of pin A. The reaction $\mathbf{R}_A$ and the forces $\mathbf{F}_{AC}$ and $\mathbf{F}_{AD}$ exerted on pin A by members

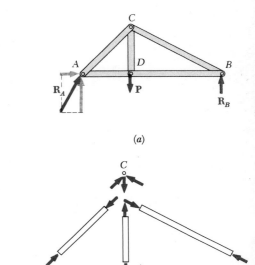

(a)

(b)

Fig. 6.7

AC and AD, respectively, must form a force triangle. First we draw $\mathbf{R}_A$ (Fig. 6.8); noting that $\mathbf{F}_{AC}$ and $\mathbf{F}_{AD}$ are directed along AC and AD, respectively, we complete the triangle and determine the magnitude and sense of $\mathbf{F}_{AC}$ and $\mathbf{F}_{AD}$. The magnitudes F_{AC} and F_{AD} represent the forces in members AC and AD. Since $\mathbf{F}_{AC}$ is directed down and to the left, that is, toward joint A, member AC pushes on pin A and is in compression. On the other hand, since $\mathbf{F}_{AD}$ is directed away from the joint, member AD pulls on pin A and is in tension.

We may now proceed to joint D, where only two forces, $\mathbf{F}_{DC}$ and $\mathbf{F}_{DB}$, are still unknown. The other forces are the load $\mathbf{P}$, which is given, and the force $\mathbf{F}_{DA}$ exerted on the pin by member AD. As indicated above, this force is equal and opposite to the force $\mathbf{F}_{AD}$ exerted by the same member on pin A. We may draw the force polygon corresponding to joint D, as shown in Fig. 6.8, and determine the forces $\mathbf{F}_{DC}$ and $\mathbf{F}_{DB}$ from that polygon. How-

	Free-body diagram	Force polygon
Joint A		
Joint D		
Joint C		
Joint B		

Fig. 6.8

ever, when more than three forces are involved, it is usually more conven- ient to write the equations of equilibrium $\Sigma F_x = 0$, $\Sigma F_y = 0$ and solve these equations for the two unknown forces. Since both of these forces are found to be directed away from joint D, members DC and DB pull on the pin and are in tension.

Next, joint C is considered; its free-body diagram is shown in Fig. 6.8. It is noted that both $\mathbf{F}_{CD}$ and $\mathbf{F}_{CA}$ are known from the analysis of the preced- ing joints and that only $\mathbf{F}_{CB}$ is unknown. Since the equilibrium of each pin provides sufficient information to determine two unknowns, a check of our analysis is obtained at this joint. The force triangle is drawn, and the mag- nitude and sense of $\mathbf{F}_{CB}$ are determined. Since $\mathbf{F}_{CB}$ is directed toward joint C, member CB pushes on pin C and is in compression. The check is ob- tained by verifying that the force $\mathbf{F}_{CB}$ and member CB are parallel.

At joint B, all the forces are known. Since the corresponding pin is in equilibrium, the force triangle must close and an additional check of the analysis is obtained.

It should be noted that the force polygons shown in Fig. 6.8 are not unique. Each of them could be replaced by an alternate configuration. For example, the force triangle corresponding to joint A could be drawn as shown in Fig. 6.9. The triangle actually shown in Fig. 6.8 was obtained by drawing the three forces $\mathbf{R}_A$, $\mathbf{F}_{AC}$, and $\mathbf{F}_{AD}$ in tip-to-tail fashion in the order in which their lines of action are encountered when moving clockwise around joint A. The other force polygons in Fig. 6.8, having been drawn in the same way, can be made to fit into a single diagram, as shown in Fig. 6.10. Such a diagram, known as *Maxwell's diagram*, greatly facilitates the *graphical analysis* of truss problems.

Fig. 6.9

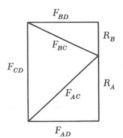

Fig. 6.10

6.5. Joints under Special Loading Conditions. Consider

the joint shown in Fig. 6.11a, which connects four members lying in two intersecting straight lines. The free-body diagram of Fig. 6.11b shows that pin A is subjected to two pairs of directly opposite forces. The correspond- ing force polygon, therefore, must be a parallelogram (Fig. 6.11c), and *the forces in opposite members must be equal.*

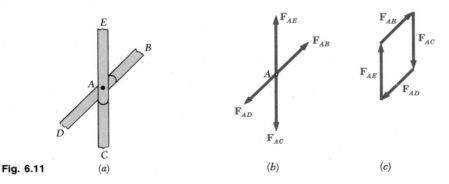

Fig. 6.11 (a) (b) (c)

(a)   **(b)**

Fig. 6.12

(a)   **(b)**

Fig. 6.13

Fig. 6.14

Consider next the joint shown in Fig. 6.12a, which connects three members and supports a load **P**. Two of the members lie in the same line, and the load **P** acts along the third member. The free-body diagram of pin A and the corresponding force polygon will be as shown in Fig. 6.11b and c with $\mathbf{F}_{AE}$ replaced by the load **P**. Thus, *the forces in the two opposite members must be equal, and the force in the other member must equal P.* A particular case of special interest is shown in Fig. 6.12b. Since, in this case, no external load is applied to the joint, we have $P = 0$, and the force in member AC is zero. Member AC is said to be a *zero-force member*.

Consider now a joint connecting two members only. From Sec. 2.9, we know that a particle which is acted upon by two forces will be in equilibrium if the two forces have the same magnitude, same line of action, and opposite sense. In the case of the joint of Fig. 6.13a, which connects two members AB and AD lying in the same line, the equilibrium of pin A requires therefore that *the forces in the two members be equal.* In the case of the joint of Fig. 6.13b, the equilibrium of pin A is impossible unless the forces in both members are zero. Members connected as shown in Fig. 6.13b, therefore, must be *zero-force members*.

Spotting the joints which are under the special loading conditions listed above will expedite the analysis of a truss. Consider, for example, a Howe truss loaded as shown in Fig. 6.14. All the members represented by colored lines will be recognized as zero-force members. Joint C connects three members, two of which lie in the same line, and is not subjected to any external load; member BC is thus a zero-force member. Applying the same reasoning to joint K, we find that member JK is also a zero-force member. But joint J is now in the same situation as joints C and K, and member IJ must be a zero-force member. The examination of joints C, J, and K also shows that the forces in members AC and CE are equal, that the forces in members HJ and JL are equal, and that the forces in members IK and KL are equal. Furthermore, now turning our attention to joint I, where the 20-kN load and member HI are collinear, we note that the force in member HI is 20 kN (tension) and that the forces in members GI and IK are equal. Hence, the forces in members GI, IK, and KL are equal.

Students, however, should be warned against misusing the rules established in this section. For example, it would be wrong to assume that the force in member DE is 25 kN or that the forces in members AB and BD are equal. The conditions discussed above do not apply to joints B and D. The forces in these members and in all remaining members should be found by carrying out the analysis of joints A, B, D, E, F, G, H, and L in the usual manner. Until they have become thoroughly familiar with the conditions of application of the rules established in this section, students would be well advised to draw the free-body diagrams of all pins and to write the corresponding equilibrium equations (or draw the corresponding force polygons), whether or not the joints considered fall into the categories listed above.

A final remark concerning zero-force members: These members are not useless. While they do not carry any load under the particular loading conditions shown, the zero-force members of Fig. 6.14 will probably carry loads if the loading conditions are changed. Besides, even in the case considered, these members are needed to support the weight of the truss and to maintain the truss in the desired shape.

*6.6. Space Trusses. When several straight members are joined together at their extremities to form a three-dimensional configuration, the structure obtained is called a *space truss*.

We recall from Sec. 6.3 that the most elementary two-dimensional rigid truss consisted of three members joined at their extremities to form the sides of a triangle; by adding two members at a time to this basic configuration, and connecting them at a new joint, it was possible to obtain a larger rigid structure which was defined as a simple truss. Similarly, the most elementary rigid space truss consists of six members joined at their extremities to form the edges of a tetrahedron $ABCD$ (Fig. 6.15a). By adding three members at a time to this basic configuration, such as AE, BE, and CE, attaching them at separate existing joints, and connecting them at a new joint, we can obtain a larger rigid structure which is defined as a *simple space truss* (Fig. 6.15b).† Observing that the basic tetrahedron has six members and four joints and that every time three members are added, the number of joints is increased by one, we conclude that in a simple space truss the total number of members is $m = 3n - 6$, where n is the total number of joints.

If a space truss is to be completely constrained and if the reactions at its supports are to be statically determinate, the supports should consist of a combination of balls, rollers, and balls and sockets which provides six unknown reactions (see Sec. 4.8). These unknown reactions may be readily determined by solving the six equations expressing that the three-dimensional truss is in equilibrium.

Although the members of a space truss are actually joined together by means of riveted or welded connections, it is assumed that each joint consists of a ball-and-socket connection. Thus, no couple will be applied to the members of the truss, and each member may be treated as a two-force member. The conditions of equilibrium for each joint will be expressed by the three equations $\Sigma F_x = 0$, $\Sigma F_y = 0$, and $\Sigma F_z = 0$. In the case of a simple space truss containing n joints, writing the conditions of equilibrium for each joint will thus yield $3n$ equations. Since $m = 3n - 6$, these equations suffice to determine all unknown forces (forces in m members and six reactions at the supports). However, to avoid solving many simultaneous equations, care should be taken to select joints in such an order that no selected joint will involve more than three unknown forces.

† The four joints must not lie in a plane.

(a)

(b)

Fig. 6.15

Using the method of joints, determine the force in each member of the truss shown.

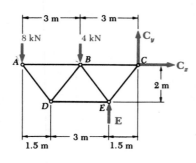

Solution. A free-body diagram of the entire truss is drawn; external forces acting on this free body consist of the applied loads and the reactions at C and E.

Equilibrium of Entire Truss.

$+ \;\text{\small ↻}\;\Sigma M_C = 0$: $(8 \text{ kN})(6 \text{ m}) + (4 \text{ kN})(3 \text{ m}) - E(1.5 \text{ m}) = 0$

$E = +40 \text{ kN}$ **E = 40 kN ↑**

$\xrightarrow{+}\Sigma F_x = 0$:   **$C_x = 0$**

$+\uparrow \Sigma F_y = 0$: $-8 \text{ kN} - 4 \text{ kN} + 40 \text{ kN} + C_y = 0$

$C_y = -28 \text{ kN}$ **$C_y = 28$ kN ↓**

Joint A. This joint is subjected to only two unknown forces, namely, the forces exerted by members AB and AD. A force triangle is used to determine $\mathbf{F}_{AB}$ and $\mathbf{F}_{AD}$. We note that member AB pulls on the joint and thus is in tension and that member AD pushes on the joint and thus is in compression. The magnitudes of the two forces are obtained from the proportion

$$\frac{8 \text{ kN}}{4} = \frac{F_{AB}}{3} = \frac{F_{AD}}{5}$$

$F_{AB} = 6 \text{ kN } T$ ◄
$F_{AD} = 10 \text{ kN } C$ ◄

Joint D. Since the force exerted by member AD has been determined, only two unknown forces are now involved at this joint. Again, a force triangle is used to determine the unknown forces in members DB and DE.

$F_{DB} = F_{DA}$ $F_{DB} = 10 \text{ kN } T$ ◄
$F_{DE} = 2(\tfrac{3}{5})F_{DA}$ $F_{DE} = 12 \text{ kN } C$ ◄

$F_{BA} = 6$ kN

4 kN

F_{BC}

$F_{BD} = 10$ kN F_{BE}

Joint B. Since more than three forces act at this joint, we determine the two unknown forces $\mathbf{F}_{BC}$ and $\mathbf{F}_{BE}$ by solving the equilibrium equations $\Sigma F_x = 0$ and $\Sigma F_y = 0$. We arbitrarily assume that both unknown forces act away from the joint, i.e., that the members are in tension. The positive value obtained for F_{BC} indicates that our assumption was correct; member BC is in tension. The negative value of F_{BE} indicates that our assumption was wrong; member BE is in compression.

$$+\uparrow \Sigma F_y = 0: \quad -4 \text{ kN} - \tfrac{4}{5}(10 \text{ kN}) - \tfrac{4}{5}F_{BE} = 0$$
$$F_{BE} = -15 \text{ kN} \qquad F_{BE} = 15 \text{ kN } C \quad \blacktriangleleft$$

$$\xrightarrow{+}\Sigma F_x = 0: \quad F_{BC} - 6 \text{ kN} - \tfrac{3}{5}(10 \text{ kN}) - \tfrac{3}{5}(15 \text{ kN}) = 0$$
$$F_{BC} = +21 \text{ kN} \qquad F_{BC} = 21 \text{ kN } T \quad \blacktriangleleft$$

$F_{EB} = 15$ kN F_{EC}

$F_{ED} = 12$ kN E

$E = 40$ kN

Joint E. The unknown force $\mathbf{F}_{EC}$ is assumed to act away from the joint. Summing x components, we write

$$\xrightarrow{+}\Sigma F_x = 0: \quad \tfrac{3}{5}F_{EC} + 12 \text{ kN} + \tfrac{3}{5}(15 \text{ kN}) = 0$$
$$F_{EC} = -35 \text{ kN} \qquad F_{EC} = 35 \text{ kN } C \quad \blacktriangleleft$$

Summing y components, we obtain a check of our computations:

$$+\uparrow \Sigma F_y = 40 \text{ kN} - \tfrac{4}{5}(15 \text{ kN}) - \tfrac{4}{5}(35 \text{ kN})$$
$$= 40 \text{ kN} - 12 \text{ kN} - 28 \text{ kN} = 0 \qquad \text{(checks)}$$

$C_y = 28$ kN

$F_{CB} = 21$ kN C $C_x = 0$

$F_{CE} = 35$ kN

Joint C. Using the computed values of $\mathbf{F}_{CB}$ and $\mathbf{F}_{CE}$, we may determine the reactions $\mathbf{C}_x$ and $\mathbf{C}_y$ by considering the equilibrium of this joint. Since these reactions have already been determined from the equilibrium of the entire truss, we will obtain two checks of our computations. We may also merely use the computed values of all forces acting on the joint (forces in members and reactions) and check that the joint is in equilibrium:

$$\xrightarrow{+} \Sigma F_x = -21 \text{ kN} + \tfrac{3}{5}(35 \text{ kN}) = -21 \text{ kN} + 21 \text{ kN} = 0 \qquad \text{(checks)}$$
$$+\uparrow\Sigma F_y = -28 \text{ kN} + \tfrac{4}{5}(35 \text{ kN}) = -28 \text{ kN} + 28 \text{ kN} = 0 \qquad \text{(checks)}$$

234

Problems

6.1 through 6.12 Using the method of joints, determine the force in each member of the truss shown. State whether each member is in tension or compression.

Fig. P6.1

Fig. P6.2

Fig. P6.3

Fig. P6.4

Fig. P6.5

Fig. P6.6

Fig. P6.7

Fig. P6.8

Fig. P6.9

Fig. P6.10

Fig. P6.11

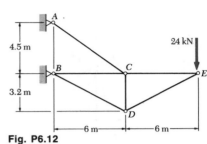

Fig. P6.12

6.13   Solve Prob. 6.10, assuming that the vertical 50-kN load is applied at joint C.

6.14   Determine whether the trusses given in Probs. 6.11, 6.15, 6.16, and 6.17 are simple trusses.

6.15 through 6.17   Determine the zero-force members in the truss shown for the given loading.

Fig. P6.15

Fig. P6.16

Fig. P6.17

*6.18   Six bars, each of length L, are connected to form a regular tetrahedron which rests on a frictionless horizontal surface. Determine the force in each of the six members when a vertical force $\mathbf{P}$ is applied at A.

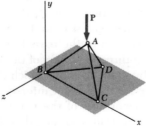

Fig. P6.18

*6.19   Twelve members, each of length L, are connected to form a regular octahedron. Determine the force in each member if two vertical loads are applied as shown.

Fig. P6.19

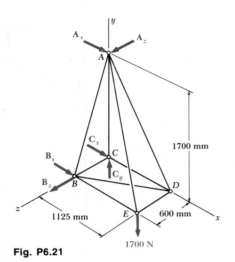

Fig. P6.21

5400 N

Fig. P6.20

*6.20 The three-dimensional truss is supported by the six reactions shown. If a vertical 5400-N load is applied at A, determine (a) the reactions, (b) the force in each member.

*6.21 The three-dimensional truss is supported by the six reactions shown. If a vertical 1700-N load is applied at E, determine (a) the reactions, (b) the force in each member.

6.7. Analysis of Trusses by the Method of Sections.

The method of joints is most effective when the forces in all the members of a truss are to be determined. If, however, the force in only one member or the forces in a very few members are desired, another method, the method of sections, will prove more efficient.

Assume, for example, that we want to determine the force in member BD of the truss shown in Fig. 6.16a. To do this, we must determine the force with which member BD acts on either joint B or joint D. If we were to use the method of joints, we would choose either joint B or joint D as a free body. However, we may also choose as a free body a larger portion of the truss, composed of several joints and members, provided that the desired force is one of the external forces acting on that portion. If, in addition, the portion of the truss is chosen so that there is a total of only three unknown forces acting upon it, the desired force may be obtained by solving the equations of equilibrium for this portion of the truss. In practice, the portion of the truss to be utilized is obtained by *passing a section* through three members of the truss, one of which is the desired member, i.e., by drawing a line which divides the truss into two completely separate parts but does not intersect more than three members. Either of the two portions of the truss obtained after the intersected members have been removed may then be used as a free body.†

---

† In the analysis of certain trusses, sections are passed which intersect more than three members; the forces in one, or possibly two, of the intersected members may be obtained if equilibrium equations can be found, each of which involves only one unknown (see Probs. 6.38 through 6.40).

In Fig. 6.16a, the section nn has been passed through members BD, BE, and CE, and the portion ABC of the truss is chosen as the free body (Fig. 6.16b). The forces acting on the free body are the loads P_1 and P_2 at points A and B and the three unknown forces F_{BD}, F_{BE}, and F_{CE}. Since it is not known whether the members removed were in tension or compression, the three forces have been arbitrarily drawn away from the free body as if the members were in tension.

The fact that the rigid body ABC is in equilibrium can be expressed by writing three equations which may be solved for the three unknown forces. If only the force F_{BD} is desired, we need write only one equation, provided that the equation does not contain the other unknowns. Thus the equation $\Sigma M_E = 0$ yields the value of the magnitude F_{BD} of the force F_{BD}. A positive sign in the answer will indicate that our original assumption regarding the sense of F_{BD} was correct and that member BD is in tension; a negative sign will indicate that our assumption was incorrect and that BD is in compression.

On the other hand, if only the force F_{CE} is desired, an equation which does not involve F_{BD} or F_{BE} should be written; the appropriate equation is $\Sigma M_B = 0$. Again a positive sign for the magnitude F_{CE} of the desired force indicates a correct assumption, hence tension; and a negative sign indicates an incorrect assumption, hence compression.

If only the force F_{BE} is desired, the appropriate equation is $\Sigma F_y = 0$. Whether the member is in tension or compression is again determined from the sign of the answer.

When the force in only one member is determined, no independent check of the computation is available. However, when all the unknown forces acting on the free body are determined, the computations can be checked by writing an additional equation. For instance, if F_{BD}, F_{BE}, and F_{CE} are determined as indicated above, the computation can be checked by verifying that $\Sigma F_x = 0$.

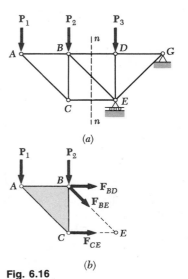

Fig. 6.16

*6.8. Trusses Made of Several Simple Trusses.

Consider two simple trusses ABC and DEF. If they are connected by three bars BD, BE, and CE as shown in Fig. 6.17a, they will form together a rigid truss ABDF. The trusses ABC and DEF can also be combined into a single rigid truss by joining joints B and D into a single joint B and by connecting joints C and E by a bar CE (Fig. 6.17b). The truss thus obtained is known as a Fink truss. It should be noted that the trusses of Fig. 6.17a and b are *not* simple trusses; they cannot be constructed from a triangular truss by adding successive pairs of members as prescribed in Sec. 6.3. They are rigid trusses, however, as we may check by comparing the systems of connections used to hold the simple trusses ABC and DEF together (three bars in Fig. 6.17a, one pin and one bar in Fig. 6.17b) with the systems of supports discussed in Secs. 4.4 and 4.5. Trusses made of several simple trusses rigidly connected are known as *compound trusses*.

It may be checked that in a compound truss the number of members m and the number of joints n are still related by the formula $m = 2n - 3$. If

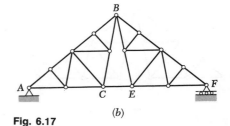

Fig. 6.17

a compound truss is supported by a frictionless pin and a roller (involving three unknown reactions), the total number of unknowns is $m + 3$ and this number is therefore equal to the number $2n$ of equations obtained by expressing that the n pins are in equilibrium. Compound trusses supported by a pin and a roller, or by an equivalent system of supports, are *statically determinate*, *rigid*, and *completely constrained*. This means that all unknown reactions and forces in members can be determined by the methods of statics and that all equilibrium equations being satisfied, the truss will neither collapse nor move. The forces in the members, however, cannot all be determined by the method of joints, except by solving a large number of simultaneous equations. In the case of the compound truss of Fig. 6.17a, for example, it will be found more expeditious to pass a section through members BD, BE, and CE to determine their forces.

Suppose, now, that the simple trusses ABC and DEF are connected by *four* bars BD, BE, CD, and CE (Fig. 6.18). The number of members m is now larger than $2n - 3$; the truss obtained is *overrigid*, and one of the four members BD, BE, CD, or CE is said to be *redundant*. If the truss is supported by a pin at A and a roller at F, the total number of unknowns is $m + 3$. This number is now larger than the number $2n$ of available independent equations; the truss is *statically indeterminate*.

Finally, we shall assume that the two simple trusses ABC and DEF are joined by a pin as shown in Fig. 6.19a. The number of members m is smaller than $2n - 3$. If the truss is supported by a pin at A and a roller at F, the total number of unknowns is $m + 3$. This number is now smaller than the number $2n$ of equilibrium equations which should be satisfied; the truss is *nonrigid* and will collapse under its own weight. However, if two pins are used to support it, the truss becomes *rigid* and will not collapse (Fig. 6.19b). We note that the total number of unknowns is now $m + 4$ and is equal to the number $2n$ of equations. More generally, if the reactions at the supports involve r unknowns, the condition for a compound truss to be statically determinate, rigid, and completely constrained is $m + r = 2n$. While necessary, this condition, however, is not sufficient for the equilibrium of a structure which ceases to be rigid when detached from its supports (see Sec. 6.11).

Fig. 6.18

(a)

Fig. 6.19

(b)

140 kN   140 kN

5 m

B

K 80 kN

├─4 m─┼─4 m─┼─4 m─┼─4 m─┼─4 m─┤

SAMPLE PROBLEM 6.2

Determine the force in members EF and GI of the truss shown.

140 kN   140 kN

K 80 kN

5 m

B_x

B_y

├─4 m─┼─4 m─┼─4 m─┼─4 m─┼─4 m─┤

Solution. A free-body diagram of the entire truss is drawn; external forces acting on this free body consist of the applied loads and the reactions at B and J.

Equilibrium of the Entire Truss.

$+\uparrow\Sigma M_B = 0$:

$$-(140 \text{ kN})(4 \text{ m}) - (140 \text{ kN})(12 \text{ m}) - (80 \text{ kN})(5 \text{ m}) + J(16 \text{ m}) = 0$$

$$J = +165 \text{ kN} \qquad \mathbf{J} = 165 \text{ kN} \uparrow$$

$\xrightarrow{+}\Sigma F_x = 0; \qquad B_x + 80 \text{ kN} = 0$

$$B_x = -80 \text{ kN} \qquad \mathbf{B_x} = 80 \text{ kN} \uparrow$$

$+\uparrow\Sigma M_J = 0$:

$$(140 \text{ kN})(12 \text{ m}) + (140 \text{ kN})(4 \text{ m}) - (80 \text{ kN})(5 \text{ m}) - B_y(16 \text{ m}) = 0$$

$$B_y = +115 \text{ kN} \qquad \mathbf{B_y} = 115 \text{ kN} \uparrow$$

140 kN   140 kN

n   m

K 80 kN

80 kN

115 kN   n   165 kN   m

Force in Member EF. Section nn is passed through the truss so that it intersects member EF and only two additional members. After the intersected members have been removed, the left-hand portion of the truss is chosen as a free body. Three unknowns are involved; to eliminate the two horizontal forces, we write

$$+\uparrow\Sigma F_y = 0: \qquad +115 \text{ kN} - 140 \text{ kN} - F_{EF} = 0$$

$$F_{EF} = -25 \text{ kN}$$

The sense of $\mathbf{F}_{EF}$ was chosen assuming member EF to be in tension; the negative sign obtained indicates that the member is in compression.

$$F_{EF} = 25 \text{ kN } C \qquad \blacktriangleleft$$

140 kN

A   C   E

$\mathbf{F}_{EG}$

$\mathbf{F}_{EF}$

80 kN B   D $\mathbf{F}_{DF}$

115 kN

$\mathbf{F}_{GI}$ I   K

$\mathbf{F}_{HI}$ 80 kN

5 m

H $\mathbf{F}_{HJ}$ J

165 kN

├─4 m─┤

Force in Member GI. Section mm is passed through the truss so that it intersects member GI and only two additional members. After the intersected members have been removed, we choose the right-hand portion of the truss as a free body. Three unknown forces are again involved; to eliminate the two forces passing through point H, we write

$$+\uparrow\Sigma M_H = 0: \qquad (165 \text{ kN})(4 \text{ m}) - (80 \text{ kN})(5 \text{ m}) + F_{GI}(5 \text{ m}) = 0$$

$$F_{GI} = -52 \text{ kN} \qquad F_{GI} = 52 \text{ kN } C \qquad \blacktriangleleft$$

1 kN
1 kN
1 kN

Determine the force in members *FH*, *GH*, and *GI* of the roof truss shown.

5 kN 5 kN 5 kN

6 panels @ 5 m = 30 m

$\alpha = 28.07°$

12.50 kN   7.50 kN

Solution. Section *nn* is passed through the truss as shown. The right-hand portion of the truss will be taken as a free body. Since the reaction at *L* acts on this free body, the value of **L** must be calculated separately, using the entire truss as a free body; the equation $\Sigma M_A = 0$ yields **L** = 7.50 kN↑.

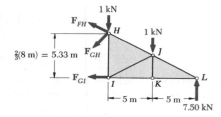

$\frac{2}{3}(8\ m) = 5.33\ m$

7.50 kN

Force in Member GI. Using the portion *HLI* of the truss as a free body, the value of F_{GI} is obtained by writing

$+\uparrow \Sigma M_H = 0$: $(7.50\ \text{kN})(10\ \text{m}) - (1\ \text{kN})(5\ \text{m}) - F_{GI}(5.33\ \text{m}) = 0$
$$F_{GI} = +13.13\ \text{kN} \qquad F_{GI} = 13.13\ \text{kN}\ T \blacktriangleleft$$

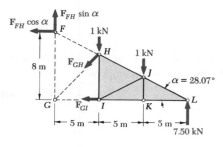

8 m

$\alpha = 28.07°$

7.50 kN

Force in Member FH. The value of F_{FH} is obtained from the equation $\Sigma M_G = 0$. We move $\mathbf{F}_{FH}$ along its line of action until it acts at point *F*, where it is resolved into its *x* and *y* components. The moment of $\mathbf{F}_{FH}$ with respect to point *G* is now equal to $(F_{FH} \cos \alpha)(8\ \text{m})$.

$+\uparrow \Sigma M_G = 0$:
$$(7.50\ \text{kN})(15\ \text{m}) - (1\ \text{kN})(10\ \text{m}) - (1\ \text{kN})(5\ \text{m}) + (F_{FH} \cos \alpha)(8\ \text{m}) = 0$$
$$F_{FH} = -13.81\ \text{kN} \qquad F_{FH} = 13.81\ \text{kN}\ C \blacktriangleleft$$

$\beta = 43.15°$

7.50 kN

Force in Member GH. The value of F_{GH} is determined by first resolving the force $\mathbf{F}_{GH}$ into *x* and *y* components at point *G* and then solving the equation $\Sigma M_L = 0$.

$+\uparrow \Sigma M_L = 0$: $(1\ \text{kN})(10\ \text{m}) + (1\ \text{kN})(5\ \text{m}) + (F_{GH} \cos \beta)(15\ \text{m}) = 0$
$$F_{GH} = -1.371\ \text{kN} \qquad F_{GH} = 1.371\ \text{kN}\ C \blacktriangleleft$$

Problems

6.22 Determine the force in members *CD* and *DF* of the truss shown.

6.23 Determine the force in members *FG* and *FH* of the truss shown.

6.24 Determine the force in members *FG* and *FH* of the truss shown when $P = 35$ kN.

Fig. P6.22 and P6.23

Fig. P6.24 and P6.25

6.25 Determine the force in members *EF* and *EG* of the truss shown when $P = 35$ kN.

6.26 Determine the force in members *DE* and *DF* of the truss shown when $P = 100$ kN.

6.27 Determine the force in members *EG* and *EF* of the truss shown when $P = 100$ kN.

6.28 Determine the force in members *DF* and *DE* of the truss shown.

Fig. P6.26 and P6.27

Fig. P6.28 and P6.29

6.29 Determine the force in members *CD* and *CE* of the truss shown.

6.30 Determine the force in members *BD* and *DE* of the truss shown.

6.31 Determine the force in members *DG* and *EG* of the truss shown.

Fig. P6.30 and P6.31

6.32 Determine the force in member *CD* of the Fink roof truss shown when *P* = 25 kN.

Fig. P6.32

6.33 Determine the force in members *CE*, *DE*, and *DF* of the truss shown.

6.34 Determine the force in members *DF*, *EF*, and *EG* of the truss shown.

6.35 Determine the force in members *GI*, *GJ*, and *HI* of the truss shown.

6.36 Determine the force in members *AD*, *CD*, and *CE* of the truss shown.

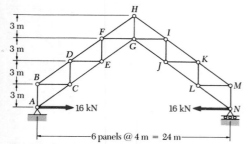

Fig. P6.33, P6.34, and P6.35

Fig. P6.36 and P6.37

6.37 Determine the force in members *DG*, *FG*, and *FH* of the truss shown.

6.38 Determine the force in members *FK* and *JO* of the truss shown. (*Hint.* Use section *a-a*.)

6.39 Determine the force in members *DG* and *FH* of the truss shown. (*Hint.* Use section *a-a*.)

Fig. P6.38

Fig. P6.39

Fig. P6.40

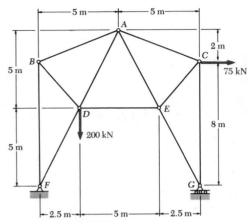

Fig. P6.41 and P6.42

6.40 Determine the force in member *IK* of the truss shown. (*Hint.* Use section *a-a*.)

6.41 Determine the force in members *DE* and *AE* of the truss shown.

6.42 Determine the force in members *AB* and *AD* of the truss shown.

6.43 The diagonal members in the center panel of the truss shown are very slender and can act only in tension; such members are known as *counters*. Determine the force in member *DE* and in the counters which are acting under the given loading.

6.44 Solve the Prob. 6.43, assuming that the 30-kN load has been removed.

6.45 Solve Prob. 6.43 assuming that the 45-kN load has been removed.

Fig. P6.43

6.46 and 6.47 Classify each of the given structures as completely, partially, or improperly constrained; if completely constrained, further classify as determinate or indeterminate. (All members can act both in tension and in compression.)

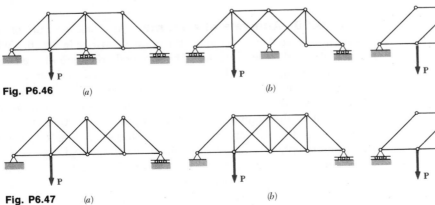

Fig. P6.46   (a)   (b)   (c)

Fig. P6.47   (a)   (b)   (c)

6.48 and 6.49 Classify each of the given structures as completely, partially, or improperly constrained; if completely constrained, further classify as determinate or indeterminate. (All members can act both in tension and in compression.)

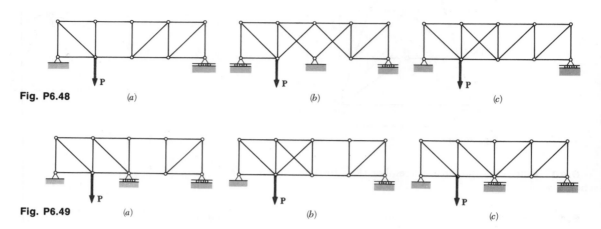

Fig. P6.48   (a)   (b)   (c)

Fig. P6.49   (a)   (b)   (c)

FRAMES AND MACHINES

6.9. Structures Containing Multiforce Members. Under Trusses, we have considered structures consisting entirely of pins and of straight two-force members. The forces acting on the two-force members were known to be directed along the members themselves. We shall now consider structures in which at least one of the members is a *multiforce* member, i.e., a member acted upon by three or more forces. These forces will generally not be directed along the members on which they act; their direction is unknown, and they should be represented therefore by two unknown components.

Frames and machines are structures containing multiforce members. *Frames* are designed to support loads and are usually stationary, fully constrained structures. *Machines* are designed to transmit and modify forces; they may or may not be stationary and will always contain moving parts.

6.10. Analysis of a Frame. As a first example of analysis of a frame, we shall consider again the crane described in Sec. 6.1, which carries a given load W (Fig. 6.20a). The free-body diagram of the entire frame is shown in Fig. 6.20b. This diagram may be used to determine the external forces acting on the frame. Summing moments about A, we first determine the force **T** exerted by the cable; summing x and y components, we then determine the components A_x and A_y of the reaction at the pin A.

In order to determine the internal forces holding the various parts of a frame together, we must dismember the frame and draw a free-body diagram for each of its component parts (Fig. 6.20c). First, the two-force members should be considered. In this frame, member BE is the only two-force member. The forces acting at each end of this member must have the same magnitude, same line of action, and opposite sense (Sec. 4.6). They are therefore directed along BE and will be denoted, respectively, by $\mathbf{F}_{BE}$

and $-\mathbf{F}_{BE}$. Their sense will be arbitrarily assumed as shown in Fig. 6.20c, and the correctness of this assumption will be checked later by the sign obtained for the common magnitude F_{BE} of the two forces.

Next, we consider the multiforce members, i.e., the members which are acted upon by three or more forces. According to Newton's third law, the force exerted at B by member BE on member AD must be equal and opposite to the force $\mathbf{F}_{BE}$ exerted by AD on BE. Similarly, the force exerted at E by member BE on member CF must be equal and opposite to the force $-\mathbf{F}_{BE}$ exerted by CF on BE. The forces that the two-force member BE exerts on AD and CF are therefore respectively equal to $-\mathbf{F}_{BE}$ and $\mathbf{F}_{BE}$; they have the same magnitude F_{BE} and opposite sense, and should be directed as shown in Fig. 6.20c.

At C two multiforce members are connected. Since neither the direction nor the magnitude of the forces acting at C is known, these forces will be represented by their x and y components. The components $\mathbf{C}_x$ and $\mathbf{C}_y$ of the force acting on member AD will be arbitrarily directed to the right and upward. Since, according to Newton's third law, the forces exerted by member CF on AD and by member AD on CF are equal and opposite, the components of the force acting on member CF *must* be directed to the left and downward; they will be denoted, respectively, by $-\mathbf{C}_x$ and $-\mathbf{C}_y$. Whether the force $\mathbf{C}_x$ is actually directed to the right and the force $-\mathbf{C}_x$ is actually directed to the left will be determined later from the sign of their common magnitude C_x, a plus sign indicating that the assumption made was correct, and a minus sign that it was wrong. The free-body diagrams of the multiforce members are completed by showing the external forces acting at A, D, and F.†

The internal forces may now be determined by considering the free-body diagram of either of the two multiforce members. Choosing the free-body diagram of CF, for example, we write the equations $\Sigma M_C = 0$, $\Sigma M_E = 0$, and $\Sigma F_x = 0$, which yield the values of the magnitudes F_{BE}, C_y, and C_x, respectively. These values may be checked by verifying that member AD is also in equilibrium.

It should be noted that the free-body diagrams of the pins were not shown in Fig. 6.20c. This was because the pins were assumed to form an integral part of one of the two members they connected. This assumption can always be used to simplify the analysis of frames and machines. When a pin connects three or more members, however, or when a pin connects a support and two or more members, or when a load is applied to a pin, a clear decision must be made in choosing the member to which the pin will be assumed to belong. (If multiforce members are involved, the pin should be attached to one of these members.) The various forces exerted on the pin should then be clearly identified. This is illustrated in Sample Prob. 6.6.

† The use of a minus sign to distinguish the force exerted by one member on another from the equal and opposite force exerted by the second member on the first is not strictly necessary, since the two forces belong to different free-body diagrams and thus cannot easily be confused. In the Sample Problems, we shall represent by the same symbol equal and opposite forces which are applied to different free bodies. It should be noted that, under these conditions, the sign obtained for a given force component will not directly relate the sense of that component to the sense of the corresponding coordinate axis. Rather, a positive sign will indicate that *the sense assumed for that component in the free-body diagram* is correct, and a negative sign that it is wrong.

(a)

(b)

(c)

Fig. 6.20

6.11. Frames Which Cease to Be Rigid When Detached from Their Supports.

The crane analyzed in Sec. 6.10 was so constructed that it could keep the same shape without the help of its supports; it was therefore considered as a rigid body. Many frames, however, will collapse if detached from their supports; such frames cannot be considered as rigid bodies. Consider, for example, the frame shown in Fig. 6.21a, which consists of two members AC and CB carrying loads P and Q at their midpoints; the members are supported by pins at A and B and are connected by a pin at C. If detached from its supports, this frame will not maintain its shape; it should therefore be considered as made of *two distinct rigid parts AC and CB*.

The equations $\Sigma F_x = 0$, $\Sigma F_y = 0$, $\Sigma M = 0$ (about any given point) express the conditions for the *equilibrium of a rigid body* (Chap. 4); we should use them, therefore, in connection with the free-body diagrams of rigid bodies, namely, the free-body diagrams of members AC and CB (Fig. 6.21b). Since these members are multiforce members, and since pins are used at the supports and at the connection, the reactions at A and B and the

(a)

Fig. 6.21

(b) (c)

forces at C will each be represented by two components. In accordance with Newton's third law, the components of the force exerted by CB on AC and the components of the force exerted by AC on CB will be represented by vectors of the same magnitude and opposite sense; thus, if the first pair of components consists of C_x and C_y, the second pair will be represented by $-C_x$ and $-C_y$. We note that four unknown force components act on free body AC, while only three independent equations may be used to express that the body is in equilibrium; similarly, four unknowns, but only three equations, are associated with CB. However, only six different unknowns are involved in the analysis of the two members, and altogether six equations are available to express that the members are in equilibrium. Writing $\Sigma M_A = 0$ for free body AC and $\Sigma M_B = 0$ for CB, we obtain two simultaneous equations which may be solved for the common magnitude C_x of the components C_x and $-C_x$, and for the common magnitude C_y of the components C_y and $-C_y$. Writing, then, $\Sigma F_x = 0$ and $\Sigma F_y = 0$ for each of the two free bodies, we obtain successively the magnitudes A_x, A_y, B_x, and B_y.

We shall observe now that since the equations of equilibrium $\Sigma F_x = 0$, $\Sigma F_y = 0$, $\Sigma M = 0$ (about any given point) are satisfied by the forces acting on free body AC, and since they are also satisfied by the forces acting on free body CB, they must be satisfied when the forces acting on the two free bodies are considered simultaneously. Since the internal forces at C cancel each other, we find that the equations of equilibrium must be satisfied by the external forces shown on the free-body diagram of the frame ACB itself (Fig. 6.21c), although the frame is not a rigid body. These equations may be used to determine some of the components of the reactions at A and B. We shall note, however, that *the reactions cannot be completely determined from the free-body diagram of the whole frame*. It is thus necessary to dismember the frame and to consider the free-body diagrams of its component parts (Fig. 6.21b), even when we are interested only in finding external reactions. This may be explained by the fact that the equilibrium equations obtained for free body ACB are *necessary conditions* for the equilibrium of a nonrigid structure, *but not sufficient conditions*.

The method of solution outlined in the second paragraph of this section involved simultaneous equations. We shall now discuss a more expeditious method, which utilizes the free body ACB as well as the free bodies AC and CB. Writing $\Sigma M_A = 0$ and $\Sigma M_B = 0$ for free body ACB, we obtain B_y and A_y. Writing $\Sigma M_C = 0$, $\Sigma F_x = 0$, and $\Sigma F_y = 0$ for free body AC, we obtain successively A_x, C_x, and C_y. Finally, writing $\Sigma F_x = 0$ for ACB, we obtain B_x.

We noted above that the analysis of the frame of Fig. 6.21 involves six unknown force components and six independent equilibrium equations (the equilibrium equations for the whole frame were obtained from the original six equations and, therefore, are not independent). Moreover, we checked that all unknowns could be actually determined and that all equations could be satisfied. The frame considered is *statically determinate and rigid*.† In general, to determine whether a structure is statically determinate and rigid, we should draw a free-body diagram for each of its component parts and count the reactions and internal forces involved. We should also determine the number of independent equilibrium equations (excluding equations expressing the equilibrium of the whole structure or of groups of component parts already analyzed). If there are more unknowns than equations, the structure is *statically indeterminate*. If there are fewer unknowns than equations, the structure is *nonrigid*. If there are as many unknowns as equations, *and if all unknowns may be determined and all equations satisfied* under general loading conditions, the structure is *statically determinate and rigid;* if, however, due to an *improper arrangement* of members and supports, all unknowns cannot be determined and all equations cannot be satisfied, the structure is *statically indeterminate and nonrigid*.

† The word "rigid" is used here to indicate that the frame will maintain its shape as long as it remains attached to its supports.

SAMPLE PROBLEM 6.4

In the frame shown, members ACE and BCD are connected by a pin at C and by the link DE. For the loading shown, determine the force in link DE and the components of the force exerted at C on member BCD.

Entire Frame. Since the external reactions involve only three unknowns, we compute the reactions by considering the free-body diagram of the entire frame.

$$+\uparrow\Sigma F_y = 0: \quad A_y - 480\text{ N} = 0 \quad\quad A_y = +480\text{ N} \quad\quad \mathbf{A}_y = 480\text{ N}\uparrow$$

$$+\uparrow\Sigma M_A = 0: \quad -(480\text{ N})(100\text{ mm}) + B(160\text{ mm}) = 0$$
$$B = +300\text{ N} \quad\quad \mathbf{B} = 300\text{ N}\rightarrow$$

$$\xrightarrow{+}\Sigma F_x = 0: \quad B + A_x = 0$$
$$300\text{ N} + A_x = 0 \quad\quad A_x = -300\text{ N} \quad\quad \mathbf{A}_x = 300\text{ N}\leftarrow$$

Members. We now dismember the frame. Since only two members are connected at C, the components of the unknown forces acting on ACE and BCD are, respectively, equal and opposite and are assumed directed as shown. We assume that link DE is in tension and exerts at D and E equal and opposite forces directed as shown.

Member BCD. Using the free body BCD, we write

$$+\curvearrowleft\Sigma M_C = 0: \quad (F_{DE}\sin\alpha)(250\text{ mm}) + (300\text{ N})(60\text{ mm}) + (480\text{ N})(100\text{ mm}) = 0$$
$$F_{DE} = -561\text{ N} \quad\quad\quad F_{DE} = 561\text{ N } C \quad\blacktriangleleft$$

$$\xrightarrow{+}\Sigma F_x = 0: \quad C_x - F_{DE}\cos\alpha + 300\text{ N} = 0$$
$$C_x - (-561\text{ N})\cos 28.07° + 300\text{ N} = 0 \quad C_x = -795\text{ N}$$

$$+\uparrow\Sigma F_y = 0: \quad C_y - F_{DE}\sin\alpha - 480\text{ N} = 0$$
$$C_y - (-561\text{ N})\sin 28.07° - 480\text{ N} = 0 \quad C_y = +216\text{ N}$$

From the signs obtained for C_x and C_y we conclude that the force components $\mathbf{C}_x$ and $\mathbf{C}_y$ exerted on member BCD are directed respectively to the left and up. We have

$$\mathbf{C}_x = 795\text{ N}\leftarrow, \ \mathbf{C}_y = 216\text{ N}\uparrow \ \blacktriangleleft$$

Member ACE (Check). The computations are checked by considering the free body ACE. For example,

$$+\uparrow\Sigma M_A = (F_{DE}\cos\alpha)(300\text{ mm}) + (F_{DE}\sin\alpha)(100\text{ mm}) - C_x(220\text{ mm})$$
$$= (-561\cos\alpha)(300) + (-561\sin\alpha)(100) - (-795)(220) = 0$$

Determine the components of the forces acting on each member of the frame shown.

Entire Frame. Since the external reactions involve only three unknowns, we compute the reactions by considering the free-body diagram of the entire frame.

$$+\uparrow \Sigma M_E = 0: \qquad -(2400 \text{ N})(3.6 \text{ m}) + F(4.8 \text{ m}) = 0$$
$$F = +1800 \text{ N} \qquad\qquad \mathbf{F = 1800 \text{ N} \uparrow} \blacktriangleleft$$
$$+\uparrow \Sigma F_y = 0: \qquad -2400 \text{ N} + 1800 \text{ N} + E_y = 0$$
$$E_y = +600 \text{ N} \qquad\qquad \mathbf{E_y = 600 \text{ N} \uparrow} \blacktriangleleft$$

$$\overset{+}{\rightarrow} \Sigma F_x = 0: \qquad\qquad\qquad\qquad\qquad\qquad \mathbf{E_x = 0} \blacktriangleleft$$

The frame is now dismembered; since only two members are connected at each joint, equal and opposite components are shown on each member at each joint.

Member BCD

$$+\uparrow \Sigma M_B = 0: \quad -(2400 \text{ N})(3.6 \text{ m}) + C_y(2.4 \text{ m}) = 0 \quad C_y = +3600 \text{ N} \blacktriangleleft$$
$$+\uparrow \Sigma M_C = 0: \quad -(2400 \text{ N})(1.2 \text{ m}) + B_y(2.4 \text{ m}) = 0 \quad B_y = +1200 \text{ N} \blacktriangleleft$$
$$\overset{+}{\rightarrow} \Sigma F_x = 0: \qquad -B_x + C_x = 0$$

We note that neither B_x nor C_x can be obtained by considering only member *BCD*. The positive values obtained for B_y and C_y indicate that the force components $\mathbf{B}_y$ and $\mathbf{C}_y$ are directed as assumed.

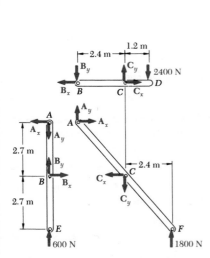

Member ABE

$$+\uparrow \Sigma M_A = 0: \qquad B_x(2.7 \text{ m}) = 0 \qquad\qquad B_x = 0 \blacktriangleleft$$
$$\overset{+}{\rightarrow} \Sigma F_x = 0: \qquad +B_x - A_x = 0 \qquad\qquad A_x = 0 \blacktriangleleft$$
$$+\uparrow \Sigma F_y = 0: \qquad -A_y + B_y + 600 \text{ N} = 0$$
$$-A_y + 1200 \text{ N} + 600 \text{ N} = 0 \qquad A_y = +1800 \text{ N} \blacktriangleleft$$

Member BCD. Returning now to member *BCD*, we write

$$\overset{+}{\rightarrow} \Sigma F_x = 0: \qquad -B_x + C_x = 0 \qquad 0 + C_x = 0 \qquad C_x = 0 \blacktriangleleft$$

Member ACF (Check). All unknown components have now been found; to check the results, we verify that member *ACF* is in equilibrium.

$$+\uparrow \Sigma M_C = (1800 \text{ N})(2.4 \text{ m}) - A_y(2.4 \text{ m}) - A_x(2.7 \text{ m})$$
$$= (1800 \text{ N})(2.4 \text{ m}) - (1800 \text{ N})(2.4 \text{ m}) - 0 = 0 \quad \text{(checks)}$$

300 N

0.5 m
0.5 m
0.5 m
0.5 m

—1.2 m—

A 300 N horizontal force is applied to pin A of the frame shown. Determine the forces acting on the two vertical members of the frame.

Entire Frame. The entire frame is chosen as a free body; although the reactions involve four unknowns, E_y and F_y may be determined by writing

$$+\uparrow\Sigma M_E = 0: \qquad -(300 \text{ N})(2 \text{ m}) + F_y(1.2 \text{ m}) = 0$$
$$F_y = +500 \text{ N} \qquad\qquad F_y = 500 \text{ N}\uparrow \quad \blacktriangleleft$$

$$+\uparrow\Sigma F_y = 0: \qquad E_y + F_y = 0$$
$$E_y = -500 \text{ N} \qquad\qquad E_y = 500 \text{ N}\downarrow \quad \blacktriangleleft$$

The equations of equilibrium of the entire frame are not sufficient to determine E_x and F_x. The equilibrium of the various members must now be considered in order to proceed with the solution. In dismembering the frame we shall assume that pin A is attached to the multiforce member ACE and, thus, that the 300-N force is applied to that member. We also note that AB and CD are two-force members.

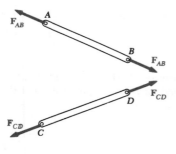

Member ACE

$$+\uparrow\Sigma F_y = 0: \quad -\tfrac{5}{13}F_{AB} + \tfrac{5}{13}F_{CD} - 500 \text{ N} = 0$$

$$+\Sigma M_E = 0: \quad -(300 \text{ N})(2 \text{ m}) - (\tfrac{12}{13}F_{AB})(2 \text{ m}) - (\tfrac{12}{13}F_{CD})(0.5 \text{ m}) = 0$$

Solving these equations simultaneously, we find

$$F_{AB} = -520 \text{ N} \qquad F_{CD} = +780 \text{ N} \qquad \blacktriangleleft$$

The signs obtained indicate that the sense assumed for F_{CD} was correct and the sense for F_{AB} incorrect. Summing now x components:

$$\xrightarrow{+}\Sigma F_x = 0: \quad 300 \text{ N} + \tfrac{12}{13}(-520 \text{ N}) + \tfrac{12}{13}(780 \text{ N}) + E_x = 0$$
$$E_x = -540 \text{ N} \qquad\qquad E_x = 540 \text{ N}\leftarrow \quad \blacktriangleleft$$

Entire Frame. Since E_x has been determined, we may return to the free-body diagram of the entire frame and write

$$\xrightarrow{+}\Sigma F_x = 0: \quad 300 \text{ N} - 540 \text{ N} + F_x = 0$$
$$F_x = +240 \text{ N} \qquad\qquad F_x = 240 \text{ N}\rightarrow \quad \blacktriangleleft$$

Member BDF (Check). We may check our computations by verifying that the equation $\Sigma M_B = 0$ is satisfied by the forces acting on member BDF.

$$+\Sigma M_B = -(\tfrac{12}{13}F_{CD})(0.5 \text{ m}) + (F_x)(1.5 \text{ m})$$
$$= -\tfrac{12}{13}(780 \text{ N})(0.5 \text{ m}) + (240 \text{ N})(1.5 \text{ m})$$
$$= -360 \text{ N·m} + 360 \text{ N·m} = 0 \qquad\qquad \text{(checks)}$$

Problems

6.50 and 6.51 Determine the force in member BD and the components of the reaction at C.

Fig. P6.50   **Fig. P6.51**

6.52 Determine the components of all forces acting on member $ABCD$ of the assembly shown.

6.53 Solve Prob. 6.52, assuming that the 600-N force applied at E is directed vertically downward.

Fig. P6.52

6.54 An aircraft tow bar is positioned by means of a single hydraulic cylinder CD which is connected to two identical arm-and-wheel units DEF. The entire tow bar has a mass of 200 kg and its center of gravity is located at G. For the position shown, determine (a) the force exerted by the cylinder on bracket C, (b) the force exerted on each arm by the pin at E.

Fig. P6.54

6.55 Solve Prob. 6.54, assuming that a 70-kg mechanic is standing on the tow bar at point B.

6.56 Determine the components of all forces acting on member *ABCD* when $\theta = 0$.

6.57 Determine the components of all forces acting on member *ABCD* when $\theta = 90°$.

Fig. P6.56 and P6.57

Fig. P6.58

6.58 The low-bed trailer shown is designed so that the rear end of the bed can be lowered to ground level in order to facilitate the loading of equipment or wrecked vehicles. A 1400-kg vehicle has been hauled to the position shown by a winch; the trailer is then returned to a traveling position where $\alpha = 0$ and both *AB* and *BE* are horizontal. Considering only the weight of the disabled automobile, determine the force which must be exerted by the hydraulic cylinder to maintain a position with $\alpha = 0$.

6.59 For the marine crane shown, which is used in offshore drilling operations, determine (*a*) the force in link *CD*, (*b*) the force in the brace *AC*, (*c*) the force exerted at *A* on the boom *AB*.

Fig. P6.59

6.60 Knowing that $P = 450$ N and $Q = 300$ N, determine the components of all forces acting on member *BCDE* of the assembly shown.

Fig. P6.60 and P6.61

6.61 Knowing that $P = 300$ N and $Q = 450$ N, determine the components of all forces acting on membeer *BCDE* of the assembly shown.

6.62 Determine the components of the reactions at D and E if the frame is loaded by a clockwise couple of magnitude 150 N·m applied (a) at point A, (b) at point B.

Fig. P6.62

6.63 Determine the components of the reactions at A and B, (a) if the 500-N load is applied as shown, (b) if the 500-N load is moved along its line of action and is applied at point F.

6.64 Determine all the forces exerted on member AI if the frame is loaded by a clockwise couple of magnitude 230 N·m applied (a) at point D, (b) at point E.

Fig. P6.63

Fig. P6.64 and P6.65

6.65 Determine all the forces exerted on member AI if the frame is loaded by a 240-N force directed horizontally to the right and applied (a) at point D, (b) at point E.

6.66 The hydraulic cylinder CF, which partially controls the position of rod DE, has been locked in the position shown. Knowing that $\theta = 60°$, determine (a) the force **P** for which the tension in link AB is 410 N, (b) the corresponding force exerted on member BCD at point C.

6.67 The hydraulic cylinder CF, which partially controls the position of rod DE, has been locked in the position shown. Knowing that $P = 400$ N and $\theta = 75°$, determine (a) the force in link AB, (b) the force exerted on member BCD at point C.

Fig. P6.66 and P6.67

125 mm

75 mm

300 mm — 300 mm

240 N

Fig. P6.68

6.68 Knowing that the pulley has a radius of 75 mm, determine the components of the reactions at A and B.

2 m — 2 m

1.5 m

4.8 kN

Fig. P6.69

6.69 Knowing that each pulley has a radius of 250 mm, determine the components of the reactions at D and E.

6.70 A 0.6-m-diameter pipe is supported every 4.8 m by a small frame; a typical frame is shown. Knowing that the combined weight of the pipe and its contents is 4500 N/m and neglecting the effect of friction, determine the components (a) of the reaction at E, (b) of the force exerted at C on member CDE.

6.71 Solve Prob. 6.70, for a frame where h = 1.35 m.

1.8 m

r = 0.3 m

h = 2.25 m

1.35 m

Fig. P6.70

6.72 The cab and motor units of the front-end loader shown are connected by a vertical pin located 1500 mm behind the cab wheels. The distance from C to D is 750 mm. The center of gravity of the 250-kN motor unit is located at G_m, while the centers of gravity of the 90-kN cab and 80-kN load are located, respectively, at G_c and G_l. Knowing that the machine is at rest with its brakes released, determine (a) the reactions at each of the four wheels, (b) the forces exerted on the motor unit at C and D.

875 mm   90 kN

625 mm   250 kN

-2375 mm-

80 kN

G_c

G_m

G_l

C

D

A   B

1500 mm   2125 mm

Fig. P6.72

6.73 Solve Prob. 6.72, assuming that the 80-kN load has been removed.

6.74 A 1000-kg trailer is attached to a 1250-kg automobile by a ball-and-socket trailer hitch at D. Determine (a) the reactions at each of the six wheels when the automobile and trailer are at rest, (b) the additional load on each of the automobile wheels due to the trailer.

Fig. P6.74

6.75 In order to obtain a better weight distribution over the four wheels of the automobile of Prob. 6.74, a compensating hitch of the type shown is used to attach the trailer to the automobile. This hitch consists of two bar springs (only one is shown in the figure) which fit into bearings inside a support rigidly attached to the automobile. The springs are also connected by chains to the trailer frame, and specially designed hooks make it possible to place both chains under tension. (a) Determine the tension T required in each of the two chains if the additional load due to the trailer is to be evenly distributed over the four wheels of the automobile. (b) What are the corresponding reactions at each of the six wheels of the trailer-automobile combination?

Fig. P6.75

6.76 For the frame and loading shown, determine the components of all forces acting on member $GBEH$.

Dimensions in mm

Fig. P6.76

6.77 Solve Prob. 6.76, assuming that the 900-N load is applied at F instead of C.

6.78 and 6.79 For the frame and loading shown, determine the components of all forces acting on member *ABD*.

Dimensions in mm
Fig. P6.78

Fig. P6.79

6.80 Solve Prob. 6.79, assuming that the 1800-N load has been removed.

6.81 Solve Prob. 6.78, assuming that the 4-kN load has been removed.

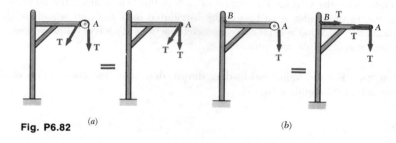

Fig. P6.82   (a)   (b)

6.82 (a) Show that when a frame supports a pulley at *A*, an equivalent loading of the frame and of each of its component parts may be obtained by removing the pulley and applying at *A* two forces equal and parallel to the forces of tension in the cable. (b) Further, show that if one end of the cable is attached to the frame at a point *B*, a force of magnitude equal to the tension should also be applied at *B*.

6.83 The axis of the three-hinged arch *ABC* is a parabola with vertex at *B*. Knowing that $P = 546$ kN and $Q = 364$ kN, determine (a) the components of the reaction at *C*, (b) the components of the force exerted at *B* on segment *AB*.

6.84 The axis of the three-hinged arch *ABC* is a parabola with vertex at *B*. Knowing that $P = 364$ kN and $Q = 546$ kN, determine (a) the components of the reaction at *C*, (b) the components of the force exerted at *B* on segment *AB*.

Fig. P6.83 and P6.84

6.85 Members *ABC* and *CDE* are pin-connected at *C* and supported by the four links *AF*, *BG*, *DG*, and *EH*. Determine the force in each link when a load **P** is applied at *B* as shown.

Fig. P6.85

6.86 Solve Prob. 6.85, assuming that the load **P** has been replaced by a clockwise couple of moment **M₀** applied to member *ABC* at *B*.

6.87 Members *ABC* and *CDE* are pin-connected at *C* and supported by the four links *AF*, *BG*, *GD*, and *EH*. For the loading shown, determine the force in each link.

6.88 Solve Prob. 6.87, assuming that the force **P** has been replaced by a clockwise couple of moment **M₀** applied at the same point.

Fig. P6.87

Fig. P6.89   800 N   **Fig. P6.90**   800 N   **Fig. P6.91**   800 N

6.89 through 6.91 The frame shown consists of members *AD* and *EH*, which are connected by two links. Determine the force in each link for the given loading.

6.92 A vertical load **P** of magnitude 750 N is applied to member *ABC*. Members *ABC* and *DEF* are parallel and are placed between two frictionless walls and connected by the link *BE*. Knowing that $a = 0.75$ m, determine the reactions at points *A*, *C*, *D*, and *F*.

6.93 The two parallel members *ABC* and *DEF* are placed between two frictionless walls and connected by a link *BE*. Determine the range of values of the distance *a* for which the load **P** can be supported.

Fig. P6.92 and P6.93

6.94 Three beams are nailed together at their midpoints to form the support system shown. Assuming that only vertical forces are exerted at the connections, determine the vertical reactions at A, D, and F.

Fig. P6.94

Fig. P6.95

6.95 Four beams, each of length $2a$, are nailed together at their midpoints to form the support system shown. Assuming that only vertical forces are exerted at the connections, determine the vertical reactions at A, D, E, and H.

6.96 and 6.97 Each of the frames shown consists of two L-shaped members connected by two rigid links. For each frame, determine the reactions at the supports and indicate whether the frame is rigid.

Fig. P6.96

Fig. P6.97

6.12. Machines.

Machines are structures designed to transmit and modify forces. Whether they are simple tools or include complicated mechanisms, their main purpose is to transform *input forces* into *output forces*. Consider, for example, a pair of cutting pliers used to cut a wire (Fig. 6.22*a*). If we apply two equal and opposite forces **P** and −**P** on their handles, they will exert two equal and opposite forces **Q** and −**Q** on the wire (Fig. 6.22*b*).

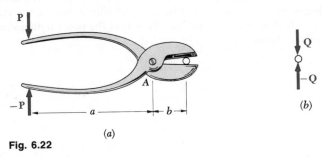

(a)

(b)

Fig. 6.22

To determine the magnitude Q of the output forces when the magnitude P of the input forces is known (or, conversely, to determine P when Q is known), we draw a free-body diagram of the pliers *alone*, showing the input forces **P** and −**P** and the *reactions* −**Q** and **Q** that the wire exerts on the pliers (Fig. 6.23). However, since a pair of pliers forms a nonrigid

Fig. 6.23

structure, we must use one of the component parts as a free body in order to determine the unknown forces. Considering Fig. 6.24*a*, for example, and taking moments about A, we obtain the relation $Pa = Qb$, which defines the magnitude Q in terms of P or P in terms of Q. The same free-body diagram may be used to determine the components of the internal force at A; we find $A_x = 0$ and $A_y = P + Q$.

In the case of more complicated machines, it generally will be necessary to use several free-body diagrams and, possibly, to solve simultaneous equations involving various internal forces. The free bodies should be chosen to include the input forces and the reactions to the output forces, and the total number of unknown force components involved should not exceed the number of available independent equations. While it is advisable to check whether the problem is determinate before attempting to solve it, there is no point in discussing the rigidity of a machine. A machine includes moving parts and thus must be nonrigid.

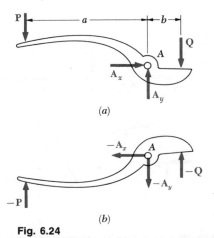

(a)

(b)

Fig. 6.24

A hydraulic-lift table is used to raise a 1000-kg crate. It consists of a platform and two identical linkages on which hydraulic cylinders exert equal forces. (Only one linkage and one cylinder are shown.) Members *EDB* and *CG* are each of length $2a$, and member *AD* is pinned to the midpoint of *EDB*. If the crate is placed on the table, so that half of its weight is supported by the system shown, determine the force exerted by each cylinder in raising the crate for $\theta = 60°$, $a = 0.70$ m, and $L = 3.20$ m. Show that the result obtained is independent of the distance d.

Solution. The machine considered consists of the platform and of the linkage, with an input force $\mathbf{F}_{DH}$ exerted by the cylinder and an output force equal and opposite to $\frac{1}{2}\mathbf{W}$. Since more than three unknowns would be involved, the entire mechanism is not used as a free body. The mechanism is dismembered and free-body diagrams are drawn for platform *ABC*, for roller *C*, and for member *EDB*. Since *AD*, *BC*, and *CG* are two-force members, their free-body diagrams have been omitted, and the forces they exert on the other parts of the mechanism have been drawn parallel to these members.

Platform ABC.

$$\xrightarrow{+}\Sigma F_x = 0: \qquad -F_{AD}\cos\theta = 0 \qquad F_{AD} = 0$$
$$+\uparrow\Sigma F_y = 0: \qquad B + C - \tfrac{1}{2}W = 0 \qquad B + C = \tfrac{1}{2}W \tag{1}$$

Roller C. We draw a force triangle and obtain $F_{BC} = C\cot\theta$.

Member EDB. Recalling that $F_{AD} = 0$,

$$+\uparrow\Sigma M_E = 0: \qquad F_{DH}\cos(\phi - 90°)a - B(2a\cos\theta) - F_{BC}(2a\sin\theta) = 0$$
$$F_{DH}a\sin\phi - B(2a\cos\theta) - (C\cot\theta)(2a\sin\theta) = 0$$
$$F_{DH}\sin\phi - 2(B + C)\cos\theta = 0$$

Recalling Eq. (1), we have

$$F_{DH} = W\,\frac{\cos\theta}{\sin\phi} \tag{2}$$

and we observe that the result obtained is independent of d. ◀

Applying first the law of sines to triangle *EDH*, we write

$$\frac{\sin\phi}{EH} = \frac{\sin\theta}{DH} \qquad \sin\phi = \frac{EH}{DH}\sin\theta \tag{3}$$

Using now the law of cosines, we have

$$(DH)^2 = a^2 + L^2 - 2aL\cos\theta$$
$$= (0.70)^2 + (3.20)^2 - 2(0.70)(3.20)\cos 60°$$
$$(DH)^2 = 8.49 \qquad DH = 2.91\text{ m}$$

We also note that

$$W = mg = (1000\text{ kg})(9.81\text{ m/s}^2) = 9810\text{ N} = 9.81\text{ kN}$$

Substituting for $\sin\phi$ from (3) into (2) and using the numerical data, we write

$$F_{DH} = W\,\frac{DH}{EH}\cot\theta = (9.81\text{ kN})\frac{2.91\text{ m}}{3.20\text{ m}}\cot 60°$$

$$F_{DH} = 5.15\text{ kN} \quad \blacktriangleleft$$

Fig. P6.98

Problems

6.98 The shear shown is used to cut and trim electronic-circuit-board laminates. For the position shown, determine (*a*) the vertical component of the force exerted on the shearing blade at *D*, (*b*) the reaction at *C*.

6.99 The control rod *CE* passes through a horizontal hole in the body of the toggle clamp shown. Determine (*a*) the force **Q** required to hold the clamp in equilibrium, (*b*) the corresponding force in link *BD*.

Fig. P6.99

6.100 Water pressure in the supply system exerts a downward force of 100 N on the vertical plug at *A*. Determine the tension in the fusible link *DE* and the force exerted on member *BCE* at *B*.

6.101 Solve Prob. 6.98, assuming that the 400-N force is applied vertically downward at *A*.

Fig. P6.100

Fig. P6.102

6.102 The jaw crusher shown consists of a fixed jaw and a moving jaw *AB* which is attached to a large pin at *A*. Power is delivered to shaft *C* to which a circular disk *D* is attached eccentrically. As shaft *C* rotates, the connecting rod *EF* moves toggle *GFH*. For the position shown, the magnitude of the resultant force **F** on jaw *AB* is 360 kN and the arms *GF* and *FH* of the toggle each form an angle of 5° with the horizontal. Neglecting the effect of friction, determine the force in rod *EF*. (*Note:* At the end of each crushing cycle springs, which are not shown, return the jaw and toggle to their initial positions.)

6.103 A 9-m length of railroad track of mass 40 kg/m is lifted by the rail tongs shown. Determine the forces exerted at D and F on tong BDF.

Fig. P6.103

6.104 A 3600-kg steel ingot is lifted by a pair of tongs as shown. Determine the forces exerted at C and E on tong BCE.

Fig. P6.104

Fig. P6.105

6.105 If the toggle shown is added to the tongs of Prob. 6.104 and the load is lifted by applying a single force at G, determine the forces exerted at C and E on the tong BCE.

6.106 The action of the roll clamp is controlled by the two hydraulic cylinders shown. In order to hold firmly the 2000-kg paper roll, a vertical 6-kN force is applied at the top of the roll by arm CAF. Determine (a) the force exerted by each cylinder, (b) the force exerted at C on arm $BCEH$.

Fig. P6.106

Fig. P6.107

6.107 The gear-pulling assembly shown consists of a crosshead CF, two grip arms ABC and FGH, two links BD and EG, and a threaded center rod JK. Knowing that the center rod JK must exert a 4800-N force on the vertical shaft KL in order to start the removal of the gear, determine all forces acting on grip arm ABC. Assume that the rounded ends of the crosshead are smooth and exert horizontal forces on the grip arms.

6.108 A force **P** of magnitude 2.4 kN is applied to the piston of the engine system shown. For each of the two positions shown, determine the couple **M** required to hold the system in equilibrium.

(a)   (b)
Fig. P6.108 and P6.109

6.109 A couple **M** of magnitude 315 N · m is applied to the crank of the engine system shown. For each of the two positions shown, determine the force **P** required to hold the system in equilibrium.

6.110 and 6.111 Two rods are connected by a frictionless collar B. Knowing that the magnitude of the couple $\mathbf{M}_A$ is 20 N·m, determine (a) the couple $\mathbf{M}_C$ required for equilibrium, (b) the corresponding components of the reaction at C.

Fig. P6.110   **Fig. P6.111**

6.112 The upper blade and lower handle of the compound-lever shears are pin-connected to the main element *ABE* at *A* and *B*, respectively, and to the short link *CD* at *C* and *D*, respectively. Determine the forces exerted on a twig when two 120-N forces are applied to the handles.

Fig. P6.112

Fig. P6.113

6.113 The specialized plumbing wrench shown is used in confined areas (e.g., under a basin or sink). It consists essentially of a jaw *BC* pinned at *B* to a long rod. Knowing that the forces exerted on the nut are equivalent to a clockwise couple (when viewed from above) of magnitude 8.80 N · m, determine (*a*) the magnitude of the force exerted by pin *B* on jaw *BC*, (*b*) the couple $\mathbf{M}_0$ which is applied to the wrench.

6.114 The tool shown is used to crimp terminals onto electric wires. Knowing that a worker will apply forces of magnitude $P = 135$ N to the handles, determine the magnitude of the crimping forces which will be exerted on the terminal.

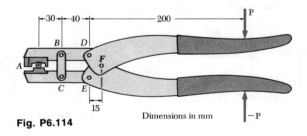

Fig. P6.114

6.115 The pliers shown are used to attach electrical connectors to flat cables which carry many separate wires. The clamping jaws remain parallel as the connectors are attached. Knowing that 380-N forces directed along line *a-a* are required to complete the attachment, determine the magnitude *P* of the forces which must be applied to the handles. Assume that pins *A* and *D* slide freely in slots cut in the jaws.

Fig. P6.115

6.116 A hand-operated hydraulic cylinder has been designed for use where space is severely limited. Determine the magnitude of the force exerted on the piston at *D* when two 450-N forces are applied as shown.

Fig. P6.116

Fig. P6.117

6.117 Determine the magnitude of the gripping forces produced when two 300-N forces are applied as shown.

6.118 Since the brace shown must remain in position even when the magnitude of **P** is very small, a single safety spring is attached at *D* and *E*. The spring *DE* has a constant of 8750 N/m and an unstretched length of 175 mm. Knowing that *l* = 250 mm and that the magnitude of **P** is 4000 N, determine the force **Q** required to release the brace.

Fig. P6.118

Fig. P6.119

Fig. P6.120

6.119 and 6.120 Determine the force **P** which must be applied to the toggle *CDE* to maintain bracket *ABC* in the position shown.

6.121 The shelf *ABC* is held horizontally by a self-locking brace which consists of two parts *BDE* and *EDF* hinged at *E* and bearing against each other at *D*. Knowing that the shelf is 384 mm wide and has a mass of 18 kg, determine the force **P** required to release the brace. (*Hint.* To release the brace, the forces of contact at *D* must be zero.)

Fig. P6.121

6.122 The telescoping arm *ABC* is used to raise a worker to the elevation of overhead electric and telephone wires. For the extension shown, the center of gravity of the 625-kg arm is located at point *G*. The worker, the bucket, and equipment attached to the bucket together have a mass of 200 kg and have a combined center of gravity at *C*. Determine the force exerted at *B* by the single hydraulic cylinder used when $\theta = 35°$.

Fig. P6.122

Fig. P6.123

6.123 The position of the spindle *DE* of a lift truck is partially controlled by two identical linkage-and-hydraulic-cylinder systems, only one of which is shown. A 15-kN spool of electric cable is held by the spindle in the position shown. Knowing that the load supported by the one system shown is 7.5 kN, determine (*a*) the force exerted by the hydraulic cylinder on point *G*, (*b*) the components of the force exerted on member *BCF* at point *C*.

6.124 A 500-kg concrete slab is supported by a chain and sling attached to the bucket of the front-end loader shown. The action of the bucket is controlled by two identical mechanisms, only one of which is shown. Knowing that the mechanism shown supports one-half of the 500-kg slab, determine the force exerted (*a*) by cylinder *CD*, (*b*) by cylinder *FH*.

Fig. P6.124

Fig. P6.125

6.125 The motion of the backhoe bucket is controlled by the hydraulic cylinders *AB*, *DE*, and *FI*. Determine the force exerted by each cylinder in supporting the 7.5-kN load shown.

6.126 The elevation of the platform is controlled by two identical mechanisms, only one of which is shown. A load of 5 kN is applied to the mechanism shown. Knowing that the pin at *C* can transmit only a horizontal force, determine (*a*) the force in link *BE*, (*b*) the components of the force exerted by the hydraulic cylinder on pin *H*.

Fig. P6.126

Fig. P6.127

6.127 The gears *D* and *G* are rigidly attached to shafts which are held by frictionless bearings. If $r_D = 108$ mm and $r_G = 36$ mm, determine (*a*) the couple $\mathbf{M}_0$ which must be applied for equilibrium, (*b*) the reactions at *A* and *B*.

6.128 In the planetary-gear system shown, the radius of the central gear A is a, the radius of each planetary gear is b, and the radius of the outer gear E is $(a + 2b)$. In a particular gear system where $a = 50$ mm and $b = 30$ mm, a clockwise couple $\mathbf{M}_A$ is applied to gear A. If the system is to be in equilibrium, determine (a) the couple $\mathbf{M}_S$ which must be applied to the spider BCD, (b) the couple $\mathbf{M}_E$ which must be applied to the outer gear E.

6.129 In the planetary-gear system shown, the radius of the central gear A is a, the radius of each of the planetary gears is b, and the radius of the outer gear E is $(a + 2b)$. A clockwise couple of magnitude M_A is applied to the central gear A and a counterclockwise couple of magnitude $3.5M_A$ is applied to the spider BCD. If the system is to be in equilibrium, determine (a) the required ratio b/a, (b) the couple $\mathbf{M}_E$ which must be applied to the outer gear E.

*6.130 Two shafts AC and EG, which lie in the vertical yz plane, are connected by a universal joint at D. The bearings at B and E do not exert any axial force. A couple of magnitude 30 N·m (clockwise when viewed from the positive z axis) is applied to shaft AC at A. At a time when the arm of the crosspiece attached to shaft AC is vertical, determine (a) the magnitude of the couple $\mathbf{M}_G$ which must be applied to shaft EG to maintain equilibrium, (b) the reactions at B, C, and E. (*Hint.* The sum of the couples exerted on the crosspiece must be zero.)

Fig. P6.128 and P6.129

Fig. P6.130

*6.131 Solve Prob. 6.130, assuming that the arm of the crosspiece attached to shaft ABC is horizontal.

*6.132 The large mechanical tongs shown are used to grab and lift a thick 8000-kg steel slab HJ. Knowing that slipping does not occur between the tong grips and the slab at H and J, determine the components of all forces acting on member EFH. (*Hint.* Consider the symmetry of the tongs to establish relationships between the components of the force acting at E on EFH and the components of the force acting at D on CDF.)

Fig. P6.132

*6.133 The mechanism shown is installed at some loading docks so that the dock edge C can be brought to the same elevation as the beds of various trucks. The weight of the platform and mechanism is roughly balanced by the force exerted by spring DE, while the final adjustment in elevation is controlled by the hydraulic cylinder GJ. Knowing that the weight of all moving parts is equivalent to the single force **W** of magnitude 7.5 kN, determine the required tension in spring DE if the force exerted by the hydraulic cylinder is to be zero in the position shown.

Fig. P6.133

*6.134 The weight of the platform and mechanism of Prob. 6.133 is exactly balanced by the force exerted by spring DE in the position shown and the force exerted by the hydraulic cylinder GJ is zero. A 1-kN force directed vertically downward is then applied at edge C. Determine the force which must be exerted by the hydraulic cylinder if the mechanism is to remain in the same position.

Review and Summary

In this chapter we learned to determine the *internal forces* holding together the various parts of a structure.

Analysis of trusses

    The first half of the chapter was devoted to the analysis of *trusses*, i.e., to the analysis of structures consisting of *straight members connected at their extremities only*. The members being slender and unable to support lateral loads, all the loads must be applied at the joints; a truss may thus be assumed to consist of *pins and two-force members* [Sec. 6.2].

Simple trusses

    A truss is said to be *rigid* if it is designed in such a way that it will not greatly deform and collapse under a small load. A triangular truss consisting of three members connected at three joints is clearly a rigid truss (Fig. 6.25a), and so will the truss obtained by adding two new members to the first one and connecting them at a new joint (Fig. 6.25b). Trusses obtained by repeating this procedure are called *simple trusses*. We may *(a)* *(b)* **Fig. 6.25**

check that in a simple truss the total number of members is $m = 2n - 3$, where n is the total number of joints [Sec. 6.3].

The forces in the various members of a simple truss may be determined by the *method of joints* [Sec. 6.4]. First, the reactions at the supports may be obtained by considering the entire truss as a free body. The free-body diagram of each pin is then drawn, showing the forces exerted on the pin by the members or supports it connects. Since the members are straight two-force members, the force exerted by a member on the pin is directed along that member, and only the magnitude of the force is unknown. It is always possible in the case of a simple truss to draw the free-body diagrams of the pins in such an order that only two unknown forces are included in each diagram. These forces may be obtained from the corresponding two equilibrium equations or—if only three forces are involved—from the corresponding force triangle. If the force exerted by a member on a pin is directed toward that pin, the member is in *compression;* if it is directed away from the pin, the member is in *tension* [Sample Prob. 6.1]. The analysis of a truss may sometimes be expedited by recognizing *joints under special loading conditions* [Sec. 6.5]. The method of joints may also be extended to the analysis of three-dimensional or *space trusses* [Sec. 6.6].

The *method of sections* is usually preferred to the method of joints when the force in only one member—or very few members—of a truss is desired [Sec. 6.7]. To determine the force in member *BD* of the truss of Fig. 6.26a, for example, we *pass a section* through members *BD*, *BE*, and *CE*, remove these members, and use the portion *ABC* of the truss as a free body (Fig. 6.26b). Writing $\Sigma M_E = 0$, we determine the magnitude of the force $\mathbf{F}_{BD}$, which represents the force in member *BD*. A positive sign indicates that the member is in *tension*, a negative sign that it is in *compression* [Sample Probs. 6.2 and 6.3].

The method of sections is particularly useful in the analysis of *compound trusses*, i.e., trusses which cannot be constructed from the basic triangular truss of Fig. 6.25a. These trusses may be obtained by rigidly connecting several simple trusses [Sec. 6.8]. If the component trusses have been properly connected (e.g., one pin and one link, or three nonconcurrent and nonparallel links) and if the resulting structure is properly supported (e.g., one pin and one roller), the compound truss is *statically determinate, rigid, and completely constrained*. The following

Method of joints

Method of sections

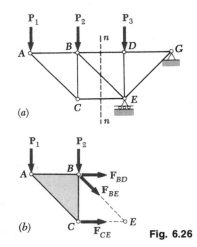

Fig. 6.26

necessary—but not sufficient—condition is then satisfied: $m + r = 2n$, where m is the number of members, r is the number of unknowns representing the reactions at the supports, and n is the number of joints.

Frames and machines

The second part of the chapter was devoted to the analysis of *frames and machines*. Frames and machines are structures which contain *multiforce members*, i.e., members acted upon by three or more forces. Frames are designed to support loads and are usually stationary, fully constrained structures. Machines are designed to transmit or modify forces and always contain moving parts [Sec. 6.9].

Analysis of a frame

To *analyze a frame*, we first consider the *entire frame as a free body* and write three equilibrium equations [Sec. 6.10]. If the frame remains rigid when detached from its supports, the reactions involve only three unknowns and may be determined from these equations [Sample Probs. 6.4 and 6.5]. On the other hand, if the frame ceases to be rigid when detached from its supports, the reactions involve more than three unknowns and cannot be completely determined [Sec. 6.11; Sample Prob. 6.6].

Multiforce members

We then *dismember the frame* and identify the various members as either two-force members or multiforce members; pins are assumed to form an integral part of one of the members they connect. We draw the free-body diagram of each of the multiforce members, noting that when two multiforce members are connected to the same two-force member, they are acted upon by that member with *equal and opposite forces of unknown magnitude but known direction*. When two multiforce members are connected by a pin, they exert on each other *equal and opposite forces of unknown direction*, which should be represented by *two unknown components*. The equilibrium equations obtained from the free-body diagrams of the multiforce members may then be solved for the various internal forces [Sample Probs. 6.4 and 6.5]. They may also be used to complete the determination of the reactions at the supports [Sample Prob. 6.6]. Actually, if the frame is *statically determinate and rigid*, the free-body diagrams of the multiforce members could provide as many equations as there are unknown forces (including the reactions) [Sec. 6.11]. However, as suggested above, it is advisable to first consider the free-body diagram of the entire frame to minimize the number of equations to be solved simultaneously.

Analysis of a machine

To *analyze a machine*, we dismember it and, following the same procedure as for a frame, draw the free-body diagram of each of the multiforce members. The corresponding equilibrium equations yield the *output forces* exerted by the machine in terms of the *input forces* applied to it, as well as the *internal forces* at the various connections [Sec. 6.12; Sample Prob. 6.7].

Review Problems

6.135 The Whitworth mechanism shown is used to produce a quick-return motion of point D. The block at B is pinned to the crank AB and is free to slide in a slot cut in member CD. Determine the couple **M** which must be applied to the crank AB to hold the mechanism in equilibrium when (*a*) $\alpha = 0$, (*b*) $\alpha = 30°$.

6.136 Solve Prob. 6.135, when (*a*) $\alpha = 60°$, (*b*) $\alpha = 90°$.

6.137 Determine the reactions at the supports of the beams shown.

Fig. P6.135

(*a*)

(*b*)

Fig. P6.137

6.138 The truck shown is used to facilitate work on overhead wires by raising a pair of buckets to the required elevation. Two tubular members AB and BC, each of length 3.6 m, form the main supporting mechanism; the position of AB is controlled by means of the hydraulic cylinder DE. Two 0.6-m diameter sheaves, one on each side, are rigidly attached to member BC at B. Cables are fastened to the sheaves, pass over pulleys at H, and are fastened to a common movable block at F. The position of block F is controlled by a second hydraulic cylinder EF. Knowing that the workmen, buckets, and equipment attached to the buckets together have a total mass of 300 kg and have a combined center of gravity at G, determine the force which must be exerted by each hydraulic cylinder to maintain the position shown. Neglect the weight of the mechanism.

Fig. P6.138

Fig. P6.139

Fig. P6.141 and P6.142

Fig. P6.143

Fig. P6.145

6.139 A 48-mm-diameter pipe is gripped by the Stillson wrench shown. Portions AB and DE of the wrench are rigidly attached to each other and portion CF is connected by a pin at D. Assuming that no slipping occurs between the pipe and the wrench, determine the components of the forces exerted on the pipe at A and at C.

6.140 Knowing that the surfaces at A and D are frictionless, determine the components of all forces exerted on member ACD.

Fig. P6.140   Dimensions in mm

6.141 Determine the force in members DE and EF of the truss shown.

6.142 Determine the force in members FG and FH of the truss shown.

6.143 Using the method of joints, determine the force in each member of the truss shown. State whether each member is in tension or compression.

Fig. P6.144   16 mm   18 mm

6.144 The compound-lever pruning shears shown can be adjusted by placing pin A at varius ratchet positions on blade ACE. Knowing that 1460-N vertical forces are required to complete the pruning of a twig, determine the magnitude P of the forces which must be applied to the handles when the shears are adjusted as shown.

6.145 The bent rod DEF fits into the bent pipe ABC as shown. Neglecting the effect of friction, determine the reactions at A and F due to the 360-N force applied at B.

6.146 A 400-kg block may be supported by a small frame in each of the four ways shown. The diameter of the pulley is 250 mm. For each case, determine (*a*) the force components and the couple representing the reaction at *A*, (*b*) the force exerted at *D* on the vertical member.

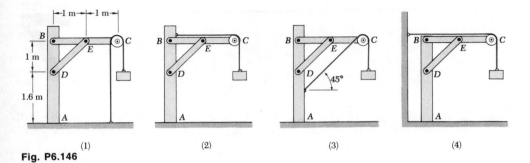

(1)   (2)   (3)   (4)

Fig. P6.146

The following problems are designed to be solved with a computer.

6.C1 For the truss and loading shown, write a computer program and calculate the force in each member for values of θ from 0 to 90° at 5° intervals.

6.C2 Several comparative designs of the truss of Sample Prob. 6.3 are to be made. Write a computer program and calculate the force in members *FH*, *GH*, and *GI* for values of *h* from 4 to 12 m at 1-m intervals.

6.C3 Various configurations of the frame shown are being investigated. (*a*) Write a computer program and calculate the force in links *CF* and *DG* for values of *a* from 0 to 0.3 m at 0.05-m intervals. (*b*) Explain what happens when $a = 0.15$ m.

Fig. P6.C1

Fig. P6.C3

6.C4 Write a computer program which can be used to determine the couple **M** required to hold the system shown in equilibrium for values of θ from 0 to 180° at 15° intervals. For the case when $b = 100$ mm, $l = 350$ mm, and $P = 1.5$ kN, calculate (*a*) the magnitude *M* of the couple at 15° intervals, (*b*) the value of θ for which *M* is maximum and the corresponding value of *M*.

Fig. P6.C4

Forces in Beams and Cables

Fig. 7.1

Fig. 7.2

* **7.1. Introduction.** In preceding chapters, two basic problems involving structures were considered: (1) the determination of the external forces acting on a structure (Chap. 4) and (2) the determination of the forces which hold together the various members forming a structure (Chap. 6). We shall now consider the problem of determining the internal forces which hold together the various parts of a given member.

We shall first analyze the internal forces in the members of a frame, such as the crane considered earlier in Chap. 6 (Secs. 6.1 and 6.10) and note that whereas the internal forces in a straight two-force member can produce only *tension* or *compression* in that member, the internal forces in any other type of member will usually produce *shear* and *bending* as well.

Most of this chapter will be devoted to the analysis of the internal forces in two important types of engineering structures, namely,

1. *Beams,* which are usually long, straight prismatic members designed to support loads applied at various points along the member.
2. *Cables,* which are flexible members capable of withstanding only tension, designed to support either concentrated or distributed loads. Cables are used in many engineering applications, such as suspension bridges and transmission lines.

* **7.2. Internal Forces in Members.** We shall first consider a *straight two-force member AB* (Fig. 7.1a). From Sec. 4.6, we know that the forces **F** and −**F** acting at A and B, respectively, must be directed along AB in opposite sense and have the same magnitude F. Now, let us cut the member at C. To maintain the equilibrium of the free bodies AC and CB thus obtained, we must apply to AC a force −**F** equal and opposite to **F**, and to CB a force **F** equal and opposite to −**F** (Fig. 7.1b). These new forces are directed along AB in opposite sense and have the same magnitude F. Since the two parts AC and CB were in equilibrium before the member was cut, *internal forces* equivalent to these new forces must have

276

Fig. 7.3

existed in the member itself. We see that in the case of a straight two-force member, the internal forces acting on each part of the member are equivalent to an axial force. The magnitude F of this force does not depend upon the location of the section C and is referred to as the *force in member AB*. In the case considered, the member is in tension and will elongate under the action of the internal forces. In the case represented in Fig. 7.2, the member is in compression and will decrease in length under the action of the internal forces.

Next we shall consider a *multiforce member*. Take, for instance, member AD of the crane analyzed in Sec. 6.10. This crane is shown again in Fig. 7.3*a*, and the free-body diagram of member AD is drawn in Fig. 7.3*b*. We now cut member AD at J and draw a free-body diagram for each of the portions JD and AJ of the member (Fig. 7.3*c* and *d*). Considering the free body JD, we find that its equilibrium will be maintained if we apply at J a force F to balance the vertical component of T, a force V to balance the horizontal component of T, and a couple M to balance the moment of T about J. Again we conclude that internal forces must have existed at J before member AD was cut. The internal forces acting on the portion JD of member AD are equivalent to the force-couple system shown in Fig. 7.3*c*. According to Newton's third law, the internal forces acting on AJ must be equivalent to an equal and opposite force-couple system, as shown in Fig. 7.3*d*. It clearly appears that the action of the internal forces in member AD *is not limited to producing tension or compression* as in the case of straight two-force members; the internal forces *also produce shear and bending*. The force F is again in this case called an *axial force*; the force V is called a *shearing force*; and the moment M of the couple is known as the *bending moment at J*. We note that when determining internal forces in a member, we should clearly indicate on which portion of the member the forces are supposed to act. The deformation which will occur in member AD is sketched in Fig. 7.3*e*. The actual analysis of such a deformation is part of the study of mechanics of materials.

It should be noted that in a *two-force member which is not straight*, the internal forces are also equivalent to a force-couple system. This is shown in Fig. 7.4, where the two-force member ABC has been cut at D.

Fig. 7.4

SAMPLE PROBLEM 7.1

In the frame shown, determine the internal forces (a) in member ACF at point J and (b) in member BCD at point K. This frame has been previously considered in Sample Prob. 6.5.

Solution. The reactions and the forces acting on each member of the frame are determined; this has been previously done in Sample Prob. 6.5, and the results are repeated here.

a. Internal Forces at J. Member ACF is cut at point J, and the two parts shown are obtained. The internal forces at J are represented by an equivalent force-couple system and may be determined by considering the equilibrium of either part. Considering the *free body AJ*, we write

$+\uparrow \Sigma M_J = 0:$ $-(1800 \text{ N})(1.2 \text{ m}) + M = 0$
$M = +2160 \text{ N·m}$ $M = 2160 \text{ N·m} \uparrow$ ◄

$+\searrow \Sigma F_x = 0:$ $F - (1800 \text{ N}) \cos 41.7° = 0$
$F = +1344 \text{ N}$ $F = 1344 \text{ N} \searrow$ ◄

$+\nearrow \Sigma F_y = 0:$ $-V + (1800 \text{ N}) \sin 41.7° = 0$
$V = +1197 \text{ N}$ $V = 1197 \text{ N} \swarrow$ ◄

The internal forces at J are therefore equivalent to a couple **M**, an axial force **F**, and a shearing force **V**. The internal force-couple system acting on part JCF is equal and opposite.

b. Internal Forces at K. We cut member BCD at K and obtain the two parts shown. Considering the *free body BK*, we write

$+\uparrow \Sigma M_K = 0:$ $(1200 \text{ N})(1.5 \text{ m}) + M = 0$
$M = -1800 \text{ N·m}$ $M = 1800 \text{ N·m} \downarrow$ ◄

$\xrightarrow{+} \Sigma F_x = 0:$ $F = 0$ $F = 0$ ◄

$+\uparrow \Sigma F_y = 0:$ $-1200 \text{ N} - V = 0$
$V = -1200 \text{ N}$ $V = 1200 \text{ N} \uparrow$ ◄

Problems

7.1 and 7.2 Determine the internal forces (axial force, shearing force, and bending moment) at point J of the structure indicated:

    7.1   Frame and loading of Prob. 6.57

    7.2   Frame and loading of Prob. 6.56.

7.3 and 7.4 For the frame and loading shown, determine the internal forces at the point indicated:

    7.3   Point J.

    7.4   Point K.

Fig. P7.3 and P7.4

7.5 A 4.5-kg uniform rod $ABCDE$ has been bent and is held by a wire sling as shown. Determine the internal forces (*a*) at point C, (*b*) just to the right of point B.

7.6 Determine the internal forces at point J when $\alpha = 90°$.

7.7 Determine the internal forces at point J when $\alpha = 0$.

Fig. P7.5

Fig. P7.6 and P7.7

Fig. P7.8 and P7.9

7.8 Determine the internal forces at point J when $\alpha = 90°$.

7.9 Determine the internal forces at point J when $\alpha = 0$.

7.10 Knowing that the radius of each pulley is 120 mm, determine the internal forces at (*a*) point C, (*b*) point J which is 100 mm to the left of C.

7.11 Knowing that the radius of each pulley is 100 mm, determine the internal forces at (*a*) point C, (*b*) point J which is 100 mm to the left of C.

Fig. P7.10 and P7.11

7.12 A force **P** is applied to a bent rod *AD* which may be supported in three different ways as shown. In each case determine the internal forces just to the right of point *B*.

(a)   (b)   (c)

Fig. P7.12

Fig. P7.13 and P7.14

7.13 The axis of the curved member *AB* is a parabola with vertex at *A*. If a vertical load **P** of magnitude 2250 N is applied at *A*, determine the internal forces at *J* when $h = 300$ mm, $L = 1000$ mm, and $a = 600$ mm.

7.14 Knowing that the axis of the curved member *AB* is a parabola with vertex at *A*, determine the magnitude and location of the maximum bending moment.

7.15 and 7.16 A half section of pipe rests on a frictionless horizontal surface as shown. If the half section of pipe has a mass of 9 kg and a diameter of 300 mm, determine the bending moment at point *J* when $\theta = 90°$.

Fig. P7.15 and P7.17   **Fig. P7.16 and P7.18**

*7.17 and 7.18 A half section of pipe, of weight *W* and of unit length, rests on a frictionless horizontal surface. Determine the internal force at point *J* in terms of *W*, *r*, and θ.

*7.19 In Prob. 7.18, determine the magnitude and location of the maximum internal axial force.

BEAMS

* 7.3. **Various Types of Loading and Support.** A structural member designed to support loads applied at various points along the member is known as a *beam*. In most cases, the loads are perpendicular to the axis of the beam and will cause only shear and bending in the beam. When the loads are not at a right angle to the beam, they will also produce axial forces in the beam.

Beams are usually long, straight prismatic bars. Designing a beam consists essentially in selecting the cross section which will provide the most effective resistance to the shear and bending produced by the applied loads. The design of the beam, therefore, includes two distinct parts. In the first part, the shearing forces and bending moments produced by the loads are determined. The second part is concerned with the selection of the cross section best suited to resist the shearing forces and bending moments determined in the first part. This portion of the chapter, Beams, deals with the first part of the problem of beam design, namely, the determination of the shearing forces and bending moments in beams subjected to various loading conditions and supported in various ways. The second part of the problem belongs to the study of mechanics of materials.

A beam may be subjected to *concentrated loads* P_1, P_2, ..., expressed in newtons, or its multiple kilonewtons (Fig. 7.5a), to a *distributed load* w, expressed in N/m, or· kN/m (Fig. 7.5b), or to a combination of both. When the load w per unit length has a constant value over part of the beam (as between A and B in Fig. 7.5b), the load is said to be *uniformly distributed* over that part of the beam. The determination of the reactions at the supports may be considerably simplified if distributed loads are replaced by equivalent concentrated loads, as explained in Sec. 5.8. This substitution, however, should not be performed, or at least should be performed with care, when internal forces are being computed (see Sample Prob. 7.3).

Beams are classified according to the way in which they are supported. Several types of beams frequently used are shown in Fig. 7.6. The distance L between supports is called the *span*. It should be noted that the

(a) Concentrated loads

(b) Distributed load

Fig. 7.5 Types of loadings.

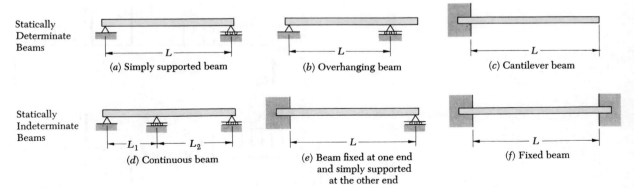

Statically Determinate Beams

(a) Simply supported beam   *(b)* Overhanging beam   *(c)* Cantilever beam

Statically Indeterminate Beams

(d) Continuous beam   *(e)* Beam fixed at one end and simply supported at the other end   *(f)* Fixed beam

Fig. 7.6 Types of beams.

(a)

(b)

Fig. 7.7 Combined beams.

reactions will be determinate if the supports involve only three unknowns. The reactions will be statically indeterminate if more unknowns are involved; the methods of statics are not sufficient then to determine the reactions, and the properties of the beam with regard to its resistance to bending must be taken into consideration. Beams supported by two rollers are not shown here; such beams are only partially constrained and will move under certain loading conditions.

Sometimes two or more beams are connected by hinges to form a single continuous structure. Two examples of beams hinged at a point H are shown in Fig. 7.7. It will be noted that the reactions at the supports involve four unknowns and cannot be determined from the free-body diagram of the two-beam system. They can be determined, however, by considering the free-body diagram of each beam separately; six unknowns are involved (including two force components at the hinge), and six equations are available.

*7.4. Shear and Bending Moment in a Beam. Consider a

beam AB subjected to various concentrated and distributed loads (Fig. 7.8a). We propose to determine the shearing force and bending moment at any point of the beam. In the example considered here, the beam is simply supported, but the method used could be applied to any type of statically determinate beam.

First we determine the reactions at A and B by choosing the entire beam as a free body (Fig. 7.8b); writing $\Sigma M_A = 0$ and $\Sigma M_B = 0$, we obtain, respectively, $\mathbf{R}_B$ and $\mathbf{R}_A$.

To determine the internal forces at C, we cut the beam at C and draw the free-body diagrams of the portions AC and CB of the beam (Fig. 7.8c).

Fig. 7.8

Using the free-body diagram of AC, we may determine the shearing force $\mathbf{V}$ at C by equating to zero the sum of the vertical components of all forces acting on AC. Similarly, the bending moment $\mathbf{M}$ at C may be found by equating to zero the sum of the moments about C of all forces and couples acting on AC. We could have used just as well, however, the free-body diagram of CB† and determined the shearing force $\mathbf{V}'$ and the bending moment $\mathbf{M}'$ by equating to zero the sum of the vertical components and the sum of the moments about C of all forces and couples acting on CB. While this possible choice of alternate free bodies may facilitate the computation of the numerical values of the shearing force and bending moment, it makes it necessary to indicate on which portion of the beam the internal forces considered are acting. If the shearing force and bending moment, however, are to be computed at every point of the beam and efficiently recorded, we should not have to specify every time which portion of the beam is used as a free body. We shall adopt, therefore, the following conventions:

To determine the shearing force in a beam, *we shall always assume* that the internal forces $\mathbf{V}$ and $\mathbf{V}'$ are directed as shown in Fig. 7.8c. A positive value obtained for their common magnitude V will indicate that this assumption was correct and that the shearing forces are actually directed as shown. A negative value obtained for V will indicate that the assumption was wrong and that the shearing forces are directed in the opposite way. Thus, only the magnitude V, together with a plus or minus sign, needs to be recorded to define completely the shearing forces at a given point of the beam. The scalar V is commonly referred to as the *shear* at the given point of the beam.

Similarly, *we shall always assume* that the internal couples $\mathbf{M}$ and $\mathbf{M}'$ are directed as shown in Fig. 7.8c. A positive value obtained for their magnitude M, commonly referred to as the bending moment, will indicate that this assumption was correct, and a negative value that it was wrong. Summarizing the sign conventions we have presented, we state:

The shear V and the bending moment M at a given point of a beam are said to be positive when the internal forces and couples acting on each portion of the beam are directed as shown in Fig. 7.9a.

These conventions may be more easily remembered if we note that:

1. *The shear at C is positive when the* **external** *forces (loads and reactions) acting on the beam tend to shear off the beam at C as indicated in Fig. 7.9b.*
2. *The bending moment at C is positive when the* **external** *forces acting on the beam tend to bend the beam at C as indicated in Fig. 7.9c.*

It may also help to note that the situation described in Fig. 7.9, and corresponding to positive values of the shear and of the bending moment, is

---

† The force and couple representing the internal forces acting on CB will now be denoted by $\mathbf{V}'$ and $\mathbf{M}'$, rather than by $-\mathbf{V}$ and $-\mathbf{M}$ as done earlier, in order to avoid confusion when applying the sign convention which we are about to introduce.

(a) Internal forces at section
(positive shear and positive bending moment)

(b) Effect of external forces
(positive shear)

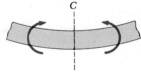

(c) Effect of external forces
(positive bending moment)

Fig. 7.9

precisely the situation which occurs in the left half of a simply supported beam carrying a single concentrated load at its midpoint. This particular example is fully discussed in the following section.

* 7.5. Shear and Bending-Moment Diagrams. Now that shear and bending moment have been clearly defined in sense as well as in magnitude, we may easily record their values at any point of a beam by plotting these values against the distance x measured from one end of the beam. The graphs obtained in this way are called, respectively, the *shear diagram* and the *bending-moment diagram*. As an example, consider a simply supported beam AB of span L subjected to a single concentrated load $\mathbf{P}$ applied at its midpoint D (Fig. 7.10a). We first determine the reactions at the supports from the free-body diagram of the entire beam (Fig. 7.10b); we find that the magnitude of each reaction is equal to $P/2$.

Next we cut the beam at a point C between A and D and draw the free-body diagrams of AC and CB (Fig. 7.10c). *Assuming that shear and bending moment are positive*, we direct the internal forces $\mathbf{V}$ and $\mathbf{V}'$ and the internal couples $\mathbf{M}$ and $\mathbf{M}'$ as indicated in Fig. 7.9a. Considering the free body AC and writing that the sum of the vertical components and the sum of the moments about C of the forces acting on the free body are zero, we find $V = +P/2$ and $M = +Px/2$. Both shear and bending moment are therefore positive; this may be checked by observing that the reaction at A tends to shear off and to bend the beam at C as indicated in Fig. 7.9b and c. We may plot V and M between A and D (Fig. 7.10e and f); the shear has a constant value $V = P/2$, while the bending moment increases linearly from $M = 0$ at $x = 0$ to $M = PL/4$ at $x = L/2$.

Cutting, now, the beam at a point E between D and B and considering the free body EB (Fig. 7.10d), we write that the sum of the vertical components and the sum of the moments about E of the forces acting on the free body are zero. We obtain $V = -P/2$ and $M = P(L - x)/2$. The shear is therefore negative and the bending moment positive; this may be checked by observing that the reaction at B bends the beam at E as indicated in Fig. 7.9c but tends to shear it off in a manner opposite to that shown in Fig. 7.9b. We can complete, now, the shear and bending-moment diagrams of Fig. 7.10e and f; the shear has a constant value $V = -P/2$ between D and B, while the bending moment decreases linearly from $M = PL/4$ at $x = L/2$ to $M = 0$ at $x = L$.

We shall note that when a beam is subjected to concentrated loads only, the shear is of constant value between loads and the bending moment varies linearly between loads. On the other hand, when a beam is subjected to distributed loads, the shear and bending moment vary quite differently (see Sample Prob. 7.3).

Fig. 7.10

20 kN   40 kN

A   B   C   D

├─2.5 m─┼──3 m──┼─2 m─┤

SAMPLE PROBLEM 7.2

Draw the shear and bending-moment diagram for the beam and loading shown.

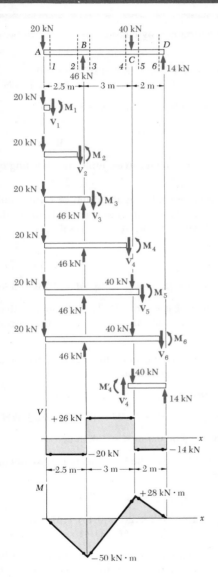

Solution. The reactions are determined by considering the entire beam as a free body; they are

$$\mathbf{R}_B = 46 \text{ kN} \uparrow \qquad \mathbf{R}_D = 14 \text{ kN} \uparrow$$

We first determine the internal forces just to the right of the 20-kN load at A. Considering the stub of beam to the left of section 1 as a free body and assuming V and M to be positive (according to the standard convention), we write

$$+\uparrow \Sigma F_y = 0: \qquad -20 \text{ kN} - V_1 = 0 \qquad\qquad V_1 = -20 \text{ kN}$$

$$+\uparrow \Sigma M_1 = 0: \qquad (20 \text{ kN})(0 \text{ m}) + M_1 = 0 \qquad\qquad M_1 = 0$$

We next consider as a free body the portion of beam to the left of section 2 and write

$$+\uparrow \Sigma F_y = 0: \qquad -20 \text{ kN} - V_2 = 0 \qquad\qquad V_2 = -20 \text{ kN}$$

$$+\uparrow \Sigma M_2 = 0: \qquad (20 \text{ kN})(2.5 \text{ m}) + M_2 = 0 \qquad\qquad M_2 = -50 \text{ kN} \cdot \text{m}$$

The shear and bending moment at sections 3, 4, 5, and 6 are determined in a similar way from the free-body diagrams shown. We obtain

$$V_3 = +26 \text{ kN} \qquad M_3 = -50 \text{ kN} \cdot \text{m}$$

$$V_4 = +26 \text{ kN} \qquad M_4 = +28 \text{ kN} \cdot \text{m}$$

$$V_5 = -14 \text{ kN} \qquad M_5 = +28 \text{ kN} \cdot \text{m}$$

$$V_6 = -14 \text{ kN} \qquad M_6 = 0$$

For several of the latter sections, the results may be more easily obtained by considering as a free body the portion of the beam to the right of the section. For example, considering the portion of the beam to the right of section 4, we write

$$+\uparrow \Sigma F_y = 0: \qquad V_4 - 40 \text{ kN} + 14 \text{ kN} = 0 \qquad\qquad V_4 = +26 \text{ kN}$$

$$+\uparrow \Sigma M_4 = 0: \qquad -M_4 + (14 \text{ kN})(2 \text{ m}) = 0 \qquad\qquad M_4 = +28 \text{ kN} \cdot \text{m}$$

We may now plot the six points shown on the shear and bending-moment diagrams. As indicated in Sec. 7.5, the shear is of constant value between concentrated loads, and the bending moment varies linearly; we obtain therefore the shear and bending-moment diagrams shown.

7 kN/m

SAMPLE PROBLEM 7.3

Draw the shear and bending-moment diagrams for the beam AB. The distributed load of 7 kN/m extends over 300 mm of the beam, from A to C, and the 2-kN load is applied at E.

Solution. The reactions are determined by considering the entire beam as a free body.

$$+\uparrow \Sigma M_A = 0: \qquad B_y(0.8\text{ m}) - (2.1\text{ kN})(0.15\text{ m}) - (2\text{ kN})(0.55\text{ m}) = 0$$
$$B_y = 1.77\text{ kN} \qquad\qquad \mathbf{B_y = 1.77\text{ kN} \uparrow}$$

$$+\uparrow \Sigma M_B = 0: \qquad (2.1\text{ kN})(0.65\text{ m}) + (2\text{ kN})(0.25\text{ m}) - A(0.8\text{ m}) = 0$$
$$A = +2.33\text{ kN} \qquad\qquad \mathbf{A = 2.33\text{ kN} \uparrow}$$

$$\xrightarrow{+}\Sigma F_x = 0: \qquad B_x = 0 \qquad\qquad\qquad \mathbf{B_x = 0}$$

The 2-kN load is now replaced by an equivalent force-couple system acting on the beam at point D.

From A to C. We determine the internal forces at a distance x from point A by considering the portion of beam to the left of section 1. That part of the distributed load acting on the free body is replaced by its resultant, and we write

$$+\uparrow\Sigma F_y = 0: \qquad 2.33 - 7x - V = 0 \qquad\qquad V = 2.33 - 7x$$

$$+\uparrow \Sigma M_1 = 0: \qquad -2.33x + 7x(\tfrac{1}{2}x) + M = 0 \qquad M = 2.33x - 3.5x^2$$

Since the free-body diagram shown may be used for all values of x smaller than 0.3 m, the expressions obtained for V and M are valid in the region $0 < x < 0.3$ m.

From C to D. Considering the portion of beam to the left of section 2 and again replacing the distributed load by its resultant, we obtain

$$+\uparrow\Sigma F_y = 0: \qquad 2.33 - 2.1 - V = 0 \qquad V = 0.23\text{ kN}$$

$$+\uparrow \Sigma M_2 = 0: \qquad -2.33x + 2.1(x - 0.15) + M = 0 \quad M = (0.315 + 0.23x)\text{kN·m}$$

These expressions are valid in the region $0.3\text{ m} < x < 0.45\text{ m}$

From D to B. Using the portion of beam to the left of section 3, we obtain for the region $0.45\text{ m} < x < 0.8\text{ m}$.

$$+\uparrow\Sigma F_y = 0: \qquad 2.33 - 2.1 - 2 - V = 0 \qquad V = 1.77\text{ kN}$$

$$+\uparrow\Sigma M_3 = 0: \qquad -2.33x + 2.1(x - 0.15) - 0.2 + 2(x - 0.45) + M = 0$$
$$M = (1.415 - 1.77x)\text{kN·m}$$

The shear and bending-moment diagrams for the entire beam may now be plotted. We note that the couple of moment 0.2 kN·m applied at point D introduces a discontinuity into the bending-moment diagram.

Problems

7.20 through 7.25 Draw the shear and bending-moment diagrams for the beam and loading shown.

Fig. P7.20

Fig. P7.21

Fig. P7.22

Fig. P7.23

Fig. P7.24

Fig. P7.25

7.26 and 7.27 Draw the shear and bending-moment diagrams for the beam *AB*.

Fig. P7.26

Fig. P7.27

7.28 Draw the shear and bending-moment diagrams for the beam *AB* if the magnitude of the distributed load is $w = 2$ kN/m.

7.29 Draw the shear and bending-moment diagrams for the beam *AB* if $a = 0.4$ m.

*7.30 Determine the distributed load w for which the maximum absolute value of the bending moment in the beam is as small as possible. (*Hint.* Draw the bending-moment diagram and then equate the absolute values of the largest positive and negative bending moments obtained.)

*7.31 Determine the distance a for which the maximum absolute value of the bending moment in the beam is as small as possible. (See hint of Prob. 7.30.)

Fig. P7.28 and P7.30

Fig. P7.29 and P7.31

7.32 through 7.34 Assuming the upward reaction of the ground to be uniformly distributed, draw the shear and bending-moment diagrams for the beam AB.

Fig. P7.32

Fig. P7.33

Fig. P7.34

7.35 Solve Prob. 7.34, assuming that the 60-kN load has been removed.

7.36 through 7.38 Draw the shear and bending-moment diagrams for the beam AB.

Fig. P7.36

Fig. P7.37

Fig. P7.38

7.39 Solve Prob. 7.38, assuming that the 500-N load has been removed.

Fig. P7.40 and P7.41

7.40 Draw the shear and bending-moment diagram for beam AB if $a = 180$ mm.

*7.41 Determine the distance a for which the maximum absolute value of the bending moment in beam AB is as small as possible. (See hint of Prob. 7.30.)

*7.42 A uniform beam is to be picked up by crane cables attached at A and B. Determine the distance a from the ends of the beam to the points where the cables should be attached if the maximum absolute value of the bending moment in the beam is to be as small as possible. (*Hint.* Draw the bending-moment diagram in terms of a, L, and the weight w per unit length, and then equate the absolute values of the largest positive and negative bending moments obtained.)

Fig. P7.42

*7.43 In order to reduce the bending moment in the cantilever beam AB, a cable and counterweight are permanently attached at end B. Determine the magnitude of the counterweight for which the maximum absolute value of the bending moment in the beam is as small as possible. (*a*) Consider only the case when the force **P** is actually applied at C. (*b*) Consider the more general case when the force **P** may either be applied at C or removed.

Fig. P7.43

* 7.6. Relations among Load, Shear, and Bending Moment.

When a beam carries more than two or three concentrated loads, or when it carries distributed loads, the method outlined in Sec. 7.5 for plotting shear and bending moment may prove quite cumbersome. The construction of the shear diagram and, especially, of the bending-moment diagram will be greatly facilitated if certain relations existing among load, shear, and bending moment are taken into consideration.

Let us consider a simply supported beam AB carrying a distributed load w per unit length (Fig. 7.11*a*), and let C and C' be two points of the beam at a distance Δx from each other. The shear and bending moment at C will be denoted by V and M, respectively, and will be assumed positive; the shear and bending moment at C' will be denoted by $V + \Delta V$ and $M + \Delta M$.

We shall now detach the portion of beam CC' and draw its free-body diagram (Fig. 7.11*b*). The forces exerted on the free body include a load of magnitude $w\,\Delta x$ and internal forces and couples at C and C'. Since shear and bending moment have been assumed positive, the forces and couples will be directed as shown in the figure.

Relations between Load and Shear. We write that the sum of the vertical components of the forces acting on the free body CC' is zero:

$$V - (V + \Delta V) - w\,\Delta x = 0$$
$$\Delta V = -w\,\Delta x$$

Dividing both members of the equation by Δx and then letting Δx approach zero, we obtain

$$\frac{dV}{dx} = -w \qquad (7.1)$$

Fig. 7.11

Formula (7.1) indicates that for a beam loaded as shown in Fig. 7.11*a*, the slope dV/dx of the shear curve is negative; the numerical value of the slope at any point is equal to the load per unit length at that point.

Integrating (7.1) between points C and D, we obtain

$$V_D - V_C = -\int_{x_C}^{x_D} w\,dx \qquad (7.2)$$

$$V_D - V_C = -(\text{area under load curve between } C \text{ and } D) \qquad (7.2')$$

(a)

Fig. 7.11 (repeated)

(b)

Note that this result could also have been obtained by considering the equilibrium of the portion of beam CD, since the area under the load curve represents the total load applied between C and D.

It should be observed that formula (7.1) *is not valid* at a point where a concentrated load is applied; the shear curve is discontinuous at such a point, as seen in Sec. 7.5. Similarly, formulas (7.2) and (7.2′) cease to be valid when concentrated loads are applied between C and D, since they do not take into account the sudden change in shear caused by a concentrated load. Formulas (7.2) and (7.2′), therefore, should be applied only between successive concentrated loads.

Relations between Shear and Bending Moment. Returning to the free-body diagram of Fig. 7.11*b*, and writing now that the sum of the moments about C' is zero, we obtain

$$(M + \Delta M) - M - V\,\Delta x + w\,\Delta x \frac{\Delta x}{2} = 0$$

$$\Delta M = V\,\Delta x - \tfrac{1}{2}w(\Delta x)^2$$

Dividing both members of the equation by Δx and then letting Δx approach zero, we obtain

$$\frac{dM}{dx} = V \tag{7.3}$$

Formula (7.3) indicates that the slope dM/dx of the bending-moment curve is equal to the value of the shear. This is true at any point where the shear has a well-defined value, i.e., at any point where no concentrated load is applied. Formula (7.3) also shows that the shear is zero at points where the bending moment is maximum. This property facilitates the determination of the points where the beam is likely to fail under bending.

Integating (7.3) between points C and D, we obtain

$$M_D - M_C = \int_{x_C}^{x_D} V\,dx \tag{7.4}$$

$$M_D - M_C = \text{area under shear curve between } C \text{ and } D \tag{7.4′}$$

Note that the area under the shear curve should be considered positive where the shear is positive and negative where the shear is negative. Formulas (7.4) and (7.4′) are valid even when concentrated loads are applied between C and D, as long as the shear curve has been correctly drawn. The formulas cease to be valid, however, if a *couple* is applied at a point between C and D, since they do not take into account the sudden change in bending moment caused by a couple (see Sample Prob. 7.7).

Example. Let us consider a simply supported beam AB of span L carrying a uniformly distributed load w (Fig. 7.12a). From the free-body diagram of the entire beam we determine the magnitude of the reactions at the supports: $R_A = R_B = wL/2$ (Fig. 7.12b). Next, we draw the shear diagram. Close to the end A of the beam, the shear is equal to R_A, that is, to $wL/2$, as we may check by considering as a free body a very small portion of the beam. Using formula (7.2), we may then determine the shear V at any distance x from A; we write

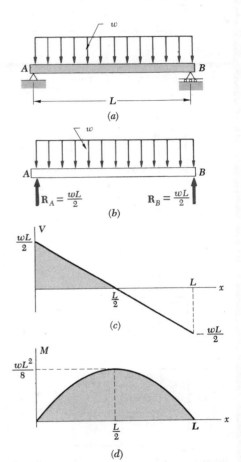

$$V - V_A = -\int_0^x w\,dx = -wx$$

$$V = V_A - wx = \frac{wL}{2} - wx = w\left(\frac{L}{2} - x\right)$$

The shear curve is thus an oblique straight line which crosses the x axis at $x = L/2$ (Fig. 7.12c). Considering, now, the bending moment, we first observe that $M_A = 0$. The value M of the bending moment at any distance x from A may then be obtained from formula (7.4); we have

$$M - M_A = \int_0^x V\,dx$$

$$M = \int_0^x w\left(\frac{L}{2} - x\right)dx = \frac{w}{2}(Lx - x^2)$$

The bending-moment curve is a parabola. The maximum value of the bending moment occurs when $x = L/2$, since V (and thus dM/dx) is zero for that value of x. Substituting $x = L/2$ in the last equation, we obtain $M_{max} = wL^2/8$.

In most engineering applications, the value of the bending moment needs to be known only at a few specific points. Once the shear diagram has been drawn, and after M has been determined at one of the ends of the beam, the value of the bending moment may then be obtained at any given point by computing the area under the shear curve and using formula (7.4′). For instance, since $M_A = 0$ for the beam of Fig. 7.12, the maximum value of the bending moment for that beam may be obtained simply by measuring the area of the shaded triangle in the shear diagram:

$$M_{max} = \frac{1}{2}\frac{L}{2}\frac{wL}{2} = \frac{wL^2}{8}$$

Fig. 7.12

We note that in this example, the load curve is a horizontal straight line, the shear curve an oblique straight line, and the bending-moment curve a parabola. If the load curve had been an oblique straight line (first degree), the shear curve would have been a parabola (second degree) and the bending-moment curve a cubic (third degree). The shear and bending-moment curves will always be, respectively, one and two degrees higher than the load curve. With this in mind, we should be able to sketch the shear and bending-moment diagrams without actually determining the functions $V(x)$ and $M(x)$, once a few values of the shear and bending moment have been computed. The sketches obtained will be more accurate if we make use of the fact that at any point where the curves are continuous, the slope of the shear curve is equal to $-w$ and the slope of the bending-moment curve is equal to V.

100 kN   60 kN   15 kN/m

SAMPLE PROBLEM 7.4

Draw the shear and bending-moment diagrams for the beam and loading shown.

Solution. Considering the entire beam as a free body, we determine the reactions:

$+\Sigma\uparrow M_A = 0:$

$$D(12\ m) - (100\ kN)(3\ m) - (60\ kN)(7\ m) - (60\ kN)(14\ m) = 0$$

$$D = +130\ kN \qquad\qquad \mathbf{D = 130\ kN \uparrow}$$

$+\uparrow \Sigma F_y = 0: \qquad A_y - 100\ kN - 60\ kN + 130\ kN - 60\ kN = 0$

$$A_y = +90\ kN \qquad\qquad A_y = 90\ kN \uparrow$$

$\xrightarrow{+}\Sigma F_x = 0: \qquad A_x = 0 \qquad\qquad\qquad \mathbf{A_x = 0}$

We also note that at both A and E the bending moment is zero; thus two points (indicated by dots) are obtained on the bending-moment diagram.

Shear Diagram. Since $dV/dx = -w$, we find that between concentrated loads and reactions the slope of the shear diagram is zero (i.e., the shear is constant). The shear at any point is determined by dividing the beam into two parts and considering either part as a free body. For example, using the portion of beam to the left of section *1*, we obtain the shear between B and C:

$+\uparrow \Sigma F_y = 0: \qquad +90\ kN - 100\ kN - V = 0 \qquad V = -10\ kN$

We also find that the shear is $+60$ kN just to the right of D and zero at end E. Since the slope $dV/dx = -w$ is constant between D and E, the shear diagram between these two points is a straight line.

Bending-Moment Diagram. We recall that the area under the shear curve between two points is equal to the change in bending moment between the same two points. For convenience, the area of each portion of the shear diagram is computed and is indicated on the diagram. Since the bending moment M_A at the left end is known to be zero, we write

$$
\begin{array}{ll}
M_B - M_A = +270 & M_B = +270\ kN\cdot m \\
M_C - M_B = -\ 40 & M_C = +230\ kN\cdot m \\
M_D - M_C = -350 & M_D = -120\ kN\cdot m \\
M_E - M_D = +120 & M_B = 0
\end{array}
$$

Since M_E is known to be zero, a check of the computations is obtained.

Between the concentrated loads and reactions the shear is constant, thus the slope dM/dx is constant and the bending-moment diagram is drawn by connecting the known points with straight lines. Between D and E where the shear diagram is an oblique straight line, the bending-moment diagram is a parabola.

From the V and M diagrams we note that $V_{max} = 90$ kN and $M_{max} = 270$ kN·m.

20 kN/m

A   C
    B

|← 6 m →|← 3 m →|

Draw the shear and bending-moment diagrams for the beam and loading shown.

Solution. Considering the entire beam as a free body, we obtain the reactions

$$\mathbf{R}_A = 80 \text{ kN} \uparrow \qquad \mathbf{R}_C = 40 \text{ kN} \uparrow$$

Shear Diagram. The shear just to the right of A is $V_A = +80$ kN. Since the change in shear between two points is equal to *minus* the area under the load curve between the same two points, we obtain V_B by writing

$$V_B - V_A = -(20 \text{ kN/m})(6 \text{ m}) = -120 \text{ kN}$$
$$V_B = -120 + V_A = -120 + 80 = -40 \text{ kN}$$

The slope $dV/dx = -w$ being constant between A and B, the shear diagram between these two points is represented by a straight line. Between B and C, the area under the load curve is zero; therefore,

$$V_C - V_B = 0 \qquad V_C = V_B = -40 \text{ kN}$$

and the shear is constant between B and C.

Bending-Moment Diagram. We note that the bending moment at each end of the beam is zero. In order to determine the maximum bending moment, we locate the section D of the beam where $V = 0$. Considering the portion of the shear diagram between A and B, we note that the triangles DAa and DBb are similar; thus,

$$\frac{x}{80 \text{ kN}} = \frac{6 - x}{40 \text{ kN}} \qquad x = 4 \text{ m}$$

The maximum bending moment occurs at point D, where we have $dM/dx = V = 0$. The areas of the various portions of the shear diagram are computed and are given (in parentheses) on the diagram. Since the area of the shear diagram between two points is equal to the change in bending moment between the same two points, we write

$$
\begin{aligned}
M_D - M_A &= +160 \text{ kN·m} & M_D &= +160 \text{ kN·m} \\
M_B - M_D &= - 40 \text{ kN·m} & M_B &= +120 \text{ kN·m} \\
M_C - M_B &= -120 \text{ kN·m} & M_C &= 0
\end{aligned}
$$

The bending-moment diagram consists of an arc of parabola followed by a segment of straight line; the slope of the parabola at A is equal to the value of V at that point.

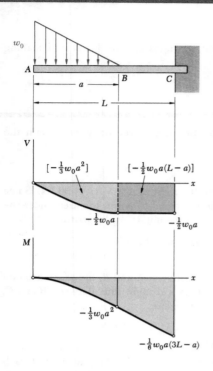

SAMPLE PROBLEM 7.6

Sketch the shear and bending-moment diagrams for the cantilever beam shown.

Solution. *Shear Diagram.* At the free end of the beam, we find $V_A = 0$. Between A and B, the area under the load curve is $\frac{1}{2}w_0 a$; we find V_B by writing

$$V_B - V_A = -\tfrac{1}{2}w_0 a \qquad V_B = -\tfrac{1}{2}w_0 a$$

Between B and C, the beam is not loaded; thus $V_C = V_B$. At A, we have $w = w_0$ and, according to Eq. (7.1), the slope of the shear curve is $dV/dx = -w_0$, while at B the slope is $dV/dx = 0$. Between A and B, the loading decreases linearly, and the shear diagram is parabolic. Between B and C, $w = 0$, and the shear diagram is a horizontal line.

Bending-Moment Diagram. The bending moment M_A at the free end of the beam is zero. We compute the area under the shear curve and write

$$M_B - M_A = -\tfrac{1}{3}w_0 a^2 \qquad M_B = -\tfrac{1}{3}w_0 a^2$$
$$M_C - M_B = -\tfrac{1}{2}w_0 a(L - a)$$
$$M_C = -\tfrac{1}{6}w_0 a(3L - a)$$

The sketch of the bending-moment diagram is completed by recalling that $dM/dx = V$. We find that between A and B the diagram is represented by a cubic curve with zero slope at A, and between B and C by a straight line.

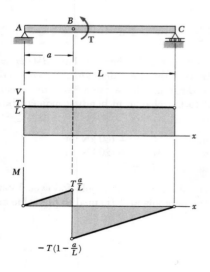

SAMPLE PROBLEM 7.7

The simple beam AC is loaded by a couple of magnitude T applied at point B. Draw the shear and bending-moment diagrams of the beam.

Solution. The entire beam is taken as a free body, and we obtain

$$\mathbf{R}_A = \frac{T}{L}\uparrow \qquad \mathbf{R}_C = \frac{T}{L}\downarrow$$

The shear at any section is constant and equal to T/L. Since a couple is applied at B, the bending-moment diagram is discontinuous at B; the bending moment decreases suddenly by an amount equal to T.

Problems

7.44 Using the methods of Sec. 7.6, solve Prob. 7.20.
7.45 Using the methods of Sec. 7.6, solve Prob. 7.21.
7.46 Using the methods of Sec. 7.6, solve Prob. 7.22.
7.47 Using the methods of Sec. 7.6, solve Prob. 7.23.
7.48 Using the methods of Sec. 7.6, solve Prob. 7.26.
7.49 Using the methods of Sec. 7.6, solve Prob. 7.27.
7.50 Using the methods of Sec. 7.6, solve Prob. 7.28.
7.51 Using the methods of Sec. 7.6, solve Prob. 7.29.
7.52 Using the methods of Sec. 7.6, solve Prob. 7.32.
7.53 Using the methods of Sec. 7.6, solve Prob. 7.33.
7.54 Using the methods of Sec. 7.6, solve Prob. 7.34.
7.55 Using the methods of Sec. 7.6, solve Prob. 7.37.

7.56 through 7.59 Draw the shear and bending-moment diagrams for the beam and loading shown.

Fig. P7.56

Fig. P7.57

Fig. P7.58

Fig. P7.59

7.60 through 7.65 Draw the shear and bending-moment diagrams for the beam and loading shown, and determine the location and magnitude of the maximum bending moment.

Fig. P7.60

Fig. P7.61

Fig. P7.62

Fig. P7.63

Fig. P7.64

Fig. P7.65

7.66 Determine the equations of the shear and bending-moment curves for the beam and loading of Prob. 7.24. (Place the origin at point A.)

7.67 through 7.69 Determine the equations of the shear and bending-moment curves for the given beam and loading. Also determine the magnitude and location of the maximum bending moment in the beam.

Fig. P7.67

Fig. P7.68

Fig. P7.69

Fig. P7.70

7.70 The beam AB supports the uniformly distributed load of 1000 N/m and two concentrated loads $\mathbf{P}$ and $\mathbf{Q}$. It has been experimentally determined that the bending moment is -395 N·m at point A and -215 N·m at point C. Determine $\mathbf{P}$ and $\mathbf{Q}$ and draw the shear and bending-moment diagrams for the beam.

*7.71 The beam AB is acted upon by the uniformly distributed load of 30 kN/m and by two forces $\mathbf{P}$ and $\mathbf{Q}$. It has been experimentally determined that the bending moment is $+235$ kN·m at point D and $+320$ kN·m at point E. Determine $\mathbf{P}$ and $\mathbf{Q}$, and draw the shear and bending-moment diagrams for the beam.

Fig. P7.71

*7.72 Solve Prob. 7.71, assuming that the uniformly distributed load of 30 kN/m extends over the entire beam AB.

*7.73 Solve Prob. 7.70, assuming that the uniformly distributed load of 1000 N/m extends over the entire beam AB.

Fig. P7.74

*7.74 A uniform beam of weight w per unit length is supported as shown. Determine the distance a if the maximum absolute value of the bending moment is to be as small as possible. (See hint of Prob. 7.42.)

Fig. P7.75

*7.75 A beam AB is loaded by couples spaced uniformly along its length from end A to point C. Assuming that the couples may be represented by a uniformly distributed couple loading of m N·m/m, draw the shear and bending-moment diagrams for the beam.

* 7.7. Cables with Concentrated Loads.

Cables are used in many engineering applications, such as suspension bridges, transmission lines, aerial tramways, guy wires for high towers, etc. Cables may be divided into two categories, according to their loading: (1) cables supporting concentrated loads, (2) cables supporting distributed loads. In this section, we shall examine cables of the first category.

Consider a cable attached to two fixed points A and B and supporting n given vertical concentrated loads $\mathbf{P}_1, \mathbf{P}_2, \ldots, \mathbf{P}_n$ (Fig. 7.13a). We assume that the cable is *flexible*, i.e., that its resistance to bending is small and may be neglected. We further assume that the *weight of the cable is negligible* compared with the loads supported by the cable. Any portion of cable between successive loads may therefore be considered as a two-force member, and the internal forces at any point in the cable reduce to a *force of tension directed along the cable*.

We assume that each of the loads lies in a given vertical line, i.e., that the horizontal distance from support A to each of the loads is known; we also assume that the horizontal and vertical distances between the supports are known. We propose to determine the shape of the cable, i.e., the vertical distance from support A to each of the points $C_1, C_2, \ldots, C_n$, and also the tension T in each portion of the cable.

(a)   (b)

Fig. 7.13

We first draw the free-body diagram of the entire cable (Fig. 7.13b). Since the slope of the portions of cable attached at A and B is not known, the reactions at A and B must be represented by two components each. Thus, four unknowns are involved, and the three equations of equilibrium are not sufficient to determine the reactions at A and B.† We must therefore obtain an additional equation by considering the equilibrium of a por-

---

† Clearly, the cable is not a rigid body; the equilibrium equations represent, therefore, *necessary but not sufficient conditions* (see Sec. 6.11).

(a)

Fig. 7.13 (repeated)

(b)

(a)

(b)

Fig. 7.14

tion of the cable. This is possible if we know the coordinates x and y of a point D of the cable. Drawing the free-body diagram of the portion of cable AD (Fig. 7.14a) and writing $\Sigma M_D = 0$, we obtain an additional relation between the scalar components A_x and A_y and may determine the reactions at A and B. The problem would remain indeterminate, however, if we did not know the coordinates of D, unless some other relation between A_x and A_y (or between B_x and B_y) were given. The cable might hang in any of various possible ways, as indicated by the dashed lines in Fig. 7.13b.

Once A_x and A_y have been determined, the vertical distance from A to any point of the cable may be easily found. Considering point C_2, for example, we draw the free-body diagram of the portion of cable AC_2 (Fig. 7.14b). Writing $\Sigma M_{C_2} = 0$, we obtain an equation which may be solved for y_2. Writing $\Sigma F_x = 0$ and $\Sigma F_y = 0$, we obtain the components of the force $\mathbf{T}$ representing the tension in the portion of cable to the right of C_2. We observe that $T \cos \theta = -A_x$; *the horizontal component of the tension force is the same at any point of the cable.* It follows that the tension T is maximum when $\cos \theta$ is minimum, i.e., in the portion of cable which has the largest angle of inclination θ. Clearly, this portion of cable must be adjacent to one of the two supports of the cable.

* 7.8. Cables with Distributed Loads. Consider a cable attached to two fixed points A and B and carrying a *distributed load* (Fig. 7.15a). We saw in the preceding section that for a cable supporting concentrated loads, the internal force at any point is a force of tension directed along the cable. In the case of a cable carrying a distributed load, the cable hangs in the shape of a curve, and the internal force at a point D is a force of tension $\mathbf{T}$ *directed along the tangent to the curve.* Given a certain distributed load, we propose in this section to determine the tension at any point of the cable. We shall also see in the following sections how the shape of the cable may be determined for two particular types of distributed loads.

Considering the most general case of distributed load, we draw the free-body diagram of the portion of cable extending from the lowest point

Fig. 7.15   (a)   (b)   (c)

C to a given point D of the cable (Fig. 7.15b). The forces acting on the free body are the tension force $\mathbf{T_0}$ at C, which is horizontal, the tension force $\mathbf{T}$ at D, directed along the tangent to the cable at D, and the resultant $\mathbf{W}$ of the distributed load supported by the portion of cable CD. Drawing the corresponding force triangle (Fig. 7.15c), we obtain the following relations:

$$T \cos \theta = T_0 \qquad T \sin \theta = W \tag{7.5}$$

$$T = \sqrt{T_0^2 + W^2} \qquad \tan \theta = \frac{W}{T_0} \tag{7.6}$$

From the relations (7.5), it appears that the horizontal component of the tension force $\mathbf{T}$ is the same at any point and that the vertical component of $\mathbf{T}$ is equal to the magnitude W of the load measured from the lowest point. Relations (7.6) show that the tension T is minimum at the lowest point and maximum at one of the two points of support.

* 7.9. Parabolic Cable.   Let us assume, now, that the cable AB carries a load *uniformly distributed along the horizontal* (Fig. 7.16a). Cables of suspension bridges may be assumed loaded in this way, since the weight of the cables is small compared with the weight of the roadway. We denote by w the load per unit length (*measured horizontally*) and express it in N/m. Choosing coordinate axes with origin at the lowest point C of the cable, we find that the magnitude W of the total load carried by the portion of cable extending from C to the point D of coordinates x and y is $W = wx$. The relations (7.6) defining the magnitude and direction of the tension force at D become

$$T = \sqrt{T_0^2 + w^2x^2} \qquad \tan \theta = \frac{wx}{T_0} \tag{7.7}$$

Moreover, the distance from D to the line of action of the resultant $\mathbf{W}$ is equal to half the horizontal distance from C to D (Fig. 7.16b). Summing moments about D, we write

$+\uparrow \ \Sigma M_D = 0: \qquad wx\dfrac{x}{2} - T_0 y = 0$

(a)

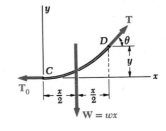

(b)

Fig. 7.16

and, solving for y,

$$y = \frac{wx^2}{2T_0} \tag{7.8}$$

This is the equation of a *parabola* with a vertical axis and its vertex at the origin of coordinates. The curve formed by cables loaded uniformly along the horizontal is thus a parabola.†

When the supports A and B of the cable have the same elevation, the distance L between the supports is called the *span* of the cable and the vertical distance h from the supports to the lowest point is called the *sag* of the cable (Fig. 7.17*a*). If the span and sag of a cable are known, and if the load w per unit horizontal length is given, the minimum tension T_0 may be found by substituting $x = L/2$ and $y = h$ in formula (7.8). Formulas (7.7) and (7.8) will then define the tension at any point and the shape of the cable.

When the supports have different elevations, the position of the lowest point of the cable is not known and the coordinates x_A, y_A and x_B, y_B of the supports must be determined. To this effect, we express that the coordinates of A and B satisfy Eq. (7.8) and that $x_B - x_A = L$, $y_B - y_A = d$, where L and d denote, respectively, the horizontal and vertical distances between the two supports (Fig. 7.17*b* and *c*).

The length of the cable from its lowest point C to its support B may be obtained from the formula

(a)

(b)

$$s_B = \int_0^{x_B} \sqrt{1 + \left(\frac{dy}{dx}\right)^2}\, dx \tag{7.9}$$

Differentiating (7.8), we obtain the derivative $dy/dx = wx/T_0$; substituting into (7.9) and using the binomial theorem to expand the radical in an infinite series, we have

$$s_B = \int_0^{x_B} \sqrt{1 + \frac{w^2 x^2}{T_0^2}}\, dx = \int_0^{x_B} \left(1 + \frac{w^2 x^2}{2T_0^2} - \frac{w^4 x^4}{8T_0^4} + \cdots\right) dx$$

$$s_B = x_B \left(1 + \frac{w^2 x_B^2}{6T_0^2} - \frac{w^4 x_B^4}{40T_0^4} + \cdots\right)$$

(c)

Fig. 7.17

and, since $wx_B^2/2T_0 = y_B$,

$$s_B = x_B \left[1 + \frac{2}{3}\left(\frac{y_B}{x_B}\right)^2 - \frac{2}{5}\left(\frac{y_B}{x_B}\right)^4 + \cdots\right] \tag{7.10}$$

The series converges for values of the ratio y_B/x_B less than 0.5; in most cases, this ratio is much smaller, and only the first two terms of the series need be computed.

---

† Cables hanging under their own weight are not loaded uniformly along the horizontal, and they do not form a parabola. The error introduced by assuming a parabolic shape for cables hanging under their own weight, however, is small when the cable is sufficiently taut. A complete discussion of cables hanging under their own weight is given in the next section.

The cable AE supports three vertical loads from the points indicated. If point C is 1.5 m below the left support, determine (a) the elevations of points B and D, (b) the maximum slope and the maximum tension in the cable.

Solution. The reaction components $\mathbf{A}_x$ and $\mathbf{A}_y$ are determined as follows:

Free Body: Entire Cable

$+\curvearrowleft\Sigma M_E = 0$:

$A_x(6 \text{ m}) - A_y(18 \text{ m}) + (30 \text{ kN})(12 \text{ m})$
$$+ (60 \text{ kN})(9 \text{ m}) + (20 \text{ kN})(4.5 \text{ m}) = 0$$
$$6A_x - 18A_y + 990 = 0$$

Free Body: ABC

$+\curvearrowleft\Sigma M_C = 0$: $\quad - A_x(1.5 \text{ m}) - A_y(9 \text{ m}) + (30 \text{ kN})(3 \text{ m}) = 0$
$$- 1.5 A_x - 9 A_y + 90 = 0$$

Solving the two equations simultaneously, we obtain

$$A_x = - 90 \text{ kN} \qquad \mathbf{A}_x = 90 \text{ kN} \leftarrow$$
$$A_y = + 25 \text{ kN} \qquad \mathbf{A}_y = 25 \text{ kN}\uparrow$$

a. Elevation of Point B. Considering the portion of cable AB as a free body, we write

$+\curvearrowleft\Sigma M_B = 0$: $\quad (90 \text{ kN})y_B - (25 \text{ kN})(6 \text{ m}) = 0$
$$y_B = 1.667 \text{ m below } A \quad \blacktriangleleft$$

Elevation of Point D. Using the portion of cable $ABCD$ as a free body, we write

$+\curvearrowleft\Sigma M_D = 0$:
$- (90 \text{ kN})y_D - (25 \text{ kN})(13.5 \text{ m}) + (30 \text{ kN})(7.5 \text{ m}) + (60 \text{ kN})(4.5 \text{ m}) = 0$
$$y_D = 1.75 \text{ m above } A \quad \blacktriangleleft$$

b. Maximum Slope and Maximum Tension. We observe that the maximum slope occurs in portion DE. Since the horizontal component of the tension is constant and equal to 90 kN, we write

$$\tan \theta = \frac{4.25 \text{ m}}{4.5 \text{ m}} \qquad \theta = 43.4° \quad \blacktriangleleft$$

$$T_{\text{max}} = \frac{90 \text{ kN}}{\cos \theta} \qquad T_{\text{max}} = 123.8 \text{ kN} \quad \blacktriangleleft$$

SAMPLE PROBLEM 7.9

A light cable is attached to a support at A, passes over a small pulley at B, and supports a load $\mathbf{P}$. Knowing that the sag of the cable is 0.5 m and that the mass per unit length of the cable is 0.75 kg/m, determine (a) the magnitude of the load $\mathbf{P}$, (b) the slope of the cable at B, and (c) the total length of the cable from A to B. Since the ratio of the sag to the span is small, assume the cable to be parabolic. Also, neglect the weight of the portion of cable from B to D.

a. **Load P.** We denote by C the lowest point of the cable and draw the free-body diagram of the portion CB of cable. Assuming the load to be uniformly distributed along the horizontal, we write

$$w = (0.75 \text{ kg/m})(9.81 \text{ m/s}^2) = 7.36 \text{ N/m}$$

The total load for the portion CB of the cable is

$$W = wx_B = (7.36 \text{ N/m})(20 \text{ m}) = 147.2 \text{ N}$$

and is applied halfway between C and B. Summing moments about B, we write

$$+\uparrow \Sigma M_B = 0: \qquad (147.2 \text{ N})(10 \text{ m}) - T_0(0.5 \text{ m}) = 0 \qquad T_0 = 2944 \text{ N}$$

From the force triangle we obtain

$$T_B = \sqrt{T_0^2 + W^2}$$
$$= \sqrt{(2944 \text{ N})^2 + (147.2 \text{ N})^2} = 2948 \text{ N}$$

Since the tension on each side of the pulley is the same, we find

$$P = T_B = 2948 \text{ N} \quad \blacktriangleleft$$

b. **Slope of Cable at B.** We also obtain from the force triangle

$$\tan \theta = \frac{W}{T_0} = \frac{147.2 \text{ N}}{2944 \text{ N}} = 0.05$$

$$\theta = 2.9° \quad \blacktriangleleft$$

c. **Length of Cable.** Applying Eq. (7.10) between C and B, we write

$$s_B = x_B \left[1 + \frac{2}{3}\left(\frac{y_B}{x_B}\right)^2 + \cdots \right]$$
$$= (20 \text{ m})\left[1 + \frac{2}{3}\left(\frac{0.5 \text{ m}}{20 \text{ m}}\right)^2 + \cdots \right] = 20.00833 \text{ m}$$

The total length of the cable between A and B is twice this value,

$$\text{Length} = 2s_B = 40.0167 \text{ m} \quad \blacktriangleleft$$

Problems

7.76 Three loads are suspended as shown from the cable. Knowing that $h_C = 4$ m, determine (a) the components of the reaction at E, (b) the maximum value of the tension in the cable.

Fig. P7.76 and P7.77

7.77 Determine the sag at point C if the maximum tension in the cable is 25 kN.

7.78 If $a = 3.2$ m and $b = 4$ m, determine the components of the reaction at E for the cable and loading shown.

7.79 If $a = b = 2.4$ m, determine (a) the components of the reaction at E, (b) the maximum tension in the cable.

7.80 If $h_C = 8$ m, determine (a) the components of the reaction at E, (b) the maximum tension in the cable.

Fig. P7.78 and P7.79

Fig. P7.80 and P7.81

7.81 Determine (a) the distance h_C for which the portion CD of the cable is horizontal, (b) the corresponding components of the reaction at E.

7.82 Cable ABC supports two loads as shown. Knowing that the distance b is to be 6 m, determine (a) the required magnitude of the force $\mathbf{P}$, (b) the corresponding distance a.

7.83 Cable ABC supports two loads as shown. Determine the distances a and b when a horizontal force $\mathbf{P}$ of magnitude 800 N is applied at C.

Fig. P7.82 and P7.83

7.84 Knowing that the 1300-N force applied at B and the block attached at C maintain cable $ABCD$ in the position shown, determine (a) the reaction at A, (b) the required weight W of the block, (c) the tension in each portion of the cable.

Fig. P7.84

7.85 Knowing that the 440-N force applied at C and the block attached at B maintain the cable $ABCD$ in the position shown, determine (a) the reaction at D, (b) the required weight W of the block, (c) the tension in each portion of the cable.

Fig. P7.85

7.86 An electric wire having a mass per unit length of 0.6 kg/m is strung between two insulators at the same elevation and 60 m apart. Knowing that the sag of the wire is 1.5 m, determine (a) the maximum tension in the wire, (b) the length of the wire.

7.87 The center span of the George Washington Bridge, as originally constructed, consisted of a uniform roadway suspended from four cables. The uniform load supported by each cable was $w = 142$ kN/m along the horizontal. Knowing that the span L is 1050 m and the sag h is 94.8 m, determine (a) the maximum tension in each cable, (b) the length of each cable.

7.88 The center span of the Verrazano-Narrows Bridge consists of two uniform roadways suspended from four cables. The design of the bridge included the effect of extreme temperature changes which cause the sag of the center span to vary from $h_w = 115.8$ m in winter to $h_s = 118.2$ m in summer. Knowing that the span is $L = 1278$ m, determine the change in length of the cables due to extreme temperature variation.

7.89 A 76-m length of wire having a mass per unit length of 2.2 kg/m is used to span a horizontal distance of 75 m. Determine (a) the approximate sag of the wire, (b) the maximum tension in the wire. [*Hint.* Use only the first two terms of Eq. (7.10).]

7.90 The total mass of cable ACB is 10 kg. Assuming that the mass of the cable is distributed uniformly along the horizontal, determine (a) the sag h, (b) the slope of the cable at A.

Fig. P7.90

7.91   The total mass of cable AC is 25 kg. Assuming that the mass of the cable is distributed uniformly along the horizontal, determine the sag h and the slope of the cable at A and C.

Fig. P7.91

7.92   Cable AB supports a load distributed uniformly along the horizontal as shown. The lowest point of the cable is located at a distance $a = 3$ m below the support A. Determine the maximum and minimum values of the tension in the cable.

Fig. P7.92

7.93   Before being fed into a printing press located to the right of D, a continuous sheet of paper having a mass per unit length of 300 g/m passes over rollers at A and B. Assuming that the curve formed by the sheet is parabolic, determine (a) the location of the lowest point C, (b) the maximum tension in the sheet.

Fig. P7.93

7.94   Solve Prob. 7.93, assuming that $a = 120$ mm.

7.95   Solve Prob. 7.92, assuming that $a = 2$ m.

*7.96   A cable AB of span L and a simple beam $A'B'$ of the same span are subjected to identical vertical loadings as shown. Show that the magnitude of the bending moment at a point C' in the beam is equal to the product of T_0h, where T_0 is the magnitude of the horizontal component of the tension force in the cable and h is the vertical distance between point C of the cable and the chord joining the points of support A and B.

Fig. P7.96

*7.97   Show that the curve assumed by a cable which carries a distributed load $w(x)$ is defined by the differential equation $d^2y/dx^2 = w(x)/T_0$, where T_0 is the tension at the lowest point.

Fig. P7.98

*7.98 If the weight per unit length of the cable AB is $w_0/\cos^2\theta$, prove that the curve formed by the cable is a circular arc. (*Hint:* Use the property indicated in Prob. 7.97.)

*7.99 A large number of ropes are tied to a light wire which is suspended from two points A and B at the same level. Show that, if the lower ends of the ropes have been cut so that they lie in the same horizontal line and if the ropes are kept uniformly spaced, the curve assumed by the wire ACB is

$$y + d = d\cosh\left(\frac{w_r}{T_0 e}\right)^{1/2} x$$

where w_r is the weight per unit length of the ropes, d is the length of the shortest rope, and e is the horizontal distance between adjacent ropes. (*Hint.* Use the property indicated in Prob. 7.97.)

Fig. P7.99

*7.10. Catenary. We shall consider now a cable AB carrying a load *uniformly distributed along the cable itself* (Fig. 7.18a). Cables hanging under their own weight are loaded in this way. We denote by w the load per unit length (*measured along the cable*) and express it in N/m. The magnitude W of the total load carried by a portion of cable of length s extending from the lowest point C to a point D is $W = ws$. Substituting this value for W in formula (7.6), we obtain the tension at D:

$$T = \sqrt{T_0^2 + w^2 s^2}$$

In order to simplify the subsequent computations, we shall introduce the constant $c = T_0/w$. We thus write

$$T_0 = wc \qquad W = ws \qquad T = w\sqrt{c^2 + s^2} \tag{7.11}$$

The free-body diagram of the portion of cable CD is shown in Fig. 7.18b. This diagram, however, cannot be used to obtain directly the equa-

(a)

Fig. 7.18

(b)

(c)

tion of the curve assumed by the cable, since we do not know the horizontal distance from D to the line of action of the resultant $\mathbf{W}$ of the load. To obtain this equation, we shall write first that the horizontal projection of a small element of cable of length ds is $dx = ds \cos \theta$. Observing from Fig. 7.18c that $\cos \theta = T_0/T$ and using (7.11), we write

$$dx = ds \cos \theta = \frac{T_0}{T} ds = \frac{wc \, ds}{w\sqrt{c^2 + s^2}} = \frac{ds}{\sqrt{1 + s^2/c^2}}$$

Selecting the origin O of the coordinates at a distance c directly below C (Fig. 7.18a) and integrating from $C(0, c)$ to $D(x, y)$, we obtain†

$$x = \int_0^s \frac{ds}{\sqrt{1 + s^2/c^2}} = c\left[\sinh^{-1}\frac{s}{c} \right]_0^s = c \sinh^{-1}\frac{s}{c}$$

This equation, which relates the length s of the portion of cable CD and the horizontal distance x, may be written in the form

$$s = c \sinh \frac{x}{c} \tag{7.15}$$

The relation between the coordinates x and y may now be obtained by writing $dy = dx \tan \theta$. Observing from Fig. 7.18c that $\tan \theta = W/T_0$ and using (7.11) and (7.15), we write

$$dy = dx \tan \theta = \frac{W}{T_0} dx = \frac{s}{c} dx = \sinh \frac{x}{c} dx$$

Integrating from $C(0, c)$ to $D(x, y)$ and using (7.12) and (7.13), we obtain

$$y - c = \int_0^x \sinh \frac{x}{c} dx = c\left[\cosh \frac{x}{c} \right]_0^x = c\left(\cosh \frac{x}{c} - 1 \right)$$

$$y - c = c \cosh \frac{x}{c} - c$$

---

†This integral may be found in all standard integral tables. The function

$$z = \sinh^{-1} u$$

(read "arc hyperbolic sine u") is the *inverse* of the function $u = \sinh z$ (read "hyperbolic sine z"). This function and the function $v = \cosh z$ (read "hyperbolic cosine z") are defined as follows:

$$u = \sinh z = \tfrac{1}{2}(e^z - e^{-z}) \qquad v = \cosh z = \tfrac{1}{2}(e^z + e^{-z})$$

Numerical values of the functions $\sinh z$ and $\cosh z$ are found in *tables of hyperbolic functions*. They may also be computed on most calculators either directly or from the above definitions. The student is referred to any calculus text for a complete description of the properties of these functions. In this section, we shall make use only of the following properties, which may be easily derived from the above definitions:

$$\frac{d \sinh z}{dz} = \cosh z \qquad \frac{d \cosh z}{dz} = \sinh z \tag{7.12}$$

$$\sinh 0 = 0 \qquad \cosh 0 = 1 \tag{7.13}$$

$$\cosh^2 z - \sinh^2 z = 1 \tag{7.14}$$

which reduces to

$$y = c \cosh \frac{x}{c} \tag{7.16}$$

This is the equation of a *catenary* with vertical axis. The ordinate c of the lowest point C is called the *parameter* of the catenary. Squaring both sides of Eqs. (7.15) and (7.16), subtracting, and taking (7.14) into account, we obtain the following relation between y and s:

$$y^2 - s^2 = c^2 \tag{7.17}$$

Solving (7.17) for s^2 and carrying into the last of the relations (7.11), we write these relations as follows:

$$T_0 = wc \qquad W = ws \qquad T = wy \tag{7.18}$$

The last relation indicates that the tension at any point P of the cable is proportional to the vertical distance from D to the horizontal line representing the x axis.

When the supports A and B of the cable have the same elevation, the distance L between the supports is called the *span* of the cable and the vertical distance h from the supports to the lowest point C is called the *sag* of the cable. These definitions are the same that were given in the case of parabolic cables, but it should be noted that because of our choice of coordinate axes, the sag h is now

$$h = y_A - c \tag{7.19}$$

It should also be observed that certain catenary problems involve transcendental equations which must be solved by successive approximations (see Sample Prob. 7.10). When the cable is fairly taut, however, the load may be assumed uniformly distributed *along the horizontal* and the catenary may be replaced by a parabola. The solution of the problem is thus greatly simplified, while the error introduced is small.

When the supports A and B have different elevations, the position of the lowest point of the cable is not known. The problem may be solved then in a manner similar to that indicated for parabolic cables, by expressing that the cable must pass through the supports and that $x_B - x_A = L$, $y_B - y_A = d$, where L and d denote, respectively, the horizontal and vertical distances between the two supports.

SAMPLE PROBLEM 7.10

A uniform cable having a mass per unit length of 5 kg/m is suspended between two points A and B as shown. Determine (a) the maximum and minimum values of the tension in the cable, (b) the length of the cable.

Solution. *Equation of Cable.* The origin of coordinates is placed at a distance c below the lowest point of the cable. The equation of the cable is given by Eq. (7.16),

$$y = c \cosh \frac{x}{c}$$

The coordinates of point B are

$$x_B = 75 \text{ m} \qquad y_B = 30 \text{ m} + c$$

Substituting these coordinates into the equation of the cable, we obtain

$$30 + c = c \cosh \frac{75}{c}$$

$$\frac{30}{c} + 1 = \cosh \frac{75}{c}$$

The value of c is determined by assuming successive trial values, as shown in the following table:

c	$\dfrac{75}{c}$	$\dfrac{30}{c}$	$\dfrac{30}{c} + 1$	$\cosh \dfrac{75}{c}$
90	0.833	0.333	1.333	1.367
100	0.750	0.300	1.300	1.295
95	0.789	0.316	1.316	1.328
98	0.765	0.306	1.306	1.307
98.4	0.762	0.305	1.305	1.305

Taking $c = 98.4$, we have

$$y_B = 30 + c = 128.4 \text{ m}$$

a. Maximum and Minimum Values of the Tension. Using Eqs. (7.18) with $w = (5 \text{ kg/m})(9.81 \text{ m/s}^2) = 49.05 \text{ N/m}$, we obtain

$$T_{\min} = T_0 = wc = (49.05 \text{ N/m})(98.4 \text{ m}) \qquad T_{\min} = 4.83 \text{ kN} \blacktriangleleft$$
$$T_{\max} = T_B = wy_B = (49.05 \text{ N/m})(128.4 \text{ m}) \qquad T_{\max} = 6.30 \text{ kN} \blacktriangleleft$$

b. Length of Cable. One-half the length of the cable is found by solving Eq. (7.17),

$$y_B^2 - s_{CB}^2 = c^2 \qquad s_{CB}^2 = y_B^2 - c^2 = (128.4)^2 - (98.4)^2 \qquad s_{CB} = 82.5 \text{ m}$$

The total length of the cable is therefore

$$s_{AB} = 2s_{CB} = 2(82.5 \text{ m}) \qquad s_{AB} = 165 \text{ m} \blacktriangleleft$$

Problems

7.100 A 40-m rope is strung between the roofs of two buildings, each 14 m high. The maximum tension is found to be 350 N and the lowest point of the cable is observed to be 6 m above the ground. Determine (*a*) the horizontal distance between the buildings, (*b*) the total mass of the rope.

7.101 A 50-m steel surveying tape has a mass of 1.6 kg. If the tape is stretched between two points at the same elevation and pulled until the tension at each end is 60 N, determine the horizontal distance between the ends of the tape. Neglect the elongation of the tape due to the tension.

7.102 An aerial tramway cable of length 150 m and with a mass per unit length of 4 kg/m is suspended between two points at the same elevation. Knowing that the sag is 37.5 m, find (*a*) the horizontal distance between the supports, (*b*) the maximum tension in the cable.

7.103 A 7.5-m chain of mass 13 kg is suspended between two points at the same elevation. Knowing that the sag is observed to be 3 m, determine (*a*) the distance between the supports (*b*) the maximum tension in the chain.

Fig. P7.104

7.104 A counterweight *D* of mass 40 kg is attached to a cable which passes over a small pulley at *A* and is attached to a support at *B*. Knowing that *L* = 15 m and *h* = 5 m, determine (*a*) the length of the cable from *A* to *B*, (*b*) the mass per unit length of the cable. Neglect the mass of the cable from *A* to *D*.

7.105 Solve Prob. 7.104, assuming that the mass of the counterweight *D* is 60 kg.

7.106 The 3-m cable *AB* has a mass of 9 kg and is attached to collars at *A* and *B* which may slide freely on the rods shown. Neglecting the weight of the collars, determine (*a*) the magnitude of the horizontal force **F** so that *h* = *a*, (*b*) the corresponding value of *h* and *a*, (*c*) the maximum tension in the cable.

7.107 A 90-m wire is suspended between two points at the same elevation and 60 m apart. Knowing that the maximum tension is 300 N, determine the sag and the total weight of the wire.

Fig. P7.106

7.108 A uniform cord 900 mm long passes over a frictionless pulley at *B* and is attached to a rigid support at *A*. Knowing that *L* = 300 mm, determine the smaller of the two values of *h* for which the cord is in equilibrium.

Fig. P7.108 and P7.109

7.109 A uniform cord 1500 mm long passes over a frictionless pulley at *B* and is attached to a rigid support at *A*. Knowing that *L* = 600 mm, determine the smaller of the two values of *h* for which the cord is in equilibrium.

7.110 To the left of point B the long cable $ABDE$ rests on the rough horizontal surface shown. Knowing that the cable has a mass per unit length of 2.7 kg/m, determine the force $\mathbf{F}$ required when $a = 2.7$ m.

7.111 Solve Prob. 7.110 when $a = 4.5$ m.

7.112 Denoting by θ the angle formed by a uniform cable and the horizontal, show that at any point $y = c/\cos\theta$.

***7.113** (a) Determine the maximum allowable horizontal span for a uniform cable of weight w per unit length if the tension in the cable is not to exceed the value T_m. (b) Using the result of part a, find the maximum span of a drawn-steel wire for which $w = 3.6$ N/m and $T_m = 40$ kN.

***7.114** A cable has a mass per unit length of 4 kg/m and is supported as shown. Knowing that the span L is 6 m, determine the *two* values of the sag h for which the maximum tension is 500 N.

***7.115** Determine the sag-to-span ratio for which the maximum tension in the cable is equal to the total weight of the entire cable AB.

***7.116** A cable, of weight w per unit length, is suspended between two points at the same elevation and a distance L apart. Determine the sag-to-span ratio for which the maximum tension is as small as possible. What are the corresponding values of θ_B and T_m?

Fig. P7.110

Fig. P7.114, P7.115, and P7.116

Review and Summary

In this chapter we learned to determine the internal forces which hold together the various parts of a given member in a structure.

Fig. 7.19 (a)   (b)

Considering first a *straight two-force member AB* [Sec. 7.2], we recall that such a member is subjected at A and B to equal and opposite forces $\mathbf{F}$ and $-\mathbf{F}$ directed along AB (Fig. 7.19a). Cutting member AB at C and drawing the free-body diagram of portion AC, we conclude that the internal forces which existed at C in member AB are equivalent to an *axial force* $-\mathbf{F}$ equal and opposite to $\mathbf{F}$ (Fig. 7.19b). We note that in the case of a two-force member which is not straight, the internal forces reduce to a force-couple system and not to a single force.

Forces in straight two-force members

Forces in Beams and Cables

Fig. 7.20 (a)

Forces in multiforce members

Considering next a *multiforce member AD* (Fig. 7.20a), cutting it at *J*, and drawing the free-body diagram of portion *JD*, we conclude that the internal forces at *J* are equivalent to a force-couple system consisting of the *axial force* **F**, the *shearing force* **V**, and a couple **M** (Fig. 7.20b). The magnitude of the shearing force measures the *shear* at point *J* and the moment of the couple is referred to as the *bending moment* at *J*. Since an equal and opposite force-couple system would have been obtained by considering the free-body diagram of portion *AJ*, it is necessary to specify which portion of member *AD* was used when recording the answers [Sample Prob. 7.1].

Forces in beams

Most of the chapter was devoted to the analysis of the internal forces in two important types of engineering structures: *beams and cables*. *Beams* are usually long, straight prismatic members designed to support loads applied at various points along the member. In general the loads are perpendicular to the axis of the beam and produce only *shear and bending* in the beam. The loads may be either *concentrated* at specific points, or *distributed* along the entire length or a portion of the beam. The beam itself may be supported in various ways; since only statically determinate beams are considered in this text, we limited our analysis to that of *simply supported beams*, *overhanging beams*, and *cantilever beams* [Sec. 7.3].

Shear and bending moment in a beam

Internal forces at section
(positive shear and positive bending moment)
Fig. 7.21

To obtain the *shear V* and *bending moment M* at a given point *C* of a beam, we first determine the reactions at the supports by considering the entire beam as a free body. We then cut the beam at *C* and use the free-body diagram of one of the two portions obtained in this fashion to determine *V* and *M*. In order to avoid any confusion regarding the sense of the shearing force **V** and couple **M** (which act in opposite directions on the two portions of the beam), the sign convention illustrated in Fig. 7.21 was adopted [Sec. 7.4]. Once the values of the shear and bending moment have been determined at a few selected points of the beam, it is usually possible to draw a *shear diagram* and a *bending-moment diagram* representing, respectively, the shear and the bending moment at any point of the beam [Sec. 7.5]. When a beam is subjected to concentrated loads only, the shear is of constant value between loads and the bending moment varies linearly between loads [Sample Prob. 7.2]. On the other hand, when a beam is subjected to distributed loads, the shear and bending moment vary quite differently [Sample Prob. 7.3].

The construction of the shear and bending-moment diagrams is facilitated if the following relations are taken into account. Denoting by w the distributed load per unit length (assumed positive if directed downward), we have [Sec. 7.5]:

$$\frac{dV}{dx} = -w \qquad (7.1)$$

$$\frac{dM}{dx} = V \qquad (7.3)$$

or, in integrated form,

$$V_D - V_C = -(\text{area under load curve between } C \text{ and } D) \qquad (7.2')$$
$$M_D - M_C = \text{area under shear curve between } C \text{ and } D \qquad (7.4')$$

Equation (7.2') makes it possible to draw the shear diagram of a beam from the curve representing the distributed load on that beam and the value of V at one end of the beam. Similarly, Eq. (7.4') makes it possible to draw the bending-moment diagram from the shear diagram and the value of M at one end of the beam. However, concentrated loads introduce discontinuities in the shear diagram and concentrated couples in the bending-moment diagram, none of which is accounted for in these equations [Sample Probs. 7.4 and 7.7]. Finally, we note from Eq. (7.3) that the points of the beam where the bending moment is maximum or minimum are also the points where the shear is zero [Sample Prob. 7.5].

The second half of the chapter was devoted to the analysis of *flexible cables*. We first considered a cable of negligible weight supporting *concentrated loads* [Sec. 7.7]. Using the entire cable AB as a free body (Fig. 7.22), we noted that the three available equilibrium equations were not sufficient to determine the four unknowns representing the reactions at the supports A and B. However, if the coordinates of a point D of the cable are known, an additional equation may be obtained by considering the free-body diagram of the portion AD or DB of the cable. Once the reactions at the supports have been determined, the elevation of any point of the cable and the tension in any portion of the cable may be found from the appropriate free-body diagram [Sample Prob. 7.8]. It was noted that the horizontal component of the force $\mathbf{T}$ representing the tension is the same at any point of the cable.

We next considered cables carrying *distributed loads* [Sec. 7.8]. Using as a free body a portion of cable CD extending from the lowest point C to an arbitrary point D of the cable (Fig. 7.23), we observed that the horizontal component of the tension force $\mathbf{T}$ at D is constant and equal to the tension T_0 at C, while its vertical component is equal to the weight W of the portion of cable CD. The magnitude and direction of $\mathbf{T}$ were obtained from the force triangle:

$$T = \sqrt{T_0^2 + W^2} \qquad \tan \theta = \frac{W}{T_0} \qquad (7.6)$$

Relations among load, shear, and bending moment

Cables with concentrated loads

Fig. 7.22

Cables with distributed loads

Fig. 7.23

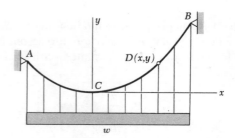

Fig. 7.24

Parabolic cable

In the case of a load *uniformly distributed along the horizontal*—as in a suspension bridge (Fig. 7.24)—the load supported by portion CD is $W = wx$, where w is the constant load per unit horizontal length [Sec. 7.9]. We also found that the curve formed by the cable is a *parabola* of equation

$$y = \frac{wx^2}{2T_0} \tag{7.8}$$

and that the length of the cable may be found by using the expansion in series given in Eq. (7.10) [Sample Prob. 7.9].

Catenary

In the case of a load *uniformly distributed along the cable itself*—e.g., a cable hanging under its own weight (Fig. 7.25)—the load supported by portion CD is $W = ws$, where s is the length measured along the cable and w is the constant load per unit length [Sec. 7.10]. Choosing the origin O of the coordinate axes at a distance $c = T_0/w$ below C, we derived the relations

$$s = c \sinh \frac{x}{c} \tag{7.15}$$

$$y = c \cosh \frac{x}{c} \tag{7.16}$$

$$y^2 - s^2 = c^2 \tag{7.17}$$

$$T_0 = wc \qquad W = ws \qquad T = wy \tag{7.18}$$

which may be used to solve problems involving cables hanging under their own weight [Sample Prob. 7.10]. Equation (7.16), which defines the shape of the cable, is the equation of a *catenary*.

Fig. 7.25

Fig. P7.117

Review Problems

7.117 Two cables of the same gage are attached to a transmission tower at B. Since the tower is slender, the horizontal component of the resultant of the forces exerted by the cable at B is to be zero. Assuming the cables to be parabolic, determine the required sag h of cable AB.

Fig. P7.118

Fig. P7.119 and P7.120

7.118 Draw the shear and bending-moment diagrams for the beam and loading shown.

7.119 Draw the shear and bending-moment diagrams for the beam AB if the magnitude of the force **P** is 2.7 kN.

7.120 Determine the range of values of P for which the maximum absolute value of the bending moment in the beam is equal to or less than 3.6 kN · m.

7.121 A 16-mm-diameter wire rope has a mass per unit length of 0.9 kg/m and is suspended from two supports at the same elevation and 160 m apart. If the sag is 40 m, determine (a) the total length of the cable, (b) the maximum tension.

7.122 Knowing that the radius of each pulley is 150 mm and that $\alpha = 20°$, determine the internal forces at (a) point J, (b) point K.

Fig. P7.122 and 7.123

7.123 Knowing that the radius of each pulley is 150 mm and that $\alpha = 30°$, determine the internal forces at (a) point J, (b) point K.

7.124 A 2-kN load is attached to a small pulley which may roll on the cable ACB. The pulley and load are held in the position shown by a second cable DE which is parallel to the portion CB of the main cable. Determine (a) the reactions at A and B, (b) the tension in cable ACB, (c) the tension in cable DE. Neglect the radius of the pulleys and the weight of the cables.

Fig. P7.124

7.125 A cable of length $L + \Delta$ is suspended between two points which are at the same elevation and a distance L apart. (a) Assuming that Δ is small compared with L and that the cable is parabolic, determine the approximate sag in terms of L and Δ. (b) If $L = 30$ m and $\Delta = 0.8$ m and the mass of the wire is 0.35 kg/m, use the result of part a to determine approximate values for the sag and the maximum tension in the wire. [*Hint.* Use only the first two terms of Eq. (7.10).]

7.126 Determine the equations of the shear and bending-moment curves for portion AC of the beam AB. Also, determine the maximum bending moment in the beam.

Fig. P7.126

Fig. P7.C1

Fig. P7.C2

Fig. P7.C4

7.127 A 5-kN load is applied at point F of plank EFG, which is suspended as shown from cable $ABCD$. If $h_B = 1.5$ m, determine (a) the distance a, (b) the corresponding maximum tension in cable $ABCD$.

7.128 A 5-kN load is applied at point F of plank EFG, which is suspended as shown from cable $ABCD$. If $a = 2.5$ m, determine (a) the sag h_B, (b) the corresponding maximum tension in cable $ABCD$.

The following problems are designed to be solved with a computer.

7.C1 Write a computer program which can be used to calculate the shearing force and the bending moment along the beam AB from $x = 0$ to $x = L$ at intervals ΔL Use this program to calculate the values of V and M for each of the following cases:

	L	ΔL	a	w_1	w_2
(a)	9 m	1 m	6 m	20 kN/m	0
(b)	9 m	1 m	6 m	0	20 kN/m
(c)	6 m	0.5 m	2 m	6 kN/m	15 kN/m

7.C2 Write a computer program which can be used to calculate the shearing force and the bending moment along the beam AB from $x = 0$ to $x = L$ at intervals ΔL. Use this program to calculate values of V and M for each of the following cases:

	L	ΔL	a	b	w	P	
(a)	9 m	1 m	6 m	—	20 kN/m	0	[Sample Prob. 7.5]
(b)	4 m	0.4 m	4 m	3.2 m	2 kN/m	4 kN	[Prob. 7.61]
(c)	4 m	0.2 m	2.6 m	1.6 m	1.8 kN/m	4 kN	[Prob. 7.26]

Fig. P7.C3

7.C3 For the beam and loading shown, write a computer program which can be used to calculate the bending moment in beam AB at the location of each concentrated load. Use this program to solve (a) Prob. 7.56, (b) Prob. 7.57.

7.C4 Write a computer program which can be used to calculate the horizontal and vertical components of the reaction at the support A_n from the values of the loads P_1, P_2, . . . , P_{n-1}, the horizontal distances d_1, d_2, . . . , d_n, and the two vertical distances h_0 and h_k. Use this program to solve part a of Probs. 7.76, 7.78, 7.79, and 7.80.

Friction

8.1. Introduction. In the preceding chapters, it was assumed that surfaces in contact were either *frictionless* or *rough*. If they were frictionless, the force each surface exerted on the other was normal to the surfaces and the two surfaces could move freely with respect to each other. If they were rough, it was assumed that tangential forces could develop to prevent the motion of one surface with respect to the other.

This view was a simplified one. Actually, no perfectly frictionless surface exists. When two surfaces are in contact, tangential forces, called *friction forces*, will always develop if one attempts to move one surface with respect to the other. On the other hand, these friction forces are limited in magnitude and will not prevent motion if sufficiently large forces are applied. The distinction between frictionless and rough surfaces is thus a matter of degree. This will be seen more clearly in the present chapter, which is devoted to the study of friction and of its applications to common engineering situations.

There are two types of friction: *dry friction*, sometimes called *Coulomb friction*, and *fluid friction*. Fluid friction develops between layers of fluid moving at different velocities. Fluid friction is of great importance in problems involving the flow of fluids through pipes and orifices or dealing with bodies immersed in moving fluids. It is also basic in the analysis of the motion of *lubricated mechanisms*. Such problems are considered in texts on fluid mechanics. We shall limit our present study to dry friction, i.e., to problems involving rigid bodies which are in contact along *nonlubricated* surfaces.

In the first part of this chapter, we shall analyze the equilibrium of various rigid bodies and structures, assuming dry friction at the surfaces of contact. Later we shall consider a number of specific engineering applications where dry friction plays an important role. These are wedges, square-threaded screws, journal bearings, thrust bearings, rolling resistance, and belt friction.

(a)

(b)

Fig. 8.1

(c)

8.2. The Laws of Dry Friction. Coefficients of Friction.

The laws of dry friction are best understood by the following experiment. A block of weight **W** is placed on a horizontal plane surface (Fig. 8.1a). The forces acting on the block are its weight **W** and the reaction of the surface. Since the weight has no horizontal component, the reaction of the surface also has no horizontal component; the reaction is therefore *normal* to the surface and is represented by **N** in Fig. 8.1a. Suppose, now, that a horizontal force **P** is applied to the block (Fig. 8.1b). If **P** is small, the block will not move; some other horizontal force must therefore exist, which balances **P**. This other force is the *static-friction force* **F**, which is actually the resultant of a great number of forces acting over the entire surface of contact between the block and the plane. The nature of these forces is not known exactly, but it is generally assumed that these forces are due to the irregularities of the surfaces in contact and also, to a certain extent, to molecular attraction.

If the force **P** is increased, the friction force **F** also increases, continuing to oppose **P**, until its magnitude reaches a certain *maximum value F_m* (Fig. 8.1c). If **P** is further increased, the friction force cannot balance it any more and the block starts sliding.† As soon as the block has been set in motion, the magnitude of **F** drops from F_m to a lower value F_k. This is because there is less interpenetration between the irregularities of the surfaces in contact when these surfaces move with respect to each other. From then on, the block keeps sliding with increasing velocity while the friction force, denoted by F_k and called the *kinetic-friction force*, remains approximately constant.

Experimental evidence shows that the maximum value F_m of the static-friction force is proportional to the normal component N of the reaction of the surface. We have

$$F_m = \mu_s N \tag{8.1}$$

where μ_s is a constant called the *coefficient of static friction*. Similarly, the magnitude F_k of the kinetic-friction force may be put in the form

$$F_k = \mu_k N \tag{8.2}$$

where μ_k is a constant called the *coefficient of kinetic friction*. The coefficients of friction μ_s and μ_k do not depend upon the area of the surfaces in contact. Both coefficients, however, depend strongly on the *nature* of the surfaces in contact. Since they also depend upon the exact condition of the

† It should be noted that, as the magnitude F of the friction force increases from 0 to F_m, the point of application A of the resultant **N** of the normal forces of contact moves to the right, so that the couples formed, respectively, by **P** and **F** and by **W** and **N** remain balanced. If **N** reaches B before F reaches its maximum value F_m, the block will tip about B before it can start sliding (see Probs. 8.19 to 8.22).

Table 8.1 Approximate Values of Coefficient of Static Friction for Dry Surfaces

Metal on metal	0.15–0.60
Metal on wood	0.20–0.60
Metal on stone	0.30–0.70
Metal on leather	0.30–0.60
Wood on wood	0.25–0.50
Wood on leather	0.25–0.50
Stone on stone	0.40–0.70
Earth on earth	0.20–1.00
Rubber on concrete	0.60–0.90

surfaces, their value is seldom known with an accuracy greater than 5 percent. Approximate values of coefficients of static friction are given in Table 8.1 for various dry surfaces. The corresponding values of the coefficient of kinetic friction would be about 25 percent smaller. We note that coefficients of friction are dimensionless quantities.

From the description given above, it appears that four different situations may occur when a rigid body is in contact with a horizontal surface:

$F = 0$

$N = P + W$

(a) No friction $(P_x = 0)$

1. The forces applied to the body do not tend to move it along the surface of contact; there is no friction force (Fig. 8.2a).

$F = P_x$
$F < \mu_s N$
$N = P_y + W$

(b) No motion $(P_x < F_m)$

2. The applied forces tend to move the body along the surface of contact but are not large enough to set it in motion. The friction force **F** which has developed may be found by solving the equations of equilibrium for the body. Since there is no evidence that **F** has reached its maximum value, the equation $F_m = \mu_s N$ *cannot be used* to determine the friction force (Fig. 8.2b).

F_m
$F_m = P_x$
$F_m = \mu_s N$
$N = P_y + W$

(c) Motion impending $\longrightarrow (P_x = F_m)$

3. The applied forces are such that the body is just about to slide. We say that *motion is impending*. The friction force **F** has reached its maximum value F_m and, together with the normal force **N**, balances the applied forces. Both the equations of equilibrium and the equation $F_m = \mu_s N$ *may be used*. We also note that the friction force has a sense opposite to the sense of impending motion (Fig. 8.2c).

F_k
$F_k < P_x$
$F_k = \mu_k N$
$N = P_y + W$

(d) Motion $\longrightarrow (P_x > F_m)$

Fig. 8.2

4. The body is sliding under the action of the applied forces, and the equations of equilibrium do not apply any more. However, **F** is now equal to $\mathbf{F}_k$ and the equation $F_k = \mu_k N$ may be used. The sense of $\mathbf{F}_k$ is opposite to the sense of motion (Fig. 8.2d).

(a) No friction

(b) No motion

(c) Motion impending ⟶

(d) Motion ⟶

Fig. 8.3

8.3. Angles of Friction. It is sometimes found convenient to replace the normal force **N** and the friction force **F** by their resultant **R**. Let us consider again a block of weight **W** resting on a horizontal plane surface. If no horizontal force is applied to the block, the resultant **R** reduces to the normal force **N** (Fig. 8.3a). However, if the applied force **P** has a horizontal component P_x which tends to move the block, the force **R** will have a horizontal component **F** and, thus, will form a certain angle with the vertical (Fig. 8.3b). If P_x is increased until motion becomes impending, the angle between **R** and the vertical grows and reaches a maximum value (Fig. 8.3c). This value is called the *angle of static friction* and is denoted by ϕ_s. From the geometry of Fig. 8.3c, we note that

$$\tan \phi_s = \frac{F_m}{N} = \frac{\mu_s N}{N}$$

$$\boxed{\tan \phi_s = \mu_s} \tag{8.3}$$

If motion actually takes place, the magnitude of the friction force drops to F_k; similarly, the angle between **R** and **N** drops to a lower value ϕ_k, called the *angle of kinetic friction* (Fig. 8.3d). From the geometry of Fig. 8.3d, we write

$$\tan \phi_k = \frac{F_k}{N} = \frac{\mu_k N}{N}$$

$$\boxed{\tan \phi_k = \mu_k} \tag{8.4}$$

Another example will show how the angle of friction may be used to advantage in the analysis of certain types of problems. Consider a block resting on a board which may be given any desired inclination; the block is subjected to no other force than its weight **W** and the reaction **R** of the board. If the board is horizontal, the force **R** exerted by the board on the block is perpendicular to the board and balances the weight **W** (Fig. 8.4a). If the board is given a small angle of inclination θ, the force **R** will deviate from the perpendicular to the board by the angle θ and will keep balancing **W** (Fig. 8.4b); it will then have a normal component **N** of magnitude $N = W \cos \theta$ and a tangential component **F** of magnitude $F = W \sin \theta$.

If we keep increasing the angle of inclination, motion will soon become impending. At that time, the angle between **R** and the normal will have reached its maximum value ϕ_s (Fig. 8.4c). The value of the angle of inclination corresponding to impending motion is called the *angle of repose*. Clearly, the angle of repose is equal to the angle of static friction ϕ_s. If the angle of inclination θ is further increased, motion starts and the angle between **R** and the normal drops to the lower value ϕ_k (Fig. 8.4d). The reaction **R** is not vertical any more, and the forces acting on the block are unbalanced.

(a) No friction

$\theta = 0$

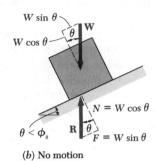

(b) No motion

$W \sin \theta$
$W \cos \theta$
$N = W \cos \theta$
$\theta < \phi_s$
$F = W \sin \theta$

(c) Motion impending

$\theta = \phi_s$
$N = W \cos \theta$
$F_m = W \sin \theta$
$\theta = \phi_s = $ angle of repose

(d) Motion

$N = W \cos \theta$
ϕ_k
$F_k < W \sin \theta$
$\theta > \phi_s$

Fig. 8.4

8.4. Problems Involving Dry Friction. Problems involving dry friction are found in many engineering applications. Some deal with simple situations such as the block sliding on a plane described in the preceding sections. Others involve more complicated situations as in Sample Prob. 8.3; many deal with the stability of rigid bodies in accelerated motion and will be studied in dynamics. Also, a number of common machines and mechanisms may be analyzed by applying the laws of dry friction. These include wedges, screws, journal and thrust bearings, and belt transmissions. They will be studied in the following sections.

The *methods* which should be used to solve problems involving dry friction are the same that were used in the preceding chapters. If a problem involves only a motion of translation, with no possible rotation, the body under consideration may usually be treated as a particle, and the methods of Chap. 2 may be used. If the problem involves a possible rotation, the body must be considered as a rigid body and the methods of Chap. 4 should be used. If the structure considered is made of several parts, the principle of action and reaction must be used as was done in Chap. 6.

If the body considered is acted upon by more than three forces (including the reactions at the surfaces of contact), the reaction at each surface will be represented by its components **N** and **F** and the problem will be solved from the equations of equilibrium. If only three forces act on the body under consideration, it may be found more convenient to represent each reaction by the single force **R** and to solve the problem by drawing a force triangle.

Most problems involving friction fall into one of the following *three groups:* In the *first group* of problems, all applied forces are given, and the coefficients of friction are known; we are to determine whether the body considered will remain at rest or slide. The friction force **F** *required to maintain equilibrium* is unknown (its magnitude is *not* equal to $\mu_s N$) and should be determined, together with the normal force **N**, by drawing a free-body diagram and *solving the equations of equilibrium* (Fig. 8.5a).

(a)

(b)

(c)

Fig. 8.5

The value found for the magnitude F of the friction force is then compared with the maximum value $F_m = \mu_s N$. If F is smaller than or equal to F_m, the body remains at rest. If the value found for F is larger than F_m, equilibrium cannot be maintained and motion takes place; the actual magnitude of the friction force is then $F_k = \mu_k N$.

In problems of the *second group*, all applied forces are given, and the motion is known to be impending; we are to determine the value of the coefficient of static friction. Here again, we determine the friction force and the normal force by drawing a free-body diagram and solving the equations of equilibrium (Fig. 8.5b). Since we know that the value found for F is the maximum value F_m, the coefficient of friction may be found by writing and solving the equation $F_m = \mu_s N$.

In problems of the *third group*, the coefficient of static friction is given, and it is known that the motion is impending in a given direction; we are to determine the magnitude or the direction of one of the applied forces. The friction force should be shown in the free-body diagram with a *sense opposite to that of the impending motion* and with a magnitude $F_m = \mu_s N$ (Fig. 8.5c). The equations of equilibrium may then be written, and the desired force may be determined.

As noted above, it may be more convenient when only three forces are involved to represent the reaction of the surface by a single force **R** and to solve the problem by drawing a force triangle. Such a solution is used in Sample Prob. 8.2.

When two bodies A and B are in contact (Fig. 8.6a), the forces of friction exerted, respectively, by A on B and by B on A are equal and opposite (Newton's third law). It is important in drawing the free-body diagram of one of the bodies, to include the appropriate friction force with its correct sense. The following rule should then be observed: *The sense of the friction force acting on A is opposite to that of the motion (or impending motion) of A as observed from B* (Fig. 8.6b).† The sense of the friction force acting on B is determined in a similar way (Fig. 8.6c). Note that the motion of A as observed from B is a *relative motion*. Body A may be fixed; yet it will have a relative motion with respect to B if B itself moves. Also, A may actually move down yet be observed from B to move up if B moves down faster than A.

† It is therefore *the same as that of the motion of B as observed from A.*

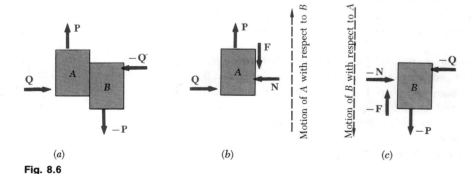

(a) (b) (c)

Fig. 8.6

SAMPLE PROBLEM 8.1

A 500-N force acts as shown on a 150-kg block placed on an inclined plane. The coefficients of friction between the block and the plane are $\mu_s = 0.25$ and $\mu_k = 0.20$. Determine whether the block is in equilibrium, and find the value of the friction force.

Force Required for Equilibrium. We first determine the value of the friction force *required to maintain equilibrium*. Assuming that **F** is directed down and to the left, we draw the free-body diagram of the block. The weight of the block is

$$W = mg = (150 \text{ kg})(9.81 \text{ m/s}^2) = 1472 \text{ N}$$

The equilibrium equations yield

$$+\nearrow \Sigma F_x = 0: \qquad 500 \text{ N} - \tfrac{3}{5}(1472 \text{ N}) - F = 0$$
$$F = -383 \text{ N} \qquad F = 383 \text{ N} \nearrow$$

$$+\nwarrow \Sigma F_y = 0: \qquad N - \tfrac{4}{5}(1472 \text{ N}) = 0$$
$$N = +1178 \text{ N} \qquad N = 1178 \text{ N} \nwarrow$$

The force **F** required to maintain equilibrium is a 383-N force directed up and to the right; the tendency of the block is thus to move down the plane.

Maximum Friction Force. The magnitude of the maximum friction force which may be developed is

$$F_{\text{max}} = \mu_s N \qquad F_{\text{max}} = 0.25(1178 \text{ N}) = 294 \text{ N}$$

Since the value of the force required to maintain equilibrium (383 N) is larger than the maximum value which may be obtained (294 N), equilibrium will not be maintained and, *the block will slide down the plane.*

Actual Value of Friction Force. The magnitude of the actual friction force is obtained as follows:

$$F_{\text{actual}} = F_k = \mu_k N$$
$$= 0.20(1178 \text{ N}) = 236 \text{ N}$$

The sense of this force is opposite to the sense of motion; the force is thus directed up and to the right,

$$F_{\text{actual}} = 236 \text{ N} \nearrow \quad \blacktriangleleft$$

It should be noted that the forces acting on the block are not balanced; the resultant is

$$\tfrac{3}{5}(1472 \text{ N}) - 500 \text{ N} - 236 \text{ N} = 147 \text{ N} \swarrow$$

SAMPLE PROBLEM 8.2

A support block is acted upon by two forces as shown. Knowing that the coefficients of friction between the block and the incline are $\mu_s = 0.35$ and $\mu_k = 0.25$, determine the force **P** required (*a*) to start the block moving up the incline, (*b*) to keep it moving up, (*c*) to prevent it from sliding down.

Solution. For each part of the problem we draw a free-body diagram of the block and a force triangle including the 800-N vertical force, the horizontal force **P**, and the force **R** exerted on the block by the incline. The direction of **R** must be determined in each separate case. We note that since **P** is perpendicular to the 800-N force, the force triangle is a right triangle, which may easily be solved for **P**. In most other problems, however, the force triangle will be an oblique triangle and should be solved by applying the law of sines.

a. Force P to Start Block Moving Up

$$\tan \phi_s = \mu_s$$
$$= 0.35$$
$$\phi_s = 19.29°$$
$$25° + 19.29° = 44.29°$$

$$P = (800 \text{ N}) \tan 44.29°$$

$$P = 780 \text{ N} \leftarrow \quad \blacktriangleleft$$

b. Force P to Keep Block Moving Up

$$\tan \phi_k = \mu_k$$
$$= 0.25$$
$$\phi_k = 14.04°$$
$$25° + 14.04° = 39.04°$$

$$P = (800 \text{ N}) \tan 39.04°$$

$$P = 649 \text{ N} \leftarrow \quad \blacktriangleleft$$

c. Force P to Prevent Block from Sliding Down

$$\phi_s = 19.29°$$
$$25° - 19.29° = 5.71°$$

$$P = (800 \text{ N}) \tan 5.71°$$

$$P = 80.0 \text{ N} \leftarrow \quad \blacktriangleleft$$

The movable bracket shown may be placed at any height on the 60-mm-diameter pipe. If the coefficient of static friction between the pipe and bracket is 0.25, determine the minimum distance x at which the load W can be supported. Neglect the weight of the bracket.

Solution. We draw the free-body diagram of the bracket. When W is placed at the minimum distance x from the axis of the pipe, the bracket is just about to slip, and the forces of friction at A and B have reached their maximum values:

$$F_A = \mu N_A = 0.25 N_A$$
$$F_B = \mu N_B = 0.25 N_B$$

Equilibrium Equations

$\xrightarrow{+} \Sigma F_x = 0: \qquad N_B - N_A = 0$
$$N_B = N_A$$

$+\uparrow \Sigma F_y = 0: \qquad F_A + F_B - W = 0$
$$0.25 N_A + 0.25 N_B = W$$

And, since N_B has been found equal to N_A,

$$0.50 N_A = W$$
$$N_A = 2W$$

$+\!\uparrow\!\Sigma M_B = 0: \qquad N_A(120 \text{ mm}) - F_A(60 \text{ mm}) - W(x - 30 \text{ mm}) = 0$
$$120 N_A - 60(0.25 N_A) - Wx + 30W = 0$$
$$120(2W) - 15(2W) - Wx + 30W = 0$$

Dividing through by W and solving for x:

$$x = 240 \text{ mm} \quad \blacktriangleleft$$

Problems

Fig. P8.1

Fig. P8.3

Fig. P8.7 and P8.8

Fig. P8.11

8.1 The coefficients of friction between the block and the incline are $\mu_s = 0.35$ and $\mu_k = 0.25$. Determine whether the block is in equilibrium and find the magnitude and direction of the friction force when $\theta = 25°$ and $P = 750$ N.

8.2 Solve Prob. 8.1 when $\theta = 30°$ and $P = 150$ N.

8.3 The coefficients of friction between the 20-kg block and the incline are $\mu_s = 0.40$ and $\mu_k = 0.30$. Determine whether the block is in equilibrium and find the magnitude and direction of the friction force when $P = 600$ N.

8.4 Solve Prob. 8.3, assuming that $P = 400$ N.

8.5 For the block of Prob. 8.1 and $\theta = 25°$, find the smallest value of P required (*a*) to start the block up the incline, (*b*) to keep it moving up.

8.6 For the block of Prob. 8.3, find the smallest value of P required (*a*) to start the block up the incline, (*b*) to keep it moving up.

8.7 The coefficients of friction between the block and the rail are $\mu_s = 0.30$ and $\mu_k = 0.25$. Knowing that $\theta = 65°$, determine the smallest value of P required (*a*) to start the block up the rail, (*b*) to keep it from moving down.

8.8 The coefficients of friction between the block and the rail are $\mu_s = 0.30$ and $\mu_k = 0.25$. Find the magnitude and direction of the smallest force **P** required (*a*) to start the block up the rail, (*b*) to keep it from moving down.

Fig. P8.9

8.9 The 10-kg block is attached to link *AB* and rests on a conveyor belt which is moving to the left. Knowing that the coefficients of friction between the block and the belt are $\mu_s = 0.30$ and $\mu_k = 0.25$ and neglecting the weight of the link, determine (*a*) the force in link *AB*, (*b*) the horizontal force **P** which should be applied to the belt to maintain its motion.

8.10 Solve Prob. 8.9, assuming that the belt is moving to the right.

8.11 The 8-kg block *A* hangs from a cable as shown. Pulley *C* is connected by a short link to block *E*, which rests on a horizontal rail. Knowing that the coefficient of static friction between block *E* and the rail is 0.35, and neglecting the weight of block *E* and the friction in the pulleys, determine the maximum allowable value of θ if the system is to remain in equilibrium.

8.12 The coefficients of friction are $\mu_s = 0.30$ and $\mu_k = 0.25$ between all surfaces of contact. Determine the smallest force **P** required to start block D moving if (a) block C is restrained by cable AB as shown, (b) cable AB is removed.

Fig. P8.12 and P8.13

8.13 The coefficients of friction are $\mu_s = 0.30$ and $\mu_k = 0.25$ between all surfaces of contact. Knowing that $P = 900$ N, determine (a) the resultant of the friction forces exerted on block D if block C is restrained as shown, (b) the friction force exerted by the ground on block D if cable AB is removed.

8.14 Three 4-kg packages A, B, and C are placed on a conveyor belt which is at rest. Between the belt and both packages A and C the coefficients of friction are $\mu_s = 0.30$ and $\mu_k = 0.20$; between package B and the belt the coefficients are $\mu_s = 0.10$ and $\mu_k = 0.08$. The packages are placed on the belt so that they are in contact with each other and at rest. Determine which, if any, of the packages will move and the friction force acting on each package.

Fig. P8.14

8.15 Solve Prob. 8.14, assuming that package B is placed to the right of both packages A and C.

8.16 Block A has a mass of 20 kg and block B has a mass of 10 kg. Knowing that the coefficient of static friction is 0.15 between all surfaces of contact, determine the value of θ for which motion is impending.

8.17 Solve Prob. 8.16, assuming that the coefficient of static friction is 0.15 between the two blocks, and zero between block B and the incline.

Fig. P8.16

8.18 For the system of Prob. 8.16, and assuming that the coefficients of friction are $\mu_s = 0.15$ and $\mu_k = 0.12$ between the two blocks, and zero between block B and the incline, determine the magnitude of the friction force between the two blocks when (a) $\theta = 40°$, (b) $\theta = 30°$.

8.19 A 60-kg cabinet is mounted on casters which can be locked to prevent their rotation. The coefficient of static friction is 0.35. If $h = 600$ mm, determine the magnitude of the force **P** required to move the cabinet to the right (a) if all casters are locked, (b) if the casters at B are locked and the casters at A are free to rotate, (c) if the casters at A are locked and the casters at B are free to rotate.

8.20 A 60-kg cabinet is mounted on casters which can be locked to prevent their rotation. The coefficient of static friction between the floor and each caster is 0.35. Assuming that the casters at both A and B are locked, determine (a) the force **P** required to move the cabinet to the right, (b) the largest allowable value of h if the cabinet is not to tip over.

Fig. P8.19 and P8.20

8.21 A packing crate of mass 40 kg must be moved to the left along the floor without tipping. Knowing that the coefficient of static friction between the crate and the floor is 0.35, determine (a) the largest allowable value of α, (b) the corresponding magnitude of the force **P**.

Fig. P8.21 and P8.22

8.22 A packing crate of mass 40 kg is pulled by a rope as shown. The coefficient of static friction between the crate and the floor is 0.35. If $\alpha = 40°$, determine (a) the magnitude of the force **P** required to move the crate, (b) whether the crate will slide or tip.

8.23 A couple of magnitude 70 N·m is applied to the drum. Determine the smallest force which must be exerted by the hydraulic cylinder if the drum is not to rotate, when the applied couple is directed (a) clockwise, (b) counterclockwise.

$\mu_s = 0.40$
$\mu_k = 0.30$

Fig. P8.23 and P8.24

8.24 The hydraulic cylinder exerts on point B a force of 3 kN directed to the right. Determine the moment of the friction force about the axle of the drum when the drum is rotating (a) clockwise, (b) counterclockwise.

8.25 Find the magnitude of the largest couple **M** which may be applied to the cylinder if it is not to spin. The cylinder has a weight W and a radius r, and the coefficient of static friction μ_s is the same at A and B.

Fig. P8.25 and P8.26

8.26 The cylinder has a weight W and a radius r. Express in terms of W and r the magnitude of the largest couple **M** which may be applied to the cylinder if it is not to spin, assuming the coefficient of static friction to be (a) zero at A and 0.35 at B, (b) 0.28 at A and 0.35 at B.

*8.27 A cord is attached to and partially wound around a cylinder of weight W and radius r which rests on an incline as shown. Knowing that the coefficient of static friction between the cylinder and the incline is 0.35, find (a) the smallest allowable value of θ if the cylinder is to remain in equilibrium, (b) the corresponding value of the tension in the cord.

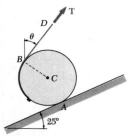

Fig. P8.27 and P8.28

*8.28 A cord is attached to and partially wound around a cylinder of weight W and radius r which rests on an incline as shown. Knowing that $\theta = 30°$, find (a) the tension in the cord, (b) the smallest value of the coefficient of static friction between the cylinder and the incline for which equilibrium is maintained.

8.29 A car is stopped with its front wheels resting against a curb when its driver starts the engine and tries to drive over the curb. Knowing that the radius of the wheels is 280 mm, that the coefficient of static friction between the tires and the pavement is 0.85, and that 60 percent of the weight of the car is distributed over its front wheels and 40 percent over its rear wheels, determine the largest curb height h that the car can negotiate, assuming (a) front-wheel drive, (b) rear-wheel drive.

Fig. P8.29

8.30 Solve Prob. 8.29, assuming that the weight of the car is equally distributed over its front and rear wheels.

8.31 The end A of a slender, uniform rod of length L and weight W bears on a horizontal surface, while its end B is supported by a cord BC. Knowing that the coefficients of friction are $\mu_s = 0.30$ and $\mu_k = 0.25$, determine (a) the maximum value of θ for which equilibrium is maintained, (b) the corresponding value of the tension in the cord.

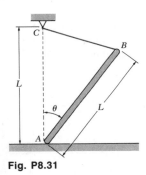

Fig. P8.31

8.32 Determine whether the rod of Prob. 8.31 is in equilibrium when $\theta = 30°$ and find the magnitude and direction of the friction force exerted on the rod.

8.33 A slender rod of length L is lodged between peg C and the vertical wall and supports a load $\mathbf{P}$ at end A. Knowing that $\theta = 35°$ and that the coefficient of static friction is 0.20 at both B and C, find the range of values of the ratio L/a for which equilibrium is maintained.

8.34 Solve Prob. 8.33, assuming that the coefficient of static friction is 0.20 at B and zero at C.

8.35 Solve Prob. 8.33, assuming that the coefficient of static friction is 0.20 at C and zero at B.

Fig. P8.33 and P8.36

8.36 A slender rod of length L is lodged between peg C and the vertical wall and supports a load $\mathbf{P}$ at end A. Knowing that $L = 12.5a$ and $\theta = 30°$ and that the coefficients of friction are $\mu_s = 0.20$ and $\mu_k = 0.15$ at C, and zero at B, determine whether the rod is in equilibrium.

8.37 Solve Prob. 8.36, assuming that $L = 6a$ and $\theta = 30°$ and that the coefficients of friction are $\mu_s = 0.20$ and $\mu_k = 0.15$ at B, and zero at C.

Dimensions in mm

Fig. P8.38

*8.38 A worker is trying to hold in place a hand truck carrying a compressed-air cylinder. Knowing that the combined weight of the truck and cylinder is 900 N, determine the magnitude and direction of (*a*) the force the worker should exert on each handle if the wheels are free to rotate, (*b*) the smallest force he should exert on each handle if brakes have been applied to prevent the wheels from rotating. The coefficients of friction between the steel wheels and the incline are $\mu_s = 0.30$ and $\mu_k = 0.25$.

8.39 The worker of Prob. 8.38 wishes to ease the hand truck down the incline by slowly stepping backward at a constant speed. Determine the magnitude and direction of the force he should exert on each handle (*a*) if the wheels are free to rotate, (*b*) if brakes have been applied to prevent the wheels from rotating.

8.40 The shear shown is used to cut and trim electronic-circuit-board laminates. Knowing that the coefficient of kinetic friction between the blade and the vertical guide is 0.20, determine the force exerted by the edge E of the blade on the laminate.

Fig. P8.40

Fig. P8.41

8.41 The friction tongs shown are used to lift a 350-kg casting. Knowing that $h = 864$ mm, determine the smallest allowable value of the coefficient of static friction between the casting and blocks D and D'.

8.42 For the friction tongs of Prob. 8.41, determine the smallest allowable value of h if the coefficient of static friction between the casting and blocks D and D' is 0.25.

8.43 A rod DE and a small cylinder are placed between two guides as shown. The rod is not to slip downward, however large the force **P** may be; i.e., the arrangement is to be *self-locking*. Neglecting the weight of the cylinder, determine the minimum allowable coefficients of static friction at A, B, and C.

8.44 A safety device used by workers climbing ladders fixed to high structures consists of a rail attached to the ladder and a sleeve which may slide on the flange of the rail. A chain connects the worker's belt to the end of an eccentric cam which may rotate about an axle attached to the sleeve at C. Determine the smallest allowable common value of the coefficient of static friction between the flange of the rail, the pins at A and B, and the eccentric cam if the sleeve is not to slide down when the chain is pulled vertically downward.

Fig. P8.43

Fig. P8.44

Fig. P8.45

8.45 To be of practical use, the safety sleeve described in the preceding problem must be free to slide along the rail when pulled upward. Determine the largest allowable value of the coefficient of static friction between the flange of the rail and the pins at A and B if the sleeve is to be free to slide when pulled as shown in the figure, assuming (a) $\theta = 60°$, (b) $\theta = 50°$, (c) $\theta = 40°$.

8.46 A light metal panel is welded to two short sleeves of 25-mm inside diameter which may slide on a horizontal rod. The coefficients of friction between the sleeves and the rod are $\mu_s = 0.40$ and $\mu_k = 0.30$. A cord attached to corner C is used to move the panel along the rod. Determine the range of values of θ for which the panel will start moving to the right.

8.47 (a) Solve Prob. 8.46, assuming that the cord is attached at point E at a distance $x = 100$ mm from corner C. (b) Determine the largest value of x for which the panel may be moved to the right.

Fig. P8.46

8.48 A 3-m beam, with a mass of 500 kg, is to be moved to the left onto the platform. A horizontal force **P** is applied to the dolly, which is mounted on frictionless wheels. The coefficients of friction between all surfaces are $\mu_s = 0.30$ and $\mu_k = 0.25$ and initially $x = 0.6$ m. Knowing that the top surface of the dolly is slightly higher than the platform, determine the force **P** required to start moving the beam. (*Hint.* The beam is supported at A and D.)

Fig. P8.48

8.49 (*a*) Show that the beam of Prob. 8.48 *cannot* be moved if the top surface of the dolly is slightly *lower* than the platform. (*b*) Show that the beam *can* be moved if two 78-kg workers stand on the beam at B and determine how far to the left the beam can be moved.

8.50 Denoting by μ_s the coefficient of static friction between the collar C and the horizontal rod, determine the largest magnitude of the couple **M** for which equilibrium is maintained. Explain what happens if $\mu_s \geq \tan \theta$.

Fig. P8.50

Fig. P8.51

8.51 The slender rod AB of length $l = 300$ mm is attached to a collar at A and rests on a wheel located at a vertical distance $a = 50$ mm from the horizontal rod on which the collar slides. Neglecting the friction at C and knowing that the coefficient of static friction between the collar and the horizontal rod is 0.25, determine the range of values of Q for which equilibrium is maintained when $P = 60$ N and $\theta = 20°$.

8.52 Solve Prob. 8.51, assuming that the wheel at C is frozen in its bearings and that the coefficient of static friction between the wheel and rod AB is also 0.25.

*8.53 Two 2.5-m beams are pin-connected at D and support two loads **P** and **Q** as shown. Knowing that the coefficient of static friction is zero at A and $\frac{1}{3}$ at B and C, determine the smallest value of P for which equilibrium is maintained when $Q = 650$ N. (*Hint.* Note that C moves up when B moves to the right.)

Fig. P8.53

*8.54 Solve Prob. 8.53, assuming that the coefficient of static friction is $\frac{1}{3}$ at all surfaces of contact.

*8.55 Two slender rods of negligible weight are pin-connected at A and attached to the 8-kg block B and the 36-kg block C as shown. The coefficient of static friction is 0.55 between all surfaces of contact. Determine the range of values of P for which equilibrium is maintained.

Fig. P8.55 and P8.56

*8.56 Two slender rods of negligible weight are pin-connected at A and attached to the 8-kg block B and the 36-kg block C as shown. A vertical load of magnitude $P = 1500$ N is applied at A. Determine (*a*) the minimum value of the coefficient of static friction (at both B and C) for which equilibrium is maintained, (*b*) whether sliding is impending at B or at C.

*8.57 Solve Prob. 8.56, assuming that $P = 1000$ N.

*8.58 A 3-m plank lies on two rollers A and B, located 1.5 m apart on a 10° incline. Roller A rotates slowly clockwise at a constant speed; roller B is idle. Initially, the plank is placed on the rollers with its center of gravity at A ($x = 0$) and its end C at B. Knowing that the coefficients of friction between the board and roller A are $\mu_s = 0.35$ and $\mu_k = 0.28$, (*a*) determine the value reached by x when the plank starts slipping on roller A, (*b*) describe what happens next.

Fig. P8.58

*8.59 Solve Prob. 8.58, assuming that roller B is frozen in its bearings and that the coefficients of friction are the same at B as at A.

Fig. P8.60

*8.60 The mathematical model shown, consisting of blocks connected by springs, has been developed for the analysis of a certain structure. The weight of each block is $W = 5$ N, the constant of each spring is $k = 20$ N/m, and the coefficient of friction between the base and each block is 0.40. Knowing that the initial tension in each spring is zero, construct a graph showing the magnitude of the force **P** versus the position of block A as P increases from zero to 5 N and then decreases to zero.

(a)

(b)

(c)

Fig. 8.7

8.5. Wedges. Wedges are simple machines used to raise large stone blocks and other heavy loads. These loads may be raised by applying to the wedge a force usually considerably smaller than the weight of the load. Besides, because of the friction existing between the surfaces in contact, a wedge, if properly shaped, will remain in place after being forced under the load. Wedges may thus be used advantageously to make small adjustments in the position of heavy pieces of machinery.

Consider the block A shown in Fig. 8.7a. This block rests against a vertical wall B and is to be raised slightly by forcing a wedge C between block A and a second wedge D. We want to find the minimum value of the force **P** which must be applied to the wedge C to move the block. We shall assume that the weight **W** of the block is known. It may have been given or determined in newtons from the mass of the block expressed in kilograms.

The free-body diagrams of block A and of wedge C have been drawn in Fig. 8.7b and c. The forces acting on the block include its weight and the normal and friction forces at the surfaces of contact with wall B and wedge C. The magnitudes of the friction forces $\mathbf{F}_1$ and $\mathbf{F}_2$ are equal, respectively, to $\mu_s N_1$ and $\mu_s N_2$ since the motion of the block must be started. It is important to show the friction forces with their correct sense. Since the block will move upward, the force $\mathbf{F}_1$ exerted by the wall on the block must be directed downward. On the other hand, since the wedge C moves to the right, the relative motion of A with respect to C is to the left and the force $\mathbf{F}_2$ exerted by C on A must be directed to the right.

Considering now the free body C in Fig. 8.7c, we note that the forces acting on C include the applied force **P** and the normal and friction forces at the surfaces of contact with A and D. The weight of the wedge is small compared with the other forces involved and may be neglected. The forces acting on C are equal and opposite to the forces $\mathbf{N}_2$ and $\mathbf{F}_2$ acting on A and are denoted, respectively, by $-\mathbf{N}_2$ and $-\mathbf{F}_2$; the friction force $-\mathbf{F}_2$ must therefore be directed to the left. We check that the force $\mathbf{F}_3$ is also directed to the left.

The total number of unknowns involved in the two free-body diagrams may be reduced to four if the friction forces are expressed in terms of the normal forces. Expressing that block A and wedge C are in equilibrium will provide four equations which may be solved to obtain the magnitude of **P**. It should be noted that in the example considered here, it will be more convenient to replace each pair of normal and friction forces by their resultant. Each free body is then subjected to only three forces, and the problem may be solved by drawing the corresponding force triangles (see Sample Prob. 8.4).

8.6. Square-Threaded Screws. Square-threaded screws are frequently used in jacks, presses, and other mechanisms. Their analysis is similar to that of a block sliding along an inclined plane.

Consider the jack shown in Fig. 8.8. The screw carries a load **W** and is supported by the base of the jack. Contact between screw and base takes place along a portion of their threads. By applying a force **P** on the handle, the screw may be made to turn and to raise the load **W**.

The thread of the base has been unwrapped and shown as a straight line in Fig. 8.9a. The correct slope was obtained by plotting horizontally the product $2\pi r$, where r is the mean radius of the thread, and vertically the *lead L* of the screw, i.e., the distance through which the screw advances in one turn. The angle θ this line forms with the horizontal is the *lead angle*. Since the force of friction between two surfaces in contact does not depend upon the area of contact, the two threads may be assumed to be in contact over a much smaller area than they actually are and the screw may be represented by the block shown in Fig. 8.9a. It should be noted, however, that in this analysis of the jack, the friction between cap and screw is neglected.

The free-body diagram of the block should include the load **W**, the reaction **R** of the base thread, and a horizontal force **Q** having the same effect as the force **P** exerted on the handle. The force **Q** should have the same moment as **P** about the axis of the screw and its magnitude should thus be $Q = Pa/r$. The force **Q**, and thus the force **P** required to raise the load **W**, may be obtained from the free-body diagram shown in Fig. 8.9a. The friction angle is taken equal to ϕ_s since the load will presumably be raised through a succession of short strokes. In mechanisms providing for the continuous rotation of a screw, it may be desirable to distinguish between the force required to start motion (using ϕ_s) and that required to maintain motion (using ϕ_k).

Fig. 8.8

(a) Impending motion upward

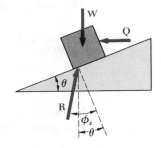

(b) Impending motion downward with $\phi_s > \theta$

(c) Impending motion downward with $\phi_s < \theta$

Fig. 8.9 Block-and-incline analysis of a screw.

If the friction angle ϕ_s is larger than the lead angle θ, the screw is said to be *self-locking*; it will remain in place under the load. To lower the load, we must then apply the force shown in Fig. 8.9b. If ϕ_s is smaller than θ, the screw will unwind under the load; it is then necessary to apply the force shown in Fig. 8.9c to maintain equilibrium.

The lead of a screw should not be confused with its *pitch*. The lead was defined as the distance through which the screw advances in one turn; the pitch is the distance measured between two consecutive threads. While lead and pitch are equal in the case of *single-threaded* screws, they are different in the case of *multiple-threaded* screws, i.e., screws having several independent threads. It is easily verified that for double-threaded screws, the lead is twice as large as the pitch; for triple-threaded screws, it is three times as· large as the pitch; etc.

SAMPLE PROBLEM 8.4

The position of the machine block B is adjusted by moving the wedge A. Knowing that the coefficient of static friction is 0.35 between all surfaces of contact, determine the force P required (a) to raise block B, (b) to lower block B.

Solution. For each part, the free-body diagrams of block B and wedge A are drawn, together with the corresponding force triangles, and the law of sines is used to find the desired forces. We note that since $\mu_s = 0.35$, the angle of friction is

$$\phi_s = \tan^{-1} 0.35 = 19.3°$$

a. Force P to Raise Block
Free Body: Block B

$$\frac{R_1}{\sin 109.3°} = \frac{2 \text{ kN}}{\sin 43.4°}$$

$$R_1 = 2.75 \text{ kN}$$

Free Body: Wedge A

$$\frac{P}{\sin 46.6°} = \frac{2.75 \text{ kN}}{\sin 70.7°}$$

$$P = 2.12 \text{ kN}$$

$P = 2.12$ kN← ◄

b. Force P to Lower Block
Free Body: Block B

$$\frac{R_1}{\sin 70.7°} = \frac{2 \text{ kN}}{\sin 98.0°}$$

$$R_1 = 1.91 \text{ kN}$$

Free Body: Wedge A

$$\frac{P}{\sin 30.6°} = \frac{1.91 \text{ kN}}{\sin 70.7°}$$

$$P = 1.03 \text{ kN}$$

$P = 1.03$ kN→ ◄

SAMPLE PROBLEM 8.5

A clamp is used to hold two pieces of wood together as shown. The clamp has a double square thread of mean diameter equal to 10 mm and with a pitch of 2 mm. The coefficient of friction between threads is $\mu_s = 0.30$. If a maximum torque of 40 N·m is applied in tightening the clamp, determine (a) the force exerted on the pieces of wood, (b) the torque required to loosen the clamp.

a. **Force Exerted by Clamp.** The mean radius of the screw is $r = 5$ mm. Since the screw is double-threaded, the lead L is equal to twice the pitch: $L = 2(2 \text{ mm}) = 4$ mm. The lead angle θ and the friction angle ϕ_s are obtained by writing

$$\tan \theta = \frac{L}{2\pi r} = \frac{4 \text{ mm}}{10\pi \text{ mm}} = 0.1273 \qquad \theta = 7.3°$$

$$\tan \phi_s = \mu_s = 0.30 \qquad\qquad\qquad \phi_s = 16.7°$$

The force **Q** which should be applied to the block representing the screw is obtained by expressing that its moment Qr about the axis of the screw is equal to the applied torque.

$$Q(5 \text{ mm}) = 40 \text{ N·m}$$

$$Q = \frac{40 \text{ N·m}}{5 \text{ mm}} = \frac{40 \text{ N·m}}{5 \times 10^{-3} \text{ m}} = 8000 \text{ N} = 8 \text{ kN}$$

The free-body diagram and the corresponding force triangle may now be drawn for the block; the magnitude of the force **W** exerted on the pieces of wood is obtained by solving the triangle.

$$W = \frac{Q}{\tan (\theta + \phi_s)} = \frac{8 \text{ kN}}{\tan 24.0°}$$

$$W = 17.97 \text{ kN} \quad \blacktriangleleft$$

b. **Torque Required to Loosen Clamp.** The force **Q** required to loosen the clamp and the corresponding torque are obtained from the free-body diagram and force triangle shown.

$$Q = W \tan (\phi_s - \theta) = (17.97 \text{ kN}) \tan 9.4°$$
$$= 2.975 \text{ kN}$$

$$\text{Torque} = Qr = (2.975 \text{ kN})(5 \text{ mm})$$
$$= (2.975 \times 10^3 \text{ N})(5 \times 10^{-3} \text{ m}) = 14.87 \text{ N·m}$$

$$\text{Torque} = 14.87 \text{ N·m} \quad \blacktriangleleft$$

Fig. P8.61

Fig. P8.63

Fig. P8.65

Fig. P8.66

Fig. P8.67

Problems

8.61 A 6-m long wide-flange beam weighing 6650 N is supported by a 15° wedge at each end. Wedge A is fairly smooth ($\mu_s = 0.20$ at all surfaces of contact) and may be forced under the beam to adjust its position. Wedge B is rough ($\mu_s = 0.50$) and the right end of the beam may be considered as fixed. Determine the horizontal force **P** which should be applied to wedge A to raise the left end of the beam.

8.62 In Prob. 8.61, determine the horizontal force **P** which should be applied to wedge A to lower the left end of the beam.

8.63 A 100-kg block rests as shown on a wedge of negligible weight. Knowing that the coefficient of static friction is 0.25 at all surfaces of contact, determine the angle θ for which sliding is impending and compute the corresponding value of the normal force exerted on the block by the vertical wall.

8.64 Solve Prob. 8.63, assuming (a) that the coefficient of static friction is zero between the block and the vertical wall and 0.25 at the other two surfaces of contact, (b) that the coefficient of static friction is zero between the block and the wedge and 0.25 at the other two surfaces of contact.

8.65 and 8.66 Two 8° wedges of negligible weight are used to move and position the 800-kg block. Knowing that the coefficient of static friction is 0.30 at all surfaces of contact, determine the smallest force **P** which should be applied as shown to one of the wedges.

8.67 The elevation of the end of the steel floor beam is adjusted by means of the steel wedges E and F. The steel base plate CD has been welded to the lower flange of the beam; the end reaction of the beam is known to be 90 kN. The coefficient of static friction is 0.30 between the two steel surfaces and 0.60 between the steel and concrete. If horizontal motion of the base plate is prevented by the force **Q**, determine (a) the force **P** required to raise the beam, (b) the corresponding force **Q**.

8.68 Solve Prob. 8.67, assuming that the end of the beam is to be lowered.

8.69 High-strength bolts are used in the construction of many modern steel structures. For a 24-mm nominal-diameter bolt the required minimum bolt tension is 236 kN. Assuming the coefficient of static friction to be 0.35, determine the required torque which must be applied to the bolt and nut. The mean diameter of the thread is 22.6 mm, and the lead is 3 mm. Neglect friction between the nut and washer, and assume the bolt to be square-threaded.

8.70 The spring of the door latch has a constant of 400 N/m and in the position shown exerts a 2.8-N force on the bolt. The coefficient of static friction between the bolt and the guide plate is 0.35; all other surfaces are well lubricated and may be assumed frictionless. Determine the magnitude of the force **P** required to start closing the door.

Fig. P8.69

Fig. P8.70

8.71 In Prob. 8.70, determine the angle which the face of the bolt should form with the line BC if the force **P** required to close the door is to be the same for both the position shown and the position when B is almost at the guide plate.

8.72 A 12° wedge is used to split a log. The coefficient of friction between the wedge and the wood is 0.40. Knowing that a force **P** of magnitude 3.2 kN was required to insert the wedge, determine the magnitude of the forces exerted on the log by the wedge after it has been inserted.

8.73 A 5° wedge is to be forced under a 625-kg machine base at A. Knowing that the coefficient of static friction is 0.20 at all surfaces, (*a*) determine the force **P** required to move the wedge, (*b*) indicate whether the machine will move.

Fig. P8.72

Fig. P8.73

8.74 Solve Prob. 8.73, assuming that the wedge is to be forced under the machine base at B instead of A.

Fig. P8.75

8.75 The square-threaded worm gear shown has a mean radius of 50 mm and a pitch 12.5 mm. The large gear is subjected to a constant clockwise torque of 1100 N·m. Knowing that the coefficient of static friction between gear teeth is 0.12, determine the torque which must be applied to shaft AB in order to rotate the large gear counterclockwise. Neglect friction in the bearings at A, B, and C.

8.76 In Prob. 8.75, determine the torque which must be applied to shaft AB in order to rotate the large gear clockwise.

8.77 The main features of a screw-luffing crane are shown. Distances AD and CD are each 9 m. The position of the 6-Mg boom CDE is controlled by the screw ABC, which is double-threaded at each end (left-handed thread at A, right-handed thread at C). Each thread has a pitch of 16 mm and a mean diameter of 200 mm. If the coefficient of static friction is 0.08, determine the magnitude of the couple which must be applied to the screw (a) to raise the boom, (b) to lower the boom.

Fig. P8.77

8.78 Derive the following formulas relating the load $\mathbf{W}$ and the force $\mathbf{P}$ exerted on the handle of the jack discussed in Sec. 8.6: (a) $P = (Wr/a) \tan (\theta + \phi_s)$, to raise the load; (b) $P = (Wr/a) \tan (\phi_s - \theta)$, to lower the load if the screw is self-locking; (c) $P = (Wr/a) \tan (\theta - \phi_s)$, to hold the load if the screw is not self-locking.

8.79 The position of the automobile jack shown is controlled by a screw ABC which is single-threaded at each end (right-handed thread at A, left-handed thread at C). Each thread has a pitch of 2.5 mm and a mean diameter of 9 mm. If the coefficient of static friction is 0.15, determine the magnitude and sense of the couple $\mathbf{M}$ which must be applied to the screw to raise the automobile.

8.80 For the jack of Prob. 8.79, determine the magnitude and sense of the couple $\mathbf{M}$ which must be applied to lower the automobile.

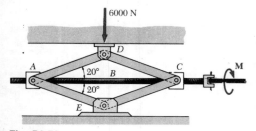

Fig. P8.79

8.81 The vise shown consists of two members connected by two double-threaded screws of mean radius 6.25 mm and pitch 2 mm. The lower member is threaded at A and B ($\mu_s = 0.35$), but the upper member is not threaded. It is desired to apply two equal and opposite forces of 600 N on the blocks held between the jaws. (*a*) What screw should be adjusted first? (*b*) What is the maximum torque applied in tightening the second screw?

$\leftarrow$125 mm$\rightarrow$$\leftarrow$125 mm$\rightarrow$

Fig. P8.81

8.82 Solve part *b* of Prob. 8.81, assuming that the wrong screw is adjusted first.

8.83 In the machinist's vise shown, the movable jaw D is rigidly attached to the tongue AB which fits loosely into the fixed body of the vise. The screw is single-threaded into the fixed base and has a mean diameter of 18 mm and a pitch of 6 mm. The coefficient of static friction is 0.25 between the threads and also between the tongue and the body. Neglecting bearing friction between the screw and the movable head, determine the torque which must be applied to the handle in order to produce a clamping force of 5 kN.

8.84 In Prob. 8.83, a clamping force of 5 kN was obtained by tightening the vise. Determine the torque which must be applied to the screw to loosen the vise.

42 mm
18 mm
30 mm
72 mm

Fig. P8.83

* 8.7. Journal Bearings. Axle Friction. Journal bearings are used to provide lateral support to rotating shafts and axles. Thrust bearings, which will be studied in the next section, are used to provide axial support to shafts and axles. If the journal bearing is fully lubricated, the frictional resistance depends upon the speed of rotation, the clearance between axle and bearing, and the viscosity of the lubricant. As indicated in Sec. 8.1, such problems are studied in fluid mechanics. The methods of this chapter, however, may be applied to the study of axle friction when the bearing is not lubricated or only partially lubricated. We may then assume that the axle and the bearing are in direct contact along a single straight line.

(a)

(b)

(c)

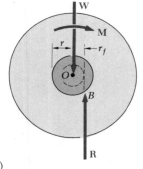

(d)

(e)

Fig. 8.10

Consider two wheels, each of weight **W**, rigidly mounted on an axle supported symmetrically by two journal bearings (Fig. 8.10a). If the wheels rotate, we find that to keep them rotating at constant speed, it is necessary to apply to each of them a couple **M**. A free-body diagram has been drawn in Fig. 8.10c, which represents one of the wheels and the corresponding half axle in projection on a plane perpendicular to the axle. The forces acting on the free body include the weight **W** of the wheel, the couple **M** required to maintain its motion, and a force **R** representing the reaction of the bearing. This force is vertical, equal, and opposite to **W** but does not pass through the center O of the axle; **R** is located to the right of O at a distance such that its moment about O balances the moment **M** of the couple. Contact between the axle and bearing, therefore, does not take place at the lowest point A when the axle rotates. It takes place at point B (Fig. 8.10b) or, rather, along a straight line intersecting the plane of the figure at B. Physically, this is explained by the fact that when the wheels are set in motion, the axle "climbs" in the bearings until slippage occurs. After sliding back slightly, the axle settles more or less in the position shown. This position is such that the angle between the reaction **R** and the normal to the surface of the bearing is equal to the angle of kinetic friction ϕ_k. The distance from O to the line of action of **R** is thus $r \sin \phi_k$, where r is the radius of the axle. Writing that $\Sigma M_O = 0$ for the forces acting on the free body considered, we obtain the magnitude of the couple **M** required to overcome the frictional resistance of one of the bearings:

$$M = Rr \sin \phi_k \tag{8.5}$$

Observing that, for small values of the angle of friction, $\sin \phi_k$ may be replaced by $\tan \phi_k$, that is, by μ_k, we write the approximate formula

$$M \approx Rr\mu_k \tag{8.6}$$

In the solution of certain problems, it may be more convenient to let the line of action of **R** pass through O, as it does when the axle does not rotate. A couple $-$**M** of the same magnitude as the couple **M** but of opposite sense must then be added to the reaction **R** (Fig. 8.10d). This couple represents the frictional resistance of the bearing.

In case a graphical solution is preferred, the line of action of **R** may be readily drawn (Fig. 8.10e) if we note that it must be tangent to a circle centered at O and of radius

$$r_f = r \sin \phi_k \approx r\mu_k \tag{8.7}$$

This circle is called the *circle of friction* of the axle and bearing and is independent of the loading conditions of the axle.

* 8.8. Thrust Bearings. Disk Friction.

Thrust bearings are used to provide axial support to rotating shafts and axles. They are of two types: (1) *end bearings* and (2) *collar bearings* (Fig. 8.11). In the case of collar bearings, friction forces develop between the two ring-shaped areas which are in contact. In the case of end bearings, friction takes place over full circular areas, or over ring-shaped areas when the end of the shaft is hollow. Friction between circular areas, called *disk friction*, also occurs in other mechanisms, such as *disk clutches*.

To obtain a formula which is valid in the most general case of disk friction, we shall consider a rotating hollow shaft. A couple **M** keeps the shaft rotating at constant speed while a force **P** maintains it in contact with a fixed bearing (Fig. 8.12). Contact between the shaft and the bearing takes place over a ring-shaped area of inner radius R_1 and outer radius R_2. Assuming that the pressure between the two surfaces in contact is uniform, we find that the magnitude of the normal force ΔN exerted on an element of area ΔA is $\Delta N = P\,\Delta A/A$, where $A = \pi(R_2^2 - R_1^2)$, and that the magnitude of the friction force ΔF acting on ΔA is $\Delta F = \mu_k\,\Delta N$. Denoting by r the distance from the axis of the shaft to the element of area ΔA, we express as follows the moment ΔM of ΔF about the axis of the shaft:

$$\Delta M = r\,\Delta F = \frac{r\mu_k P\,\Delta A}{\pi(R_2^2 - R_1^2)}$$

The equilibrium of the shaft requires that the moment **M** of the couple applied to the shaft be equal in magnitude to the sum of the moments of the friction forces $\Delta \mathbf{F}$. Replacing ΔA by the infinitesimal element $dA = r\,d\theta\,dr$ used with polar coordinates, and integrating over the area of contact, we thus obtain the following expression for the magnitude of the couple **M**

(a) End bearing

(b) Collar bearing

Fig. 8.11 Thrust bearings.

Fig. 8.12

required to overcome the frictional resistance of the bearing:

$$M = \frac{\mu_k P}{\pi(R_2^2 - R_1^2)} \int_0^{2\pi} \int_{R_1}^{R_2} r^2 \, dr \, d\theta$$

$$= \frac{\mu_k P}{\pi(R_2^2 - R_1^2)} \int_0^{2\pi} \tfrac{1}{3}(R_2^3 - R_1^3) \, d\theta$$

$$M = \tfrac{2}{3}\mu_k P \frac{R_2^3 - R_1^3}{R_2^2 - R_1^2} \tag{8.8}$$

When contact takes place over a full circle of radius R, formula (8.8) reduces to

$$M = \tfrac{2}{3}\mu_k PR \tag{8.9}$$

The value of M is then the same as would be obtained if contact between shaft and bearing took place at a single point located at a distance $2R/3$ from the axis of the shaft.

The largest torque which may be transmitted by a disk clutch without causing slippage is given by a formula similar to (8.9), where μ_k has been replaced by the coefficient of static friction μ_s.

* 8.9. Wheel Friction. Rolling Resistance.

The wheel is one of the most important inventions of our civilization. Its use makes it possible to move heavy loads with relatively little effort. Because the point of the wheel in contact with the ground at any given instant has no relative motion with respect to the ground, the wheel eliminates the large friction forces which would arise if the load were in direct contact with the ground. In practice, however, the wheel is not perfect, and some resistance to its motion exists. This resistance has two distinct causes. It is due (1) to a combined effect of axle friction and friction at the rim and (2) to the fact that the wheel and the ground deform, with the result that contact between wheel and ground takes place, not at a single point, but over a certain area.

To understand better the first cause of resistance to the motion of a wheel, we shall consider a railroad car supported by eight wheels mounted on axles and bearings. The car is assumed to be moving to the right at constant speed along a straight horizontal track. The free-body diagram of one of the wheels is shown in Fig. 8.13a. The forces acting on the free body include the load $\mathbf{W}$ supported by the wheel and the normal reaction $\mathbf{N}$ of the track. Since $\mathbf{W}$ is drawn through the center O of the axle, the frictional resistance of the bearing should be represented by a counterclockwise couple $\mathbf{M}$ (see Sec. 8.7). To keep the free body in equilibrium, we must add two equal and opposite forces $\mathbf{P}$ and $\mathbf{F}$, forming a clockwise couple of moment $-\mathbf{M}$. The force $\mathbf{F}$ is the friction force exerted by the track on the wheel, and $\mathbf{P}$ represents the force which should be applied to the wheel to keep it rolling at constant speed. Note that the forces $\mathbf{P}$ and $\mathbf{F}$ would not exist if there were no friction between wheel and track. The couple $\mathbf{M}$ representing the axle friction would then be zero; the wheel would slide on the track without turning in its bearing.

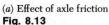
(a) Effect of axle friction   (b) Free wheel   (c) Rolling resistance
Fig. 8.13

The couple **M** and the forces **P** and **F** also reduce to zero when there is no axle friction. For example, a wheel which is not held in bearings and rolls freely and at constant speed on horizontal ground (Fig. 8.13b) will be subjected to only two forces: its own weight **W** and the normal reaction **N** of the ground. No friction force will act on the wheel, regardless of the value of the coefficient of friction between wheel and ground. A wheel rolling freely on horizontal ground should thus keep rolling indefinitely.

Experience, however, indicates that the wheel will slow down and eventually come to rest. This is due to the second type of resistance mentioned at the beginning of this section, known as the *rolling resistance*. Under the load **W**, both the wheel and the ground deform slightly, causing the contact between wheel and ground to take place over a certain area. Experimental evidence shows that the resultant of the forces exerted by the ground on the wheel over this area is a force **R** applied at a point B, which is not located directly under the center O of the wheel, but slightly in front of it (Fig. 8.13c). To balance the moment of **W** about B and to keep the wheel rolling at constant speed, it is necessary to apply a horizontal force **P** at the center of the wheel. Writing $\Sigma M_B = 0$, we obtain

$$Pr = Wb \qquad (8.10)$$

where r = radius of wheel
  b = horizontal distance between O and B

The distance b is commonly called the *coefficient of rolling resistance*. It should be noted that b is not a dimensionless coefficient since it represents a length; b is usually expressed in millimetres. The value of b depends upon several parameters in a manner which has not yet been clearly established. Values of the coefficient of rolling resistance vary from about 0.25 mm for a steel wheel on a steel rail to 125 mm for the same wheel on soft ground.

A pulley of diameter 100 mm can rotate about a fixed shaft of diameter 50 mm. The coefficients of static and kinetic friction between the pulley and shaft are both assumed equal to 0.20. Determine (*a*) the smallest vertical force **P** required to raise a 2-kN load, (*b*) the smallest vertical force **P** required to hold the load, (*c*) the smallest horizontal force **P** required to raise the same load.

a. Vertical Force P Required to Raise the Load. When the forces in both parts of the rope are equal, contact between the pulley and shaft takes place at *A*. When **P** is increased, the pulley rolls around the shaft slightly and contact takes place at *B*. The free-body diagram of the pulley when motion is impending is drawn. The perpendicular distance from the center *O* of the pulley to the line of action of **R** is

$$r_f = r \sin \phi \approx r\mu \qquad r_f \approx (25 \text{ mm})0.20 = 5 \text{ mm}$$

Summing moments about *B*, we write

$$+ \rangle \Sigma M_B = 0: \qquad (55 \text{ mm})(2 \text{ kN}) - (45 \text{ mm}) P = 0$$
$$P = 2.44 \text{ kN} \qquad\qquad \mathbf{P = 2.44 \text{ kN} \downarrow} \blacktriangleleft$$

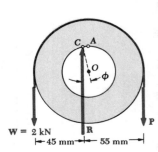

b. Vertical Force P to Hold the Load. As the force **P** is decreased, the pulley rolls around the shaft and contact takes place at *C*. Considering the pulley as a free body and summing moments about *C*, we write

$$+ \rangle \Sigma M_C = 0: \qquad (45 \text{ mm})(2 \text{ kN}) - (55 \text{ mm}) P = 0$$
$$P = 1.64 \text{ kN} \qquad\qquad \mathbf{P = 1.64 \text{ kN} \downarrow} \blacktriangleleft$$

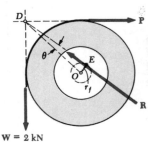

c. Horizontal Force P to Raise the Load. Since the three forces **W**, **P**, and **R** are not parallel, they must be concurrent. The direction of **R** is thus determined from the fact that its line of action must pass through the point of intersection *D* of **W** and **P**, and must be tangent to the circle of friction. Recalling that the radius of the circle of friction is $r_f = 5$ mm, we write

$$\sin \theta = \frac{OE}{OD} = \frac{5 \text{ mm}}{(50 \text{ mm})\sqrt{2}} = 0.0707 \qquad \theta = 4.1°$$

From the force triangle, we obtain

$$P = W \cot (45° - \theta) = (2 \text{ kN}) \cot 40.9°$$
$$= 2.31 \text{ kN} \qquad\qquad \mathbf{P = 2.31 \text{ kN} \rightarrow} \blacktriangleleft$$

Problems

8.85 A windlass of 250-mm diameter is used to raise or lower a 70-kg load. It is supported by two poorly lubricated bearings ($\mu_s = 0.50$) of 75-mm diameter. For each of the two positions shown, determine the magnitude of the force **P** required to start raising the load.

250 mm

P

200 mm

70 kg

(a)

P

70 kg

(b)

Fig. P8.85

8.86 For the windlass of Prob. 8.85, and for each of the two positions shown, determine the magnitude of the smallest force **P** which will hold the load in place.

8.87 A hot-metal ladle and its contents have a mass of 50 Mg. Knowing that the coefficient of static friction between the hooks and the pinion is 0.30, determine the tension in cable AB required to start tipping the ladle.

T

1.6 m

A

360 mm

B

Fig. P8.87

75 mm

A

O

B

C

D

20 kg

30 kg

150 mm

100 mm

Fig. P8.88

8.88 A lever of negligible weight is loosely fitted onto a 75-mm-diameter fixed shaft. It is observed that the lever will just start rotating if a 3-kg mass is added at C. Determine the coefficient of static friction between the shaft and the lever.

8.89 An 800-N load is to be raised by the block and tackle shown. Each of the 50-mm-diameter pulleys rotates on a 10-mm-diameter axle. Knowing that $\mu = 0.25$, determine the tension in each portion of the rope as the load is slowly raised.

8.90 In Prob. 8.89, determine the tension in each portion of the rope as the 800-N load is slowly lowered.

8.91 A bushing of 75-mm outside diameter fits loosely on a horizontal 50-mm-diameter shaft. If a force **P** forming an angle of 30° with the horizontal and having a magnitude $P = 800$ N is required to start raising the 45-kg load, determine the coefficient of static friction between the shaft and the bushing. Assume that the rope does not slip on the bushing.

Fig. P8.89

Fig. P8.91

8.92 Knowing that the coefficient of static friction between the shaft and the bushing of Prob. 8.91 is 0.35, determine the magnitude of the smallest force **P** required (*a*) to start raising the 45-kg load, (*b*) to hold the 45-kg load in place.

8.93 A loaded railroad car has a mass of 25 Mg and is supported by eight wheels of 800-mm diameter with 125-mm-diameter axles. Knowing that the coefficients of friction are $\mu_s = 0.025$ and $\mu_k = 0.020$, determine the horizontal force required (*a*) to get the car in motion, (*b*) to keep it moving with a constant velocity. Neglect the rolling resistance between the wheels and the track.

8.94 A scooter is to be designed to roll down a 3 percent slope at a constant speed. Assuming that the coefficient of kinetic friction between the 25-mm-diameter axles and the bearings is 0.12, determine the required diameter of the wheels. Neglect the rolling resistance between the wheels and the ground.

8.95 A couple of magnitude $M = 150$ N · m is required to start the vertical shaft rotating. Determine the coefficient of static friction.

8.96 A vertical force of 250 N is applied to a 6-kg electric polisher as it is operated on a horizontal surface. Knowing that the coefficient of kinetic friction is 0.30, determine the magnitude Q of the forces required to prevent rotation of the handles. Assume the force between the disk and the surface to be uniformly distributed.

Fig. P8.95

Fig. P8.96

8.97 Four springs, each of constant 7 kN/m, are used to press plate AB against the head on the vertical rod. In the position shown each spring has been compressed 50 mm. The plate AB may move vertically, but it is constrained against rotation by bolts which pass through holes cut in the plate. Knowing that $\mathbf{P} = 0$ and that the coefficient of friction is 0.40, determine the magnitude of the couple $\mathbf{M}$ required to rotate the rod.

8.98 In Prob. 8.97, determine the required magnitude of the force $\mathbf{P}$ if the rod is to rotate when the magnitude of the couple $\mathbf{M}$ is 35 N·m. For what magnitude of the force $\mathbf{P}$ is the rod most easily rotated?

*8.99 As the surfaces of shaft and bearing wear out, the frictional resistance of a thrust bearing decreases. It is generally assumed that the wear is directly proportional to the distance traveled by any given point of the shaft, and thus to the distance r from the point to the axis of the shaft. Assuming, then, that the normal force per unit area is inversely proportional to r, show that the magnitude M of the couple required to overcome the frictional resistance of a worn-out end bearing (with contact over the full circular area) is equal to 75 percent of the value given by formula (8.9) for a new bearing.

Fig. P8.97

*8.100 Assuming that bearings wear out as indicated in Prob. 8.99, show that the magnitude M of the couple required to overcome the frictional resistance of a worn-out collar bearing is

$$M = \tfrac{1}{2}\mu_k P(R_1 + R_2)$$

where P = magnitude of the total axial force
R_1, R_2 = inner and outer radii of collar

*8.101 Assuming that the pressure between the surfaces of contact is uniform, show that the magnitude M of the couple required to overcome frictional resistance for the conical pivot shown is

$$M = \frac{2}{3}\frac{\mu_k P}{\sin\theta}\frac{R_2^3 - R_1^3}{R_2^2 - R_1^2}$$

8.102 Solve Prob. 8.96, assuming that the normal force per unit area between the disk and the surface varies linearly from a maximum at the center to zero at the circumference of the disk.

Fig. P8.101

8.103 A circular disk of 200-mm diameter rolls at a constant velocity down a 3 percent incline. Determine the coefficient of rolling resistance.

8.104 Determine the horizontal force required to move a 1340-kg automobile along a horizontal road at a constant velocity. Neglect all forms of friction except rolling resistance, and assume the coefficient of rolling resistance to be 1.5 mm. The diameter of each tire is 575 mm.

8.105 Solve Prob. 8.93, including the effect of a coefficient of rolling resistance of 0.5 mm.

8.106 Solve Prob. 8.94, including the effect of a coefficient of rolling resistance of 1.75 mm.

(a)

(b)

Fig. 8.14

8.10. Belt Friction. Consider a flat belt passing over a fixed cylindrical drum (Fig. 8.14a). We propose to determine the relation existing between the values T_1 and T_2 of the tension in the two parts of the belt when the belt is just about to slide toward the right.

Let us detach from the belt a small element PP' subtending an angle $\Delta\theta$. Denoting by T the tension at P and by $T + \Delta T$ the tension at P', we draw the free-body diagram of the element of the belt (Fig. 8.14b). Besides the two forces of tension, the forces acting on the free body are the normal component $\Delta\mathbf{N}$ of the reaction of the drum and the friction force $\Delta\mathbf{F}$. Since motion is assumed to be impending, we have $\Delta F = \mu_s\,\Delta N$. It should be noted that if $\Delta\theta$ is made to approach zero, the magnitudes ΔN, ΔF, and the *difference* ΔT between the tension at P and the tension at P' will also approach zero; the value T of the tension at P, however, will remain unchanged. This observation helps in understanding our choice of notations.

Choosing the coordinate axes shown in Fig. 8.14b, we write the equations of equilibrium for the element PP':

$$\Sigma F_x = 0: \quad (T + \Delta T)\cos\frac{\Delta\theta}{2} - T\cos\frac{\Delta\theta}{2} - \mu_s\,\Delta N = 0 \tag{8.11}$$

$$\Sigma F_y = 0: \quad \Delta N - (T + \Delta T)\sin\frac{\Delta\theta}{2} - T\sin\frac{\Delta\theta}{2} = 0 \tag{8.12}$$

Solving Eq. (8.12) for ΔN and substituting into (8.11), we obtain after reductions

$$\Delta T\cos\frac{\Delta\theta}{2} - \mu_s(2T + \Delta T)\sin\frac{\Delta\theta}{2} = 0$$

We shall now divide both terms by $\Delta\theta$; as far as the first term is concerned, this will be simply done by dividing ΔT by $\Delta\theta$. The division of the second term is carried out by dividing the terms in the parentheses by 2 and the sine by $\Delta\theta/2$. We write

$$\frac{\Delta T}{\Delta\theta}\cos\frac{\Delta\theta}{2} - \mu_s\left(T + \frac{\Delta T}{2}\right)\frac{\sin\left(\Delta\theta/2\right)}{\Delta\theta/2} = 0$$

If we now let $\Delta\theta$ approach 0, the cosine approaches 1 and $\Delta T/2$ approaches zero as noted above. On the other hand, the quotient of $\sin\left(\Delta\theta/2\right)$ over $\Delta\theta/2$ approaches 1, according to a lemma derived in all calculus textbooks. Since the limit of $\Delta T/\Delta\theta$ is by definition equal to the derivative $dT/d\theta$, we write

$$\frac{dT}{d\theta} - \mu_s T = 0 \qquad \frac{dT}{T} = \mu_s\,d\theta$$

We shall now integrate both members of the last equation obtained from P_1 to P_2 (Fig. 8.14a). At P_1, we have $\theta = 0$ and $T = T_1$; at P_2, we have $\theta = \beta$ and $T = T_2$. Integrating between these limits, we write

$$\int_{T_1}^{T_2}\frac{dT}{T} = \int_0^\beta \mu_s\,d\theta$$

$$\ln T_2 - \ln T_1 = \mu_s\beta$$

or, noting that the left-hand member is equal to the natural logarithm of the quotient of T_2 and T_1,

$$\ln \frac{T_2}{T_1} = \mu_s \beta \qquad (8.13)$$

This relation may also be written in the form

$$\frac{T_2}{T_1} = e^{\mu_s \beta} \qquad (8.14)$$

The formulas we have derived apply equally well to problems involving flat belts passing over fixed cylindrical drums and to problems involving ropes wrapped around a post or capstan. They may also be used to solve problems involving band brakes. In such problems, it is the drum which is about to rotate, while the band remains fixed. The formulas may also be applied to problems involving belt drives. In these problems, both the pulley and the belt rotate; our concern is then to find whether the belt will slip, i.e., whether it will move *with respect* to the pulley.

Formulas (8.13) and (8.14) should be used only if the belt, rope, or brake is *about to slip*. Formula (8.14) will be used if T_1 or T_2 is desired; formula (8.13) will be preferred if either μ_s or the angle of contact β is desired. We should note that T_2 is always larger than T_1; T_2 therefore represents the tension in that part of the belt or rope which *pulls*, while T_1 is the tension in the part which *resists*. We should also observe that the angle of contact β must be expressed in *radians*. The angle β may be larger than 2π; for example, if a rope is wrapped n times around a post, β is equal to $2\pi n$.

If the belt, rope, or brake is actually slipping, formulas similar to (8.13) and (8.14), but involving the coefficient of kinetic friction μ_k, should be used. If the belt, rope, or brake does not slip and is not about to slip, none of these formulas may be used.

The belts used in belt drives are often V-shaped. Such a belt, called a *V belt*, is shown in Fig. 8.15a. It is seen that contact between belt and pulley takes place along the sides of the groove. The relation existing between the values T_1 and T_2 of the tension in the two parts of the belt when the belt is just about to slip may again be obtained by drawing the free-body diagram of an element of belt (Fig. 8.15b and c). Equations similar to (8.11) and (8.12) are derived, but the magnitude of the total friction force acting on the element is now $2 \Delta F$, and the sum of the y components of the normal forces is $2 \Delta N \sin (\alpha/2)$. Proceeding as above, we obtain

$$\frac{T_2}{T_1} = e^{\mu_s \beta / \sin (\alpha/2)} \qquad (8.15)$$

(a)

(b)

(c)

Fig. 8.15

SAMPLE PROBLEM 8.7

A hawser thrown from a ship to a pier is wrapped two full turns around a capstan. The tension in the hawser is 7500 N; by exerting a force of 150 N on its free end, a dock worker can just keep the hawser from slipping. (a) Determine the coefficient of friction between the hawser and the capstan. (b) Determine the tension in the hawser that could be resisted by the 150-N force if the hawser were wrapped three full turns around the capstan.

a. **Coefficient of Friction.** Since slipping of the hawser is impending, we use Eq. (8.13):

$$\ln \frac{T_2}{T_1} = \mu_s \beta$$

Since the hawser is wrapped two full turns around the capstan, we have

$$\beta = 2(2\pi \text{ rad}) = 12.6 \text{ rad}$$
$$T_1 = 150 \text{ N} \qquad T_2 = 7500 \text{ N}$$

Therefore,

$$\mu_s \beta = \ln \frac{T_2}{T_1}$$

$$\mu_s (12.6 \text{ rad}) = \ln \frac{7500 \text{ N}}{150 \text{ N}} = \ln 50 = 3.91$$

$$\mu_s = 0.31 \quad \blacktriangleleft$$

b. **Hawser Wrapped Three Turns around Capstan.** Using the value of μ_s obtained in part *a*, we have now

$$\beta = 3(2\pi \text{ rad}) = 18.9 \text{ rad}$$
$$T_1 = 150 \text{ N} \qquad \mu_s = 0.31$$

Substituting these values into Eq. (8.14), we obtain

$$\frac{T_2}{T_1} = e^{\mu_s \beta}$$

$$\frac{T_2}{150 \text{ N}} = e^{(0.31)(18.9)} = e^{5.86} = 350$$

$$T_2 = 52\,500 \text{ N} \qquad T_2 = 52.5 \text{ kN} \quad \blacktriangleleft$$

SAMPLE PROBLEM 8.8

A flat belt connects pulley A, which drives a machine tool, to pulley B, which is attached to the shaft of an electric motor. The coefficients of friction are $\mu_s = 0.25$ and $\mu_k = 0.20$ between both pulleys and the belt. Knowing that the maximum allowable tension in the belt is 3 kN, determine the largest torque which can be exerted by the belt on pulley A.

Solution. Since the resistance to slippage depends upon the angle of contact β between pulley and belt, as well as upon the coefficient of static friction μ_s, and since μ_s is the same for both pulleys, slippage will occur first on pulley B, for which β is smaller.

Pulley B. Using Eq. (8.14) with $T_2 = 3$ kN, $\mu_s = 0.25$, and $\beta = 120°$ $= 2\pi/3$ rad, we write

$$\frac{T_2}{T_1} = e^{\mu_s \beta} \qquad \frac{3 \text{ kN}}{T_1} = e^{0.25(2\pi/3)} = 1.688$$

$$T_1 = \frac{3 \text{ kN}}{1.688} = 1.777 \text{ kN}$$

Pulley A. We draw the free-body diagram of pulley A. The couple $\mathbf{M}_A$ is applied to the pulley by the machine tool to which it is attached and is equal and opposite to the torque exerted by the belt. We write

$$+\uparrow \Sigma M_A = 0: \qquad M_A - (3 \text{ kN})(0.2 \text{ m}) + (1.777 \text{ kN})(0.2 \text{ m}) = 0$$
$$M_A = 0.245 \text{ kN·m} \qquad\qquad M_A = 245 \text{ N·m} \blacktriangleleft$$

Note. We may check that the belt does not slip on pulley A by computing the value of μ_s required to prevent slipping at A and verifying that it is smaller than the actual value of μ_s. From Eq. (8.13) we have

$$\mu_s \beta = \ln \frac{T_2}{T_1} = \ln \frac{3 \text{ kN}}{1.777 \text{ kN}} = 0.524$$

and, since $\beta = 240° = 4\pi/3$ rad,

$$\frac{4\pi}{3}\mu_s = 0.524 \qquad \mu_s = 0.125 < 0.25$$

Fig. P8.108

Fig. P8.109 and P8.110

Fig. P8.113

Fig. P8.114

Problems

8.107 A hawser is wrapped two full turns around a capstan head. By exerting a force of 750 N on the free end of the hawser, a seaman can resist a force of 45 kN on the other end of the hawser. Determine (a) the coefficient of static friction, (b) the number of times the hawser should be wrapped around the capstan if a 300-kN force is to be resisted by the same 750-N force.

8.108 A rope having a mass per unit length of 0.6 kg/m is wound $2\frac{1}{2}$ times around a horizontal rod. What length x of rope should be left hanging if a 50-kg load is to be supported? The coefficient of static friction between the rope and the rod is 0.30.

8.109 Knowing that the coefficient of static friction is 0.25 between the rope and the horizontal pipe and 0.20 between the rope and the vertical pipe, determine the range of values of P for which equilibrium is maintained.

8.110 Knowing that the coefficient of static friction is 0.30 between the rope and the horizontal pipe and that the smallest value of P for which equilibrium is maintained is 80 N, determine (a) the largest value of P for which equilibrium is maintained, (b) the coefficient of static friction between the rope and the vertical pipe.

8.111 Assume that the bushing of Prob. 8.91 has become frozen to the shaft and cannot rotate. Determine the coefficient of static friction between the bushing and the rope if a force **P** of magnitude 1 kN is required to start raising the 45-kg load.

8.112 Assume that the bushing of Prob. 8.91 has become frozen to the shaft and cannot rotate. If the coefficient of static friction between the bushing and the rope is 0.35, determine the magnitude of the smallest force **P** required (a) to start raising the 45-kg load, (b) to hold the 45-kg load in place.

8.113 A flat belt is used to transmit the 40-N·m torque developed by an electric motor. The drum in contact with the belt has a diameter of 200 mm, and the coefficient of static friction between the belt and the drum is 0.30. Determine the minimum allowable value of the tension in each part of the belt if the belt is not to slip.

8.114 A flat belt is used to transmit a torque from pulley A to pulley B. The radius of each pulley is 50 mm and the coefficient of static friction is 0.30. Determine the largest torque which can be transmitted if the allowable belt tension is 3 kN.

8.115 Solve Prob. 8.114, assuming that the belt is looped around the pulleys in a figure 8.

8.116 The setup shown is used to measure the output of a small turbine. When the flywheel is at rest, the reading of each spring scale is 70 N. If a 12.60-N·m couple must be applied to the flywheel to keep it rotating clockwise at a constant speed, determine (a) the reading of each scale at that time, (b) the coefficient of kinetic friction. Assume that the length of the belt does not change.

Fig. P8.116 and P8.117

8.117 The setup shown is used to measure the output of a small turbine. The coefficient of kinetic friction is 0.20 and the reading of each spring scale is 80 N when the flywheel is at rest. Determine (a) the reading of each scale when the flywheel is rotating clockwise at a constant speed, (b) the couple which must be applied to the flywheel. Assume that the length of the belt does not change.

8.118 A band brake is used to control the speed of a flywheel as shown. The coefficients of friction are $\mu_s = 0.30$ and $\mu_k = 0.25$. What couple should be applied to the flywheel to keep it rotating counterclockwise at a constant speed when $P = 50$ N?

Fig. P8.118

8.119 Solve Prob. 8.118, assuming that the flywheel rotates clockwise.

8.120 A brake drum of radius $r = 150$ mm is rotating counterclockwise when a force **P** of magnitude 60 N is applied at A. Knowing that the coefficient of kinetic friction is 0.40, determine the moment about O of the friction forces applied to the drum when $a = 250$ mm and $b = 300$ mm.

8.121 Knowing that $r = 150$ mm and $a = 250$ mm, determine the maximum value of the coefficient of kinetic friction for which the brake is not self-locking when the drum rotates counterclockwise.

8.122 Knowing that the coefficient of kinetic friction is 0.40, determine the minimum value of the ratio a/r for which the brake is not self-locking. Assume that $a > r$ and that the drum rotates counterclockwise.

Fig. P8.120, P8.121, and P8.122

200 mm

70 kg

m

Fig. P8.123

8.123 A cord is placed over two cylinders, each of 100-mm diameter. Knowing that the coefficients of friction are $\mu_s = 0.30$ and $\mu_k = 0.25$, determine the largest mass m which can be raised when cylinder B is rotated slowly and cylinder A is kept fixed.

300 mm   300 mm

A   B   C

50 kg m

Fig. P8.124

8.124 A cable is placed around three pipes, each of 150 mm outside diameter, located in the same horizontal plane. Two of the pipes are fixed and do not rotate; the third pipe is rotated slowly. Knowing that the coefficients of friction are $\mu_s = 0.25$ and $\mu_k = 0.20$ for each pipe, determine the largest mass m which can be raised (a) if only pipe A is rotated, (b) if only pipe B is rotated, (c) if only pipe C is rotated.

8.125 The strap wrench shown is used to grip the pipe firmly and at the same time not mar the external surface of the pipe. Knowing that $a = 360$ mm and $r = 40$ mm, determine the minimum coefficient of static friction for which the wrench will be self-locking.

r

a

P

Fig. P8.125

8.126 For the strap wrench of Prob. 8.125, determine the minimum value of the ratio r/a for which the strap will be self-locking if the coefficient of static friction between the strap and the pipe is 0.25.

β

T_1 T_2

Fig. P8.127

8.127 Prove that Eqs. (8.13) and (8.14) are valid for any shape of surface provided that the coefficient of friction is the same at all points of contact.

8.128 Complete the derivation of Eq. (8.15), which relates the tension in both parts of a V belt.

8.129 Solve Prob. 8.113, assuming that the flat belt and pulley are replaced by a V belt and V pulley with $\alpha = 36°$. (The angle α is as shown in Fig. 8.15a.)

Review and Summary

This chapter was devoted to the study of *dry friction*, i.e., to problems involving rigid bodies which are in contact along *nonlubricated surfaces*.

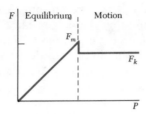

Fig. 8.16

Static and kinetic friction

Considering a block resting on a horizontal surface [Sec. 8.2] and applying to it a horizontal force **P**, we note that the block at first does not move. This shows that a *friction force* **F** must have developed to balance **P** (Fig. 8.16). As the magnitude of **P** is increased, the magnitude of **F** also increases until it reaches a maximum value F_m. If **P** is further increased, the block starts sliding and the magnitude of **F** drops from F_m to a lower value F_k. Experimental evidence shows that F_m and F_k are proportional to the normal component N of the reaction of the surface. We have

$$F_m = \mu_s N \qquad F_k = \mu_k N \qquad (8.1,\ 8.2)$$

where μ_s and μ_k are called, respectively, the *coefficient of static friction* and the *coefficient of kinetic friction*. These coefficients depend upon the nature and the condition of the surfaces in contact. Approximate values of the coefficients of static friction were given in Table 8.1.

Angles of friction

It is sometimes convenient to replace the normal force **N** and the friction force **F** by their resultant **R** (Fig. 8.17). As the friction force increases and reaches its maximum value $F_m = \mu_s N$, the angle ϕ that **R** forms with the normal to the surface increases and reaches a maximum value ϕ_s, called the *angle of static friction*. If motion actually takes place, the magnitude of **F** drops to F_k; similarly the angle ϕ drops to a lower value ϕ_k, called the *angle of kinetic friction*. As shown in Sec. 8.3, we have

$$\tan \phi_s = \mu_s \qquad \tan \phi_k = \mu_k \qquad (8.3,\ 8.4)$$

Fig. 8.17

(a)   (b)

Fig. 8.18

Problems involving friction

When solving equilibrium problems involving friction, we should keep in mind that the magnitude F of the friction force is equal to $F_m = \mu_s N$ *only if the body is about to slide* [Sec. 8.4]. *If motion is not impending,* F and N should be considered as *independent unknowns* to be determined from the equilibrium equations (Fig. 8.18a). We should also check that the value of F required to maintain equilibrium is not larger than F_m; if it were, the body would move and the magnitude of the friction force would be $F_k = \mu_k N$ [Sample Prob. 8.1]. On the other hand, *if motion is known to be impending,* F has reached its maximum value $F_m = \mu_s N$ (Fig. 8.18b) and this expression may be substituted for F in the equilibrium equations [Sample Prob. 8.3]. When only three forces are involved in a free-body diagram, including the reaction **R** of the surface in contact with the body, it is usually more convenient to solve the problem by drawing a force triangle [Sample Prob. 8.2].

When a problem involves the analysis of the forces exerted on each other by *two bodies A and B,* it is important to show the friction forces with their correct sense. The correct sense for the friction force exerted by B on A, for instance, is opposite to that of the *relative motion* (or impending motion) of A with respect to B [Fig. 8.6 of Sec. 8.4].

Wedges and screws

In the second part of the chapter we considered a number of specific engineering applications where dry friction plays an important role. In the case of *wedges,* which are simple machines used to raise heavy loads [Sec. 8.5], two or more free-body diagrams were drawn and care was taken to show each friction force with its correct sense [Sample Prob. 8.4]. The analysis of *square-threaded screws,* which are frequently used in jacks, presses, and other mechanisms, was reduced to the analysis of a block sliding on an incline by unwrapping the thread of the screw and showing it as a straight line [Sec. 8.6]. This is done again in Fig. 8.19, where r denotes the *mean radius* of the thread, L the *lead* of the screw, i.e., the distance through which the screw advances in one turn, W the load, and where Qr is equal to the torque exerted on the screw. It was noted that in the case of multiple-threaded screws the lead L of the screw is *not* equal to its pitch, which is the distance measured between two consecutive threads.

Fig. 8.19

Other applications

Other engineering applications considered in this chapter were *journal bearings* and *axle friction* [Sec. 8.7], *thrust bearings* and *disk friction* [Sec. 8.8], *wheel friction* and *rolling resistance* [Sec. 8.9], and *belt friction* [Sec. 8.10].

In solving a problem involving a *flat belt* passing over a fixed cylinder, it is important to first determine the direction in which the belt slips or is about to slip. If the drum is rotating, the motion or impending motion of the belt should be determined *relative* to the rotating drum. For instance, if the belt of Fig. 8.20 is about to slip to the right relative to the drum, the friction forces exerted by the drum on the belt will be directed to the left and the tension will be larger in the right-hand portion of the belt than in the left-hand portion. Denoting by T_2 the larger tension, by T_1 the smaller tension, by μ_s the coefficient of static friction, and by β the angle (in radians) subtended by the belt, we derived in Sec. 8.10 the formulas

$$\ln \frac{T_2}{T_1} = \mu_s \beta \tag{8.13}$$

$$\frac{T_2}{T_1} = e^{\mu_s \beta} \tag{8.14}$$

which were used in solving Sample Probs. 8.7 and 8.8. If the belt actually slips on the drum, the coefficient of static friction μ_s should be replaced by the coefficient of kinetic friction μ_k in both of these formulas.

Belt friction

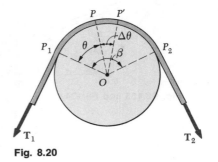

Fig. 8.20

Review Problems

8.130 Two large cylinders, each of radius $r = 500$ mm, rotate in opposite directions and form the main elements of a crusher for stone aggregate. The distance d is set equal to the maximum desired size of the crushed aggregate. If $d = 20$ mm and $\mu_s = 0.30$, determine the size s of the largest stones which will be pulled through the crusher by friction alone.

Fig. P8.130

8.131 In the vise shown, the screw is single-threaded in the upper member; it passes through the lower member and is held by a frictionless washer. The pitch of the screw is 3 mm, its mean radius is 12 mm, and the coefficient of static friction is 0.15. Determine the magnitude P of the forces exerted by the jaws when a 75-N·m couple is applied to the screw.

8.132 Solve Prob. 8.131, assuming that the screw is single-threaded at both A and B (right-handed thread at A and left-handed thread at B).

Fig. P8.131

8.133 The uniform rod AB lies in a vertical plane with its ends resting against the surfaces AC and BC. Determine the range of values of θ corresponding to equilibrium in terms of α and the angle of static friction ϕ_s between the rod and the two surfaces. Consider the case when (a) $\alpha > 2\phi_s$, (b) $\alpha \le 2\phi_s$.

8.134 The uniform rod AB lies in a vertical plane with its ends resting against the surfaces AC and BC. Knowing that the coefficient of static friction is 0.25 between the rod and each of the surfaces, determine the range of values of θ corresponding to equilibrium when (a) $\alpha = 45°$, (b) $\alpha = 25°$.

Fig. P8.133 and P8.134

8.135 A uniform bar of length 600 mm is supported by a horizontal shaft of diameter 50 mm. The shaft fits loosely in a circular hole in the bar and the coefficient of static friction is 0.40. If $x = 100$ mm and the shaft is slowly rotated, determine the angle at which the bar will slip.

Fig. P8.135

Fig. P8.136

8.136 A flat belt passes over two idler pulleys and under a rotating drum of diameter 200 mm. The axle of the drum is free to move vertically in a slot, and a spring keeps the drum in contact with the belt. What is the minimum force which should be exerted by the spring if slippage is not to occur when a 45 N·m couple is applied to the drum? The coefficient of static friction between belt and drum is 0.30.

Fig. P8.137

8.137 The uniform rod AB of radius a and weight W is attached to collars at A and B which may slide on the rods shown. Denoting by μ_s the coefficient of static friction between each collar and the rod upon which it may slide, determine the smallest value of μ_s for which the rod will remain in equilibrium in the position shown.

8.138 A half section of pipe, with a mass of 100 kg, is to be moved to the right along the floor without tipping. Knowing that the coefficient of friction between the pipe and the floor is 0.35, determine (a) the largest allowable value of α, (b) the corresponding tension T.

8.139 A half section of pipe, with a mass of 100 kg, is pulled by a cable as shown. The coefficient of friction between the pipe and the floor is 0.35. If $\alpha = 30°$, determine (a) the tension T required to move the pipe, (b) whether the pipe will slide or tip.

Fig. P8.138 and P8.139

8.140 A slender rod of length L is lodged between peg C and the horizontal ceiling and supports a load P at end B. Knowing that $\theta = 30°$ and that the coefficient of static friction is 0.40 at both A and C, find the range of values of the ratio L/a for which equilibrium is maintained.

8.141 A slender rod of length L is lodged between peg C and the horizontal ceiling and supports a load P at end B. Knowing that $L = 8a$, $\theta = 15°$, and that the coefficients of friction are $\mu_s = 0.60$ and $\mu_k = 0.50$ at A, and zero at C, determine whether the rod is in equilibrium and find the value of the friction force at A.

Fig. P8.140 and P8.141

The following problems are designed to be solved with a computer.

8.C1 The 40-kg block A hangs from a cable as shown. Pulley C is connected by a short link to block E, which rests on a horizontal rail. Denoting by μ_s the coefficient of static friction between block E and the rail, and neglecting the weight of block E and the friction in the pulleys, write a computer program and use it to calculate the value of θ for which motion impends for values of μ_s from 0 to 0.55 at 0.05 intervals.

Fig. P8.C1

Fig. P8.C2

8.C2 The coefficient of static friction between all surfaces of contact is 0.15. Knowing that block B has a mass 25 kg, write a computer program and use it to calculate the value of θ for which motion is impending for masses of block A from 0 to 60 kg at 5-kg intervals.

Fig. P8.C3

8.C3 A slender rod of length L is lodged between peg C and the horizontal ceiling and supports a load P at end B. (*a*) Knowing that the coefficient of static friction μ_s is the same at A and C, show that the following relation exists between the angle of static friction $\phi_s = \tan^{-1} \mu_s$ and the angle θ for which sliding is impending to the right:

$$\cot 2\phi_s = \cot \theta - \frac{a}{2L \sin^2 \theta \cos \theta}$$

(*b*) Use this relation to write a computer program and calculate μ_s for values of θ from 15 to 60° at 5° intervals, assuming (1) $L = 4a$, (2) $L = 8a$. (*c*) Determine to three significant figures the value of θ for which sliding impends to the right assuming $\mu_s = 0.300$ and (1) $L = 4a$, (2) $L = 8a$.

Fig. P8.C4

8.C4 The end B of a uniform beam of length L is being pulled by a stationary crane. Initially the beam lies on the ground with A directly under pulley C. As the cable is slowly pulled in, the beam first slides to the left with $\theta = 0$ until it has moved through a distance x_0. In a second phase, end B is raised, while end A keeps sliding to the left until x reaches its maximum value x_m and θ the corresponding value θ_1. The beam then rotates about A' while θ keeps increasing. As θ reaches the value θ_2, end A starts sliding to the right and keeps sliding in an irregular manner until B reaches C. Knowing that the coefficients of friction between the beam and the ground are $\mu_s = 0.50$ and $\mu_k = 0.40$, (*a*) write a program to compute x for any value of θ while the beam is sliding to the left and use this program to determine x_0, x_m, and θ_1, (*b*) modify the program to compute for any θ the value of x for which sliding would be impending to the right and use this new program to determine the value θ_2 of θ corresponding to $x = x_m$.

Distributed Forces: Moments of Inertia

9.1. Introduction. In Chap. 5, we analyzed various systems of forces distributed over an area or volume. The three main types of forces considered were (1) weights of homogeneous plates of uniform thickness (Secs. 5.3 through 5.6), (2) distributed loads on beams and hydrostatic forces (Secs. 5.8 and 5.9), and (3) weights of homogeneous three-dimensional bodies (Secs. 5.10 and 5.11). In the case of homogeneous plates, the magnitude ΔW of the weight of an element of plate was proportional to the area ΔA of the element. In the case of distributed loads on beams, the magnitude ΔW of each elementary weight was represented by an element of area $\Delta A = \Delta W$ under the load curve; in the case of hydrostatic forces on submerged rectangular surfaces, a similar procedure was followed. In the case of homogeneous three-dimensional bodies, the magnitude ΔW of the weight of an element of the body was proportional to the volume ΔV of the element. Thus, in all cases considered in Chap. 5, the distributed forces were proportional to the elementary areas or volumes associated with them. The resultant of these forces, therefore, could be obtained by summing the corresponding areas or volumes and the moment of the resultant about any given axis could be determined by computing the first moments of the areas or volumes about that axis.

In the first part of this chapter, we shall consider distributed forces $\Delta \mathbf{F}$ whose magnitudes depend not only upon the element of area ΔA on which they act but also upon the distance from ΔA to some given axis. More precisely, the magnitude of the force per unit area $\Delta F / \Delta A$ will vary linearly with the distance to the axis. As we shall see in the next section, forces of this type are found in the study of the bending of beams and in problems involving submerged nonrectangular surfaces. Assuming that the elementary forces involved are distributed over an area A and vary linearly with the distance y to the x axis, we shall find that while the magnitude of their resultant $\mathbf{R}$ depends upon the first moment $Q_x = \int y \, dA$ of the area A, the location of the point where $\mathbf{R}$ should be applied depends upon the *second moment,* or *moment of inertia,* $I_x = \int y^2\, dA$ of the same area with respect to the x axis. We shall learn to compute the moments of inertia of various areas with respect to given x and y axes. We shall also introduce the *polar moment of inertia* $J_O = \int r^2\, dA$ of an area, where r is the distance from the element of area dA to a point O. To facilitate our computations, we shall establish a relation between the moment of inertia I_x of an area A with respect to a given x axis and its moment of inertia $I_{x'}$ with respect to a parallel centroidal x' axis (parallel-axis theorem). We shall also study the transformation of the moments of inertia of a given area under a rotation of axes (Secs. 9.9 and 9.10).

In the second part of the chapter, we shall determine the moments of inertia of various *masses* with respect to a given axis. As we shall see in Sec. 9.11, the moment of inertia of a given mass about an axis AA' is defined as the integral $I = \int r^2\, dm$, where r is the distance from the axis AA' to the element of mass dm. Moments of inertia of masses are encountered in dynamics in problems involving the rotation of a rigid body about an axis. To facilitate the computation of mass moments of inertia, we shall introduce the parallel-axis theorem (Sec. 9.12) and analyze the transformation of moments of inertia of masses under a rotation of axes (Secs. 9.16 and 9.17).

MOMENTS OF INERTIA OF AREAS

9.2. Second Moment, or Moment of Inertia, of an Area.

In the first part of this chapter, we shall consider distributed forces $\Delta \mathbf{F}$ of magnitude ΔF proportional to the element of area ΔA on which they act and varying linearly with the distance from ΔA to some given axis.

Consider, for example, a beam of uniform cross section, subjected to two equal and opposite couples applied at each end of the beam. Such a beam is said to be in *pure bending,* and it is shown in mechanics of materials that the internal forces in any section of the beam are distributed forces whose magnitudes $\Delta F = ky\, \Delta A$ vary linearly with the distance y from an axis passing through the centroid of the section. This axis, represented by the x axis in Fig. 9.1, is known as the *neutral axis* of the section. The forces on one side of the neutral axis are forces of compression and on the other side, forces of tension, while on the neutral axis itself the forces are zero.

The magnitude of the resultant $\mathbf{R}$ of the elementary forces $\Delta \mathbf{F}$ over the entire section is

$$R = \int ky\, dA = k \int y\, dA$$

The last integral obtained is recognized as the *first moment* Q_x of the section about the x axis; it is equal to $\bar{y}A$ and to zero, since the centroid of the section is located on the x axis. The system of the forces $\Delta \mathbf{F}$ thus reduces to a couple. The magnitude M of this couple (bending moment) must be equal to the sum of the moments $\Delta M_x = y\, \Delta F = ky^2\, \Delta A$ of the elementary forces. Integrating over the entire section, we obtain

$$M = \int ky^2\, dA = k \int y^2\, dA$$

Fig. 9.1

The last integral is known as the *second moment*, or *moment of inertia,*† of the beam section with respect to the x axis and is denoted by I_x. It is obtained by multiplying each element of area dA by the *square of its distance* from the x axis and integrating over the beam section. Since each product $y^2\,dA$ is positive, whether y is itself positive or negative (or zero if y is zero), the integral I_x will always be different from zero and positive.

Another example of second moment, or moment of inertia, of an area is provided by the following problem of hydrostatics: A vertical circular gate used to close the outlet of a large reservoir is submerged under water as shown in Fig. 9.2. What is the resultant of the forces exerted by the water on the gate, and what is the moment of the resultant about the line of intersection of the plane of the gate with the water surface (x axis)?

If the gate were rectangular, the resultant of the forces of pressure could be determined from the pressure curve, as was done in Sec. 5.9. Since the gate is circular, however, a more general method must be used. Denoting by y the depth of an element of area ΔA and by ρ the density of water, the pressure at the element is $p = \rho gy$, and the magnitude of the elementary force exerted on ΔA is $\Delta F = p\,\Delta A = \rho gy\,\Delta A$. The magnitude of the resultant of the elementary forces is thus

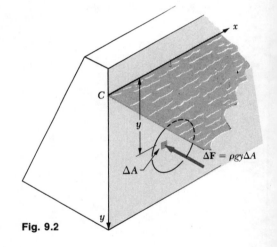

Fig. 9.2

$$R = \int \rho gy\,dA = \rho g \int y\,dA$$

and may be obtained by computing the first moment $Q_x = \int y\,dA$ of the area of the gate with respect to the x axis. The moment M_x of the resultant must be equal to the sum of the moments $\Delta M_x = y\Delta F = \rho gy^2\Delta A$ of the

---

† The term second moment is more proper than the term moment of inertia, since, logically, the latter should be used only to denote integrals of mass (see Sec. 9.11). In common engineering practice, however, moment of inertia is used in connection with areas as well as masses.

elementary forces. Integrating over the area of the gate, we have

$$M_x = \int \rho g y^2 \, dA = \rho g \int y^2 \, dA$$

Here again, the integral obtained represents the second moment, or moment of inertia, I_x of the area with respect to the x axis.

9.3. Determination of the Moment of Inertia of an Area by Integration.

We have defined in the preceding section the second moment, or moment of inertia, of an area A with respect to the x axis.

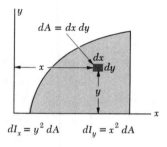

$dI_x = y^2 \, dA \qquad dI_y = x^2 \, dA$

(a)

Fig. 9.3

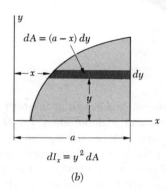

$dI_x = y^2 \, dA$

(b)

$dI_y = x^2 \, dA$

(c)

Defining in a similar way the moment of inertia I_y of the area A with respect to the y axis, we write (Fig. 9.3a)

$$I_x = \int y^2 \, dA \qquad I_y = \int x^2 \, dA \tag{9.1}$$

These integrals, known as the *rectangular moments of inertia* of the area A, may be more easily computed if we choose for dA a thin strip parallel to one of the axes of coordinates. To compute I_x, the strip is chosen parallel to the x axis, so that all the points forming the strip are at the same distance y from the x axis (Fig. 9.3b); the moment of inertia dI_x of the strip is then obtained by multiplying the area dA of the strip by y^2. To compute I_y, the strip is chosen parallel to the y axis so that all the points forming the strip are at the same distance x from the y axis (Fig. 9.3c); the moment of inertia dI_y of the strip is $x^2 \, dA$.

Moment of Inertia of a Rectangular Area. As an example, we shall determine the moment of inertia of a rectangle with respect to its base (Fig. 9.4). Dividing the rectangle into strips parallel to the x axis, we obtain

Fig. 9.4

$$dA = b \, dy \qquad dI_x = y^2 b \, dy \qquad I_x = \int_0^h by^2 \, dy = \tfrac{1}{3}bh^3 \tag{9.2}$$

Computing I_x and I_y from the Same Elementary Strips. The formula just derived may be used to determine the moment of inertia dI_x with respect to the x axis of a rectangular strip parallel to the y axis such as the one shown in Fig. 9.3c. Making $b = dx$ and $h = y$ in formula (9.2), we write

$$dI_x = \tfrac{1}{3}y^3\, dx$$

On the other hand, we have

$$dI_y = x^2\, dA = x^2 y\, dx$$

The same element may thus be used to compute the moments of inertia I_x and I_y of a given area (Fig. 9.5).

$$dI_x = \tfrac{1}{3}y^3\, dx$$
$$dI_y = x^2\, y\, dx$$

Fig. 9.5

9.4. Polar Moment of Inertia. An integral of great importance in problems concerning the torsion of cylindrical shafts and in problems dealing with the rotation of slabs is

$$J_O = \int r^2\, dA \tag{9.3}$$

where r is the distance from the element of area dA to the pole O (Fig. 9.6). This integral is the *polar moment of inertia* of the area A with respect to O.

The polar moment of inertia of a given area may be computed from the rectangular moments of inertia I_x and I_y of the area if these integrals are already known. Indeed, noting that $r^2 = x^2 + y^2$, we write

Fig. 9.6

$$J_O = \int r^2\, dA = \int (x^2 + y^2)\, dA = \int y^2\, dA + \int x^2\, dA$$

that is,

$$J_O = I_x + I_y \tag{9.4}$$

(a)

(b)

(c)

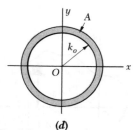

(d)

Fig. 9.7

9.5. Radius of Gyration of an Area. Consider an area A which has a moment of inertia I_x with respect to the x axis (Fig. 9.7a). Let us imagine that we concentrate this area into a thin strip parallel to the x axis (Fig. 9.7b). If the area A, thus concentrated, is to have the same moment of inertia with respect to the x axis, the strip should be placed at a distance k_x from the x axis, defined by the relation

$$I_x = k_x^2 A$$

Solving for k_x, we write

$$k_x = \sqrt{\frac{I_x}{A}} \tag{9.5}$$

The distance k_x is referred to as the *radius of gyration* of the area with respect to the x axis. We may define in a similar way the radii of gyration k_y and k_O (Fig. 9.7c and d); we write

$$I_y = k_y^2 A \qquad k_y = \sqrt{\frac{I_y}{A}} \tag{9.6}$$

$$J_O = k_O^2 A \qquad k_O = \sqrt{\frac{J_O}{A}} \tag{9.7}$$

Substituting for J_O, I_x, and I_y in terms of the radii of gyration in the relation (9.4), we observe that

$$k_O^2 = k_x^2 + k_y^2 \tag{9.8}$$

Example. As an example, let us compute the radius of gyration k_x of the rectangle shown in Fig. 9.8. Using formulas (9.5) and (9.2), we write

$$k_x^2 = \frac{I_x}{A} = \frac{\frac{1}{3}bh^3}{bh} = \frac{h^2}{3} \qquad k_x = \frac{h}{\sqrt{3}}$$

The radius of gyration k_x of the rectangle is shown in Fig. 9.8. It should not be confused with the ordinate $\bar{y} = h/2$ of the centroid of the area. While k_x depends upon the *second moment*, or moment of inertia, of the area, the ordinate $\bar{y}$ is related to the *first moment* of the area.

Fig. 9.8

Determine the moment of inertia of a triangle with respect to its base.

Solution. A triangle of base b and height h is drawn; the x axis is chosen to coincide with the base. A differential strip parallel to the x axis is chosen. Since all portions of the strip are at the same distance from the x axis, we write

$$dI_x = y^2 \, dA \qquad dA = l \, dy$$

From the similar triangles, we have

$$\frac{l}{b} = \frac{h-y}{h} \qquad l = b\frac{h-y}{h} \qquad dA = b\frac{h-y}{h} \, dy$$

Integrating dI_x from $y = 0$ to $y = h$, we obtain

$$I_x = \int y^2 \, dA = \int_0^h y^2 b\frac{h-y}{h} \, dy = \frac{b}{h}\int_0^h (hy^2 - y^3) \, dy$$

$$= \frac{b}{h}\left[h\frac{y^3}{3} - \frac{y^4}{4}\right]_0^h \qquad\qquad I_x = \frac{bh^3}{12} \quad \blacktriangleleft$$

SAMPLE PROBLEM 9.2

(*a*) Determine the centroidal polar moment of inertia of a circular area by direct integration. (*b*) Using the result of part *a*, determine the moment of inertia of a circular area with respect to a diameter.

a. **Polar Moment of Inertia.** An annular differential element of area is chosen. Since all portions of the differential area are at the same distance from the origin, we write

$$dJ_O = u^2 \, dA \qquad dA = 2\pi u \, du$$

$$J_O = \int dJ_O = \int_0^r u^2(2\pi u \, du) = 2\pi \int_0^r u^3 \, du$$

$$J_O = \frac{\pi}{2}r^4 \quad \blacktriangleleft$$

b. **Moment of Inertia with Respect to a Diameter.** Because of the symmetry of the circular area we have $I_x = I_y$. We then write

$$J_O = I_x + I_y = 2I_x \qquad \frac{\pi}{2}r^4 = 2I_x \qquad I_{\text{diameter}} = I_x = \frac{\pi}{4}r^4 \quad \blacktriangleleft$$

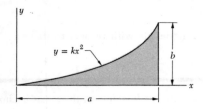

SAMPLE PROBLEM 9.3

(a) Determine the moment of inertia of the shaded area shown with respect to each of the coordinate axes. This area has also been considered in Sample Prob. 5.4. (b) Using the results of part a, determine the radius of gyration of the shaded area with respect to each of the coordinate axes.

Solution. Referring to Sample Prob. 5.4, we obtain the following expressions for the equation of the curve and the total area:

$$y = \frac{b}{a^2}x^2 \qquad A = \tfrac{1}{3}ab$$

Moment of Inertia I_x. A vertical differential element of area is chosen. Since all portions of this element are *not* at the same distance from the x axis, we must treat the element as a thin rectangle. The moment of inertia of the element with respect to the x axis is

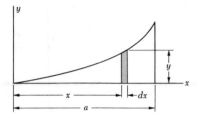

$$dI_x = \tfrac{1}{3}y^3\,dx = \frac{1}{3}\left(\frac{b}{a^2}x^2\right)^3 dx = \frac{1}{3}\frac{b^3}{a^6}x^6\,dx$$

$$I_x = \int dI_x = \int_0^a \frac{1}{3}\frac{b^3}{a^6}x^6\,dx = \left[\frac{1}{3}\frac{b^3}{a^6}\frac{x^7}{7}\right]_0^a$$

$$I_x = \frac{ab^3}{21} \quad \blacktriangleleft$$

Moment of Inertia I_y. The same vertical differential element of area is used. Since all portions of the element are at the same distance from the y axis, we write

$$dI_y = x^2\,dA = x^2(y\,dx) = x^2\left(\frac{b}{a^2}x^2\right)dx = \frac{b}{a^2}x^4\,dx$$

$$I_y = \int dI_y = \int_0^a \frac{b}{a^2}x^4\,dx = \left[\frac{b}{a^2}\frac{x^5}{5}\right]_0^a$$

$$I_y = \frac{a^3b}{5} \quad \blacktriangleleft$$

Radii of Gyration k_x and k_y

$$k_x^2 = \frac{I_x}{A} = \frac{ab^3/21}{ab/3} = \frac{b^2}{7} \qquad k_x = \sqrt{\tfrac{1}{7}}\,b \quad \blacktriangleleft$$

$$k_y^2 = \frac{I_y}{A} = \frac{a^3b/5}{ab/3} = \tfrac{3}{5}a^2 \qquad k_y = \sqrt{\tfrac{3}{5}}\,a \quad \blacktriangleleft$$

Problems

9.1 Determine the moment of inertia of the triangle of Sample Prob. 9.1 with respect to a line which passes through the upper vertex and is parallel to the x axis.

9.2 through 9.5 Determine by direct integration the moment of inertia of the shaded area with respect to the y axis.

Fig. P9.2 and P9.6   **Fig. P9.3 and P9.7**

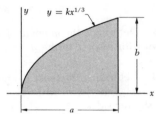

Fig. P9.4 and P9.8   **Fig. P9.5 and P9.9**

9.6 through 9.9 Determine by direct integration the moment of inertia of the shaded area with respect to the x axis.

9.10 and 9.11 Determine the moment of inertia and radius of gyration of the shaded area shown with respect to the x axis.

Fig. P9.10 and P9.12   **Fig. P9.11 and P9.13**

9.12 and 9.13 Determine the moment of inertia and radius of gyration of the shaded area shown with respect to the y axis.

9.14 Determine the moment of inertia and radius of gyration of the shaded area shown with respect to the x axis.

Fig. P9.14 and P9.15

9.15 Determine the moment of inertia and radius of gyration of the shaded area shown with respect to the y axis.

Fig. P9.16

9.16 Determine the polar moment of inertia and the polar radius of gyration of the rectangle shown with respect to the midpoint of one of its (a) longer sides, (b) shorter sides.

9.17 Determine the polar moment of inertia and the polar radius of gyration of the trapezoid shown with respect to point P.

Fig. P9.17

Fig. P9.18

9.18 Determine the polar moment of inertia and the polar radius of gyration of an equilateral triangle of side a with respect to one of its vertices.

9.19 (a) Determine by direct integration the polar moment of inertia of the annular area shown with respect to point O. (b) Using the result of part a, determine the moment of inertia of the given area with respect to the x axis.

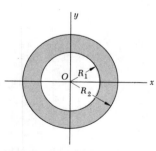

Fig. P9.19 and P9.20

9.20 (a) Show that the polar radius of gyration k_O of the annular area shown is approximately equal to the mean radius $R_m = (R_1 + R_2)/2$ for small values of the thickness $t = R_2 - R_1$. (b) Determine the percentage error introduced by using R_m in place of k_O for values of t/R_m respectively equal to 1, $\frac{1}{2}$, and $\frac{1}{10}$.

*9.21 Prove that the centroidal polar moment of inertia of a given area A cannot be smaller than $A^2/2\pi$. (Hint. Compare the moment of inertia of the given area with the moment of inertia of a circle of the same area and same centroid.)

9.6. Parallel-Axis Theorem.

9.6. Parallel-Axis Theorem. Consider the moment of inertia I of an area A with respect to an axis AA' (Fig. 9.9). Denoting by y the distance from an element of area dA to AA', we write

$$I = \int y^2 \, dA$$

Let us now draw an axis BB' parallel to AA' through the centroid C of the area; this axis is called a *centroidal axis*. Denoting by y' the distance from

Fig. 9.9

the element dA to BB', we write $y = y' + d$, where d is the distance between the axes AA' and BB'. Substituting for y in the integral representing I, we write

$$I = \int y^2 \, dA = \int (y' + d)^2 \, dA$$
$$= \int y'^2 \, dA + 2d \int y' \, dA + d^2 \int dA$$

The first integral represents the moment of inertia $\bar{I}$ of the area with respect to the centroidal axis BB'. The second integral represents the first moment of the area with respect to BB'; since the centroid C of the area is located on that axis, the second integral must be zero. Finally, we observe that the last integral is equal to the total area A. We write therefore

$$I = \bar{I} + Ad^2 \tag{9.9}$$

This formula expresses that the moment of inertia I of an area with respect to any given axis AA' is equal to the moment of inertia $\bar{I}$ of the area with respect to a centroidal axis BB' parallel to AA' *plus* the product Ad^2 of the area A and of the square of the distance d between the two axes. This theorem is known as the *parallel-axis theorem*. Substituting $k^2 A$ for I and $\bar{k}^2 A$ for $\bar{I}$, the theorem may also be expressed in the following way:

$$k^2 = \bar{k}^2 + d^2 \tag{9.10}$$

A similar theorem may be used to relate the polar moment of inertia J_O of an area about a point O and the polar moment of inertia $\bar{J}_C$ of the same area about its centroid C. Denoting by d the distance between O and C, we write

$$J_O = \bar{J}_C + Ad^2 \qquad \text{or} \qquad k_O^2 = \bar{k}_C^2 + d^2 \tag{9.11}$$

Fig. 9.10

Fig. 9.11

Example 1. As an application of the parallel-axis theorem, we shall determine the moment of inertia I_T of a circular area with respect to a line tangent to the circle (Fig. 9.10). We found in Sample Prob. 9.2 that the moment of inertia of a circular area about a centroidal axis is $\bar{I} = \frac{1}{4}\pi r^4$. We may write, therefore,

$$I_T = \bar{I} + Ad^2 = \tfrac{1}{4}\pi r^4 + \pi r^2 r^2 = \tfrac{5}{4}\pi r^4$$

Example 2. The parallel-axis theorem may also be used to determine the centroidal moment of inertia of an area when the moment of inertia of this area with respect to some parallel axis is known. Consider, for instance, a triangular area (Fig. 9.11). We found in Sample Prob. 9.1 that the moment of inertia of a triangle with respect to its base AA' is equal to $\frac{1}{12}bh^3$. Using the parallel-axis theorem, we write

$$I_{AA'} = \bar{I}_{BB'} + Ad^2$$
$$\bar{I}_{BB'} = I_{AA'} - Ad^2 = \tfrac{1}{12}bh^3 - \tfrac{1}{2}bh(\tfrac{1}{3}h)^2 = \tfrac{1}{36}bh^3$$

It should be observed that the product Ad^2 was *subtracted* from the given moment of inertia in order to obtain the centroidal moment of inertia of the triangle. While this product is *added* in transferring *from* a centroidal axis to a parallel axis, it should be *subtracted* in transferring *to* a centroidal axis. In other words, the moment of inertia of an area is always smaller with respect to a centroidal axis than with respect to any other parallel axis.

Returning to Fig. 9.11, we observe that the moment of inertia of the triangle with respect to a line DD' drawn through a vertex may be obtained by writing

$$I_{DD'} = \bar{I}_{BB'} + Ad'^2 = \tfrac{1}{36}bh^3 + \tfrac{1}{2}bh(\tfrac{2}{3}h)^2 = \tfrac{1}{4}bh^3$$

Note that $I_{DD'}$ *could not* have been obtained directly from $I_{AA'}$. The parallel-axis theorem can be applied only if one of the two parallel axes passes through the centroid of the area.

9.7. Moments of Inertia of Composite Areas.
Consider a composite area A made of several component areas A_1, A_2, etc. Since the integral representing the moment of inertia of A may be subdivided into integrals computed over A_1, A_2, etc., the moment of inertia of A with respect to a given axis will be obtained by adding the moments of inertia of the areas A_1, A_2, etc., with respect to the same axis. The moment of inertia of an area made of several of the common shapes shown in Fig. 9.12 may thus be obtained from the formulas given in that figure. Before adding the moments of inertia of the component areas, however, the parallel-axis theorem should be used to transfer each moment of inertia to the desired axis. This is shown in Sample Probs. 9.4 and 9.5.

The properties of the cross sections of various structural shapes are given in Fig. 9.13. As noted in Sec. 9.2, the moment of inertia of a beam section about its neutral axis is closely related to the value of the internal forces. The determination of moments of inertia is thus a prerequisite to the analysis and design of structural members.

It should be noted that the radius of gyration of a composite area is *not* equal to the sum of the radii of gyration of the component areas. In order to determine the radius of gyration of a composite area, it is necessary first to compute the moment of inertia of the area.

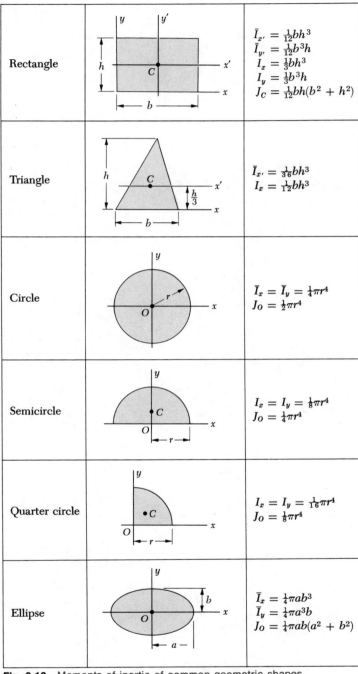

Rectangle		$\bar{I}_{x'} = \frac{1}{12}bh^3$ $\bar{I}_{y'} = \frac{1}{12}b^3h$ $I_x = \frac{1}{3}bh^3$ $I_y = \frac{1}{3}b^3h$ $J_C = \frac{1}{12}bh(b^2 + h^2)$
Triangle		$\bar{I}_{x'} = \frac{1}{36}bh^3$ $I_x = \frac{1}{12}bh^3$
Circle		$\bar{I}_x = \bar{I}_y = \frac{1}{4}\pi r^4$ $J_O = \frac{1}{2}\pi r^4$
Semicircle		$I_x = I_y = \frac{1}{8}\pi r^4$ $J_O = \frac{1}{4}\pi r^4$
Quarter circle		$I_x = I_y = \frac{1}{16}\pi r^4$ $J_O = \frac{1}{8}\pi r^4$
Ellipse		$\bar{I}_x = \frac{1}{4}\pi ab^3$ $\bar{I}_y = \frac{1}{4}\pi a^3b$ $J_O = \frac{1}{4}\pi ab(a^2 + b^2)$

Fig. 9.12 Moments of inertia of common geometric shapes.

Fig. 9.13 Properties of Rolled-Steel Shapes

	Designation	Area mm^2	Depth mm	Width mm	Axis X-X			Axis Y-Y		
					$\bar{I}_x$ 10^6 mm^4	$\bar{k}_x$ mm	$\bar{y}$ mm	$\bar{I}_y$ 10^6 mm^4	$\bar{k}_y$ mm	$\bar{x}$ mm
W Shapes (Wide-Flange Shapes)	W460 × 113†	14400	463	280	554	196.3		63.3	66.3	
	W410 × 85	10800	417	181	316	170.7		17.94	40.6	
	W360 × 57	7230	358	172	160.2	149.4		11.11	39.4	
	W200 × 46.1	5890	203	203	45.8	88.1		15.44	51.3	
S Shapes (Standard Shapes)	S460 × 81.4†	10390	457	152	335	179.6		8.66	29.0	
	S310 × 47.3	6032	305	127	90.7	122.7		3.90	25.4	
	S250 × 37.8	4806	254	118	51.6	103.4		2.83	24.2	
	S150 × 18.6	2362	152	84	9.2	62.2		0.758	17.91	
C Shapes (Standard Channels)	C310 × 30.8†	3929	305	74	53.7	117.1		1.615	20.29	17.73
	C250 × 22.8	2897	254	65	28.1	98.3		0.949	18.11	16.10
	C200 × 17.1	2181	203	57	13.57	79.0		0.549	15.88	14.50
	C150 × 12.2	1548	152	48	5.45	59.4		0.288	13.64	13.00
Angles	L152 × 152 × 25.4‡	7100			14.78	45.6	47.2	14.78	45.6	47.2
	L102 × 102 × 12.7	2420			2.31	30.9	30.0	2.31	30.9	30.0
	L76 × 76 × 6.4	929			0.516	23.6	21.4	0.516	23.6	21.4
	L152 × 102 × 12.7	3060			7.24	48.6	50.5	2.61	29.2	25.1
	L127 × 76 × 12.7	2420			3.93	40.3	44.5	1.074	21.1	19.05
	L76 × 51 × 6.4	768			0.454	24.3	25.2	0.163	14.58	12.52

†Normal depth in millimetres and mass in kilograms per metre.

‡Depth, width, and thickness in millimetres.

The strength of a W360 × 57 rolled-steel beam is increased by attaching a 225 × 20 mm plate to its upper flange as shown. Determine the moment of inertia and the radius of gyration of the composite section with respect to an axis through its centroid C and paralle to the plate.

Solution. The origin of coordinates O is placed at the centroid of the wide-flange shape, and the distance $\overline{Y}$ to the centroid of the composite section is computed by the methods of Chap. 5. The area of the wide-flange shape is found by referring to Fig. 9.13. The area and y coordinate of the centroid of the plate are

$$A = (225 \text{ mm})(20 \text{ mm}) = 4500 \text{ mm}^2$$
$$\overline{y} = \tfrac{1}{2}(358 \text{ mm}) + \tfrac{1}{2}(20 \text{ mm}) = 189 \text{ mm}$$

Section	Area, mm²	$\overline{y}$, mm	$\overline{y}A$, mm³
Plate	4500	189	850.5×10^3
Wide-flange shape	7230	0	0
	11730	...	850.5×10^3

$$\overline{Y}\Sigma A = \Sigma\overline{y}A \qquad \overline{Y}(11730) = (850.5 \times 10^3) \qquad \overline{Y} = 72.51 \text{ mm}$$

Moment of Inertia. The parallel-axis theorem is used to determine the moments of inertia of the wide-flange shape and of the plate with respect to the x' axis. This axis is a centroidal axis for the composite section, but *not* for either of the elements considered separately. The value of $\overline{I}_x$ for the wide-flange shape is obtained from Fig. 9.13.

For the wide-flange shape,

$$I_{x'} = \overline{I}_x + A\overline{Y}^2 = 160.2 \times 10^6 + (7230)(72.51)^2 = 198.2 \times 10^6 \text{ mm}^4$$

For the plate,

$$I_{x'} = \overline{I}_x + Ad^2 = (\tfrac{1}{12})(225)(20)^3 + (4500)(189 - 72.51)^2 = 61.2 \times 10^6 \text{ mm}^4$$

For the composite area,

$$I_{x'} = 192.6 \times 10^6 + 61.2 \times 10^6 = 253.8 \times 10^6 \text{ mm}^4$$

$$I_{x'} = 254 \times 10^6 \text{ mm}^4 \quad \blacktriangleleft$$

Radius of Gyration

$$k_{x'}^2 = \frac{I_{x'}}{A} = \frac{253.8 \times 10^6 \text{ mm}^4}{11730 \text{ mm}^2}$$

$$k_{x'} = 147.1 \text{ mm} \blacktriangleleft$$

SAMPLE PROBLEM 9.5

Determine the moment of inertia of the shaded area with respect to the x axis.

Solution. The given area may be obtained by subtracting a half circle from a rectangle. The moments of inertia of the rectangle and of the half circle will be computed separately.

I_x **for Rectangle.** Referring to Fig. 9.12, we obtain

$$I_x = \tfrac{1}{3}bh^3 = \tfrac{1}{3}(240 \text{ mm})(120 \text{ mm})^3 = 138.2 \times 10^6 \text{ mm}^4$$

I_x **for the Half Circle.** Referring to Fig. 5.8, we locate the centroid C of the half circle with respect to diameter AA'.

$$a = \frac{4r}{3\pi} = \frac{(4)(90 \text{ mm})}{3\pi} = 38.2 \text{ mm}$$

The distance b from the centroid C to the x axis is

$$b = 120 \text{ mm} - a = 120 \text{ mm} - 38.2 \text{ mm} = 81.8 \text{ mm}$$

Referring now to Fig. 9.12, we compute the moment of inertia of the half circle with respect to diameter AA'; we also compute the area of the half circle.

$$I_{AA'} = \tfrac{1}{8}\pi r^4 = \tfrac{1}{8}\pi(90 \text{ mm})^4 = 25.76 \times 10^6 \text{ mm}^4$$
$$A = \tfrac{1}{2}\pi r^2 = \tfrac{1}{2}\pi(90 \text{ mm})^2 = 12.72 \times 10^3 \text{ mm}^2$$

Using the parallel-axis theorem, we obtain the value of $\bar{I}_{x'}$:

$$I_{AA'} = \bar{I}_{x'} + Aa^2$$
$$25.76 \times 10^6 \text{ mm}^4 = \bar{I}_{x'} + (12.72 \times 10^3 \text{ mm}^2)(38.2 \text{ mm})^2$$
$$\bar{I}_{x'} = 7.20 \times 10^6 \text{ mm}^4$$

Again using the parallel-axis theorem, we obtain the value of I_x:

$$I_x = \bar{I}_{x'} + Ab^2 = 7.20 \times 10^6 \text{ mm}^4 + (12.72 \times 10^3 \text{ mm}^2)(81.8 \text{ mm})^2$$
$$= 92.3 \times 10^6 \text{ mm}^4$$

I_x **for Given Area.** Subtracting the moment of inertia of the half circle from that of the rectangle, we obtain

$$I_x = 138.2 \times 10^6 \text{ mm}^4 - 92.3 \times 10^6 \text{ mm}^4$$
$$I_x = 45.9 \times 10^6 \text{ mm}^4 \quad \blacktriangleleft$$

Problems

9.22 and 9.24 Determine the moment of inertia and the radius of gyration of the shaded area with respect to the x axis.

Fig. P9.22 and P9.23

Fig. P9.24 and P9.25

9.23 and 9.25 Determine the moment of inertia and the radius of gyration of the shaded area with respect to the y axis.

Fig. P9.26

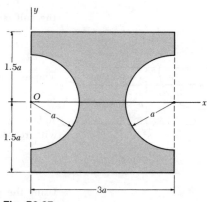

Fig. P9.27

9.26 and 9.27 Determine the moments of inertia of the shaded area shown with respect to the x and y axes when $a = 20$ mm.

9.28 Determine the shaded area and its moment of inertia with respect to a centroidal axis parallel to AA', knowing that its moments of inertia with respect to AA' and BB' are respectively 2.2×10^6 mm^4 and 4×10^6 mm^4, and that $d_1 = 25$ mm and $d_2 = 10$ mm.

Fig. P9.28 and P9.29

9.29 Knowing that the shaded area is equal to 6000 mm^2 and that its moment of inertia with respect to AA' is 18×10^6 mm^4, determine its moment of inertia with respect to BB', for $d_1 = 50$ mm and $d_2 = 10$ mm.

9.30 The shaded area is equal to 5000 mm². Determine its centroidal moments of inertia $\bar{I}_x$ and $\bar{I}_y$, knowing that $\bar{I}_y = 2\bar{I}_x$ and that the polar moment of inertia of the area about point A is $J_A = 22.5 \times 10^6$ mm⁴.

9.31 The polar moments of inertia of the shaded area with respect to points A, B, and D are, respectively, $J_A = 28.8 \times 10^6$ mm⁴, $J_B = 67.2 \times 10^6$ mm⁴, and $J_D = 45.6 \times 10^6$ mm⁴. Determine the shaded area, its centroidal moment of inertia $\bar{J}_C$, and the distance d from C to D.

9.32 and 9.33 Determine the moments of inertia $\bar{I}_x$ and $\bar{I}_y$ of the area shown with respect to centroidal axes respectively parallel and perpendicular to the side AB.

Fig. P9.30 and P9.31

Fig. P9.32

Dimensions in mm

Fig. P9.33

9.34 and 9.35 Determine the polar moment of inertia of the area shown with respect to (a) point O, (b) the centroid of the area.

Dimensions in mm

Fig. P9.34

Fig. P9.35

(a)

(b)

Fig. P9.36

9.36 Two W200 × 46.1 rolled sections may be welded at A and B in either of the two ways shown. For each arrangement, determine the moment of inertia of the section with respect to the horizontal centroidal axis.

9.37 Two $152 \times 102 \times 12.7$ mm angles are welded together to form the section shown. Determine the moments of inertia and the radii of gyration of the section with respect to the centroidal axes shown.

Fig. P9.37

Fig. P9.38

9.38 Two channels and two plates are used to form the column section shown. For $b = 200$ mm, determine the moments of inertia and the radii of gyration of the combined section with respect to the centroidal axes.

9.39 In Prob. 9.38, determine the distance b for which the centroidal moments of inertia $\bar{I}_x$ and $\bar{I}_y$ of the column section are equal.

Fig. P9.40

9.40 A channel and a plate are welded together as shown to form a section which is symmetrical with respect to the y axis. Determine the moments of inertia of the section with respect to its centroidal x and y axes.

9.41 Two $102 \times 102 \times 12.7$ mm angles are welded to a 12-mm steel plate as shown. For $b = 250$ mm, determine the moments of inertia of the combined section with respect to centroidal axes respectively parallel and perpendicular to the plate.

Fig. P9.41

9.42 Solve Prob. 9.41, assuming that $b = 300$ mm.

Fig. P9.43

9.43 The strength of the rolled S section shown is increased by welding a channel to its upper flange. Determine the moments of inertia of the combined section with respect to its centroidal x and y axes.

9.44 through 9.46 The panel shown forms the end of a trough which is filled with water to the line AA'. Referring to Sec. 9.2, determine the depth of the point of application of the resultant of the hydrostatic forces acting on the panel (center of pressure).

Fig. P9.44

Fig. P9.45

Fig. P9.46

9.47 The center of a vertical circular gate, 1.2 m in diameter, is located 1.8 m below the water surface. The gate is held by three bolts equally spaced as shown. Determine the force on each bolt.

Fig. P9.47

9.48 Solve Prob. 9.47, assuming that the center of the gate is located 1.5 m below the water surface.

9.49 A vertical circular gate of radius r is hinged about its diameter $C'C''$. Denoting the density of water by ρ, determine (a) the reaction at each of the two hinges, (b) the moment of the couple required to keep the gate closed.

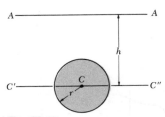

Fig. P9.49

*9.50 Determine the x coordinate of the centroid of the volume shown; this volume was obtained by intersecting a circular cylinder by an oblique plane. (*Hint.* The height of the volume is proportional to the x coordinate; consider an analogy between this height and the water pressure on a submerged surface.)

Fig. P9.50

*9.51 Determine the x coordinate of the centroid of the volume shown. (See hint of Prob. 9.50.)

Fig. P9.51

*9.52 Show that the system of hydrostatic forces acting on a submerged plane area A may be reduced to a force $\mathbf{P}$ at the centroid C of the area and two couples. The force $\mathbf{P}$ is perpendicular to the area and of magnitude $P = \rho g A \bar{y} \sin \theta$, where ρ is the density of the liquid, and the couples are represented by vectors directed as shown and of magnitude $M_{x'} = \rho g \, \bar{I}_{x'} \sin \theta$ and $M_{y'} = \rho g \bar{I}_{x'y'} \sin \theta$, where $\bar{I}_{x'y'} = \int x'y' \, dA$ (see Sec. 9.8). Note that the couples are independent of the depth at which the area is submerged.

Fig. P9.52

Fig. P9.53

*9.53 Show that the resultant of the hydrostatic forces acting on a submerged plane area A is a force $\mathbf{P}$ perpendicular to the area and of magnitude $P = \rho g A \bar{y} \sin \theta = \bar{p} A$, where ρ is the density of the liquid and $\bar{p}$ the pressure at the centroid C of the area. Show that $\mathbf{P}$ is applied at a point C_P, called the center of pressure, of coordinates $x_P = I_{xy}/A\bar{y}$ and $y_P = I_x/A\bar{y}$, where $I_{xy} = \int xy \, dA$ (see Sec. 9.8). Show also that the difference of ordinates $y_P - \bar{y}$ is equal to $\bar{k}_{x'}^2/\bar{y}$ and thus depends upon the depth at which the area is submerged.

Fig. 9.14

* 9.8. Product of Inertia. The integral

$$I_{xy} = \int xy \, dA \qquad (9.12)$$

obtained by multiplying each element dA of an area A by its coordinates x and y and integrating over the area (Fig. 9.14), is known as the *product of inertia* of the area A with respect to the x and y axes. Unlike the moments of inertia I_x and I_y, the product of inertia I_{xy} may be either positive or negative.

When one or both of the x and y axes are axes of symmetry for the area A, the product of inertia I_{xy} is zero. Consider, for example, the channel section shown in Fig. 9.15. Since this section is symmetrical with respect to the x axis, we can associate to each element dA of coordinates x and y an element dA' of coordinates x and $-y$. Clearly, the contributions of any pair of elements chosen in this way cancel out, and the integral (9.12) reduces to zero.

Fig. 9.15

A parallel-axis theorem similar to the one established in Sec. 9.6 for moments of inertia may be derived for products of inertia. Consider an area A and a system of rectangular coordinates x and y (Fig. 9.16). Through the centroid C of the area, of coordinates $\bar{x}$ and $\bar{y}$, we draw two *centroidal axes* x' and y' parallel, respectively, to the x and y axes. Denoting by x and y the coordinates of an element of area dA with respect to the original axes, and by x' and y' the coordinates of the same element with respect to the centroidal axes, we write $x = x' + \bar{x}$ and $y = y' + \bar{y}$. Substituting into (9.12), we obtain the following expression for the product of inertia I_{xy}:

$$I_{xy} = \int xy\, dA = \int (x' + \bar{x})(y' + \bar{y})\, dA$$
$$= \int x'y'\, dA + \bar{y}\int x'\, dA + \bar{x}\int y'\, dA + \bar{x}\bar{y}\int dA$$

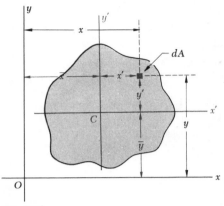

Fig. 9.16

The first integral represents the product of inertia $\bar{I}_{x'y'}$ of the area A with respect to the centroidal axes x' and y'. The next two integrals represent first moments of the area with respect to the centroidal axes; they reduce to zero, since the centroid C is located on these axes. Finally, we observe that the last integral is equal to the total area A. We write therefore

$$I_{xy} = \bar{I}_{x'y'} + \bar{x}\bar{y}A \tag{9.13}$$

*9.9. Principal Axes and Principal Moments of Inertia.

Consider the area A and the coordinate axes x and y (Fig. 9.17). We assume that the moments and product of inertia

$$I_x = \int y^2\, dA \qquad I_y = \int x^2\, dA \qquad I_{xy} = \int xy\, dA \tag{9.14}$$

of the area A are known, and we propose to determine the moments and product of inertia $I_{x'}$, $I_{y'}$, and $I_{x'y'}$ of A with respect to new axes x' and y' obtained by rotating the original axes about the origin through an angle θ.

We first note the following relations between the coordinates x', y' and x, y of an element of area dA:

$$x' = x\cos\theta + y\sin\theta \qquad y' = y\cos\theta - x\sin\theta$$

Substituting for y' in the expression for $I_{x'}$, we write

$$I_{x'} = \int (y')^2\, dA = \int (y\cos\theta - x\sin\theta)^2\, dA$$
$$= \cos^2\theta \int y^2\, dA - 2\sin\theta\cos\theta \int xy\, dA + \sin^2\theta \int x^2\, dA$$

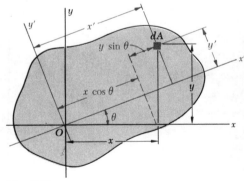

Fig. 9.17

Taking the relations (9.14) into account, we write

$$I_{x'} = I_x\cos^2\theta - 2I_{xy}\sin\theta\cos\theta + I_y\sin^2\theta \tag{9.15}$$

Similarly, we obtain for $I_{y'}$ and $I_{x'y'}$ the expressions

$$I_{y'} = I_x\sin^2\theta + 2I_{xy}\sin\theta\cos\theta + I_y\cos^2\theta \tag{9.16}$$
$$I_{x'y'} = (I_x - I_y)\sin\theta\cos\theta + I_{xy}(\cos^2\theta - \sin^2\theta) \tag{9.17}$$

Recalling the trigonometric relations

$$\sin 2\theta = 2 \sin \theta \cos \theta \qquad \cos 2\theta = \cos^2 \theta - \sin^2 \theta$$

and

$$\cos^2 \theta = \frac{1 + \cos 2\theta}{2} \qquad \sin^2 \theta = \frac{1 - \cos 2\theta}{2}$$

we may write (9.15), (9.16), and (9.17) as follows:

$$I_{x'} = \frac{I_x + I_y}{2} + \frac{I_x - I_y}{2} \cos 2\theta - I_{xy} \sin 2\theta \qquad (9.18)$$

$$I_{y'} = \frac{I_x + I_y}{2} - \frac{I_x - I_y}{2} \cos 2\theta + I_{xy} \sin 2\theta \qquad (9.19)$$

$$I_{x'y'} = \frac{I_x - I_y}{2} \sin 2\theta + I_{xy} \cos 2\theta \qquad (9.20)$$

We observe, by adding (9.18) and (9.19) member by member, that

$$I_{x'} + I_{y'} = I_x + I_y \qquad (9.21)$$

This result could have been anticipated, since both members of (9.21) are equal to the polar moment of inertia J_O.

Equations (9.18) and (9.20) are the parametric equations of a circle. This means that if we choose a set of rectangular axes and plot a point M of abscissa $I_{x'}$ and ordinate $I_{x'y'}$ for any given value of the parameter θ, all the points thus obtained will lie on a circle. To establish this property we shall eliminate θ from Eqs. (9.18) and (9.20); this is done by transposing $(I_x + I_y)/2$ in Eq. (9.18), squaring both members of Eqs. (9.18) and (9.20), and adding. We write

$$\left(I_{x'} - \frac{I_x + I_y}{2} \right)^2 + I_{x'y'}^2 = \left(\frac{I_x - I_y}{2} \right)^2 + I_{xy}^2 \qquad (9.22)$$

Setting

$$I_{\text{ave}} = \frac{I_x + I_y}{2} \qquad \text{and} \qquad R = \sqrt{\left(\frac{I_x - I_y}{2} \right)^2 + I_{xy}^2} \qquad (9.23)$$

we write the identity (9.22) in the form

$$(I_{x'} - I_{\text{ave}})^2 + I_{x'y'}^2 = R^2 \qquad (9.24)$$

which is the equation of a circle of radius R centered at the point C of abscissa I_{ave} and ordinate 0 (Fig. 9.18a). It may be observed that Eqs. (9.19) and (9.20) are the parametric equations of the same circle. Furthermore, due to the symmetry of the circle about the horizontal axis, the same result would have been obtained if instead of plotting M, we had plotted a point N of abscissa $I_{y'}$ and ordinate $-I_{x'y'}$ (Fig. 9.18b). This property will be used in Sec. 9.10.

The two points A and B where the circle obtained intersects the axis of abscissas are of special interest: Point A corresponds to the maximum value of the moment of inertia $I_{x'}$, while point B corresponds to its minimum

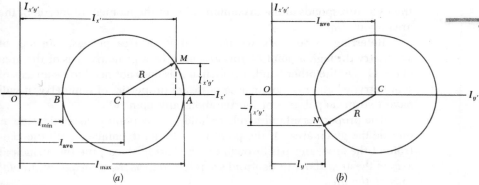

Fig. 9.18

value. Besides, both points correspond to a zero value of the product of inertia $I_{x'y'}$. Thus, the values θ_m of the parameter θ which correspond to the points A and B may be obtained by setting $I_{x'y'} = 0$ in Eq. (9.20). We obtain†

$$\tan 2\theta_m = -\frac{2I_{xy}}{I_x - I_y} \tag{9.25}$$

This equation defines two values $2\theta_m$ which are 180° apart and thus two values θ_m which are 90° apart. One of them corresponds to point A in Fig. 9.18a and to an axis through O in Fig. 9.17 with respect to which the moment of inertia of the given area is maximum; the other value corresponds to point B and an axis through O with respect to which the moment of inertia of the area is minimum. The two axes thus defined, which are perpendicular to each other, are called the *principal axes of the area about* O, and the corresponding values I_{max} and I_{min} of the moment of inertia are called the *principal moments of inertia of the area about* O. Since the two values θ_m defined by Eq. (9.25) were obtained by setting $I_{x'y'} = 0$ in Eq. (9.20), it is clear that the product of inertia of the given area with respect to its principal axes is zero.

We observe from Fig. 9.18a that

$$I_{max} = I_{ave} + R \qquad \text{and} \qquad I_{min} = I_{ave} - R \tag{9.26}$$

Substituting for I_{ave} and R from formulas (9.23), we write

$$I_{max,min} = \frac{I_x + I_y}{2} \pm \sqrt{\left(\frac{I_x - I_y}{2}\right)^2 + I_{xy}^2} \tag{9.27}$$

Unless it is possible to tell by inspection which of the two principal axes corresponds to I_{max} and which corresponds to I_{min}, it is necessary to substitute one of the values of θ_m into Eq. (9.18) in order to determine which of

---

†This relation may also be obtained by differentiating $I_{x'}$ in Eq. (9.18) and setting $dI_{x'}/d\theta = 0$.

the two corresponds to the maximum value of the moment of inertia of the area about O.

Referring to Sec. 9.8, we note that if an area possesses an axis of symmetry through a point O, this axis must be a principal axis of the area about O. On the other hand, a principal axis does not need to be an axis of symmetry; whether or not an area possesses properties of symmetry, it will have two principal axes of inertia about any point O.

The properties established here hold for any point O located inside or outside the given area. If the point O is chosen to coincide with the centroid of the area, any axis through O is a centroidal axis; the two principal axes of the area about its centroid are referred to as the *principal centroidal axes of the area*.

*9.10. Mohr's Circle for Moments and Products of Inertia.

The circle used in the preceding section to illustrate the relations existing between the moments and products of inertia of a given area with respect to axes passing through a fixed point O was first introduced by the German engineer Otto Mohr (1835–1918) and is known as *Mohr's circle*. We shall see that if the moments and product of inertia of an area A are known with respect to two rectangular x and y axes through a point O, Mohr's circle may be used to determine graphically (*a*) the principal axes and principal moments of inertia of the area about O, or (*b*) the moments and product of inertia of the area with respect to any other pair of rectangular axes x' and y' through O.

Consider a given area A and two rectangular coordinate axes x and y (Fig. 9.19*a*). We shall assume that the moments of inertia I_x and I_y and the product of inertia I_{xy} are known, and we shall represent them on a diagram by plotting a point X of coordinates I_x and I_{xy} and a point Y of coordinates I_y and $-I_{xy}$ (Fig. 9.19*b*). If I_{xy} is positive, as assumed in Fig. 9.19*a*, point X is located above the horizontal axis and point Y below, as shown in Fig. 9.19*b*. If I_{xy} is negative, X is located below the horizontal axis and Y above. Joining X and Y by a straight line, we define the point C of intersection of line XY with the horizontal axis and draw the circle of center C and diameter XY. Noting that the abscissa of C and the radius of the circle are respectively equal to the quantities I_{ave} and R defined by the formulas (9.23), we conclude that the circle obtained is Mohr's circle for the given area about point O. Thus the abscissas of the points A and B where the circle intersects the horizontal axes represent respectively the principal moments of inertia $I_{\max}$ and $I_{\min}$ of the area.

We also note that, since $\tan(XCA) = 2I_{xy}/(I_x - I_y)$, the angle XCA is equal in magnitude to one of the angles $2\theta_m$ which satisfy Eq. (9.25); thus the angle θ_m which defines in Fig. 9.19*a* the principal axis Oa corresponding to point A in Fig. 9.19*b* may be obtained by dividing in half the angle XCA measured on Mohr's circle. We further observe that if $I_x > I_y$ and $I_{xy} > 0$, as in the case considered here, the rotation which brings CX into CA is clockwise. But, in that case, the angle θ_m obtained from Eq. (9.25) and defining the principal axis Oa in Fig. 9.19*a* is negative; thus the rota-

Fig. 9.19

tion bringing Ox into Oa is also clockwise. We conclude that the senses of rotation in both parts of Fig. 9.19 are the same; if a clockwise rotation through $2\theta_m$ is required to bring CX into CA on Mohr's circle, a clockwise rotation through θ_m will bring Ox into the corresponding principal axis Oa in Fig. 9.19a.

Since Mohr's circle is uniquely defined, the same circle may be obtained by considering the moments and product of inertia of the area A with respect to the rectangular axes x' and y' (Fig. 9.19a). The point X' of coordinates $I_{x'}$ and $I_{x'y'}$ and the point Y' of coordinates $I_{y'}$ and $-I_{x'y'}$ are therefore located on Mohr's circle, and the angle $X'CA$ in Fig. 9.19b must be equal to twice the angle $x'Oa$ in Fig. 9.19a. Since, as noted above, the angle XCA is twice the angle xOa, it follows that the angle XCX' in Fig. 9.19b is twice the angle xOx' in Fig. 9.19a. The diameter $X'Y'$ defining the moments and product of inertia $I_{x'}$, $I_{y'}$, and $I_{x'y'}$ of the given area with respect to rectangular axes x' and y' forming an angle θ with the x and y axes may be obtained by rotating through an angle 2θ the diameter XY corresponding to the moments and product of inertia I_x, I_y, and I_{xy}. We note that the rotation which brings the diameter XY into the diameter $X'Y'$ in Fig. 9.19b has the same sense as the rotation which brings the xy axes into the $x'y'$ axes in Fig. 9.19a.

It should be noted that the use of Mohr's circle is not limited to graphical solutions, i.e., to solutions based on the careful drawing and measuring of the various parameters involved. By merely sketching Mohr's circle and using trigonometry, one may easily derive the various relations required for a numerical solution of a given problem. Actual computations may then be carried out on a calculator (see Sample Prob. 9.8).

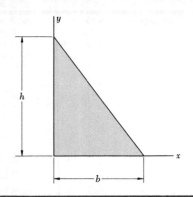

SAMPLE PROBLEM 9.6

Determine the product of inertia of the right triangle shown (*a*) with respect to the *x* and *y* axes and (*b*) with respect to centroidal axes parallel to the *x* and *y* axes.

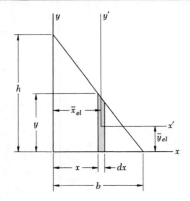

a. Product of Inertia I_{xy}. A vertical rectangular strip is chosen as the differential element of area. Using the parallel-axis theorem, we write

$$dI_{xy} = dI_{x'y'} + \bar{x}_{el}\bar{y}_{el}\, dA$$

Since the element is symmetrical with respect to the x' and y' axes, we note that $dI_{x'y'} = 0$. From the geometry of the triangle, we obtain

$$y = h\left(1 - \frac{x}{b}\right) \qquad dA = y\, dx = h\left(1 - \frac{x}{b}\right)dx$$

$$\bar{x}_{el} = x \qquad \bar{y}_{el} = \tfrac{1}{2}y = \tfrac{1}{2}h\left(1 - \frac{x}{b}\right)$$

Integrating dI_{xy} from $x = 0$ to $x = b$, we obtain

$$I_{xy} = \int dI_{xy} = \int \bar{x}_{el}\bar{y}_{el}\, dA = \int_0^b x(\tfrac{1}{2})h^2\left(1 - \frac{x}{b}\right)^2 dx$$

$$= h^2\int_0^b \left(\frac{x}{2} - \frac{x^2}{b} + \frac{x^3}{2b^2}\right)dx = h^2\left[\frac{x^2}{4} - \frac{x^3}{3b} + \frac{x^4}{8b^2}\right]_0^b$$

$$I_{xy} = \tfrac{1}{24}b^2h^2 \quad \blacktriangleleft$$

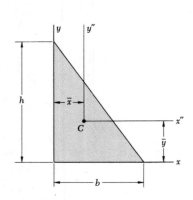

b. Product of Inertia $\bar{I}_{x''y''}$. The coordinates of the centroid of the triangle are

$$\bar{x} = \tfrac{1}{3}b \qquad \bar{y} = \tfrac{1}{3}h$$

Using the expression for I_{xy} obtained in part *a*, we apply the parallel-axis theorem and write

$$I_{xy} = \bar{I}_{x''y''} + \bar{x}\bar{y}A$$

$$\tfrac{1}{24}b^2h^2 = \bar{I}_{x''y''} + (\tfrac{1}{3}b)(\tfrac{1}{3}h)(\tfrac{1}{2}bh)$$

$$\bar{I}_{x''y''} = \tfrac{1}{24}b^2h^2 - \tfrac{1}{18}b^2h^2$$

$$\bar{I}_{x''y''} = -\tfrac{1}{72}b^2h^2 \quad \blacktriangleleft$$

SAMPLE PROBLEM 9.7

For the section shown, the moments of inertia with respect to the x and y axes have been computed and are known to be

$$I_x = 10.38 \text{ in}^4 \qquad I_y = 6.97 \text{ in}^4$$

Determine (a) the principal axes of the section about O, (b) the values of the principal moments of inertia of the section about O.

Solution. We first compute the product of inertia with respect to the x and y axes. The area is divided into three rectangles as shown. We note that the product of inertia $\bar{I}_{x'y'}$ with respect to centroidal axes parallel to the x and y axes is zero for each rectangle. Using the parallel-axis theorem $I_{xy} = \bar{I}_{x'y'} + \bar{x}\bar{y}A$, we thus find that for each rectangle, I_{xy} reduces to $\bar{x}\bar{y}A$.

Rectangle	Area, in^2	$\bar{x}$, in.	$\bar{y}$, in.	$\bar{x}\bar{y}A$, in^4
I	1.5	−1.25	+1.75	−3.28
II	1.5	0	0	0
III	1.5	+1.25	−1.75	−3.28
				−6.56

$$I_{xy} = \Sigma \bar{x}\bar{y}A = -6.56 \text{ in}^4$$

a. Principal Axes. Since the magnitudes of I_x, I_y, and I_{xy} are known, Eq. (9.25) is used to determine the values of θ_m:

$$\tan 2\theta_m = -\frac{2I_{xy}}{I_x - I_y} = -\frac{2(-6.56)}{10.38 - 6.97} = +3.85$$

$$2\theta_m = 75.4° \text{ and } 255.4°$$
$$\theta_m = 37.7° \qquad \text{and} \qquad \theta_m = 127.7° \quad \blacktriangleleft$$

b. Principal Moments of Inertia. Using Eq. (9.27), we write

$$I_{\text{max,min}} = \frac{I_x + I_y}{2} \pm \sqrt{\left(\frac{I_x - I_y}{2}\right)^2 + I_{xy}^2}$$

$$= \frac{10.38 + 6.97}{2} \pm \sqrt{\left(\frac{10.38 - 6.97}{2}\right)^2 + (-6.56)^2}$$

$$I_{\text{max}} = 15.45 \text{ in}^4 \qquad I_{\text{min}} = 1.897 \text{ in}^4 \quad \blacktriangleleft$$

Noting that the area of the section is farther away from the a axis than from the b axis, we conclude that $I_a = I_{\text{max}} = 15.45 \text{ in}^4$ and $I_b = I_{\text{min}} = 1.897 \text{ in}^4$. This conclusion may be verified by substituting $\theta = 37.7°$ into Eqs. (9.18) and (9.19).

L152×102×12.7

SAMPLE PROBLEM 9.8

For the section shown, the moments and product of inertia with respect to the x and y axes have been computed and are known to be

$$I_x = 7.24 \times 10^6 \text{ mm}^4 \qquad I_y = 2.61 \times 10^6 \text{ mm}^4 \qquad I_{xy} = -2.54 \times 10^6 \text{mm}^4$$

Using Mohr's circle, determine (a) the principal axes of the section about O, (b) the values of the principal moments of inertia of the section about O, (c) the moments and product of inertia of the section with respect to the x' and y' axes forming an angle of $60°$ with the x and y axes.

Solution. We first plot point X of coordinates $I_x = 7.24$, $I_{xy} = -2.54$, and point Y of coordinates $I_y = 2.61$, $-I_{xy} = +2.54$. Joining X and Y by a straight line, we define the center C of Mohr's circle. The abscissa of C, which represents I_{ave}, and the radius R of the circle may be measured directly or calculated as follows:

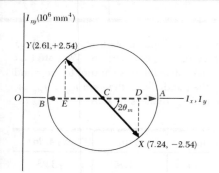

$$I_{\text{ave}} = OC = \tfrac{1}{2}(I_x + I_y) = \tfrac{1}{2}(7.24 \times 10^6 + 2.61 \times 10^6) = 4.925 \times 10^6 \text{ mm}^4$$
$$CD = \tfrac{1}{2}(I_x - I_y) = \tfrac{1}{2}(7.24 \times 10^6 - 2.61 \times 10^6) = 2.315 \times 10^6 \text{ mm}^4$$
$$R = \sqrt{(CD)^2 + (DX)^2} = \sqrt{(2.315 \times 10^6)^2 + (2.54 \times 10^6)^2} = 3.437 \times 10^6 \text{ mm}^4$$

a. Principal Axes. The principal axes of the section correspond to points A and B on Mohr's circle and the angle through which we should rotate CX to bring it into CA defines $2\theta_m$. We have

$$\tan 2\theta_m = \frac{DX}{CD} = \frac{2.54}{2.315} = 1.097 \qquad 2\theta_m = 47.6°\uparrow \qquad \theta_m = 23.8°\uparrow \quad \blacktriangleleft$$

Thus the principal axis Oa corresponding to the maximum value of the moment of inertia is obtained by rotating the x axis through $23.8°$ counterclockwise; the principal axis corresponding to the minimum value of the moment of inertia may be obtained by rotating the y axis through the same angle.

b. Principal Moments of Inertia. The principal moments of inertia are represented by the abscissas of A and B. We have

$$I_{\text{max}} = OA = OC + CA = I_{\text{ave}} + R = (4.925 + 3.437)10^6 \text{ mm}^4$$
$$I_{\text{max}} = 8.36 \times 10^6 \text{ mm}^4 \quad \blacktriangleleft$$
$$I_{\text{min}} = OB = OC - BC = I_{\text{ave}} - R = (4.925 - 3.437)10^6 \text{ mm}^4$$
$$I_{\text{min}} = 1.49 \times 10^6 \text{ mm}^4 \quad \blacktriangleleft$$

c. Moments and Product of Inertia with Respect to x'y' Axes. The points X' and Y' on Mohr's circle which correspond to the x' and y' axes are obtained by rotating CX and CY through an angle $2\theta = 2(60°) = 120°$ counterclockwise. The coordinates of X' and Y' yield the desired moments and product of inertia. Noting that the angle that CX' forms with the horizontal axis is $\phi = 120° - 47.6° = 72.4°$, we write

$$I_{x'} = OF = OC + CF = 4.925 \times 10^6 \text{ mm}^4 + (3.437 \times 10^6 \text{ mm}^4) \cos 72.4°$$
$$I_{x'} = 5.96 \times 10^6 \text{ mm}^4 \quad \blacktriangleleft$$
$$I_{y'} = OG = OC - GC = 4.925 \times 10^6 \text{ mm}^4 - (3.437 \times 10^6 \text{ mm}^4) \cos 72.4°$$
$$I_{y'} = 3.89 \times 10^6 \text{ mm}^4 \quad \blacktriangleleft$$
$$I_{x'y'} = FX' = (3.437 \times 10^6 \text{ mm}^4) \sin 72.4°$$
$$I_{x'y'} = 3.28 \times 10^6 \text{ mm}^4 \quad \blacktriangleleft$$

Problems

9.54 through 9.57 Determine by direct integration the product of inertia of the given area with respect to the x and y axes.

Fig. P9.54

Fig. P9.55

Fig. P9.56

Fig. P9.57

9.58 through 9.63 Using the parallel-axis theorem, determine the product of inertia of the area shown with respect to the centroidal x and y axes.

Dimensions in mm

Fig. P9.58

Fig. P9.59

Fig. P9.60

Fig. P9.61

Fig. P9.62

Dimensions in mm

Fig. P9.63

9.64   Determine the moments of inertia and the product of inertia of the quarter circle of Prob. 9.56 with respect to new axes obtained by rotating the x and y axes about O (a) through 30° counterclockwise, (b) through 45° counterclockwise.

9.65   Determine the moments of inertia and the product of inertia of the area of Prob. 9.61 with respect to new centroidal axes obtained by rotating the x and y axes through 30° counterclockwise.

9.66   Determine the moments of inertia and the product of inertia of the L127 × 76 × 12.7 mm angle cross section of Prob. 9.62 with respect to new centroidal axes obtained by rotating the x and y axes through 30° clockwise. (The moments of inertia $\bar{I}_x$ and $\bar{I}_y$ of the section are given in Fig. 9.13.)

9.67   Determine the moments of inertia and the product of inertia of the L 76 × 51 × 6.4 mm angle cross section of Prob. 9.63 with respect to new centroidal axes obtained by rotating the x and y axes through 30° clockwise. (The moments of inertia $\bar{I}_x$ and $\bar{I}_y$ of the section are given in Fig. 9.13.)

9.68 through 9.71   For the area indicated, determine the orientation of the principal axes through the centroid and the corresponding values of the moment of inertia.

9.68   Area of Prob. 9.58.
9.69   Area of Prob. 9.59.
9.70   Area of Prob. 9.60.
9.71   Area of Prob. 9.61.

9.72 and 9.73   For the angle cross section indicated, determine the orientation of the principal axes through the centroid and the corresponding values of the moment of inertia. (The moments of inertia $\bar{I}_x$ and $\bar{I}_y$ of the cross sections are given in Fig. 9.13.)

9.72   The L127 × 76 × 12.7 mm angle of Prob. 9.62.
9.73   The L 76 × 51 × 6.4 mm angle of Prob. 9.63.

9.74   Using Mohr's circle, determine the moments of inertia and the product of inertia of the quarter circle of Prob. 9.56 with respect to new axes obtained by rotating the x and y axes about O (a) through 30° counterclockwise, (b) through 45° counterclockwise.

9.75   Using Mohr's circle, determine the moments of inertia and the product of inertia of the area of Prob. 9.61 with respect to new centroidal axes obtained by rotating the x and y axes through 30° counterclockwise.

9.76   Using Mohr's circle, determine the moments of inertia and the product of inertia of the L127 × 76 × 12.7 mm angle cross section of Prob. 9.62 with respect to new centroidal axes obtained by rotating the x and y axes through 30° clockwise. (The moments of inertia $\bar{I}_x$ and $\bar{I}_y$ of the section are given in Fig. 9.13.)

9.77 Using Mohr's circle, determine the moments of inertia and the product of inertia of the L 76 × 51 × 6.4 mm angle cross section of Prob. 9.63 with respect to new centroidal axes obtained by rotating the x and y axes through 30° clockwise. (The moments of inertia $\bar{I}_x$ and $\bar{I}_y$ of the section are given in Fig. 9.13.)

9.78 through 9.81 Using Mohr's circle, determine for the area indicated the orientation of the principal axes through the centroid and the corresponding values of the moment of inertia.

> **9.78** Area of Prob. 9.58.
> **9.79** Area of Prob. 9.59.
> **9.80** Area of Prob. 9.60.
> **9.81** Area of Prob. 9.61.

9.82 and 9.83 Using Mohr's circle, determine for the angle cross section indicated the orientation of the principal axes through the centroid and the corresponding values of the moment of inertia. (The moments of inertia $\bar{I}_x$ and $\bar{I}_y$ of the cross sections are given in Fig. 9.13.)

> **9.82** The L127 × 76 × 12.7 mm angle of Prob. 9.62.
> **9.83** The L 76 × 51 × 6.4 mm angle of Prob. 9.63.

9.84 Using Mohr's circle, show that for any regular polygon (such as a pentagon), (a) the moment of inertia with respect to every axis through the centroid is the same, (b) the product of inertia with respect to any pair of rectangular axes through the centroid is zero.

9.85 The moments and product of inertia of an L 127 × 76 × 12.7 mm angle cross section with respect to two rectangular axes x and y through C are, respectively, $\bar{I}_x = 3.93 \times 10^6$ mm⁴, $\bar{I}_y = 1.074 \times 10^6$ mm⁴, and $\bar{I}_{xy} < 0$, with the minimum value of the moment of inertia of the area with respect to any axis through C being $\bar{I}_{min} = 0.655 \times 10^6$ mm⁴. Using Mohr's circle, determine (a) the product of inertia $\bar{I}_{xy}$ of the area, (b) the orientation of the principal axes, (c) the value of $\bar{I}_{max}$.

*9.86 Prove that the expression $I_{x'}I_{y'} - I^2_{x'y'}$, where $I_{x'}$, $I_{y'}$, and $I_{x'y'}$ represent, respectively, the moments and product of inertia of a given area with respect to two rectangular axes x' and y' through a given point O, is independent of the orientation of the x' and y' axes. Considering the particular case when the x' and y' axes correspond to the maximum value of $I_{x'y'}$, show that the given expression represents the square of the tangent drawn from the origin of the coordinates to Mohr's circle.

*9.87 Using the invariance property established in the preceding problem, express the product of inertia I_{xy} of an area A with respect to two rectangular axes through O in terms of the moments of inertia I_x and I_y of A and of the principal moments of inertia I_{min} and I_{max} of A about O. Apply the formula obtained to calculate the product of inertia I_{xy} of the L127 × 76 × 12.7 mm angle cross section shown in Fig. 9.13, knowing that its minimum moment of inertia is 0.655×106 mm⁴.

MOMENTS OF INERTIA OF MASSES

9.11. Moment of Inertia of a Mass. Consider a small mass Δm mounted on a rod of negligible mass which may rotate freely about an axis AA' (Fig. 9.20a). If a couple is applied to the system, the rod and mass, assumed initially at rest, will start rotating about AA'. The details of this motion will be studied later in dynamics. At present, we wish only to indicate that the time required for the system to reach a given speed of rotation is proportional to the mass Δm and to the square of the distance r. The product $r^2 \, \Delta m$ provides, therefore, a measure of the *inertia* of the system, i.e., of the resistance the system offers when we try to set it in motion. For this reason, the product $r^2 \, \Delta m$ is called the *moment of inertia* of the mass Δm with respect to the axis AA'.

Fig. 9.20   *(a)*   *(b)*   *(c)*

Consider now a body of mass m which is to be rotated about an axis AA' (Fig. 9.20b). Dividing the body into elements of mass Δm_1, Δm_2, etc., we find that the resistance offered by the body is measured by the sum $r_1^2 \, \Delta m_1 + r_2^2 \, \Delta m_2 + \cdots$. This sum defines, therefore, the moment of inertia of the body with respect to the axis AA'. Increasing the number of elements, we find that the moment of inertia is equal, at the limit, to the integral

$$I = \int r^2 \, dm \qquad (9.28)$$

The *radius of gyration* k of the body with respect to the axis AA' is defined by the relation

$$I = k^2 m \qquad \text{or} \qquad k = \sqrt{\frac{I}{m}} \qquad (9.29)$$

The radius of gyration k represents, therefore, the distance at which the entire mass of the body should be concentrated if its moment of inertia with respect to AA' is to remain unchanged (Fig. 9.20c). Whether it is kept in its original shape (Fig. 9.20b) or whether it is concentrated as shown in Fig. 9.20c, the mass m will react in the same way to a rotation, or *gyration*, about AA'.

The radius of gyration k is expressed in metres and the mass m in kilograms. The moment of inertia of a mass, therefore, will be expressed in $kg \cdot m^2$.

The moment of inertia of a body with respect to a coordinate axis may easily be expressed in terms of the coordinates x, y, z of the element of mass dm (Fig. 9.21). Noting, for example, that the square of the distance r from

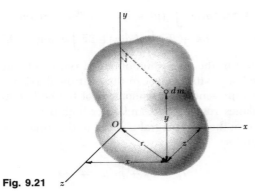

Fig. 9.21

the element dm to the y axis is $z^2 + x^2$, we express the moment of inertia of the body with respect to the y axis as

$$I_y = \int r^2 \, dm = \int (z^2 + x^2) \, dm$$

Similar expressions may be obtained for the moments of inertia with respect to the x and z axes. We write

$$
\begin{aligned}
I_x &= \int (y^2 + z^2) \, dm \\
I_y &= \int (z^2 + x^2) \, dm \\
I_z &= \int (x^2 + y^2) \, dm
\end{aligned}
\qquad (9.30)
$$

Fig. 9.22

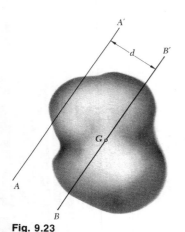

Fig. 9.23

9.12. Parallel-Axis Theorem. Consider a body of mass m. Let $Oxyz$ be a system of rectangular coordinates with origin at an arbitrary point O, and $Gx'y'z'$ a system of parallel *centroidal axes*, i.e., a system with origin at the center of gravity G of the body† and with axes x', y', z', respectively, parallel to x, y, z (Fig. 9.22). Denoting by $\bar{x}$, $\bar{y}$, $\bar{z}$ the coordinates of G with respect to $Oxyz$, we write the following relations between the coordinates x, y, z of the element dm with respect to $Oxyz$ and its coordinates x', y', z' with respect to the centroidal axes $Gx'y'z'$:

$$x = x' + \bar{x} \qquad y = y' + \bar{y} \qquad z = z' + \bar{z} \tag{9.31}$$

Referring to Eqs. (9.30), we may express the moment of inertia of the body with respect to the x axis as follows:

$$I_x = \int (y^2 + z^2)\, dm = \int [(y' + \bar{y})^2 + (z' + \bar{z})^2]\, dm$$
$$= \int (y'^2 + z'^2)\, dm + 2\bar{y} \int y'\, dm + 2\bar{z} \int z'\, dm + (\bar{y}^2 + \bar{z}^2) \int dm$$

The first integral in the expression obtained represents the moment of inertia $\bar{I}_{x'}$ of the body with respect to the centroidal axis x'; the second and third integrals represent the first moment of the body with respect to the $z'x'$ and $x'y'$ planes, respectively, and, since both planes contain G, the two integrals are zero; the last integral is equal to the total mass m of the body. We write, therefore,

$$I_x = \bar{I}_{x'} + m(\bar{y}^2 + \bar{z}^2) \tag{9.32}$$

and, similarly,

$$I_y = \bar{I}_{y'} + m(\bar{z}^2 + \bar{x}^2) \qquad I_z = \bar{I}_{z'} + m(\bar{x}^2 + \bar{y}^2) \tag{9.32'}$$

We easily verify from Fig. 9.22 that the sum $\bar{z}^2 + \bar{x}^2$ represents the square of the distance OB between the y and y' axis. Similarly, $\bar{y}^2 + \bar{z}^2$ and $\bar{x}^2 + \bar{y}^2$ represent the squares of the distances between the x and x' axes, and the z and z' axes, respectively. Denoting by d the distance between an arbitrary axis AA' and a parallel centroidal axis BB' (Fig. 9.23), we may, therefore, write the following general relation between the moment of inertia I of the body with respect to AA' and its moment of inertia $\bar{I}$ with respect to BB':

$$I = \bar{I} + md^2 \tag{9.33}$$

Expressing the moments of inertia in terms of the corresponding radii of gyration, we may also write

$$k^2 = \bar{k}^2 + d^2 \tag{9.34}$$

where k and $\bar{k}$ represent the radii of gyration about AA' and BB', respectively.

---

†Note that the term centroidal is used to define an axis passing through the center of gravity G of the body, whether or not G coincides with the centroid of the volume of the body.

9.13. Moments of Inertia of Thin Plates.

Consider a thin plate of uniform thickness t, made of a homogeneous material of density ρ (density = mass per unit volume). The mass moment of inertia of the plate with respect to an axis AA' *contained in the plane* of the plate (Fig. 9.24a) is

$$I_{AA',\text{mass}} = \int r^2 \, dm$$

Since $dm = \rho t \, dA$, we write

$$I_{AA',\text{mass}} = \rho t \int r^2 \, dA$$

But r represents the distance of the element of area dA to the axis AA'; the

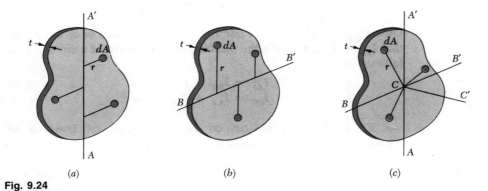

(a)   (b)   (c)

Fig. 9.24

integral is therefore equal to the moment of inertia of the area of the plate with respect to AA'. We have

$$I_{AA',\text{mass}} = \rho t I_{AA',\text{area}} \tag{9.35}$$

Similarly, we have with respect to an axis BB' perpendicular to AA' (Fig. 9.24b)

$$I_{BB',\text{mass}} = \rho t I_{BB',\text{area}} \tag{9.36}$$

Considering now the axis CC' *perpendicular* to the plate through the point of intersection C of AA' and BB' (Fig. 9.24c), we write

$$I_{CC',\text{mass}} = \rho t J_{C,\text{area}} \tag{9.37}$$

where J_C is the *polar* moment of inertia of the area of the plate with respect to point C.

Recalling the relation $J_C = I_{AA'} + I_{BB'}$ existing between polar and rectangular moments of inertia of an area, we write the following relation between the mass moments of inertia of a thin plate:

$$I_{CC'} = I_{AA'} + I_{BB'} \tag{9.38}$$

Fig. 9.25

Fig. 9.26

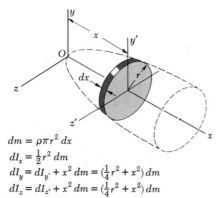

$$dm = \rho \pi r^2 \, dx$$
$$dI_x = \tfrac{1}{2} r^2 \, dm$$
$$dI_y = dI_{y'} + x^2 \, dm = (\tfrac{1}{4} r^2 + x^2) \, dm$$
$$dI_z = dI_{z'} + x^2 \, dm = (\tfrac{1}{4} r^2 + x^2) \, dm$$

Fig. 9.27 Determination of the moment of inertia of a body of revolution.

Rectangular Plate. In the case of a reactangular plate of sides a and b (Fig. 9.25), we obtain the following mass moments of inertia with respect to axes through the center of gravity of the plate:

$$I_{AA',\text{mass}} = \rho t I_{AA',\text{area}} = \rho t (\tfrac{1}{12} a^3 b)$$
$$I_{BB',\text{mass}} = \rho t I_{BB',\text{area}} = \rho t (\tfrac{1}{12} a b^3)$$

Observing that the product ρabt is equal to the mass m of the plate, we write the mass moments of inertia of a thin rectangular plate as follows:

$$I_{AA'} = \tfrac{1}{12} m a^2 \qquad I_{BB'} = \tfrac{1}{12} m b^2 \tag{9.39}$$
$$I_{CC'} = I_{AA'} + I_{BB'} = \tfrac{1}{12} m (a^2 + b^2) \tag{9.40}$$

Circular Plate. In the case of a circular plate, or disk, of radius r (Fig. 9.26), we write

$$I_{AA',\text{mass}} = \rho t I_{AA',\text{area}} = \rho t (\tfrac{1}{4} \pi r^4)$$

Observing that the product $\rho \pi r^2 t$ is equal to the mass m of the plate and that $I_{AA'} = I_{BB'}$, we write the mass moments of inertia of a circular plate as follows:

$$I_{AA'} = I_{BB'} = \tfrac{1}{4} m r^2 \tag{9.41}$$
$$I_{CC'} = I_{AA'} + I_{BB'} = \tfrac{1}{2} m r^2 \tag{9.42}$$

9.14. Determination of the Moment of Inertia of a Three-Dimensional Body by Integration. The moment of inertia of a three-dimensional body is obtained by computing the integral $I = \int r^2 \, dm$. If the body is made of a homogeneous material of density ρ, we have $dm = \rho \, dV$ and write $I = \rho \int r^2 \, dV$. This integral depends only upon the shape of the body. Thus, in order to compute the moment of inertia of a three-dimensional body, it will generally be necessary to perform a triple, or at least a double, integration.

However, if the body possesses two planes of symmetry, it is usually possible to determine the body's moment of inertia through a single integration by choosing as an element of mass dm the mass of a thin slab perpendicular to the planes of symmetry. In the case of bodies of revolution, for example, the element of mass should be a thin disk (Fig. 9.27). Using formula (9.42), the moment of inertia of the disk with respect to the axis of revolution may be readily expressed as indicated in Fig. 9.27. Its moment of inertia with respect to each of the other two axes of coordinates will be obtained by using formula (9.41) and the parallel-axis theorem. Integration of the expressions obtained will yield the desired moment of inertia of the body of revolution.

9.15. Moments of Inertia of Composite Bodies. The moments of inertia of a few common shapes are shown in Fig. 9.28. The moment of inertia with respect to a given axis of a body made of several of these simple shapes may be obtained by computing the moments of inertia of its component parts about the desired axis and adding them together. We should note, as we have already noted in the case of areas, that the radius of gyration of a composite body *cannot* be obtained by adding the radii of gyration of its component parts.

Slender rod		$I_y = I_z = \frac{1}{12}mL^2$
Thin rectangular plate		$I_x = \frac{1}{12}m(b^2 + c^2)$ $I_y = \frac{1}{12}mc^2$ $I_z = \frac{1}{12}mb^2$
Rectangular prism		$I_x = \frac{1}{12}m(b^2 + c^2)$ $I_y = \frac{1}{12}m(c^2 + a^2)$ $I_z = \frac{1}{12}m(a^2 + b^2)$
Thin disk		$I_x = \frac{1}{2}mr^2$ $I_y = I_z = \frac{1}{4}mr^2$
Circular cylinder		$I_x = \frac{1}{2}ma^2$ $I_y = I_z = \frac{1}{12}m(3a^2 + L^2)$
Circular cone		$I_x = \frac{3}{10}ma^2$ $I_y = I_z = \frac{3}{5}m(\frac{1}{4}a^2 + h^2)$
Sphere		$I_x = I_y = I_z = \frac{2}{5}ma^2$

Fig. 9.28 Mass moments of inertia of common geometric shapes.

SAMPLE PROBLEM 9.9

Determine the mass moment of inertia of a slender rod of length L and mass m with respect to an axis perpendicular to the rod and passing through one end of the rod.

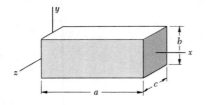

Solution. Choosing the differential element of mass shown, we write

$$dm = \frac{m}{L}\,dx$$

$$I_y = \int x^2\,dm = \int_0^L x^2 \frac{m}{L}\,dx = \left[\frac{m}{L}\frac{x^3}{3}\right]_0^L \qquad I_y = \tfrac{1}{3}mL^2 \quad \blacktriangleleft$$

SAMPLE PROBLEM 9.10

Determine the mass moment of inertia of the homogeneous rectangular prism shown with respect to the z axis.

Solution. We choose as a differential element of mass the thin slab shown for which

$$dm = \rho bc\,dx$$

Referring to Sec. 9.13, we find that the moment of inertia of the element with respect to the z' axis is

$$dI_{z'} = \tfrac{1}{12}b^2\,dm$$

Applying the parallel-axis theorem, we obtain the mass moment of inertia of the slab with respect to the z axis.

$$dI_z = dI_{z'} + x^2\,dm = \tfrac{1}{12}b^2\,dm + x^2\,dm = (\tfrac{1}{12}b^2 + x^2)\,\rho bc\,dx$$

Integrating from $x = 0$ to $x = a$, we obtain

$$I_z = \int dI_z = \int_0^a (\tfrac{1}{12}b^2 + x^2)\,\rho bc\,dx = \rho abc\,(\tfrac{1}{12}b^2 + \tfrac{1}{3}a^2)$$

Since the total mass of the prism is $m = \rho abc$, we may write

$$I_z = m(\tfrac{1}{12}b^2 + \tfrac{1}{3}a^2) \qquad I_z = \tfrac{1}{12}m(4a^2 + b^2) \quad \blacktriangleleft$$

We note that if the prism is slender, b is small compared to a and the expression for I_z reduces to $\tfrac{1}{3}ma^2$, which is the result obtained in Sample Prob. 9.9 when $L = a$.

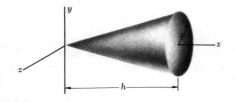

SAMPLE PROBLEM 9.11

Determine the mass moment of inertia of a right circular cone with respect to (a) its longitudinal axis, (b) an axis through the apex of the cone and perpendicular to its longitudinal axis, (c) an axis through the centroid of the cone and perpendicular to its longitudinal axis.

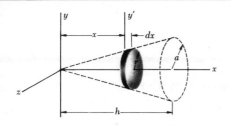

Solution. We choose the differential element of mass shown.

$$r = a\frac{x}{h} \qquad dm = \rho\pi r^2\,dx = \rho\pi\frac{a^2}{h^2}x^2\,dx$$

a. Moment of Inertia I_x. Using the expression derived in Sec. 9.13 for a thin disk, we compute the mass moment of inertia of the differential element with respect to the x axis.

$$dI_x = \tfrac{1}{2}r^2\,dm = \tfrac{1}{2}\!\left(a\frac{x}{h}\right)^{\!2}\left(\rho\pi\frac{a^2}{h^2}x^2\,dx\right) = \tfrac{1}{2}\rho\pi\frac{a^4}{h^4}x^4\,dx$$

Integrating from $x = 0$ to $x = h$, we obtain

$$I_x = \int dI_x = \int_0^h \tfrac{1}{2}\rho\pi\frac{a^4}{h^4}x^4\,dx = \tfrac{1}{2}\rho\pi\frac{a^4}{h^4}\frac{h^5}{5} = \tfrac{1}{10}\rho\pi a^4 h$$

Since the total mass of the cone is $m = \tfrac{1}{3}\rho\pi a^2 h$, we may write

$$I_x = \tfrac{1}{10}\rho\pi a^4 h = \tfrac{3}{10}a^2(\tfrac{1}{3}\rho\pi a^2 h) = \tfrac{3}{10}ma^2 \qquad I_x = \tfrac{3}{10}ma^2 \blacktriangleleft$$

b. Moment of Inertia I_y. The same differential element will be used. Applying the parallel-axis theorem and using the expression derived in Sec. 9.13 for a thin disk, we write

$$dI_y = dI_{y'} + x^2\,dm = \tfrac{1}{4}r^2\,dm + x^2\,dm = (\tfrac{1}{4}r^2 + x^2)\,dm$$

Substituting the expressions for r and dm, we obtain

$$dI_y = \left(\frac{1}{4}\frac{a^2}{h^2}x^2 + x^2\right)\!\left(\rho\pi\frac{a^2}{h^2}x^2\,dx\right) = \rho\pi\frac{a^2}{h^2}\left(\frac{a^2}{4h^2} + 1\right)x^4\,dx$$

$$I_y = \int dI_y = \int_0^h \rho\pi\frac{a^2}{h^2}\left(\frac{a^2}{4h^2} + 1\right)x^4\,dx = \rho\pi\frac{a^2}{h^2}\left(\frac{a^2}{4h^2} + 1\right)\frac{h^5}{5}$$

Introducing the total mass of the cone m, we rewrite I_y as follows:

$$I_y = \tfrac{3}{5}(\tfrac{1}{4}a^2 + h^2)\tfrac{1}{3}\rho\pi a^2 h \qquad I_y = \tfrac{3}{5}m(\tfrac{1}{4}a^2 + h^2) \blacktriangleleft$$

c. Moment of Inertia $\bar{I}_{y''}$. We apply the parallel-axis theorem and write

$$I_y = \bar{I}_{y''} + m\bar{x}^2$$

Solving for $\bar{I}_{y''}$ and recalling that $\bar{x} = \tfrac{3}{4}h$, we have

$$\bar{I}_{y''} = I_y - m\bar{x}^2 = \tfrac{3}{5}m(\tfrac{1}{4}a^2 + h^2) - m(\tfrac{3}{4}h)^2$$
$$\bar{I}_{y''} = \tfrac{3}{20}m(a^2 + \tfrac{1}{4}h^2) \blacktriangleleft$$

A steel forging consists of a rectangular prism 150 by 50 by 50 mm and of two cylinders of diameter 50 mm and length 75 mm, as shown. Determine the mass moments of inertia with respect to the coordinate axes. (Density of steel = 7850 kg/m³.)

Computation of Masses

Prism. $V = (50 \text{ mm})^2(150 \text{ mm}) = 0.375 \times 10^6 \text{ mm}^3$

or, since $1 \text{ mm}^3 = (10^{-3} \text{ m})^3 = 10^{-9} \text{ m}^3$,

$$V = 0.393 \times 10^6 \times 10^{-9} \text{ m}^3 = 0.375 \times 10^{-3} \text{ m}^3$$
$$m = \rho V = (7.85 \times 10^3 \text{ kg/m}^3)(0.375 \times 10^{-3} \text{ m}^3) = 2.94 \text{ kg}$$

Each Cylinder

$$V = \pi r^2 h = \pi(25 \text{ mm})^2(75 \text{ mm}) = 0.1473 \times 10^6 \text{ mm}^3$$
$$= 0.1473 \times 10^{-3} \text{ m}^3$$
$$m = \rho V = (7.85 \times 10^3 \text{ kg/m}^3)(0.1473 \times 10^{-3} \text{ m}^3) = 1.156 \text{ kg}$$

Mass Moments of Inertia. The mass moments of inertia of each component are computed from Fig. 9.28, using the parallel-axis theorem when necessary. Note that all lengths should be expressed in millimetres.

Prism

$$I_x = I_z = \tfrac{1}{12}(2.94 \text{ kg})[(150 \text{ mm})^2 + (50 \text{ mm})^2] = 6125 \text{ kg·mm}^2$$
$$I_y = \tfrac{1}{12}(2.94 \text{ kg})[(50 \text{ mm})^2 + (50 \text{ mm})^2] = 1225 \text{ kg·mm}^2$$

Each Cylinder

$$I_x = \tfrac{1}{2}ma^2 + m\bar{y}^2 = \tfrac{1}{2}(1.156 \text{ kg})(25 \text{ mm})^2 + (1.156 \text{ kg})(50 \text{ mm})^2$$
$$= 3250 \text{ kg·mm}^2$$
$$I_y = \tfrac{1}{12}m(3a^2 + L^2) + m\bar{x}^2 = \tfrac{1}{12}(1.156 \text{ kg})[3(25 \text{ mm})^2 + (75 \text{ mm})^2]$$
$$+ (1.156 \text{ kg})(62.5 \text{ mm})^2 = 5240 \text{ kg·mm}^2$$
$$I_z = \tfrac{1}{12}m(3a^2 + L^2) + m(\bar{x}^2 + \bar{y}^2)$$
$$= \tfrac{1}{12}(1.156 \text{ kg})[3(25 \text{ mm})^2 + (75 \text{ mm})^2]$$
$$+ (1.156 \text{ kg})[(62.5 \text{ mm})^2 + (50 \text{ mm})^2] + 8130 \text{ kg·mm}^2$$

Entire Body. Adding the values obtained, and observing that $1 \text{ mm}^2 = (10^{-3} \text{ m})^2 = 10^{-6} \text{ m}^2$, we have

$$I_x = 6125 \text{ kg·mm}^2 + 2(3250 \text{ kg·mm}^2) = 12.63 \times 10^3 \text{ kg·mm}^2$$
$$I_x = 12.63 \times 10^{-3} \text{ kg·m}^2 \blacktriangleleft$$
$$I_y = 1225 \text{ kg·mm}^2 + 2(5240 \text{ kg·mm}^2) = 11.71 \times 10^3 \text{ kg·mm}^2$$
$$I_y = 11.71 \times 10^{-3} \text{ kg·m}^2 \blacktriangleleft$$
$$I_z = 6125 \text{ kg·mm}^2 + 2(8130 \text{ kg·mm}^2) = 22.4 \times 10^3 \text{ kg·mm}^2$$
$$I_z = 22.4 \times 10^{-3} \text{ kg·m}^2 \blacktriangleleft$$

Dimensions in mm

$r = 0.08$ m

$b = 0.2$ m $\quad c = 0.16$ m

$a = 0.05$ m

$d = 0.1$ m

SAMPLE PROBLEM 9.13

A thin steel plate 4 mm thick is cut and bent to form the machine part shown. Knowing that the density of steel is 7850 kg/m³, determine the mass moment of inertia of the machine part with respect to the coordinate axes.

Solution. We observe that the machine part consists of a semicircular plate, plus a rectangular plate, minus a circular plate.

Computation of Masses. *Semicircular Plate*

$$V_1 = \tfrac{1}{2}\pi r^2 t = \tfrac{1}{2}\pi(0.08 \text{ m})^2(0.004 \text{ m}) = 40.21 \times 10^{-6} \text{ m}^3$$
$$m_1 = \rho V_1 = (7.85 \times 10^3 \text{ kg/m}^3)(40.21 \times 10^{-6} \text{ m}^3) = 0.3156 \text{ kg}$$

Rectangular Plate

$$V_2 = (0.200 \text{ m})(0.160 \text{ m})(0.004 \text{ m}) = 128 \times 10^{-6} \text{ m}^3$$
$$m_2 = \rho V_2 = (7.85 \times 10^3 \text{ kg/m}^3)(128 \times 10^{-6} \text{ m}^3) = 1.005 \text{ kg}$$

Circular Plate

$$V_3 = \pi a^2 t = \pi(0.050 \text{ m})^2(0.004 \text{ m}) = 31.42 \times 10^{-6} \text{ m}^3$$
$$m_3 = \rho V_3 = (7.85 \times 10^3 \text{ kg/m}^3)(31.42 \times 10^{-6} \text{ m}^3) = 0.2466 \text{ kg}$$

Mass Moments of Inertia. Using the method presented in Sec. 9.13, we compute the mass moment of inertia of each component.

Semicircular Plate. From Fig. 9.28, we observe that for a circular plate of mass m and radius r

$$I_x = \tfrac{1}{2}mr^2 \qquad I_y = I_z = \tfrac{1}{4}mr^2$$

Because of symmetry, we note that for a semicircular plate

$$I_x = \tfrac{1}{2}(\tfrac{1}{2}mr^2) \qquad I_y = I_z = \tfrac{1}{2}(\tfrac{1}{4}mr^2)$$

Since the mass of the semicircular plate is $m_1 = \tfrac{1}{2}m$, we have

$$I_x = \tfrac{1}{2}m_1 r^2 = \tfrac{1}{2}(0.3156 \text{ kg})(0.08 \text{ m})^2 = 1.010 \times 10^{-3} \text{ kg}\cdot\text{m}^2$$
$$I_y = I_z = \tfrac{1}{4}(\tfrac{1}{2}mr^2) = \tfrac{1}{4}m_1 r^2 = \tfrac{1}{4}(0.3156 \text{ kg})(0.08 \text{ m})^2 = 0.505 \times 10^{-3} \text{ kg}\cdot\text{m}^2$$

Rectangular Plate

$$I_x = \tfrac{1}{12}m_2 c^2 = \tfrac{1}{12}(1.005 \text{ kg})(0.16 \text{ m})^2 = 2.144 \times 10^{-3} \text{ kg}\cdot\text{m}^2$$
$$I_z = \tfrac{1}{3}m_2 b^2 = \tfrac{1}{3}(1.005 \text{ kg})(0.2 \text{ m})^2 = 13.400 \times 10^{-3} \text{ kg}\cdot\text{m}^2$$
$$I_y = I_x + I_z = (2.144 + 13.400)(10^{-3}) = 15.544 \times 10^{-3} \text{ kg}\cdot\text{m}^2$$

Circular Plate

$$I_x = \tfrac{1}{4}m_3 a^2 = \tfrac{1}{4}(0.2466 \text{ kg})(0.05 \text{ m})^2 = 0.154 \times 10^{-3} \text{ kg}\cdot\text{m}^2$$
$$I_y = \tfrac{1}{2}m_3 a^2 + m_3 d^2$$
$$= \tfrac{1}{2}(0.2466 \text{ kg})(0.05 \text{ m})^2 + (0.2466 \text{ kg})(0.1 \text{ m})^2 = 2.774 \times 10^{-3} \text{ kg}\cdot\text{m}^2$$
$$I_z = \tfrac{1}{4}m_3 a^2 + m_3 d^2 = \tfrac{1}{4}(0.2466 \text{ kg})(0.05 \text{ m})^2 + (0.2466 \text{ kg})(0.1 \text{ m})^2$$
$$= 2.620 \times 10^{-3} \text{ kg}\cdot\text{m}^2$$

Entire Machine Part

$$I_x = (1.010 + 2.144 - 0.154)(10^{-3}) \text{ kg}\cdot\text{m}^2 \qquad I_x = 3.00 \times 10^{-3} \text{ kg}\cdot\text{m}^2 \quad \blacktriangleleft$$
$$I_y = (0.505 + 15.544 - 2.774)(10^{-3}) \text{ kg}\cdot\text{m}^2 \qquad I_y = 13.28 \times 10^{-3} \text{ kg}\cdot\text{m}^2 \quad \blacktriangleleft$$
$$I_z = (0.505 + 13.400 - 2.620)(10^{-3}) \text{ kg}\cdot\text{m}^2 \qquad I_z = 11.29 \times 10^{-3} \text{ kg}\cdot\text{m}^2 \quad \blacktriangleleft$$

Problems

9.88 A thin semicircular plate has a radius a and a mass m. Determine the mass moment of inertia of the plate with respect to (*a*) the centroidal axis BB', (*b*) the centroidal axis CC'.

Fig. P9.88

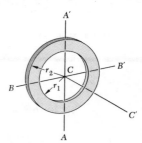

Fig. P9.89

9.89 Determine the mass moment of inertia of a ring of mass m, cut from a thin uniform plate, with respect to (*a*) the diameter AA' of the ring, (*b*) the axis CC' perpendicular to the plane of the ring.

9.90 A thin plate of mass m is cut in the shape of an isosceles triangle of base b and height h. Determine the mass moment of inertia of the plate with respect to (*a*) the centroidal axes AA' and BB' in the plane of the plate, (*b*) the centroidal axis CC' perpendicular to the plate.

9.91 Determine the mass moments of inertia of the plate of Prob. 9.90 with respect to axes DD' and EE' parallel to the centroidal axes AA' and BB' and located at a distance d from the plane of the plate.

9.92 A thin plate of mass m is cut in the shape of a parallelogram as shown. Determine the mass moment of inertia of the plate with respect to (*a*) the x axis, (*b*) the axis BB' perpendicular to the plate.

9.93 Determine the mass moment of inertia of the plate of Prob. 9.92 with respect to (*a*) the y axis, (*b*) the axis AA' perpendicular to the plate.

9.94 The area shown is revolved about the x axis to form a homogeneous solid of revolution of mass m. Express the mass moment of inertia of the solid with respect to the x axis in terms of m, a, and n.

Fig. P9.90

Fig. P9.92

Fig. P9.94

Fig. P9.95

9.95 Determine by direct integration the mass moment of inertia with respect to the y axis of the right circular cylinder shown, assuming a uniform density and a mass m.

9.96 Determine by direct integration the mass moment of inertia and the radius of gyration of the right circular cone with respect to the z axis, assuming a uniform density and a mass m.

Fig. P9.96

9.97 Determine by direct integration the mass moment of inertia and the radius of gyration with respect to the y axis of the paraboloid shown, assuming a uniform density and a mass m.

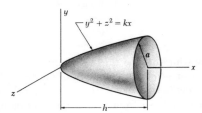

Fig. P9.97

9.98 Determine by direct integration the mass moment of inertia with respect to the x axis of the pyramid shown, assuming a uniform density and a mass m.

9.99 Determine by direct integration the mass moment of inertia with respect to the y axis of the pyramid shown, assuming a uniform density and a mass m.

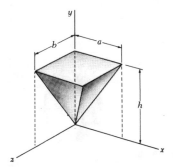

Fig. P9.98 and P9.99

9.100 A thin spherical dish of mass m is formed by passing a horizontal plane through a spherical shell of radius R and thickness t. Determine by direct integration the mass moment of inertia of the dish with respect to its vertical axis of symmetry. Check that the result obtained for $\phi = 90°$ (hemispherical shell) is the same as the answer to Prob. 9.104.

Fig. P9.100

9.101 A thin steel wire is bent into the shape of a circular arc as shown. Denoting by m' the mass per unit length of the wire, determine the mass moment of inertia of the wire with respect to each of the coordinate axes.

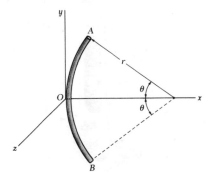

Fig. P9.101

9.102 and 9.103 Determine the mass moment of inertia and the radius of gyration of the steel flywheel shown with respect to its axis of rotation. (Density of steel = 7850 kg/m³.)

Fig. P9.102   Dimensions in mm

Fig. P9.103

9.104 Knowing that the thin hemispherical shell shown is of mass m and thickness t, determine the mass moment of inertia and the radius of gyration of the shell with respect to the x axis. (*Hint.* Consider the shell as formed by removing a hemisphere of radius r from a hemisphere of radius $r + t$; then neglect the terms containing t^2 and t^3 and keep those terms containing t.)

9.105 The machine part shown is formed by machining a conical surface into a circular cylinder. For $b = \frac{1}{2}h$, determine the mass moment of inertia and the radius of gyration of the machine part with respect to the y axis.

Fig. P9.104

Fig. P9.105

9.106 For the 2-kg connecting rod shown, it has been experimentally determined that the mass moments of inertia of the rod with respect to the centerline axes of the bearings AA' and BB' are, respectively, $I_{AA'} = 78$ g·m² and $I_{BB'} = 41$ g·m². Knowing that $r_a + r_b = 290$ mm, determine (a) the location of the centroidal axis GG', (b) the radius of gyration with respect to axis GG'.

9.107 Knowing that for the 3.25-kg connecting rod shown the mass moment of inertia with respect to axis AA' is 205 g·m², determine the mass moment of inertia with respect to axis BB', for $r_a = 225$ mm and $r_b = 140$ mm.

Fig. P9.106 and P9.107

9.108 For the homogeneous ring shown, which is of density ρ, determine (a) the mass moment of inertia with respect to the axis BB', (b) the value of a_1 for which, given a_2 and h, $I_{BB'}$ is maximum, (c) the corresponding value of $I_{BB'}$.

9.109 Determine the mass moment of inertia and the radius of gyration of the steel ring shown with respect to the axis BB' with $a_1 = 75$ mm, $a_2 = 125$ mm, and $h = 100$ mm. (Density of steel = 7850 kg/m³.)

Fig. P9.108 and P9.109

9.110 and 9.111 A section of sheet steel 2 mm thick is cut and bent into the machine component shown. Knowing that the density of steel is 7850 kg/m³, determine the mass moment of inertia of the component with respect to (a) the x axis, (b) the y axis, (c) the z axis.

Fig. P9.110

Fig. P9.111

9.112 A corner reflector for tracking by radar has two sides in the shape of a quarter circle of radius 375 mm and one side in the shape of a triangle. Each part of the reflector is formed from aluminium plate of uniform 1.25 mm thickness. Knowing that the density of the aluminium used is 2800 kg/m³, determine the mass moment of inertia of the reflector with respect to each of the coordinate axes.

Fig. P9.112

Fig. P9.113

9.113 A section of sheet steel 0.75 mm thick is cut and bent into the sheet-metal machine component shown. Knowing that the density of steel is 7850 kg/m³, determine the mass moment of inertia of the component with respect to each of the coordinate axes.

9.114 and 9.115 Determine the mass moment of inertia of the steel machine element shown with respect to the x axis. (Density of steel = 7850 kg/m³.)

Fig. P9.115 and P9.116

Dimensions in mm
Fig. P9.114 and P9.117

9.116 and 9.117 Determine the mass moment of inertia of the steel machine element shown with respect to the y axis. (Density of steel = 7850 kg/m³.)

Fig. P9.118

9.118 A homogeneous wire with a mass per unit length of 1.8 kg/m is used to form the figure shown. Determine the mass moment of inertia of the wire figure with respect to (a) the x axis, (b) the y axis.

9.119 In Prob. 9.118, determine the mass moment of inertia of the wire figure with respect to the z axis.

*9.16. Moment of Inertia of a Body with Respect to an Arbitrary Axis through O. Mass Products of Inertia.

We shall see in this section how the moment of inertia of a body may be determined with respect to an arbitrary axis OL through the origin (Fig. 9.29) if we have computed beforehand its moments of inertia with respect to the three coordinate axes, as well as certain other quantities to be defined below.

The moment of inertia of the body with respect to OL is represented by the integral $I_{OL} = \int p^2 \, dm$, where p denotes the perpendicular distance from the element of mass dm to the axis OL. But, denoting by $\boldsymbol{\lambda}$ the unit vector along OL and by $\mathbf{r}$ the position vector of the element dm, we observe that the perpendicular distance p is equal to the magnitude $r \sin \theta$ of the vector product $\boldsymbol{\lambda} \times \mathbf{r}$. We therefore write

$$I_{OL} = \int p^2 \, dm = \int |\boldsymbol{\lambda} \times \mathbf{r}|^2 \, dm \qquad (9.43)$$

Expressing the square in terms of the rectangular components of the vector product, we have

$$I_{OL} = \int [(\lambda_x y - \lambda_y x)^2 + (\lambda_y z - \lambda_z y)^2 + (\lambda_z x - \lambda_x z)^2] \, dm$$

where the components λ_x, λ_y, λ_z of the unit vector $\boldsymbol{\lambda}$ represent the direction cosines of the axis OL, and the components x, y, z of $\mathbf{r}$ represent the coordinates of the element of mass dm. Expanding the squares in the expression obtained and rearranging the terms, we write

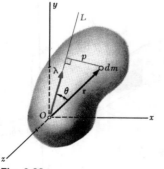

Fig. 9.29

$$I_{OL} = \lambda_x^2 \int (y^2 + z^2)\, dm + \lambda_y^2 \int (z^2 + x^2)\, dm + \lambda_z^2 \int (x^2 + y^2)\, dm$$
$$- 2\lambda_x\lambda_y \int xy\, dm - 2\lambda_y\lambda_z \int yz\, dm - 2\lambda_z\lambda_x \int zx\, dm \qquad (9.44)$$

Referring to Eqs. (9.30), we note that the first three integrals in (9.44) represent, respectively, the moments of inertia I_x, I_y, and I_z of the body with respect to the coordinate axes. The last three integrals in (9.44), which involve products of coordinates, are called the *products of inertia* of the body with respect to the x and y axes, the y and z axes, and the z and x axes, respectively. We write

$$I_{xy} = \int xy\, dm \qquad I_{yz} = \int yz\, dm \qquad I_{zx} = \int zx\, dm \qquad (9.45)$$

Substituting for the various integrals from (9.30) and (9.45) into (9.44), we have

$$I_{OL} = I_x\lambda_x^2 + I_y\lambda_y^2 + I_z\lambda_z^2 - 2I_{xy}\lambda_x\lambda_y - 2I_{yz}\lambda_y\lambda_z - 2I_{zx}\lambda_z\lambda_x \qquad (9.46)$$

We note that the definition of the products of inertia of a mass given in Eqs. (9.45) is an extension of the definition of the product of inertia of an area (Sec. 9.8). Mass products of inertia reduce to zero under the same conditions of symmetry as products of inertia of areas, and the parallel-axis theorem for mass products of inertia is expressed by relations similar to the formula derived for the product of inertia of an area. Substituting for x, y, z from Eqs. (9.31) into Eqs. (9.45), we verify that

$$\begin{aligned} I_{xy} &= \bar{I}_{x'y'} + m\bar{x}\bar{y} \\ I_{yz} &= \bar{I}_{y'z'} + m\bar{y}\bar{z} \\ I_{zx} &= \bar{I}_{z'x'} + m\bar{z}\bar{x} \end{aligned} \qquad (9.47)$$

where $\bar{x}, \bar{y}, \bar{z}$ are the coordinates of the center of gravity G of the body, and $\bar{I}_{x'y'}, \bar{I}_{y'z'}, \bar{I}_{z'x'}$ denote the products of inertia with respect to the centroidal axes x', y', z' (Fig. 9.22).

*9.17. Ellipsoid of Inertia. Principal Axes of Inertia.

Let us assume that the moment of inertia of the body considered in the preceding section has been determined with respect to a large number of axes OL through the fixed point O, and that a point Q has been plotted on each axis OL at a distance $OQ = 1/\sqrt{I_{OL}}$ from O. The locus of the points Q thus obtained forms a surface (Fig. 9.30). The equation of that surface may be obtained by substituting $1/(OQ)^2$ for I_{OL} in (9.46) and multiplying both sides of the equation by $(OQ)^2$. Observing that

$$(OQ)\lambda_x = x \qquad (OQ)\lambda_y = y \qquad (OQ)\lambda_z = z$$

where x, y, z denote the rectangular coordinates of a point Q of the surface, we write

$$I_x x^2 + I_y y^2 + I_z z^2 - 2I_{xy} xy - 2I_{yz} yz - 2I_{zx} zx = 1 \qquad (9.48)$$

The equation obtained is that of a *quadric*. Since the moment of inertia I_{OL} is different from zero for every axis OL, no point Q may be at an infinite

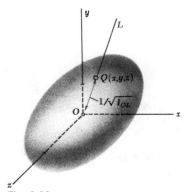

Fig. 9.30

Distributed Forces: Moments of Inertia

Fig. 9.31

Fig. 9.32

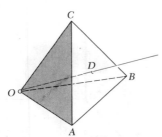

Fig. 9.33

distance from O. Thus, the quadric obtained is an *ellipsoid*. This ellipsoid, which defines the moment of inertia of the body with respect to any axis through O, is known as the *ellipsoid of inertia* of the body at O.

We observe that if the axes in Fig. 9.30 are rotated, the coefficients of the equation defining the ellipsoid change, since these are equal to the moments and products of inertia of the body with respect to the rotated coordinate axes. However, the *ellipsoid itself remains unaffected*, since its shape depends only upon the distribution of mass in the body considered. Suppose now that we choose as coordinate axes the principal axes x', y', z' of the ellipsoid of inertia (Fig. 9.31). The equation of the ellipsoid with respect to these coordinate axes will be of the form

$$I_{x'}x'^2 + I_{y'}y'^2 + I_{z'}z'^2 = 1 \qquad (9.49)$$

which does not contain any product of coordinates. Thus, the products of inertia of the body with respect to the x', y', z' axes are zero. The x', y', z' axes are known as the *principal axes of inertia* of the body at O, and the coefficients $I_{x'}$, $I_{y'}$, $I_{z'}$ as the *principal moments of inertia* of the body at O. Note that, given a body of arbitrary shape and a point O, it is always possible to find axes which are the principal axes of inertia of the body at O, that is, axes with respect to which the products of inertia of the body are zero. Indeed, no matter how odd or irregular the shape of the body may be, the moments of inertia of the body with respect to axes through O will define an ellipsoid, and this ellipsoid will have principal axes which, by definition, are the principal axes of the body at O.

If the principal axes of inertia x', y', z' are used as coordinate axes, the expression obtained in Eq. (9.46) for the moment of inertia of a body with respect to an arbitrary axis through O reduces to

$$I_{OL} = I_{x'}\lambda_{x'}^2 + I_{y'}\lambda_{y'}^2 + I_{z'}\lambda_{z'}^2 \qquad (9.50)$$

While the determination of the principal axes of inertia of a body of arbitrary shape is somewhat involved and would require solving a cubic equation, there are many cases when these axes may be spotted immediately. Consider, for instance, the homogeneous cone of elliptical base shown in Fig. 9.32; this cone possesses two mutually perpendicular planes of symmetry OAA' and OBB'. We check from the definition (9.45) that if the $x'y'$ and $y'z'$ planes are chosen to coincide with the two planes of symmetry, all the products of inertia are zero. The x', y', and z' axes thus selected are therefore the principal axes of inertia of the cone at O. In the case of the homogeneous regular tetrahedron $OABC$ shown in Fig. 9.33, the line joining the corner O to the center D of the opposite face is a principal axis of inertia at O and any line through O perpendicular to OD is also a principal axis of inertia at O. This property may be recognized if we observe that a rotation through $120°$ about OD leaves the shape and the mass distribution of the tetrahedron unchanged. It follows that the ellipsoid of inertia at O also remains unchanged under this rotation. The ellipsoid, therefore, is of revolution about OD, and the line OD, as well as any perpendicular line through O, must be a principal axis of the ellipsoid.

SAMPLE PROBLEM 9.14

Consider a rectangular prism of mass m and sides a, b, c. Determine (a) the mass moments and products of inertia of the prism with respect to the coordinate axes shown, (b) its moment of inertia with respect to the diagonal OB.

a. Moments and Products of Inertia with Respect to the Coordinate Axes. *Moments of Inertia.* Introducing the centroidal axes x', y', z', with respect to which the moments of inertia are given in Fig. 9.28, we apply the parallel-axis theorem:

$$I_x = \bar{I}_{x'} + m(\bar{y}^2 + \bar{z}^2) = \tfrac{1}{12}m(b^2 + c^2) + m(\tfrac{1}{4}b^2 + \tfrac{1}{4}c^2)$$

$$I_x = \tfrac{1}{3}m(b^2 + c^2) \blacktriangleleft$$

Similarly, $\qquad I_y = \tfrac{1}{3}m(c^2 + a^2) \qquad I_z = \tfrac{1}{3}m(a^2 + b^2) \blacktriangleleft$

Products of Inertia. Because of symmetry, the products of inertia with respect to the centroidal axes x', y', z' are zero and these axes are principal axes of inertia. Using the parallel-axis theorem, we have

$$I_{xy} = \bar{I}_{x'y'} + m\bar{x}\bar{y} = 0 + m(\tfrac{1}{2}a)(\tfrac{1}{2}b) \qquad I_{xy} = \tfrac{1}{4}mab \blacktriangleleft$$

Similarly, $\qquad\qquad I_{yz} = \tfrac{1}{4}mbc \qquad I_{zx} = \tfrac{1}{4}mca \blacktriangleleft$

b. Moment of Inertia with Respect to OB. We recall Eq. (9.46):

$$I_{OB} = I_x\lambda_x^2 + I_y\lambda_y^2 + I_z\lambda_z^2 - 2I_{xy}\lambda_x\lambda_y - 2I_{yz}\lambda_y\lambda_z - 2I_{zx}\lambda_z\lambda_x$$

where the direction cosines of OB are

$$\lambda_x = \cos\theta_x = \frac{OH}{OB} = \frac{a}{(a^2 + b^2 + c^2)^{1/2}}$$

$$\lambda_y = \frac{b}{(a^2 + b^2 + c^2)^{1/2}} \qquad \lambda_z = \frac{c}{(a^2 + b^2 + c^2)^{1/2}}$$

Substituting the values obtained for the moments and products of inertia and for the direction cosines:

$$I_{OB} = \frac{1}{a^2 + b^2 + c^2}\left[\tfrac{1}{3}m(b^2 + c^2)a^2 + \tfrac{1}{3}m(c^2 + a^2)b^2 + \tfrac{1}{3}m(a^2 + b^2)c^2\right.$$

$$\left. -\tfrac{1}{2}ma^2b^2 - \tfrac{1}{2}mb^2c^2 - \tfrac{1}{2}mc^2a^2\right]$$

$$I_{OB} = \frac{m}{6}\frac{a^2b^2 + b^2c^2 + c^2a^2}{a^2 + b^2 + c^2} \blacktriangleleft$$

Alternate Solution. The moment of inertia I_{OB} may be obtained directly from the principal moments of inertia $\bar{I}_{x'}$, $\bar{I}_{y'}$, $\bar{I}_{z'}$, since the line OB passes through the centroid O'. Since the x', y', z' axes are principal axes of inertia, we use Eq. (9.50) and write

$$I_{OB} = \bar{I}_{x'}\lambda_x^2 + \bar{I}_{y'}\lambda_y^2 + \bar{I}_{z'}\lambda_z^2$$

$$= \frac{1}{a^2 + b^2 + c^2}\left[\frac{m}{12}(b^2 + c^2)a^2 + \frac{m}{12}(c^2 + a^2)b^2 + \frac{m}{12}(a^2 + b^2)c^2\right]$$

$$I_{OB} = \frac{m}{6}\frac{a^2b^2 + b^2c^2 + c^2a^2}{a^2 + b^2 + c^2} \blacktriangleleft$$

Problems

Fig. P9.120

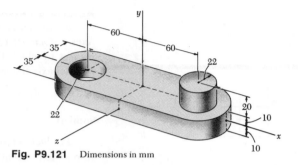

Fig. P9.121   Dimensions in mm

9.120 and 9.121 Determine the mass product of inertia I_{xy}, I_{yz}, and I_{zx} of the steel machine element shown. (Density of steel = 7850 kg/m³.)

9.122 A section of sheet steel, 2 mm thick, is cut and bent into the machine component shown. Knowing that the density of steel is 7850 kg/m³, determine the mass products of inertia I_{xy}, I_{yz}, and I_{zx} of the component.

Fig. P9.122

Fig. P9.123

9.123 A section of sheet steel, 0.75 mm thick, is cut and bent into the sheet-metal machine component shown. Knowing that the density of steel is 7850 kg/m³, determine the mass products of inertia I_{xy}, I_{yz}, and I_{zx} of the component. (*Hint.* See results of Sample Prob. 9.6.)

9.124 For the corner reflector of Prob. 9.112, determine the mass products of inertia I_{xy}, I_{yz}, and I_{zx}. (*Hint.* See results of Sample Prob. 9.6 and Prob. 9.56.)

Fig. P9.125

9.125 A homogeneous wire with a mass per unit length of 1.8 kg/m is used to form the figure shown. Determine the mass products of inertia I_{xy}, I_{yz}, and I_{zx} of the wire figure.

9.126 Complete the derivation of Eqs. (9.47), which express the parallel-axis theorem for mass products of inertia.

9.127 For the homogeneous tetrahedron of mass m which is shown, (a) determine by direct integration the mass product of inertia I_{zx}, (b) deduce I_{yz} and I_{xy} from the result obtained in part a.

9.128 Determine the mass moment of inertia of the right circular cone of Sample Prob. 9.11 with respect to a generator of the cone.

9.129 Determine the mass moment of inertia of the rectangular prism of Sample Prob. 9.14 with respect to the diagonal OF of its base.

9.130 Determine the mass moment of inertia of the corner reflector of Probs. 9.112 and 9.124 with respect to the axis through the origin which forms equal angles with the x, y, and z axes.

9.131 Determine the mass moment of inertia of the machine part of Sample Prob. 9.13 with respect to an axis through the origin characterized by the unit vector $\boldsymbol{\lambda} = \frac{2}{3}\mathbf{i} + \frac{1}{3}\mathbf{j} + \frac{2}{3}\mathbf{k}$.

Fig. P9.127

Fig. P9.132

Fig. P9.133

9.132 and 9.133 Three uniform rods, each of mass m, are welded together as shown. Determine (a) the mass moments of inertia and the mass products of inertia with respect to the coordinate axes, (b) the mass moment of inertia with respect to a line joining the origin O and point D.

9.134 The thin bent plate shown is of uniform density and mass m. Determine its mass moment of inertia with respect to a line joining points B and C.

9.135 The thin bent plate shown is of uniform density and mass m. Determine its mass moment of inertia with respect to a line joining the origin O and point A.

Fig. P9.134 and P9.135

9.136 Determine the value of the ratio a/h for which the ellipsoid of inertia of the right circular cone of Sample Prob. 9.11 is a sphere when computed (a) at the apex of the cone, (b) at the centroid of the cone.

9.137 Consider a homogeneous circular cylinder of radius a and length L. Determine the value of the ratio a/L for which the ellipsoid of inertia of the cylinder is a sphere when computed (a) at the centroid of the cylinder, (b) at the center of one of its bases.

Fig. P9.137

9.138 Given an arbitrary solid and three rectangular axes x, y, and z, prove that the mass moment of inertia of the solid with respect to any one of the three axes cannot be larger than the sum of the moments of inertia of the solid with respect to the other two axes; i.e., prove that the inequality $I_x \leq I_y + I_z$ is satisfied, as well as two similar inequalities. Further prove that, if the solid is homogeneous and of revolution, and if x is the axis of revolution and y a transverse axis, then $I_y \geq \frac{1}{2}I_x$.

9.139 Consider a cube of mass m and side a. (*a*) Show that the ellipsoid of inertia at the center of the cube is a sphere, and use this property to determine the mass moment of inertia of the cube with respect to one of its diagonals. (*b*) Show that the ellipsoid of inertia at one of the corners of the cube is an ellipsoid of revolution, and determine the principal moments of inertia of the cube at that point.

9.140 Given a homogeneous solid of mass m and of arbitrary shape, and three rectangular axes x, y, and z of origin O, prove that the sum $I_x + I_y + I_z$ of the mass moments of inertia of the solid cannot be smaller than the similar sum computed for a sphere of the same mass and same material centered at O. Further prove, using the result of Prob. 9.138, that if the solid is of revolution and if x is the axis of revolution, then its moment of inertia I_y about a transverse axis y cannot be smaller than $\frac{3}{10}ma^2$, where a is the radius of the sphere of the same mass and same material.

Review and Summary

In the first half of this chapter we were concerned with the determination of the resultant $\mathbf{R}$ of forces $\Delta \mathbf{F}$ distributed over a plane area A when their magnitude is proportional to the element of area ΔA on which they act and, at the same time, varies linearly with the distance y from ΔA to a given x axis; we thus had $\Delta F = ky\,\Delta A$. We found that the magnitude of the resultant $\mathbf{R}$ was proportional to the first moment $Q_x = \int y\,dA$ of the area A, while the moment of $\mathbf{R}$ about the x axis was proportional to the *second moment*, or *moment of inertia*, $I_x = \int y^2\,dA$ of A with respect to the same axis [Sec. 9.2].

The *rectangular moments of inertia* I_x and I_y *of an area* [Sec. 9.3] were obtained by computing the integrals

$$I_x = \int y^2\,dA \qquad I_y = \int x^2\,dA \qquad (9.1)$$

These computations may be reduced to single integrations by choosing for dA a thin strip parallel to one of the axes of coordinates. We also recall that it is possible to compute I_x and I_y from the same elementary strip (Fig. 9.34) by making use of the formula for the moment of inertia of a rectangular area [Sample Prob. 9.3].

Rectangular moments of inertia

$dI_x = \frac{1}{3}y^3\,dx$
$dI_y = x^2 y\,dx$

Fig. 9.34

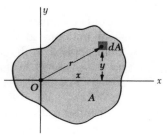

Fig. 9.35

The *polar moment of inertia of an area A* with respect to the pole O [Sec. 9.4] was defined as

$$J_O = \int r^2 \, dA \qquad (9.3)$$

where r is the distance from O to the element of area dA (Fig. 9.35). Observing that $r^2 = x^2 + y^2$, we established the relation

$$J_O = I_x + I_y \qquad (9.4)$$

The *radius of gyration of an area A* with respect to the x axis [Sec. 9.5] was defined as the distance k_x such that $I_x = k_x^2 A$. With similar definitions for the radii of gyration of A with respect to the y axis and with respect to O, we had

$$k_x = \sqrt{\frac{I_x}{A}} \qquad k_y = \sqrt{\frac{I_y}{A}} \qquad k_O = \sqrt{\frac{J_O}{A}} \qquad (9.5\text{--}9.7)$$

The *parallel-axis theorem* was presented in Sec. 9.6. It states that the moment of inertia I of an area with respect to any given axis AA' (Fig. 9.36) is equal to the moment of inertia $\bar{I}$ of the area with respect to a centroidal axis BB' parallel to AA' *plus* the product of the area A and the square of the distance d between the two axes:

$$I = \bar{I} + Ad^2 \qquad (9.9)$$

This formula may also be used to determine the moment of inertia $\bar{I}$ of an area with respect to a centroidal axis BB' when its moment of inertia I with respect to a parallel axis AA' is known. In this case, however, the product Ad^2 should be *subtracted* from the known moment of inertia I.

A similar relation holds between the polar moment of inertia J_O of an area about a point O and the polar moment of inertia $\bar{J}_C$ of the same area about its centroid C. Denoting by d the distance between O and C, we have

$$J_O = \bar{J}_C + Ad^2 \qquad (9.11)$$

The parallel-axis theorem may be used very effectively in the computation of the *moment of inertia of a composite area* with respect to a given axis [Sec. 9.7]. Considering each component area separately, we first

Polar moment of inertia

Radius of gyration

Parallel-axis theorem

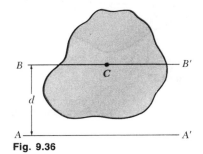

Fig. 9.36

Composite areas

Product of inertia

Rotation of axes

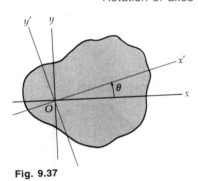

Fig. 9.37

Principal axes

Principal moments of inertia

compute the moment of inertia of each area with respect to a centroidal axis, using whenever possible the data provided in Figs. 9.12 and 9.13; the parallel-axis theorem is then applied to determine the moment of inertia of each component area with respect to the desired axis and the various values obtained are added [Sample Probs. 9.4 and 9.5].

Sections 9.8 to 9.10 were devoted to the transformation of the moments of inertia of an area *under a rotation of the coordinate axes*. First we defined the *product of inertia of an area A* as

$$I_{xy} = \int xy \, dA \tag{9.12}$$

and showed that $I_{xy} = 0$ if the area A is symmetrical with respect to either or both of the coordinate axes. We also derived the *parallel-axis theorem for products of inertia*. We had

$$I_{xy} = \bar{I}_{x'y'} + \bar{x}\bar{y}A \tag{9.13}$$

where $\bar{I}_{x'y'}$ is the product of inertia of the area with respect to centroidal axes $x'y'$ parallel to the axes xy, and $\bar{x}$ and $\bar{y}$ are the coordinates of the centroid of the area [Sec. 9.8].

In Sec. 9.9 we computed the moments and product of inertia $I_{x'}$, $I_{y'}$, and $I_{x'y'}$ of an area with respect to axes $x'y'$ obtained by rotating the original coordinate axes xy through an angle θ counterclockwise (Fig. 9.37), and expressed them in terms of the moments and product of inertia I_x, I_y, and I_{xy} computed with respect to the original xy axes. We had

$$I_{x'} = \frac{I_x + I_y}{2} + \frac{I_x - I_y}{2} \cos 2\theta - I_{xy} \sin 2\theta \tag{9.18}$$

$$I_{y'} = \frac{I_x + I_y}{2} - \frac{I_x - I_y}{2} \cos 2\theta + I_{xy} \sin 2\theta \tag{9.19}$$

$$I_{x'y'} = \frac{I_x - I_y}{2} \sin 2\theta + I_{xy} \cos 2\theta \tag{9.20}$$

The *principal axes of the area about O* were defined as the two axes perpendicular to each other, with respect to which the moments of inertia of the area are, respectively, maximum and minimum. The corresponding values of θ were denoted by θ_m and obtained from the formula

$$\tan 2\theta_m = -\frac{2I_{xy}}{I_x - I_y} \tag{9.25}$$

The corresponding maximum and minimum values of I are called the *principal moments of inertia* of the area about O; we had

$$I_{\text{max,min}} = \frac{I_x + I_y}{2} \pm \sqrt{\left(\frac{I_x - I_y}{2}\right)^2 + I_{xy}^2} \tag{9.27}$$

We also noted that the corresponding value of the product of inertia is zero.

Fig. 9.38

The transformation of the moments and product of inertia of an area under a rotation of axes may be represented graphically by drawing *Mohr's circle* [Sec. 9.10]. Given the moments and product of inertia I_x, I_y, and I_{xy} of the area with respect to the coordinate axes xy, we plot points X (I_x, I_{xy}) and Y $(I_y, -I_{xy})$ and draw the line joining these two points (Fig. 9.38). This line is a diameter of Mohr's circle and thus defines this circle. As the coordinate axes are rotated through θ, the diameter rotates through *twice that angle* and the coordinates of X' and Y' yield the new values $I_{x'}$, $I_{y'}$, and $I_{x'y'}$ of the moments and product of inertia of the area. Also, the angle θ_m and the coordinates of points A and B define the principal axes a and b and the principal moments of inertia of the area [Sample Prob. 9.8].

Mohr's circle

The second half of the chapter was devoted to the determination of *moments of inertia of masses*, which are encountered in dynamics in problems involving the rotation of a rigid body about an axis. The mass moment of inertia of a body with respect to an axis AA' (Fig. 9.39) was defined as

$$I = \int r^2 \, dm \qquad (9.28)$$

where r is the distance from AA' to the element of mass [Sec. 9.11], and its *radius of gyration* as

$$k = \sqrt{\frac{I}{m}} \qquad (9.29)$$

The moments of inertia of a body with respect to the coordinates axes were expressed as

$$I_x = \int (y^2 + z^2) \, dm$$

$$I_y = \int (z^2 + x^2) \, dm \qquad (9.30)$$

$$I_z = \int (x^2 + y^2) \, dm$$

Moments of inertia of masses

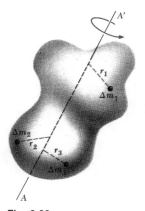

Fig. 9.39

Parallel-axis theorem

We saw that the *parallel-axis theorem* also applies to mass moments of inertia [Sec. 9.12]. Thus, the moment of inertia I of a body with respect to an arbitrary axis AA' (Fig. 9.40), may be expressed as

$$I = \bar{I} + md^2 \qquad (9.33)$$

where $\bar{I}$ is the moment of inertia of the body with respect to a centroidal axis BB' parallel to the axis AA', m the mass of the body, and d the distance between the two axes.

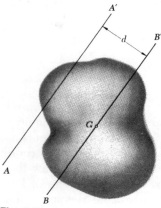

Fig. 9.40

Moments of inertia of thin plates

The moments of inertia of *thin plates* may be readily obtained from the moments of inertia of their areas [Sec. 9.13]. We found that for a *rectangular plate* the moments of inertia with respect to the axes shown (Fig. 9.41) are

$$I_{AA'} = \tfrac{1}{12}ma^2 \qquad I_{BB'} = \tfrac{1}{12}mb^2 \qquad (9.39)$$
$$I_{CC'} = I_{AA'} + I_{BB'} = \tfrac{1}{12}m(a^2 + b^2) \qquad (9.40)$$

Fig. 9.41

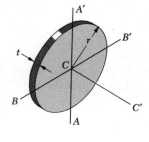

Fig. 9.42

while for a *circular plate* (Fig. 9.42) they are

$$I_{AA'} = I_{BB'} = \tfrac{1}{4}mr^2 \qquad (9.41)$$
$$I_{CC'} = I_{AA'} + I_{BB'} = \tfrac{1}{2}mr^2 \qquad (9.42)$$

When a body possesses *two planes of symmetry*, it is usually possible to determine its moment of inertia with respect to a given axis through a *single integration* by considering an element of mass dm in the shape of a thin plate [Sample Probs. 9.10 and 9.11]. On the other hand, when a body is made of *several common geometric shapes*, its moment of inertia with respect to a given axis may be obtained from the values given in Fig. 9.28 and the application of the parallel-axis theorem [Sample Probs. 9.12 and 9.13].

In the last portion of the chapter, we learned to determine the moment of inertia of a body *with respect to an arbitrary axis OL* drawn through the origin O [Sec. 9.16]. Denoting by λ_x, λ_y, λ_z the components of the unit vector $\boldsymbol{\lambda}$ along OL (Fig. 9.43) and introducing the *products of inertia*

$$I_{xy} = \int xy \, dm \qquad I_{yz} = \int yz \, dm \qquad I_{zx} = \int zx \, dm \quad (9.45)$$

we found that the moment of inertia of the body with respect to OL could be expressed as

$$I_{OL} = I_x \lambda_x^2 + I_y \lambda_y^2 + I_z \lambda_z^2 - 2I_{xy}\lambda_x\lambda_y - 2I_{yz}\lambda_y\lambda_z - 2I_{zx}\lambda_z\lambda_x \quad (9.46)$$

Fig. 9.43

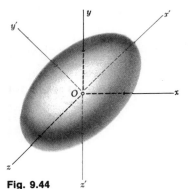

Fig. 9.44

By plotting a point Q along each axis OL at a distance $OQ = 1/\sqrt{I_{OL}}$ from O [Sec. 9.17], we obtained the surface of an ellipsoid, known as the *ellipsoid of inertia* of the body at point O. The principal axes x', y', z' of this ellipsoid (**Fig. 9.44**), are the *principal axes of inertia* of the body; that is, the products of inertia $I_{x'y'}$, $I_{y'z'}$, $I_{z'x'}$ of the body with respect to these axes are all zero. There are many situations where the principal axes of inertia of a body may be spotted from properties of symmetry of the body. Choosing these axes as coordinate axes, we may then express I_{OL} as

$$I_{OL} = I_{x'}\lambda_{x'}^2 + I_{y'}\lambda_{y'}^2 + I_{z'}\lambda_{z'}^2 \quad (9.50)$$

where $I_{x'}$, $I_{y'}$, $I_{z'}$ are the *principal moments of inertia* of the body at O.

Review Problems

9.141 A thin wire has been bent to form a half ring of radius r. Denoting the mass of the wire by m, determine the mass moment of inertia of the wire with respect to (a) the axis AA', (b) the axis BB'.

Fig. P9.141

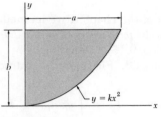

Fig. P9.142

9.142 Determine the moment of inertia of the shaded area with respect to (a) the x axis, (b) the y axis.

9.143 Determine the moment of inertia of the shaded area with respect to the y axis.

Fig. P9.143 and P9.144

9.144 Determine the product of inertia of the shaded area with respect to the x and y axes. (*Hint.* Use answer to Prob. 9.56.)

9.145 Determine the polar moment of inertia and the polar radius of gyration of the shaded area shown with respect to its centroid C.

Fig. P9.145

9.146 Determine the orientation of the principal axes through the centroid C and the corresponding values of the moment of inertia for the angle cross section shown. (The moments of inertia are $I_x = 0.152 \times 10^6 \text{ mm}^4$ and $I_y = 0.048 \times 10^6 \text{ mm}^4$.)

Fig. P9.146

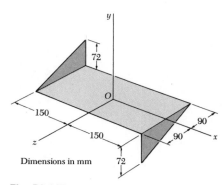

Fig. P9.147

9.147 A section of sheet steel, 2 mm thick, is cut and bent into the machine component shown. Knowing that the density of steel is 7850 kg/m^3, determine the mass moment of inertia and the radius of gyration of the component with respect to the x axis.

9.148 For the machine component of Prob. 9.147, determine the mass moment of inertia and the radius of gyration with respect to the y axis.

Fig. P9.149

9.149 Twelve uniform slender rods, each of length l, are welded together to form the cubical figure shown. Denoting by m the total mass of the twelve rods, determine the mass moment of inertia and the radius of gyration of the figure with respect to the x axis.

9.150 Knowing that the thin cylindrical shell shown is of mass m, thickness t, and height h, determine the mass moment of inertia of the shell with respect to the x axis. (*Hint.* Consider the shell as formed by removing a cylinder of radius a and height h from a cylinder of radius $a + t$ and height h; then neglect terms containing t^2 and t^3 and keep those terms containing t.)

Fig. P9.150

9.151 Determine by approximate means the moment of inertia of the shaded area with respect to (*a*) the *x* axis, (*b*) the *y* axis.

Fig. P9.151

9.152 A thin plate of mass *m* is cut in the shape of an equilateral triangle of side *a*. Determine the mass moment of inertia of the plate with respect to (*a*) the centroidal axes *AA'* and *BB'* in the plane of the plate, (*b*) the centroidal axis *CC'* perpendicular to the plate.

Fig. P9.152

The following problems are designed to be solved with a computer.

9.C1 Write a computer program which, for an area with known moments and product of inertia I_x, I_y, and I_{xy}, can be used to calculate the moments of inertia $I_{x'}$, $I_{y'}$, and $I_{x'y'}$ of the area with respect to axes x' and y' obtained by rotating the original axes counterclockwise through an angle θ. Use this program to compute $I_{x'}$, $I_{y'}$, and $I_{x'y'}$ for the section of Sample Prob. 9.8 for values of θ from 0 to 90° at 5° intervals.

9.C2 Write a computer program which, for an area with known moments and product of inertia I_x, I_y, and I_{xy}, can be used to calculate the orientation of the principal axes of the area and the corresponding values of the principal moments of inertia. Use this program to solve (*a*) Prob. 9.73, (*b*) parts *a* and *b* of Sample Prob. 9.8.

9.C3 Approximate the plane area shown by a series of rectangles of the form $bb'd'd$ and write a computer program which can be used to calculate the moment of inertia and radius of gyration of the area shown in part a of the figure with respect to each of the coordinate axes. Use this program to compute I_x, k_x, I_y, and k_y for the areas shown in parts b and c of the figure.

(a)

(b)

(c)

Fig. P9.C3

9.C4 The web of the steel flywheel shown consists of a solid plate of thickness t_2. Write a computer program which can be used to calculate the mass moment of inertia and the radius of gyration of the flywheel with respect to the axis of rotation. Use this program to solve (a) Prob. 9.102, (b) Prob. 9.103.

Fig. P9.C4

Method of
Virtual Work

* 10.1. Introduction. In the preceding chapters, problems involving the equilibrium of rigid bodies were solved by expressing that the external forces acting on the bodies were balanced. The equations of equilibrium $\Sigma F_x = 0$, $\Sigma F_y = 0$, $\Sigma M_A = 0$ were written and solved for the desired unknowns. We shall now consider a different method, which will prove more effective for solving certain types of equilibrium problems. This method is based on the *principle of virtual work* and was first formally used by the Swiss mathematician Jean Bernoulli in the eighteenth century.

As we shall see in Sec. 10.3, the principle of virtual work states that if a particle or rigid body, or, more generally, if a system of connected rigid bodies is in equilibrium under various external forces, and if the system is given an arbitrary displacement from that position of equilibrium, the total work done by the external forces during the displacement is zero. This principle may be applied particularly effectively to the solution of problems involving the equilibrium of machines or mechanisms consisting of several connected members.

In the second part of the chapter, the method of virtual work will be applied in an alternate form based on the concept of *potential energy*. As we shall see in Sec. 10.8, if a particle, rigid body, or system of rigid bodies is in equilibrium, then the derivative of its potential energy with respect to a variable defining its position must be zero.

In this chapter, we shall also learn to evaluate the mechanical efficiency of a machine (Sec. 10.5), and to determine whether a given position of equilibrium is stable, unstable, or neutral (Sec. 10.9).

*10.2. Work of a Force.

We shall first define the terms *displacement* and *work* as they are used in mechanics. Consider a particle which moves from a point A to a neighboring point A' (Fig. 10.1). If $\mathbf{r}$ denotes the position vector corresponding to point A, the small vector joining A and A' may be denoted by the differential $d\mathbf{r}$; the vector $d\mathbf{r}$ is called the *displacement* of the particle. Now let us assume that a force $\mathbf{F}$ is acting on the particle. The *work of the force* $\mathbf{F}$ *corresponding to the displacement* $d\mathbf{r}$ is defined as the quantity

$$dU = \mathbf{F} \cdot d\mathbf{r} \tag{10.1}$$

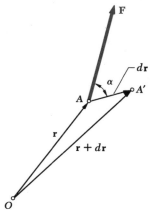

Fig. 10.1

obtained by forming the scalar product of the force $\mathbf{F}$ and of the displacement $d\mathbf{r}$. Denoting respectively by F and ds the magnitudes of the force and of the displacement, and by α the angle formed by $\mathbf{F}$ and $d\mathbf{r}$, and recalling the definition of the scalar product of two vectors (Sec. 3.9), we write

$$dU = F\, ds \cos \alpha \tag{10.1'}$$

Being a *scalar quantity*, work has a magnitude and a sign, but no direction. We also note that work should be expressed in units obtained by multiplying units of length by units of force, such as N·m. The unit of work N·m is called a *joule* (J).†

It follows from (10.1') that the work dU is positive if the angle α is acute and negative if α is obtuse. Three particular cases are of special interest. If the force $\mathbf{F}$ has the same direction as $d\mathbf{r}$, the work dU reduces to $F\, ds$. If $\mathbf{F}$ has a direction opposite to that of $d\mathbf{r}$, the work is $dU = -F\, ds$. Finally, if $\mathbf{F}$ is perpendicular to $d\mathbf{r}$, the work dU is zero.

The work dU of a force $\mathbf{F}$ during a displacement $d\mathbf{r}$ may also be considered as the product of F and of the component $ds \cos \alpha$ of the displacement $d\mathbf{r}$ along $\mathbf{F}$ (Fig. 10.2a). This view is particularly useful in the computation of the work done by the weight $\mathbf{W}$ of a body (Fig. 10.2b). The work of $\mathbf{W}$ is equal to the product of W and of the vertical displacement dy of the center of gravity G of the body. If the displacement is downward, the work is positive; if it is upward, the work is negative.

A number of forces frequently encountered in statics *do no work*. They are forces applied to fixed points ($ds = 0$) or acting in a direction perpendicular to the displacement ($\cos \alpha = 0$). Among the forces which do no work are the following: the reaction at a frictionless pin when the body

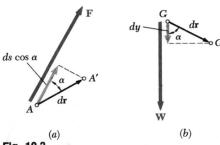

(a)   (b)

Fig. 10.2

---

† The joule is the SI unit of *energy*, whether in mechanical form (work, potential energy, kinetic energy) or in chemical, electrical, or thermal form. We should note that even though N·m = J, the moment of a force must be expressed in N·m, and not in joules, since the moment of a force is not a form of energy.

supported rotates about the pin, the reaction at a frictionless surface when the body in contact moves along the surface, the reaction at a roller moving along its track, the weight of a body when its center of gravity moves horizontally, the friction force acting on a wheel rolling without slipping (since at any instant the point of contact does not move). Examples of forces which *do work* are the weight of a body (except in the case considered above), the friction force acting on a body sliding on a rough surface, and most forces applied on a moving body.

In certain cases, the sum of the work done by several forces is zero. Consider, for example, two rigid bodies AC and BC connected at C by a *frictionless pin* (Fig. 10.3a). Among the forces acting on AC is the force $\mathbf{F}$

Fig. 10.3

(a)

(b)

exerted at C by BC. In general, the work of this force will not be zero, but it will be equal in magnitude and opposite in sign to the work of the force $-\mathbf{F}$ exerted by AC on BC, since these forces are equal and opposite and are applied to the same particle. Thus, when the total work done by all the forces acting on AB and BC is considered, the work of the two internal forces at C cancels out. A similar result is obtained if we consider a system consisting of two blocks connected by an *inextensible cord AB* (Fig. 10.3b). The work of the tension force $\mathbf{T}$ at A is equal in magnitude to the work of the tension force $\mathbf{T}'$ at B, since these forces have the same magnitude and the points A and B move through the same distance; but in one case the work is positive, and in the other it is negative. Thus, the work of the internal forces again cancels out.

It may be shown that the total work of the internal forces holding together the particles of a rigid body is zero. Consider two particles A and B of a rigid body and the two equal and opposite forces $\mathbf{F}$ and $-\mathbf{F}$ they exert on each other (Fig. 10.4). While, in general, small displacements $d\mathbf{r}$ and $d\mathbf{r}'$ of the two particles are different, the components of these displacements along AB must be equal; otherwise, the particles would not remain at the same distance from each other, and the body would not be rigid. Therefore, the work of $\mathbf{F}$ is equal in magnitude and opposite in sign to the work of $-\mathbf{F}$, and their sum is zero.

In computing the work of the external forces acting on a rigid body, it is often convenient to determine the work of a couple without considering separately the work of each of the two forces forming the couple. Consider the two forces $\mathbf{F}$ and $-\mathbf{F}$ forming a couple of moment $\mathbf{M}$ and acting on a rigid body (Fig. 10.5). Any small displacement of the rigid body bringing A

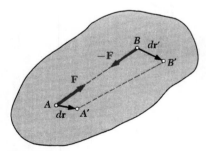

Fig. 10.4

and B, respectively, into A' and B'' may be divided into two parts, one in which points A and B undergo equal displacements $d\mathbf{r}_1$, the other in which A' remains fixed while B' moves into B'' through a displacement $d\mathbf{r}_2$ of magnitude $ds_2 = r\,d\theta$. In the first part of the motion, the work of $\mathbf{F}$ is equal in magnitude and opposite in sign to the work of $-\mathbf{F}$, and their sum is zero. In the second part of the motion, only force $\mathbf{F}$ works, and its work is $dU = F\,ds_2 = Fr\,d\theta$. But the product Fr is equal to the magnitude M of the moment of the couple. Thus, the work of a couple of moment $\mathbf{M}$ acting on a rigid body is

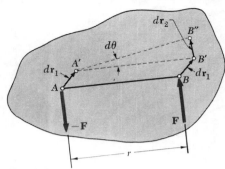

$$dU = M\,d\theta \tag{10.2}$$

where $d\theta$ is the small angle expressed in radians through which the body rotates. We again note that work should be expressed in units obtained by multiplying units of force by units of length.

Fig. 10.5

*10.3. Principle of Virtual Work. Consider a particle acted upon by several forces $\mathbf{F}_1, \mathbf{F}_2, \ldots, \mathbf{F}_n$ (Fig. 10.6). We shall assume that the particle undergoes a small displacement from A to A'. This displacement is possible, but it will not necessarily take place. The forces may be balanced and the particle at rest, or the particle may move under the action of the given forces in a direction different from that of AA'. The displacement considered is therefore an imaginary displacement; it is called a *virtual displacement* and is denoted by $\delta\mathbf{r}$. The symbol $\delta\mathbf{r}$ represents a differential of the first order; it is used to distinguish the virtual displacement from the displacement $d\mathbf{r}$ which would take place under actual motion. As we shall see, virtual displacements may be used to determine whether the conditions of equilibrium of a particle are satisfied.

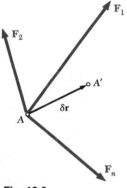

Fig. 10.6

The work of each of the forces $\mathbf{F}_1, \mathbf{F}_2, \ldots, \mathbf{F}_n$ during the virtual displacement $\delta\mathbf{r}$ is called *virtual work*. The virtual work of all the forces acting on the particle of Fig. 10.6 is

$$\delta U = \mathbf{F}_1 \cdot \delta\mathbf{r} + \mathbf{F}_2 \cdot \delta\mathbf{r} + \cdots + \mathbf{F}_n \cdot \delta\mathbf{r}$$
$$= (\mathbf{F}_1 + \mathbf{F}_2 + \cdots + \mathbf{F}_n) \cdot \delta\mathbf{r}$$

or

$$\delta U = \mathbf{R} \cdot \delta\mathbf{r} \tag{10.3}$$

where $\mathbf{R}$ is the resultant of the given forces. Thus, the total virtual work of the forces $\mathbf{F}_1, \mathbf{F}_2, \ldots, \mathbf{F}_n$ is equal to the virtual work of their resultant $\mathbf{R}$.

The principle of virtual work for a particle states that, *if a particle is in equilibrium, the total virtual work of the forces acting on the particle is zero for any virtual displacement of the particle.* This condition is necessary: if the particle is in equilibrium, the resultant $\mathbf{R}$ of the forces is zero, and it follows from (10.3) that the total virtual work δU is zero. The condition is also sufficient: if the total virtual work δU is zero for any virtual displacement, the scalar product $\mathbf{R} \cdot \delta\mathbf{r}$ is zero for any $\delta\mathbf{r}$, and the resultant $\mathbf{R}$ must be zero.

In the case of a rigid body, the principle of virtual work states that *if a rigid body is in equilibrium, the total virtual work of the external forces acting on the rigid body is zero for any virtual displacement of the body.* The condition is necessary: if the body is in equilibrium, all the particles forming the body are in equilibrium and the total virtual work of the forces acting on all the particles must be zero; but we have seen in the preceding section that the total work of the internal forces is zero; the total work of the external forces must therefore also be zero. The condition may also be proved to be sufficient.

The principle of virtual work may be extended to the case of a *system of connected rigid bodies.* If the system remains connected during the virtual displacement, *only the work of the forces external to the system need be considered,* since the total work of the internal forces at the various connections is zero.

* 10.4. Applications of the Principle of Virtual Work.

The principle of virtual work is particularly effective when applied to the solution of problems involving machines or mechanisms consisting of several connected rigid bodies. Consider, for instance, the toggle vise ACB of Fig. 10.7a, used to compress a wooden block. We wish to determine the

(a)   (b)

Fig. 10.7

force exerted by the vise on the block when a given force P is applied at C, assuming that there is no friction. Denoting by Q the reaction of the block on the vise, we draw the free-body diagram of the vise and consider the virtual displacement obtained by giving to the angle θ a positive increment $\delta\theta$ (Fig. 10.7b). Choosing a system of coordinate axes with origin at A, we note that x_B increases while y_C decreases. This is indicated in the figure by means of the positive increment δx_B and the negative increment $-\delta y_C$. The reactions A_x, A_y, and N will do no work during the virtual displacement considered, and we need only compute the work of P and Q. Since Q and δx_B have opposite senses, the virtual work of Q is $\delta U_Q = -Q\,\delta x_B$. Since P and the increment shown $(-\delta y_C)$ have the same sense, the virtual work of P is $\delta U_P = +P(-\delta y_C) = -P\,\delta y_C$. The minus signs obtained could have been predicted by simply noting that the forces Q and P are directed opposite to the positive x and y axes, respectively. Expressing the coordinates x_B and y_C in terms of the angle θ and differentiating, we obtain

$$x_B = 2l \sin \theta \qquad y_C = l \cos \theta$$
$$\delta x_B = 2l \cos \theta \; \delta\theta \qquad \delta y_C = -l \sin \theta \; \delta\theta \tag{10.4}$$

The total virtual work of the forces $\mathbf{Q}$ and $\mathbf{P}$ is thus

$$\delta U = \delta U_Q + \delta U_P = -Q \, \delta x_B - P \, \delta y_C$$
$$= -2Ql \cos \theta \; \delta\theta + Pl \sin \theta \; \delta\theta$$

Making $\delta U = 0$, we obtain

$$2Ql \cos \theta \; \delta\theta = Pl \sin \theta \; \delta\theta \tag{10.5}$$
$$Q = \tfrac{1}{2} P \tan \theta \tag{10.6}$$

The superiority of the method of virtual work over the conventional equilibrium equations in the problem considered here is clear: by using the method of virtual work, we were able to eliminate all unknown reactions, while the equation $\Sigma M_A = 0$ would have eliminated only two of the unknown reactions. We may take advantage of this characteristic of the method of virtual work to solve many problems involving machines and mechanisms. *If the virtual displacement considered is consistent with the constraints imposed by the supports and connections, all reactions and internal forces are eliminated and only the work of the loads, applied forces, and friction forces need be considered.*

We shall observe that the method of virtual work may also be used to solve problems involving completely constrained structures, although the virtual displacements considered will never actually take place. Consider, for example, the frame ACB shown in Fig. 10.8a. If point A is kept fixed, while B is given a horizontal virtual displacement (Fig. 10.8b), we need consider only the work of $\mathbf{P}$ and $\mathbf{B}_x$. We may thus determine the reaction

(a)

Fig. 10.8

(b)

component B_x in the same way as the force Q of the preceding example (Fig. 10.7b); we have

$$B_x = -\tfrac{1}{2}P \tan \theta$$

Keeping B fixed and giving to A a horizontal virtual displacement, we may similarly determine the reaction component A_x. The components A_y and B_y may be determined by rotating the frame ACB as a rigid body about B and A, respectively.

The method of virtual work may also be used to determine the configuration of a system in equilibrium under given forces. For example, the value of the angle θ for which the linkage of Fig. 10.7 is in equilibrium under two given forces P and Q may be obtained by solving Eq. (10.6) for $\tan \theta$.

It should be noted, however, that the attractiveness of the method of virtual work depends to a large extent upon the existence of simple geometric relations between the various virtual displacements involved in the solution of a given problem. When no such simple relations exist, it is usually advisable to revert to the conventional method of Chap. 6.

* 10.5. Real Machines. Mechanical Efficiency. In analyzing the toggle vise in the preceding section, we assumed that no friction forces were involved. Thus, the virtual work consisted only of the work of the applied force P and of the reaction Q. But the work of the reaction Q is equal in magnitude and opposite in sign to the work of the force exerted by the vise on the block. Equation (10.5), therefore, expresses that the *output work* $2Ql \cos \theta \; \delta\theta$ is equal to the *input work* $Pl \sin \theta \; \delta\theta$. A machine in which input and output work are equal is said to be an "ideal" machine. In a "real" machine, friction forces will always do some work, and the output work will be smaller than the input work.

Consider, for example, the toggle vise of Fig. 10.7a, and assume now that a friction force F develops between the sliding block B and the horizontal plane (Fig. 10.9). Using the conventional methods of statics and

Fig. 10.9

summing moments about A, we find $N = P/2$. Denoting by μ the coefficient of friction between block B and the horizontal plane, we have $F = \mu N = \mu P/2$. Recalling formulas (10.4), we find that the total virtual work of the forces $\mathbf{Q}$, $\mathbf{P}$, and $\mathbf{F}$ during the virtual displacement shown in Fig. 10.9 is

$$\delta U = -Q\,\delta x_B - P\,\delta y_C - F\,\delta x_B$$
$$= -2Ql\cos\theta\,\delta\theta + Pl\sin\theta\,\delta\theta - \mu Pl\cos\theta\,\delta\theta$$

Making $\delta U = 0$, we obtain

$$2Ql\cos\theta\,\delta\theta = Pl\sin\theta\,\delta\theta - \mu Pl\cos\theta\,\delta\theta \tag{10.7}$$

which expresses that the output work is equal to the input work minus the work of the friction force. Solving for Q, we have

$$Q = \tfrac{1}{2}P(\tan\theta - \mu) \tag{10.8}$$

We note that $Q = 0$ when $\tan\theta = \mu$, that is, when θ is equal to the angle of friction ϕ, and that $Q < 0$ when $\theta < \phi$. The toggle vise may thus be used only for values of θ larger than the angle of friction.

The *mechanical efficiency* of a machine is defined as the ratio

$$\eta = \frac{\text{output work}}{\text{input work}} \tag{10.9}$$

Clearly, the mechanical efficiency of an ideal machine is $\eta = 1$, since input and output work are then equal, while the mechanical efficiency of a real machine will always be less than 1.

In the case of the toggle vise we have just analyzed, we write

$$\eta = \frac{\text{output work}}{\text{input work}} = \frac{2Ql\cos\theta\,\delta\theta}{Pl\sin\theta\,\delta\theta}$$

Substituting from (10.8) for Q, we obtain

$$\eta = \frac{P(\tan\theta - \mu)l\cos\theta\,\delta\theta}{Pl\sin\theta\,\delta\theta} = 1 - \mu\cot\theta \tag{10.10}$$

We check that in the absence of friction forces, we would have $\mu = 0$ and $\eta = 1$. In the general case, when μ is different from zero, the efficiency η becomes zero for $\mu\cot\theta = 1$, that is, for $\tan\theta = \mu$, or $\theta = \tan^{-1}\mu = \phi$. We check again that the toggle vise may be used only for values of θ larger than the angle of friction ϕ.

SAMPLE PROBLEM 10.1

Using the method of virtual work, determine the magnitude of the couple **M** required to maintain the equilibrium of the mechanism shown.

Solution. Choosing a coordinate system with origin at E, we write

$$x_D = 3l \cos \theta \qquad \delta x_D = -3l \sin \theta \, \delta \theta$$

Principle of Virtual Work. Since the reactions $\mathbf{A}$, $\mathbf{E}_x$, and $\mathbf{E}_y$ will do no work during the virtual displacement, the total virtual work done by **M** and **P** must be zero. Noting that **P** acts in the positive x direction and **M** acts in the positive θ direction, we write

$$\delta U = 0: \qquad +M \, \delta \theta + P \, \delta x_D = 0$$
$$+M \, \delta \theta + P(-3l \sin \theta \, \delta \theta) = 0$$

$$M = 3Pl \sin \theta \quad \blacktriangleleft$$

SAMPLE PROBLEM 10.2

Determine the expressions for θ and for the tension in the spring which correspond to the equilibrium position of the mechanism. The unstretched length of the spring is h, and the constant of the spring is k. Neglect the weight of the mechanism.

Solution. With the coordinate system shown

$$y_B = l \sin \theta \qquad y_C = 2l \sin \theta$$
$$\delta y_B = l \cos \theta \, \delta \theta \qquad \delta y_C = 2l \cos \theta \, \delta \theta$$

The elongation of the spring is $\quad s = y_C - h = 2l \sin \theta - h$

The magnitude of the force exerted at C by the spring is

$$F = ks = k(2l \sin \theta - h) \tag{1}$$

Principle of Virtual Work. Since the reactions $\mathbf{A}_x$, $\mathbf{A}_y$, and $\mathbf{C}$ do no work, the total virtual work done by **P** and **F** must be zero.

$$\delta U = 0: \qquad P \, \delta y_B - F \, \delta y_C = 0$$
$$P(l \cos \theta \, \delta \theta) - k(2l \sin \theta - h)(2l \cos \theta \, \delta \theta) = 0$$

$$\sin \theta = \frac{P + 2kh}{4kl} \quad \blacktriangleleft$$

Substituting this expression into (1), we obtain $\qquad F = \tfrac{1}{2}P \quad \blacktriangleleft$

SAMPLE PROBLEM 10.3

A hydraulic-lift table is used to raise a 1000-kg crate. It consists of a platform and of two identical linkages on which hydraulic cylinders exert equal forces. (Only one linkage and one cylinder are shown.) Members EDB and CG are each of length $2a$, and member AD is pinned to the midpoint of EDB. If the crate is placed on the table, so that half of its weight is supported by the system shown, determine the force exerted by each cylinder in raising the crate for $\theta = 60°$, $a = 0.70$ m, and $L = 3.20$ m. This mechanism has been previously considered in Sample Prob. 6.7.

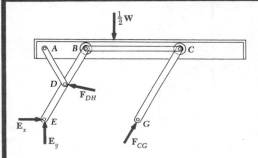

Solution. The machine considered consists of the platform and of the linkage, with an input force $\mathbf{F}_{DH}$ exerted by the cylinder and an output force equal and opposite to $\frac{1}{2}\mathbf{W}$.

Principle of Virtual Work. We first observe that the reactions at E and G do no work. Denoting by y the elevation of the platform above the base, and by s the length DH of the cylinder-and-piston assembly, we write

$$\delta U = 0: \qquad -\tfrac{1}{2}W\,\delta y + F_{DH}\,\delta s = 0 \qquad (1)$$

The vertical displacement δy of the platform is expressed in terms of the angular displacement $\delta\theta$ of EDB as follows:

$$y = (EB)\sin\theta = 2a\sin\theta$$
$$\delta y = 2a\cos\theta\,\delta\theta$$

To express δs similarly in terms of $\delta\theta$, we first note that by the law of cosines,

$$s^2 = a^2 + L^2 - 2aL\cos\theta$$

Differentiating,

$$2s\,\delta s = -2aL(-\sin\theta)\,\delta\theta$$
$$\delta s = \frac{aL\sin\theta}{s}\,\delta\theta$$

Substituting for δy and δs into (1), we write

$$(-\tfrac{1}{2}W)2a\cos\theta\,\delta\theta + F_{DH}\frac{aL\sin\theta}{s}\,\delta\theta = 0$$

$$F_{DH} = W\frac{s}{L}\cot\theta$$

With the given numerical data, we have

$$W = mg = (1000\text{ kg})(9.81\text{ m/s}^2) = 9810\text{ N} = 9.81\text{ kN}$$
$$s^2 = a^2 + L^2 - 2aL\cos\theta$$
$$= (0.70)^2 + (3.20)^2 - 2(0.70)(3.20)\cos 60° = 8.49$$
$$s = 2.91\text{ m}$$

$$F_{DH} = W\frac{s}{L}\cot\theta = (9.81\text{ kN})\frac{2.91\text{ m}}{3.20\text{ m}}\cot 60°$$

$$F_{DH} = 5.15\text{ kN} \quad \blacktriangleleft$$

Problems

Fig. P10.1

10.1 Knowing that the maximum friction force exerted by the bottle on the cork is 360 N, determine (*a*) the force **P** which must be applied to the corkscrew to open the bottle, (*b*) the maximum force exerted by the base of the corkscrew on the top of the bottle.

Fig. P10.2

10.2 Determine the force **P** required to maintain the equilibrium of the linkage.

10.3 Determine the horizontal force **P** which must be applied at *A* to maintain the equilibrium of the linkage.

Fig. P10.3 and P10.6

Fig. P10.4 and P10.5

10.4 Determine the vertical force **P** which must be applied at *C* to maintain the equilibrium of the linkage.

10.5 and 10.6 Determine the couple **M** which must be applied to member *ABC* to maintain the equilibrium of the linkage.

10.7 The mechanism shown is acted upon by the force **P**; derive an expression for the magnitude of the force **Q** required to maintain equilibrium.

Fig. P10.7

10.8 Knowing that the line of action of the force **Q** passes through point D, derive an expression for the magnitude of **Q** required to maintain equilibrium.

10.9 An overhead garage door of weight W consists of a uniform rectangular panel AC supported by a cable AE attached at the middle of the upper edge of the door and by two sets of frictionless rollers A and B which may slide in horizontal and vertical channels. Express the tension T in cable AE in terms of W, a, b, and θ.

Fig. P10.8

Fig. P10.9

Fig. P10.10

10.10 The slender rod AB is attached to a collar B and rests on a wheel at C. Neglecting the effect of friction, derive an expression for the magnitude of the force **Q** required to maintain the equilibrium of the rod.

10.11 Solve Prob. 10.10, assuming that the force **P** applied at A is vertical and directed downward.

10.12 A uniform rod AB of length l and weight W is suspended from two cords AC and BC of equal length. Derive an expression for the magnitude of the couple **M** required to maintain the equilibrium of the rod in the position shown.

Fig. P10.12

Fig. P10.13

10.13 Derive an expression for the magnitude of the couple **M** required to maintain the equilibrium of the linkage in the position shown.

10.14 A 4-kN force **P** is applied to the piston of the engine system shown. Knowing that $AB = 75$ mm and $BC = 200$ mm, determine the couple **M** required to maintain the equilibrium of the system when (a) $\theta = 30°$, (b) $\theta = 150°$.

Fig. P10.14 and P10.15

10.15 A couple **M** of magnitude 270 N·m is applied to the crank of the engine system shown. Knowing that $b = 75$ mm and $l = 200$ mm, determine the force **P** required to maintain the equilibrium of the system when (a) $\theta = 60°$, (b) $\theta = 120°$.

10.16 Collars A and B may slide freely on the frictionless rods shown. Knowing that the length of the wire AB is 550 mm and that the weight of collar A is $W = 63$ N, determine the magnitude of the force **P** required to maintain the equilibrium of the system when (a) $c = 100$ mm, (b) $c = 300$ mm.

Fig. P10.16

10.17 Solve Prob. 10.16 when (a) $c = 350$ mm, (b) $c = 450$ mm.

10.18 In Prob. 10.9, knowing that $a = 1050$ mm, $b = 700$ mm, and $W = 800$ N, determine the tension T in cable AE when the door is held in the position for which $BD = 1050$ mm.

10.19 In Prob. 10.13, determine the magnitude of the couple **M** required for equilibrium when $l = 400$ mm, $\theta = 25°$, and $P = 600$ N.

10.20 Determine the value of θ corresponding to the equilibrium position of the mechanism shown when $P = 200$ N and $Q = 800$ N.

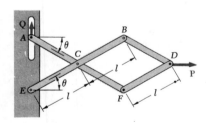

Fig. 10.20

10.21 Determine the value of θ corresponding to the equilibrium position of the mechanism of Prob. 10.7 when $P = 250$ N and $Q = 375$ N.

10.22 Determine the value of θ corresponding to the equilibrium position of the mechanism of Prob. 10.10 when $P = 250$ N, $Q = 500$ N, $l = 400$ mm, and $a = 80$ mm.

10.23 Determine the value of θ corresponding to the equilibrium position of the rod of Prob. 10.12 when $l = 300$ mm, $\alpha = 45°$, $W = 40$ N, and $M = 3$ N·m.

10.24 A vertical load **W** is applied to the linkage at B. The constant of the spring is k, and the spring is unstretched when AB and BC are horizontal. Neglecting the weight of the linkage, derive an equation in θ, W, l, and k, which must be satisfied when the linkage is in equilibrium.

Fig. P10.24 and P10.25

10.25 A load **W** of magnitude 900 N is applied to the linkage at B. Neglecting the weight of the linkage and knowing that l = 225 mm, determine the value of θ corresponding to equilibrium. The constant of the spring is k = 2 kN/m, and the spring is unstretched when AB and BC are horizontal. (*Hint.* Solve the equation obtained for θ by trial and error.)

10.26 Two bars AD and DG are connected by a pin at D and by a spring AG. Knowing that the spring is 300 mm long when unstretched and that the constant of the spring is 5 kN/m, determine the value of x corresponding to equilibrium when a 900-N load is applied at E as shown.

Fig. P10.26

10.27 Solve Prob. 10.26, assuming that the 900-N load is applied at C instead of E.

Fig. P10.28

10.28 A load **W** of magnitude 360 N is applied to the mechanism at C. Neglecting the weight of the mechanism, determine the value of θ corresponding to equilibrium. The constant of the spring is k = 3500 N/m, and the spring is unstretched when θ = 0.

10.29 A force **P** of magnitude 300 N is applied to end E of cable CDE, which passes under pulley D and is attached to the mechanism at C. Neglecting the weight of the mechanism and the radius of the pulley, determine the value of θ corresponding to equilibrium. The constant of the spring is k = 3500 N/m, and the spring is unstretched when θ = 90°

Fig. P10.29

Fig. P10.30

Fig. P10.32 and P10.33

Fig. P10.34

10.30 The lever AB is attached to the horizontal shaft BC which passes through a bearing and is welded to a fixed support at C. The torsional spring constant of the shaft BC is K; that is, a couple of magnitude K is required to rotate end B through 1 radian. Knowing that the shaft is untwisted when AB is horizontal, determine the value of θ corresponding to the position of equilibrium, if $P = 125$ N, $l = 200$ mm, and $K = 15$ N · m/rad.

10.31 Solve Prob. 10.30, if $P = 600$ N, $l = 200$ mm, and $K = 15$ N · m/rad. Obtain an answer in each of the following quadrants: $0 < \theta < 90°$, $270° < \theta < 360°$, and $360° < \theta < 450°$. (It is assumed that K remains constant for the angles of twist considered.)

10.32 The position of boom ABC is controlled by the hydraulic cylinder BD. For the loading shown, determine the force exerted by the hydraulic cylinder on pin B when $\theta = 65°$.

10.33 The position of boom ABC is controlled by the hydraulic cylinder BD. For the loading shown, (a) express the force exerted by the hydraulic cylinder on pin B as a function of the length BD, (b) determine the smallest possible value of the angle θ if the maximum force that the cylinder can exert on pin B is 12.5 kN.

10.34 The position of member ABC is controlled by the hydraulic cylinder CD. For the loading shown, determine the force exerted by the hydraulic cylinder on pin C when $\theta = 60°$.

10.35 Solve Prob. 10.34 when $\theta = 120°$.

10.36 A block of weight W is pulled up a plane forming an angle α with the horizontal by a force $\mathbf{P}$ directed along the plane. If μ is the coefficient of friction between the block and the plane, derive an expression for the mechanical efficiency of the system. Show that the mechanical efficiency cannot exceed $\frac{1}{2}$ if the block is to remain in place when the force $\mathbf{P}$ is removed.

10.37 Derive an expression for the mechanical efficiency of the jack discussed in Sec. 8.6. Show that if the jack is to be self-locking, the mechanical
efficiency cannot exceed $\frac{1}{2}$.

10.38 Denoting by μ_s the coefficient of static friction between collar C
and the vertical rod, derive an expression for the magnitude of the largest couple
M for which equilibrium is maintained in the position shown. Explain what happens if $\mu_s \geq \tan \theta$.

10.39 Knowing that the coefficient of static friction between collar C and
the vertical rod is 0.30, determine the magnitude of the largest and smallest
couple **M** for which equilibrium is maintained in the position shown, when $\theta =$
35°, $l = 500$ mm, and $P = 400$ N.

Fig. P10.38 and P10.39

10.40 Using the method of virtual work, determine the reaction at E.

10.41 Using the method of virtual work, determine separately the force
and couple representing the reaction at H.

Fig. P10.40 and P10.41

10.42 Referring to Prob. 6.122 and using the value found for F_{BD}, determine the change in length of the cylinder-and-piston assembly BD required to
raise bucket C by 75 mm.

10.43 Referring to Prob. 6.124 and using the value found for F_{CD}, determine the change in length of each of the two cylinder-and-piston assemblies CD
required to raise the 500-kg slab by 50 mm if the other two cylinders are not
activated.

10.44 Referring to Prob. 6.124 and using the value found for F_{FH}, determine the change in length of each of the two cylinder-and-piston assemblies FH
required to raise the 500-kg slab by 50 mm if the other two cylinders are not
activated.

10.45 Referring to Prob. 6.126 and using the answer obtained for the
force exerted by the cylinder, determine the change in length of the cylinder-and-
piston assembly required to raise the platform by 50 mm.

10.46 Determine the vertical movement of joint C if member FG is
lengthened by 50 mm. (*Hint*. Apply a vertical load at joint C, and using the methods of Chap. 6, compute the force exerted by member FG on joints F and G.
Then apply the method of virtual work for a virtual displacement making member
FG longer. This method should be used only for small changes in the length of
members.)

Fig. P10.46 and P10.47

10.47 Determine the horizontal movement of joint C if member FG is
lengthened by 50 mm. (Follow hint of Prob. 10.46, applying a *horizontal* force at
joint C.)

Fig. 10.10

Fig. 10.11

*10.6. Work of a Force during a Finite Displacement.

Consider a force $\mathbf{F}$ acting on a particle. The work of $\mathbf{F}$ corresponding to an infinitesimal displacement $d\mathbf{r}$ of the particle was defined in Sec. 10.2 as

$$dU = \mathbf{F} \cdot d\mathbf{r} \qquad (10.1)$$

The work of $\mathbf{F}$ corresponding to a finite displacement of the particle from A_1 to A_2 (Fig. 10.10a) is denoted by $U_{1 \to 2}$ and is obtained by integrating (10.1) along the curve described by the particle:

$$U_{1 \to 2} = \int_{A_1}^{A_2} \mathbf{F} \cdot d\mathbf{r} \qquad (10.11)$$

Using the alternate expression

$$dU = F \, ds \cos \alpha \qquad (10.1')$$

given in Sec. 10.2 for the elementary work dU, we may also express the work $U_{1 \to 2}$ as

$$U_{1 \to 2} = \int_{s_1}^{s_2} (F \cos \alpha) \, ds \qquad (10.11')$$

where the variable of integration s measures the distance along the path traveled by the particle. The work $U_{1 \to 2}$ is represented by the area under the curve obtained by plotting $F \cos \alpha$ against s (Fig. 10.10b). In the case of a force $\mathbf{F}$ of constant magnitude acting in the direction of motion, formula (10.11$'$) yields $U_{1 \to 2} = F(s_2 - s_1)$.

Recalling from Sec. 10.2 that the work of a couple of moment $\mathbf{M}$ during an infinitesimal rotation $d\theta$ of a rigid body is

$$dU = M \, d\theta \qquad (10.2)$$

we express as follows the work of the couple during a finite rotation of the body:

$$U_{1 \to 2} = \int_{\theta_1}^{\theta_2} M \, d\theta \qquad (10.12)$$

In the case of a constant couple, formula (10.12) yields

$$U_{1 \to 2} = M(\theta_2 - \theta_1)$$

Work of a Weight. It was stated in Sec. 10.2 that the work of the weight $\mathbf{W}$ of a body during an infinitesimal displacement of the body is equal to the product of W and of the vertical displacement of the center of gravity of the body. With the y axis pointing upward, the work of $\mathbf{W}$ during a finite displacement of the body (Fig. 10.11) is obtained by writing

$$dU = -W \, dy$$

Integrating from A_1 to A_2, we have

$$U_{1 \to 2} = -\int_{y_1}^{y_2} W \, dy = Wy_1 - Wy_2 \qquad (10.13)$$

or

$$U_{1 \to 2} = -W(y_2 - y_1) = -W \, \Delta y \qquad (10.13')$$

where Δy is the vertical displacement from A_1 to A_2. The work of the weight **W** is thus equal to *the product of W and of the vertical displacement of the center of gravity of the body.* The work is *positive* when $\Delta y < 0$, that is, *when the body moves down.*

Work of the Force Exerted by a Spring. Consider a body A attached to a fixed point B by a spring; it is assumed that the spring is undeformed when the body is at A_0 (Fig. 10.12a). Experimental evidence shows that the magnitude of the force **F** exerted by the spring on a body A is proportional to the deflection x of the spring measured from the position A_0. We have

$$F = kx \qquad (10.14)$$

where k is the *spring constant*, expressed in N/m. The work of the force **F** exerted by the spring during a finite displacement of the body from $A_1(x = x_1)$ to $A_2(x = x_2)$ is obtained by writing

$$dU = -F \, dx = -kx \, dx$$

$$U_{1 \to 2} = -\int_{x_1}^{x_2} kx \, dx = \tfrac{1}{2}kx_1^2 - \tfrac{1}{2}kx_2^2 \qquad (10.15)$$

We note that the work of the force **F** exerted by the spring on the body is *positive* when $x_2 < x_1$, that is, *when the spring is returning to its undeformed position.*

Since Eq. (10.14) is the equation of a straight line of slope k passing through the origin, the work $U_{1 \to 2}$ of **F** during the displacement from A_1 to A_2 may be obtained by evaluating the area of the trapezoid shown in Fig. 10.12b. This is done by computing the values F_1 and F_2 and multiplying the base Δx of the trapezoid by its mean height $\tfrac{1}{2}(F_1 + F_2)$. Since the work of the force **F** exerted by the spring is positive for a negative value of Δx, we write

$$U_{1 \to 2} = -\tfrac{1}{2}(F_1 + F_2) \, \Delta x \qquad (10.16)$$

Formula (10.16) is usually more convenient to use than (10.15) and affords fewer chances of confusing the units involved.

Fig. 10.12

Fig. 10.11 (*repeated*)

Fig. 10.12 (*a*) (*repeated*)

10.7. Potential Energy. Considering again the body of Fig. 10.11, we note from (10.13) that the work of the weight **W** during a finite displacement is obtained by subtracting the value of the function Wy corresponding to the second position of the body from its value corresponding to the first position. The work of **W** is thus independent of the actual path followed; it depends only upon the initial and final values of the function Wy. This function is called the *potential energy* of the body with respect to the *force of gravity* **W** and is denoted by V_g. We write

$$U_{1 \to 2} = (V_g)_1 - (V_g)_2 \qquad \text{with } V_g = Wy \qquad (10.17)$$

We note that if $(V_g)_2 > (V_g)_1$, that is, *if the potential energy increases* during the displacement (as in the case considered here), *the work $U_{1 \to 2}$ is negative*. If, on the other hand, the work of **W** is positive, the potential energy decreases. Therefore, the potential energy V_g of the body provides a measure of *the work which may be done* by its weight **W**. Since only the *change* in potential energy, and not the actual value of V_g, is involved in formula (10.17), an arbitrary constant may be added to the expression obtained for V_g. In other words, the level from which the elevation y is measured may be chosen arbitrarily. Note that potential energy is expressed in the same units as work, i.e., in joules (J).†

Considering now the body of Fig. 10.12a, we note from formula (10.15) that the work of the elastic force **F** is obtained by subtracting the value of the function $\frac{1}{2}kx^2$ corresponding to the second position of the body from its value corresponding to the first position. This function is denoted by V_e and is called the *potential energy* of the body with respect to the *elastic force* **F**. We write

$$U_{1 \to 2} = (V_e)_1 - (V_e)_2 \qquad \text{with } V_e = \tfrac{1}{2}kx^2 \qquad (10.18)$$

and observe that during the displacement considered, the work of the force **F** exerted by the spring on the body is negative and the potential energy V_e increases. We should note that the expression obtained for V_e is valid only if the deflection of the spring is measured from its undeformed position.

The concept of potential energy may be used when forces other than gravity forces and elastic forces are involved. It remains valid as long as the elementary work dU of the force considered is an *exact differential*. It is then possible to find a function V, called potential energy, such that

$$dU = -dV \qquad (10.19)$$

Integrating (10.19) over a finite displacement, we obtain the general formula

$$U_{1 \to 2} = V_1 - V_2 \qquad (10.20)$$

†See footnote, page 427.

which expresses that *the work of the force is independent of the path followed and is equal to minus the change in potential energy*. A force which satisfies Eq. (10.20) is said to be a *conservative force*.†

* 10.8. Potential Energy and Equilibrium. The application of the principle of virtual work is considerably simplified when the potential energy of a system is known. In the case of a virtual displacement, formula (10.19) becomes $\delta U = -\delta V$. Besides, if the position of the system is defined by a single independent variable θ, we may write $\delta V = (dV/d\theta)\,\delta\theta$. Since $\delta\theta$ must be different from zero, the condition $\delta U = 0$ for the equilibrium of the system becomes

$$\frac{dV}{d\theta} = 0 \tag{10.21}$$

In terms of potential energy, the principle of virtual work states therefore that *if a system is in equilibrium, the derivative of its total potential energy is zero*. If the position of the system depends upon several independent variables (the system is then said to possess *several degrees of freedom*), the partial derivatives of V with respect to each of the independent variables must be zero.

Consider, for example, a structure made of two members AC and CB and carrying a load W at C. The structure is supported by a pin at A and a roller at B, and a spring BD connects B to a fixed point D (Fig. 10.13a). The constant of the spring is k, and it is assumed that the natural length of the spring is equal to AD and thus that the spring is undeformed when B coincides with A. Neglecting the friction forces and the weight of the members, we find that the only forces which work during a displacement of the structure are the weight **W** and the force **F** exerted by the spring at point B (Fig. 10.13b). The total potential energy of the system will thus be obtained by adding the potential energy V_g corresponding to the gravity force **W** and the potential energy V_e corresponding to the elastic force **F**.

Choosing a coordinate system with origin at A and noting that the deflection of the spring, measured from its undeformed position, is $AB = x_B$, we write

$$V_e = \tfrac{1}{2}kx_B^2 \qquad V_g = Wy_C$$

Expressing the coordinates x_B and y_C in terms of the angle θ, we have

$$x_B = 2l \sin\theta \qquad y_C = l \cos\theta$$
$$V_e = \tfrac{1}{2}k(2l \sin\theta)^2 \qquad V_g = W(l\cos\theta)$$
$$V = V_e + V_g = 2kl^2 \sin^2\theta + Wl\cos\theta \tag{10.22}$$

The positions of equilibrium of the system are obtained by equating to zero the derivative of the potential energy V. We write

$$\frac{dV}{d\theta} = 4kl^2 \sin\theta \cos\theta - Wl\sin\theta = 0$$

† A detailed discussion of conservative forces is given in Sec. 13.7 of *Dynamics*.

(a)

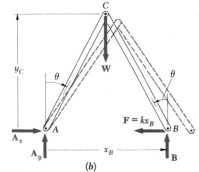

(b)

Fig. 10.13

or, factoring $l \sin \theta$,

$$\frac{dV}{d\theta} = l \sin \theta (4kl \cos \theta - W) = 0$$

There are therefore two positions of equilibrium, corresponding respectively to the values $\theta = 0$ and $\theta = \cos^{-1}(W/4kl)$.†

*10.9. Stability of Equilibrium. Consider the three uniform rods of length $2a$ and weight $\mathbf{W}$ shown in Fig. 10.14. While each rod is in equilibrium, there is an important difference between the three cases considered. Suppose that each rod is slightly disturbed from its position of equilibrium and then released: rod a will move back toward its original position, rod b will keep moving away from its original position, and rod c will remain in its new position. In case a, the equilibrium of the rod is said to be *stable;* in case b, the equilibrium is said to be *unstable;* and, in case c, to be *neutral.*

Fig. 10.14   (*a*) Stable equilibrium   (*b*) Unstable equilibrium   (*c*) Neutral equilibrium

Recalling from Sec. 10.7 that the potential energy V_g with respect to gravity is equal to Wy, where y is the elevation of the point of application of $\mathbf{W}$ measured from an arbitrary level, we observe that the potential energy of rod a is minimum in the position of equilibrium considered, that the potential energy of rod b is maximum, and that the potential energy of rod c is constant. Equilibrium is thus *stable, unstable,* or *neutral* according to whether the potential energy is *minimum, maximum,* or *constant* (Fig. 10.15).

That the result obtained is quite general may be seen as follows: We first observe that a force always tends to do positive work and thus to decrease the potential energy of the system on which it is applied. Therefore, when a system is disturbed from its position of equilibrium, the forces acting on the system will tend to bring it back to its original position if V is minimum (Fig. 10.15a) and to move it farther away if V is maximum (Fig. 10.15b). If V is constant (Fig. 10.15c), the forces will not tend to move the system either way.

†The second position does not exist if $W > 4kl$ (see Prob. 10.80 for a further discussion of the equilibrium of this system).

Recalling from calculus that a function is minimum or maximum according to whether its second derivative is positive or negative, we may summarize as follows the conditions for the equilibrium of a system with one degree of freedom (i.e., a system the position of which is defined by a single independent variable θ):

$$\frac{dV}{d\theta} = 0 \qquad \frac{d^2V}{d\theta^2} > 0: \text{ stable equilibrium}$$

$$\frac{dV}{d\theta} = 0 \qquad \frac{d^2V}{d\theta^2} < 0: \text{ unstable equilibrium}$$

(10.23)

If both the first and the second derivatives of V are zero, it is necessary to examine derivatives of a higher order to determine whether the equilibrium is stable, unstable, or neutral. The equilibrium will be neutral if all

Fig. 10.15 (*a*) Stable equilibrium   (*b*) Unstable equilibrium   (*c*) Neutral equilibrium

derivatives are zero, since the potential energy V is then a constant. The equilibrium will be stable if the first derivative found to be different from zero is of even order, and if that derivative is positive. In all other cases the equilibrium will be unstable.

If the system considered possesses *several degrees of freedom*, the potential energy V depends upon several variables and it is thus necessary to apply the theory of functions of several variables to determine whether V is minimum. It may be verified that a system with two degrees of freedom will be stable, and the corresponding potential energy $V(\theta_1, \theta_2)$ will be minimum, if the following relations are satisfied simultaneously:

$$\frac{\partial V}{\partial \theta_1} = \frac{\partial V}{\partial \theta_2} = 0$$

$$\left(\frac{\partial^2 V}{\partial \theta_1 \partial \theta_2}\right)^2 - \frac{\partial^2 V}{\partial \theta_1^2} \frac{\partial^2 V}{\partial \theta_2^2} < 0$$

(10.24)

$$\frac{\partial^2 V}{\partial \theta_1^2} > 0 \qquad \text{or} \qquad \frac{\partial^2 V}{\partial \theta_2^2} > 0$$

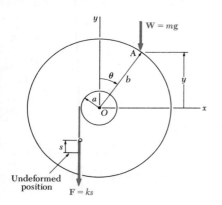

SAMPLE PROBLEM 10.4

A 10-kg block is attached to the rim of a 300-mm-radius disk as shown. Knowing that spring BC is unstretched when $\theta = 0$, determine the position or positions of equilibrium, and state in each case whether the equilibrium is stable, unstable, or neutral.

Potential Energy. Denoting by s the deflection of the spring from its undeformed position and placing the origin of coordinates at O, we obtain

$$V_e = \tfrac{1}{2}ks^2 \qquad V_g = Wy = mgy$$

Measuring θ in radians, we have

$$s = a\theta \qquad y = b\cos\theta$$

Substituting for s and y in the expressions for V_e and V_g, we write

$$V_e = \tfrac{1}{2}ka^2\theta^2 \qquad V_g = mgb\cos\theta$$
$$V = V_e + V_g = \tfrac{1}{2}ka^2\theta^2 + mgb\cos\theta$$

Positions of Equilibrium. Setting $dV/d\theta = 0$, we write

$$\frac{dV}{d\theta} = ka^2\theta - mgb\sin\theta = 0$$

$$\sin\theta = \frac{ka^2}{mgb}\theta$$

Substituting $a = 0.08$ m, $b = 0.3$ m, $k = 4$ kN/m, and $m = 10$ kg, we obtain

$$\sin\theta = \frac{(4\text{ kN/m})(0.08\text{ m})^2}{(10\text{ kg})(9.81\text{ m/s}^2)(0.3\text{ m})}\theta$$

$$\sin\theta = 0.8699\,\theta$$

where θ is expressed in radians. Solving by trial for θ, we find

$$\theta = 0 \qquad \text{and} \qquad \theta = 0.902\text{ rad}$$
$$\theta = 0 \qquad \text{and} \qquad \theta = 51.7° \quad \blacktriangleleft$$

Stability of Equilibrium. The second derivative of the potential energy V with respect to θ is

$$\frac{d^2V}{d\theta^2} = ka^2 - mgb\cos\theta$$

$$= (4\text{ kN/m})(0.08\text{ m})^2 - (10\text{ kg})(9.81\text{ m/s}^2)(0.3\text{ m})\cos\theta$$

$$= 25.6 - 29.43\cos\theta$$

For $\theta = 0$: $\quad \dfrac{d^2V}{d\theta^2} = 25.6 - 29.43\cos 0° = -3.83 < 0$

The equilibrium is unstable for $\theta = 0°$ $\quad \blacktriangleleft$

For $\theta = 51.7°$: $\quad \dfrac{d^2V}{d\theta^2} = 25.6 - 29.43\cos 51.7° = +7.36 > 0$

The equilibrium is stable for $\theta = 51.7°$ $\quad \blacktriangleleft$

Problems

10.48 Using the method of Sec. 10.8, solve Prob. 10.28.

10.49 Using the method of Sec. 10.8, solve Prob. 10.29.

10.50 Using the method of Sec. 10.8, solve Prob. 10.26.

10.51 Using the method of Sec. 10.8, solve Prob. 10.25.

10.52 Show that the equilibrium is neutral in Prob. 10.2.

10.53 Show that the equilibrium is neutral in Prob. 10.4.

10.54 Two uniform rods, each of mass m, are attached to gears of equal radii as shown. Determine the positions of equilibrium of the system and state in each case whether the equilibrium is stable, unstable, or neutral.

Fig. P10.54 and P10.55

10.55 Two uniform rods, AB and CD, are attached to gears of equal radii as shown. Knowing that $m_{AB} = 300$ g and $m_{CD} = 500$ g, determine the positions of equilibrium of the system and state in each case whether the equilibrium is stable, unstable, or neutral.

10.56 Two uniform rods, AB and CD, of the same length l, are attached to gears as shown. Knowing that rod AB has a mass of 3 kg and that rod CD has a mass of 2 kg, determine the positions of equilibrium of the system and state in each case whether the equilibrium is stable, unstable, or neutral.

Fig. P10.56

10.57 Solve Prob. 10.56, assuming that rods AB and CD have masses of 3 kg.

10.58 Using the method of Sec. 10.8, solve Prob. 10.30. Determine whether the equilibrium is stable, unstable, or neutral. (*Hint.* The potential energy corresponding to the couple exerted by a torsion spring is $\frac{1}{2}K\theta^2$, where K is the torsional spring constant and θ is the angle of twist.)

10.59 In Prob. 10.31, determine whether each of the positions of equilibrium is stable, unstable, or neutral. (See hint of Prob. 10.58.)

10.60 A load **W** of magnitude 720 N is applied to the mechanism at C. Neglecting the weight of the mechanism, determine the value of θ corresponding to equilibrium and check that the equilibrium is stable. The constant of the spring is $k = 3500$ N/m, and the spring is unstretched when $\theta = 0$.

10.61 Solve Prob. 10.60, assuming that the spring is unstretched when $\theta = 30°$.

Fig. P10.60

10.62 A collar B, of weight W, may move freely along the vertical rod shown. The constant of the spring is k and the spring is unstretched when $y = 0$. (a) Derive an equation in y, W, a, and k which must be satisfied when the collar is in equilibrium. (b) Determine the value of y corresponding to equilibrium when $W = 80$ N, $a = 300$ mm, and $k = 500$ N/m, and check that the equilibrium is stable.

Fig. P10.62

10.63 A slender rod AB, of weight W, is attached to blocks A and B which may move freely in the guides shown. The constant of the spring is k and the spring is unstretched when AB is horizontal. Neglecting the weight of the blocks, derive an equation in θ, W, l, and k which must be satisfied when the rod is in equilibrium.

Fig. P10.63

10.64 In Prob. 10.63, determine three values of θ corresponding to equilibrium when $W = 45$ N, $k = 300$ N/m, and $l = 0.5$ m. State in each case whether the equilibrium is stable, unstable, or neutral.

10.65 The constant of spring AB is k and the spring is unstretched when $\theta = 0$, (a) Neglecting the weight of the rigid arm BCD, derive an equation in θ, k, a, l, and m which must be satisfied when the arm is in equilibrium. (b) Determine three values of θ corresponding to equilibrium when $k = 13$ kN/m, $a = 250$ mm, $l = 375$ mm, and $m = 45$ kg. State in each case whether the equilibrium is stable, unstable, or neutral.

Fig. P10.65

Fig. P10.66

10.66 Bar ABC is attached to collars A and B which may move freely on the rods shown. The constant of the spring is k and the spring is unstretched when $\theta = 0$. (a) Neglecting the weight of bar ABC, derive an equation in θ, m, k, and l which must be satisfied when bar ABC is in equilibrium. (b) Determine the value of θ corresponding to equilibrium when $m = 5$ kg, $k = 800$ N/m, and $l = 250$ mm, and check that the equilibrium is stable.

10.67 Solve Prob. 10.66, assuming that the spring is unstretched when $\theta = 30°$.

10.68 A vertical load **P** is applied at end B of rod BC. The constant of the spring is k and the spring is unstretched when $\theta = 60°$. (a) Neglecting the weight of the rod, express the angle θ corresponding to equilibrium in terms of P, k, and l. (b) Determine the values of θ corresponding to equilibrium when $P = 250$ N, $k = 4400$ N/m, and $l = 200$ mm. State in each case whether the equilibrium is stable, unstable, or neutral.

10.69 A vertical load **P** of magnitude 600 N is applied at end B of rod BC. The constant of the spring is $k = 4400$ N/m, and the spring is unstretched when $\theta = 60°$. Neglecting the weight of the rod and knowing that $l = 200$ mm, determine the value of θ corresponding to equilibrium. State whether the equilibrium is stable, unstable, or neutral.

Fig. P10.68 and P10.69

10.70 A vertical load **P** is applied at end B of rod BC. The constant of the spring is k and the spring is unstretched when $\theta = 0$. (a) Neglecting the weight of the rod, express the angle θ corresponding to the equilibrium position in terms of P, k, and l. (b) Determine the value of θ corresponding to equilibrium when $P = 400$ N, $k = 800$ N/m, and $l = 250$ mm.

Fig. P10.70

Fig. P10.71

10.71 A vertical load **P** is applied at end B of rod BC. (a) Neglecting the weight of the rod, express the angle θ corresponding to the equilibrium position in terms of P, l, and the counterweight W. (b) Determine the value of θ corresponding to equilibrium when $P = 400$ N, $W = 200$ N, and $l = 250$ mm.

10.72 The rod AB is attached to a hinge at A and to two springs, each of constant k. If $h = 600$ mm, $d = 300$ mm, and $m = 75$ kg, determine the range of values of k for which the equilibrium of rod AB is stable in the position shown. Each spring can act in either tension or compression.

10.73 If $m = 60$ kg, $h = 900$ mm, and the constant of each spring is $k = 2.5$ kN/m, determine the range of values of the distance d for which the equilibrium of rod AB is stable in the position shown. Each spring can act in either tension or compression.

Fig. P10.72 and P10.73

Fig. P10.74

10.74 Two bars AB and BC of negligible weight are attached to a single spring of constant k which is undeformed when the bars are horizontal. Determine the range of values of the magnitude P of the two equal and opposite forces $\mathbf{P}$ and $-\mathbf{P}$ for which the equilibrium of the system is stable in the position shown.

10.75 Bars BC and EF are connected at G by a pin which is attached to BC and may slide freely in a slot cut in EF. Determine the smallest mass m_1 for which the equilibrium of the mechanism is stable in the position shown.

*10.76 and 10.77 The bars shown, each of length l and of negligible weight, are attached to springs each of constant k. The springs are undeformed and the system is in equilibrium when $\theta_1 = \theta_2 = 0$. Determine the range of values of P for which the equilibrium position is stable.

Fig. P10.75

Fig. P10.76

Fig. P10.77

*10.78 Solve Prob. 10.77, knowing that $l = 0.75$ mm and $k = 8750$ N/m.

*10.79 Solve Prob. 10.76, assuming that the vertical force applied at B is increased to $5\mathbf{P}$.

10.80 In Sec. 10.8, two positions of equilibrium were obtained for the system shown in Fig. 10.13, namely, $\theta = 0$ and $\theta = \cos^{-1}(W/4kl)$. Show that (a) if $W < 4kl$, the equilibrium is stable in the first position ($\theta = 0$) and unstable in the second, (b) if $W = 4kl$, the two positions coincide and the equilibrium is unstable, (c) if $W > 4kl$, the equilibrium is unstable in the first position ($\theta = 0$) and the second position does not exist. (*Note.* It is assumed that the system must deform as shown and that the system cannot rotate as a single rigid body about A when A and B coincide.)

Review and Summary

The first part of this chapter was devoted to the *principle of virtual work* and to its direct application to the solution of equilibrium problems. We first defined the *work of a force* **F** *corresponding to the small displacement d***r** [Sec. 10.2] as the quantity

$$dU = \mathbf{F} \cdot d\mathbf{r} \qquad (10.1)$$

obtained by forming the scalar product of the force **F** and of the displacement *d***r** (Fig. 10.16). Denoting respectively by F and ds the magnitudes of the force and of the displacement, and by α the angle formed by **F** and *d***r**, we wrote

$$dU = F \, ds \cos \alpha \qquad (10.1')$$

The work dU is positive if $\alpha < 90°$, zero if $\alpha = 90°$, and negative if $\alpha > 90°$. We also found that the *work of a couple of moment* **M** acting on a rigid body is

$$dU = M \, d\theta \qquad (10.2)$$

where $d\theta$ is the small angle expressed in radians through which the body rotates.

Considering a particle located at A and acted upon by several forces $\mathbf{F}_1, \mathbf{F}_2, \ldots, \mathbf{F}_n$ [Sec. 10.3], we imagined that the particle moved to a new position A' (Fig. 10.17). Since this displacement did not actually take place, it was referred to as a *virtual displacement* and denoted by $\delta\mathbf{r}$, while the corresponding work of the forces was called *virtual work* and denoted by δU. We had

$$\delta U = \mathbf{F}_1 \cdot \delta\mathbf{r} + \mathbf{F}_2 \cdot \delta\mathbf{r} + \cdots + \mathbf{F}_n \cdot \delta\mathbf{r}$$

The *principle of virtual work* states that, *if a particle is in equilibrium, the total virtual work* δU *of the forces acting on the particle is zero for any virtual displacement of the particle.*

The principle of virtual work may be extended to the case of rigid bodies and systems of rigid bodies. Since it involves *only forces which do work*, its application provides a useful alternative to the use of the equilibrium equations in the solution of many engineering problems. It is particularly effective in the case of machines and mechanisms consisting of connected rigid bodies, since the work of the reactions at the supports is zero and the work of the internal forces at the pin connections cancels out [Sec. 10.4; Sample Probs. 10.1, 10.2, and 10.3].

Work of a force

Fig. 10.16

Virtual displacement

Principle of virtual work

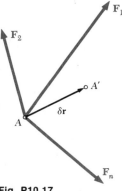

Fig. P10.17

Mechanical efficiency

Work of a force over a finite displacement

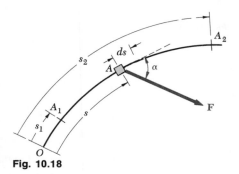

Fig. 10.18

Work of a weight

In the case of *real machines*, however [Sec. 10.5], the work of the friction forces should be taken into account, with the result that the *output work will be less than the input work*. Defining the *mechanical efficiency* of a machine as the ratio

$$\eta = \frac{\text{output work}}{\text{input work}} \tag{10.9}$$

we also noted that for an ideal machine (no friction) $\eta = 1$, while for a real machine $\eta < 1$.

In the second part of the chapter we considered the *work of forces corresponding to finite displacements* of their points of application. The work $U_{1 \to 2}$ of the force $\mathbf{F}$ corresponding to a displacement of the particle A from A_1 to A_2 (Fig. 10.18) was obtained by integrating the right-hand member of Eq. (10.1) or (10.1') along the curve described by the particle [Sec. 10.6]:

$$U_{1 \to 2} = \int_{A_1}^{A_2} \mathbf{F} \cdot d\mathbf{r} \tag{10.11}$$

or

$$U_{1 \to 2} = \int_{s_1}^{s_2} (F \cos \alpha) \, ds \tag{10.11'}$$

Similarly, the work of a couple of moment $\mathbf{M}$ corresponding to a finite rotation from θ_1 to θ_2 of a rigid body was expressed as

$$U_{1 \to 2} = \int_{\theta_1}^{\theta_2} M \, d\theta \tag{10.12}$$

The *work of the weight* $\mathbf{W}$ *of a body* as its center of gravity moves from the elevation y_1 to y_2 (Fig. 10.19) may be obtained by making $F = W$ and $\alpha = 180°$ in Eq. (10.11'):

$$U_{1 \to 2} = -\int_{y_1}^{y_2} W \, dy = W y_1 - W y_2 \tag{10.13}$$

The work of $\mathbf{W}$ is therefore positive *when the elevation y decreases.*

Fig. 10.19

Spring undeformed

Fig. 10.20

The *work of the force* **F** *exerted by a spring* on a body A as the spring is stretched from x_1 to x_2 (Fig. 10.20) may be obtained by making $F = kx$, where k is the constant of the spring, and $\alpha = 180°$ in Eq. (10.11′):

$$U_{1\to2} = -\int_{x_1}^{x_2} kx \, dx = \tfrac{1}{2}kx_1^2 - \tfrac{1}{2}kx_2^2 \qquad (10.15)$$

The work of **F** is therefore positive *when the spring is returning to its undeformed position.*

Work of the force exerted by a spring

When the work of a force **F** is independent of the path actually followed between A_1 and A_2, the force is said to be a *conservative force* and its work may be expressed as

$$U_{1\to2} = V_1 - V_2 \qquad (10.20)$$

where V is the *potential energy* associated with **F**, and V_1 and V_2 represent the values of V at A_1 and A_2, respectively [Sec. 10.7]. The potential energies associated, respectively, with the *force of gravity* **W** and the *elastic force* **F** exerted by a spring were found to be

$$V_g = Wy \qquad \text{and} \qquad V_e = \tfrac{1}{2}kx^2 \qquad (10.17, \ 10.18)$$

Potential energy

When the position of a mechanical system depends upon a single independent variable θ, the potential energy of the system is a function $V(\theta)$ of that variable and it follows from Eq. (10.20) that $\delta U = -\delta V = -(dV/d\theta)\,\delta\theta$. The condition $\delta U = 0$ required by the principle of virtual work for the equilibrium of the system may thus be replaced by the condition

$$\frac{dV}{d\theta} = 0 \qquad (10.21)$$

Alternative expression for the principle of virtual work

The use of Eq. (10.21) may be preferred to the direct application of the principle of virtual work when all the forces involved are conservative [Sec. 10.8; Sample Prob. 10.4].

Stability of equilibrium

This approach presents another advantage, since it is possible to determine from the sign of the second derivative of V whether the equilibrium of the system is *stable*, *unstable*, or *neutral* [Sec. 10.9]. If $d^2V/d\theta^2 > 0$, V is *minimum* and the equilibrium is *stable*; if $d^2V/d\theta^2 < 0$, V is *maximum* and the equilibrium is *unstable*; if $d^2V/d\theta^2 = 0$, it is necessary to examine derivatives of a higher order.

Review Problems

10.81 A spring AB of constant k is attached to two identical gears as shown. A uniform bar CD of mass m is supported by cords wrapped around drums of radius b which are attached to the gears. If the spring is undeformed when $\theta = 0$, obtain an equation defining the angle θ corresponding to the equilibrium position.

Fig. P10.81

10.82 For the mechanism of Prob. 10.81 the following numerical values are given: $k = 5$ kN/m, $a = 80$ mm, $b = 60$ mm, $r = 120$ mm, and $m = 60$ kg. Determine the values of θ corresponding to equilibrium positions and state in each case whether the equilibrium is stable, unstable, or neutral.

10.83 Collar B may slide along rod AC and is attached by a pin to a block which may slide in the vertical slot. Derive an expression for the magnitude of the couple **M** required to maintain equilibrium.

10.84 Determine the value of θ corresponding to the equilibrium position of rod AC when $R = 300$ mm, $P = 300$ N, and $M = 100$ N·m.

Fig. P10.83 and P10.84

10.85 Determine the mass m which balances the 6-kg block.

Fig. P10.85

Fig. P10.86

10.86 Knowing that rod AB is of length $2l$, derive an expression for the magnitude of the couple **M** required to maintain equilibrium.

10.87 The mechanism shown is acted upon by the force **P**; derive an expression for the magnitude of the force **Q** required to maintain equilibrium.

Fig. P10.87

Fig. P10.88

10.88 The horizontal bar AD is attached to two springs of constant k and is in equilibrium in the position shown. Determine the range of values of the magnitude P of the two equal and opposite *horizontal* forces **P** and $-$**P** for which the equilibrium position is stable (*a*) if $AB = CD$, (*b*) if $AB = 2(CD)$.

10.89 (*a*) Derive an equation defining the angle θ corresponding to the equilibrium position. (*b*) Determine the angle θ corresponding to equilibrium if $P = 2W$.

10.90 Two bars ABC and CD are attached to a single spring of constant k which is unstretched when the bars are vertical. Determine the range of values of P for which the equilibrium of the system is stable in the position shown.

Fig. P10.89

Fig. P10.90

10.91 Rod AD is acted upon by a vertical force **P** at end A and by two equal and opposite horizontal forces of magnitude Q at points B and C. Derive an expression for the magnitude Q of the horizontal forces required for equilibrium.

Fig. P10.91

Fig. P10.92

10.92 A slender rod AB, of weight W, is attached to blocks A and B which move freely in the guides shown. The blocks are connected by an elastic cord which passes over a pulley at C. (a) Express the tension in the cord in terms of W and θ. (b) Determine the value of θ for which the tension in the cord is equal to $2W$.

The following problems are designed to be solved with a computer.

10.C1 Using the principle of virtual work, write a computer program and use it to calculate the force in member CD for values of θ from 5 to 120° at 5° intervals.

Fig. P10.C1

Fig. P10.C2

10.C2 A couple $\mathbf{M}$ must be applied to crank AB to maintain the equilibrium of the engine system shown when a force $\mathbf{P}$ is applied to the piston. Knowing that $b = 75$ mm and $l = 200$ mm, write a computer program and use it to calculate the ratio M/P for values of θ from 0 to 180° at 10° intervals.

10.C3 The internal spring AC is of constant k and is undeformed when $\theta = 45°$. (a) Write a computer program which can be used to calculate the potential energy V of this system and its derivative $dV/d\theta$. (b) For $W = 100$ N, $a = 0.5$ m, $k = 3$ kN/m, calculate and plot the potential energy versus θ for values of θ from 0 to 50° at 5° intervals. (c) By examining the V-θ curve, determine the approximate values of θ corresponding to equilibrium and state in each case whether the equilibrium is stable, unstable, or neutral. (d) Determine, to three significant figures, the values of θ corresponding to equilibrium.

Fig. P10.C3

10.C4 A vertical load $\mathbf{W}$ is applied to the linkage at B. The constant of the spring is k, and the spring is unstretched when AB and BC are horizontal. (a) Neglecting the weight of the linkage, write a computer program which can be used to calculate the load W for which AB forms a given angle θ with the horizontal. (b) Use this program to compute W for values of θ from 0 to 80° at 5° intervals, assuming $l = 225$ mm and $k = 2$ kN/m. (c) Determine, to three significant figures, the value of θ for which the linkage is in equilibrium when $W = 900$ N, $l = 225$ mm, and $k = 2$ kN/m.

Fig. P10.C4

How to Use the Interactive Software

A.1. Introduction. A diskette containing interactive software is available from the publisher. This software includes 12 "Tutorials," each consisting of a problem in staties for which students are more likely to require additional help. All the tutorials were designed by the authors of this text, programmed by EnginComp Software, Inc., and should be easy to use and understand.

A.2. Equipment. This software is designed for an IBM PC or compatible computer with at least 256K of memory and DOS 2.0 and higher. Your IBM PC compatible must also have a graphics display card equivalent to the IBM color/graphics adapter.

A.3. Getting Started. In order to start the Supplementary Tutorial program, your system must be activated and the DOS version you are using must be loaded into the computer. Insert your tutorial disk into the A drive and type "A:". The computer should then prompt you with "A⟩". Simply type "TUTORIAL" following this prompt to enter the program.

The program will display a title page, and at the bottom of the screen it will type "PRESS ANY KEY TO CONTINUE". Throughout the tutorials, all inputs required and key strokes will be specified at the bottom of the screen in a similar fashion.

After striking any key, the program will display the main menu, from which all the tutorials can be accessed. The cursor can be moved by using the [↓] and [↑] arrow keys or by typing the number corresponding to your choice. Selections are made by striking the [F10] key when your choice is highlighted.

A.4. Inside the Tutorials. Once you have made your choice of tutorial on the main menu and pressed [F10], the program will show you the tutorial title page on the bottom half of the screen, and a "Help" screen on the top half. This "Help" screen lists all the special function keys and an explanation of their action. It can be displayed at any time during the program by simply striking [F1].

In a similar fashion, you can exit the tutorial at any time by striking the [Esc] key. The program will then ask you to strike [F10] if you want

459

to exit to the main menu, or any other key to continue. This prevents accidental termination of a tutorial.

The title page of each tutorial is followed by the statement of the problem, and you will be asked to select part of the data involved. This is done by entering each item and striking the [F10] key after all the data has been entered.

In several instances, and after giving a wrong answer, you will be invited to strike the [F2] key to obtain an explanatory comment before trying again or proceeding with the solution.

You may review your progress at any time by striking the [Home] key and then [F10]. This will return you to the beginning of the tutorial. Striking [F10] repeatedly will then enable you to review rapidly your solution up to the point that you had reached.

In the course of a tutorial you will sometimes encounter calculations requiring the use of a hand calculator. You will then be asked whether you wish to perform these calculations yourself, thus getting additional practical experience, or whether you wish your "Tutor"—i.e., the computer—to do the calculations for you, saving you time and effort.

At the end of each tutorial, you will be asked if you wish to try again the tutorial with some different data. Entering a "Y" (for yes) will take you to the beginning of the tutorial, while entering an "N" (for no) will take you back to the main menu.

Sometimes it is convenient to have a hard copy of tutorial screens. In order to do this, you must have a printer that can handle text and graphics information. Also, you must run the DOS Graphics program before starting the tutorials. In order to get a hard copy, simply strike the [Shift] [Prt Sc] keys.

A.5. Keeping Score of Your Correct Answers. The computer will keep score of your correct answers in the upper right-hand corner of the screen. The use of the [F9] key to supply the correct answer will count against your score, while the use of the [F10] key to review your progress will have no effect on your score at all. Your score will not be affected either, if you choose to have your "Tutor" perform the calculations for you when given that choice. However, if you choose to do the calculations yourself, your score will reflect the accuracy of your computations.

A.6. Exiting the Tutorials. To exit the tutorials, simply get back to the main menu, select the option "Exit Statics Tutorial," using the arrow keys or striking the [Esc] key, and then press [F10]. Always exit the tutorials before turning off your computer.

Index

Answers to Selected Problems†

CHAPTER 2

2.2 1391 N $\angle$ 47.8°

2.4 40.1 kN $\nearrow$ 3.8°

2.6 7.61°

2.8 (a) 3660 N (b) 3730 N

2.10 (a) 5.85 kN (b) 8.96 kN

2.12 $T_{AC} = 3330$ N; $\alpha = 34.3°$

2.16 (a) 90° (b) 1545 N

2.18 (350 N) +317 N, +147.9 N; (800 N) +274 N, +752 N; (600 N) −300 N, +520 N

2.20 (725 N) +500 N +525 N; (1000 N) +960 N, −280 N

2.22 (a) 2190 N (b) 2060 N

2.24 −879 N, +2460 N

2.28 1264 N $\nearrow$ 86.7°

2.30 1480 N $\nearrow$ 9.53°

2.32 (a) 889 N (b) 2050 N

2.34 (a) 26.8 (b) 539 N

2.36 $T_{AC} = 586$ N; $T_{BC} = 2190$ N

2.38 $T_{AC} = 12470$ N; $T_{BC} = 6370$ N

2.42 $T_B = 83.6$ kN, $T_D = 70.0$ kN

2.44 287 N $\leqslant p \leqslant$ 1600 N

2.46 (a) 784 N (b) 71.0°

2.48 1235 mm

2.50 (b) 817 N (d) 613 N

2.52 724 N $\angle$ 53.4° or 1774 N $\measuredangle$ 53.4°

2.54 27.4° < α < 222.6°

2.56 (a) −130.1 N, +816 N, +357 N (b) 98.3°, 25.0°, 66.6°

2.58 (a) +628 N, −400 N, +293 N (b) 38.3°, 120.0°, 68.5°

2.60 (a) +81.9 N, +173.2 N, −57.4 N (b) 65.8°, 30.0°, 106.7°

2.62 $F = 4750$ N; $\theta_x = 43.4°$, $\theta_y = 71.6°$, $\theta_z = 127.6°$

2.64 (a) $F_y = +654$ N, $F_z = +1186$ N; $F = 1549$ N (b) 119.0°

2.66 +250 N, +500 N, −500 N

2.68 −1350 N, +900 N, −1380 N

2.70 $R = 1171$ N; $\theta_x = 89.5°$, $\theta_y = 36.2°$, $\theta_z = 126.2°$

2.72 (a) $R = 411$ N; $\theta_x = 87.1°$, $\theta_y = 161.5°$, $\theta_z = 71.7°$ (b) $x = 31.7$ mm, $z = 198.8$ mm

2.74 548 N

2.78 9.71 kN

2.80 $T_{AB} = T_{AC} = 13.50$ kN; $T_{AD} = 20.0$ kN

2.82 (a) −(25.2 kN)$\mathbf{i}$ (b) $T_{AB} = 2.25$ kN; $T_{AC} = 16.65$ kN

2.84 $T_{AD} = 62.9$ N; $T_{BD} = T_{CD} = 57.9$ N

2.86 $T_{AD} = 376$ N; $T_{AC} = 49.4$ N

2.88 (a) 135 N (b) $T_{AB} = 156$ N; $T_{AC} = 261$ N

2.90 1372 N

2.92 (a) 1525 N (b) $T_{AD} = 205$ N; $T_{BAC} = 585$ N

2.94 (a) 550 N (b) 100 N

2.96 (a) $W = \frac{1}{2}P\sqrt{1 + (d/h)^2}$ (b) 75.6 mm

2.98 841 N $\nearrow$ 13.5°

2.100 1210 N

2.102 $T_{AC} = 134.6$ N; $T_{BC} = 110.4$ N

2.104 41.9°

2.106 61.0°; +507 N, +919 N, +582 N

2.C2 $\beta = 10°$: $F = 1012$ N, $\alpha = 69.7°$; or $F = 2850$ N, $\alpha = -69.7°$

2.C3 $a = 0.8$ m: $h = 2.25$ m, $P = 189.1$ N, $T = 544$ N; $a = 2$ m: $h = 2.95$ m, $P = 634$ N, $T = 729$ N

2.C4 (b) $R = 1025$ N; $\theta_x = 59.8°$, $\theta_y = 66.8°$, $\theta_z = 39.7°$

CHAPTER 3

3.2 14.46 N · m $\downarrow$.

3.4 $P = 400$ N; $\alpha = 22.6°$

3.6 (a) 41.7 N · m $\nwarrow$. (b) 147.4 N $\angle$ 45°

3.8 140.0 N · m $\nwarrow$.

3.10 324 N · m $\downarrow$·

3.14 $\mathbf{M}_O = \dfrac{P(x_1 y_2 - x_2 y_1)\mathbf{k}}{[(x_2 - x_1)^2 + (y_2 - y_1)^2]^{1/2}}$

3.18 (1200 N · m)$\mathbf{i}$ − (1500 N · m)$\mathbf{j}$ − (900 N · m)$\mathbf{k}$

3.20 (6000 N · m)$\mathbf{j}$ + (3600 N · m)$\mathbf{k}$

3.22 1.491 m

3.30 55.4°

3.32 (a) 70.5° (b) 180.0 N

†Partial answers are provided or referenced for all problems designed to be solved with a computer.

3.34 $33.3°$

3.38 $M_x = -1283$ N $\cdot$ m; $M_y = 770$ N $\cdot$ m;
$M_z = 1824$ N $\cdot$ m

3.40 1.532 m

3.42 $+23.0$ N $\cdot$ m

3.44 -265 N $\cdot$ m

3.46 -222 N $\cdot$ m

3.48 $+Pa/\sqrt{2}$

3.52 199.4 mm

3.54 (a) 7.33 N $\cdot$ m ↖. (b) 91.6 mm

3.56 (a) 146.5 N $\cdot$ m ↖. (b) Either A and $D \measuredangle 53.1°$ or B and $C \measuredangle 53.1°$ (c) $355.$N

3.58 $M = 13.00$ N $\cdot$ m; $\theta_x = 67.4°$, $\theta_y = 90°$, $\theta_z = 22.6°$

3.60 $M = 2.72$ N $\cdot$ m; $\theta_x = 134.9°$, $\theta_y = 58.0°$, $\theta_z = 61.9°$.

3.62 (a) $\mathbf{F} = 300$ N ↓; $\mathbf{M}_B = 54$ N $\cdot$ m ↖.
(b) $\mathbf{B} = 500$ N ←; $\mathbf{C} = 500$ N →

3.64 (a) $\mathbf{F} = 300$ N ⬈ $30°$; $\mathbf{M} = 75$ N $\cdot$ m ↖.
(b) $\mathbf{B} = 800$ N ⬈ $30°$; $\mathbf{C} = 500$ N $\measuredangle 30°$

3.68 (a) 300 N $\measuredangle 50°$; 81.0 mm from A
(b) 300 N $\measuredangle 50°$; 96.8 mm below A

3.70 $\mathbf{F} = -(250$ kN$)\mathbf{j}$;
$\mathbf{M} = (15$ kN $\cdot$ m$)\mathbf{i} + (7.5$ kN $\cdot$ m$)\mathbf{k}$

3.72 $\mathbf{F} = -(12$ kN$)\mathbf{j} + (5$ kN$)\mathbf{k}$;
$\mathbf{M} = (24$ kN $\cdot$ m$)\mathbf{i} - (16$ kN $\cdot$ m$)\mathbf{j} - (38.4$ kN $\cdot$ m$)\mathbf{k}$

3.74 (a) $\mathbf{F} = -(329$ N$)\mathbf{j}$

3.76 Force-couple system at E

3.76 Loading (f)

3.80 (a) 2.00 m from front axle (b) 50 kN; 2.80 m from front axle.

3.84 (a) 1308 N $\measuredangle 66.6°$ (b) 412 mm to the right of A and 250 mm to the right of C

3.86 (a) 7.52 N $\cdot$ m ↖. (b) 25.0 N $\cdot$ m ↖. (c) 2.50 N $\cdot$ m ↘.

3.88 (a) $\mathbf{R} = P \angle \theta$; $\mathbf{M}_D^R = Pa \sin 2\theta \cos \theta$ ↘. (b) $35.3°$

3.90 $\mathbf{R} = -(300$ N$)\mathbf{i} - (240$ N$)\mathbf{j} + (25$ N$)\mathbf{k}$;
$\mathbf{M}_A^R = -(3$ N $\cdot$ m$)\mathbf{i} + (13.5$ N $\cdot$ m$)\mathbf{j} + (9$ N $\cdot$ m$)\mathbf{k}$

3.92 $\mathbf{R} = (100$ N$)\mathbf{i} - (173$ N$)\mathbf{j}$;
$\mathbf{M}_C^R = (62.4$ N $\cdot$ m$)\mathbf{i} - (60$ N $\cdot$ m$)\mathbf{k}$
(a) Neither (b) Tighten

3.94 500 kN; 2.56 m from AD and 2.00 m from DC

3.96 $F_B = 100$ kN; $F_F = 75$ kN

3.98 (a) $R = P\sqrt{3}$; $\theta_x = \theta_y = \theta_z = 54.7°$ (b) $-a$
(c) Diagonal OC

3.100 (a) $\mathbf{R} = (2Pa/\sqrt{a^2 + c^2})\mathbf{i}$;
$\mathbf{M}_O^R = (P/\sqrt{a^2 + c^2})(bc\mathbf{i} + ca\mathbf{j} - ab\mathbf{k})$
(b) $p = bc/2a$; axis of wrench is parallel to x axis at $y = \frac{1}{2}b, z = \frac{1}{2}c$.

3.102 (a) $R = 70.7$ N; $\theta_x = 90°$, $\theta_y = \theta_z = 135°$
(b) Line defined by equations $x = -2$ mm, $y = z$.

3.104 (a) $R = 56.6$ N; $\theta_x = 45°$, $\theta_y = 90°$, $\theta_z = 45°$
(b) -25 mm (c) $y = +125$ mm, $z = +137.5$ mm

3.108 (a) $\mathbf{A} = (a + b)(R/b)\mathbf{j} + (M/b)\mathbf{k}$;
$\mathbf{B} = -(aR/b)\mathbf{j} - (M/b)\mathbf{k}$ (b) $\mathbf{A} = (525$ N$)\mathbf{j} + (400$ N$)\mathbf{k}$; $\mathbf{B} = -(375$ N$)\mathbf{j} - (400$ N$)\mathbf{k}$

3.112 $M_x = 78.9$ kN $\cdot$ m, $M_y = 13.15$ kN $\cdot$ m, $M_z = -9.86$ kN $\cdot$ m.

3.114 (a) $-(144$ N $\cdot$ m$)\mathbf{i} + (576$ N $\cdot$ m$)\mathbf{j} + (864$ N $\cdot$ m$)\mathbf{k}$
(b) 371 N $\cdot$ m

3.116 103.4 N $\cdot$ m ↙.

3.118 (a) $\mathbf{F} = 500$ N ⬋ $60°$; $\mathbf{M} = 86.2$ N $\cdot$ m ↙.
(b) $\mathbf{A} = 689$ N ↑; $\mathbf{B} = 1150$ N ⬋ $77.4°$

3.120 325 kN; $x = -0.923$ m, $z = -0.615$ m

3.122 (a) $\mathbf{R} = -(250$ N$)\mathbf{k}$;
$\mathbf{M}_A^R = (30.8$ N $\cdot$ m$)\mathbf{j} - (12.00$ N $\cdot$ m$)\mathbf{k}$
(b) $p = +48.0$ mm; axis parallel to z axis at $x = 123.2$ mm, $y = 0$.

3.C1 (b) 0.550 m; 1.150 m; 1.750 m

3.C2 $\beta = 30°$: $\mathbf{R} = 165.2$ N $\measuredangle 21.3°$,
$\mathbf{M}_D = 50.9$ N $\cdot$ m ↙;
$\beta = 150°$: $\mathbf{R} = 80.7$ N ⬊ $48.1°$,
$\mathbf{M}_D = 22.6$ N $\cdot$ m ↖.

3.C3 $z = 0.200$ m: (a) $M_x = 264$ N $\cdot$ m, $M_y = 480$ N $\cdot$ m, $M_z = -432$ N $\cdot$ m, $M_O = 698$ N $\cdot$ m(b) 333 N $\cdot$ m

3.C4 (c) 350 kN; $x = +0.75$ m, $z = -0.1860$ m

CHAPTER 4

4.2 36.8 N ↑

4.4 (a) 34.0 kN ↑ (b) 4.96 kN ↑

4.6 (a) 9.20 kN ↑ (b) 3.8 kN ↑

4.8 30 kN $\leqslant P \leqslant 135$ kN

4.10 1.25 kN $\leqslant Q \leqslant 10.25$ kN

4.12 31.0 kN

4.14 (a) 750 N (b) 1566 N $\measuredangle 69.8°$

4.16 (a) 400 N (b) 458 N $\measuredangle 49.1°$

4.18 (a) $\mathbf{A} = \mathbf{B} = 187.5$ N
(b) $\mathbf{A} = 488$ N $\measuredangle 50.2°$; $\mathbf{B} = 313$ N ←
(c) $\mathbf{A} = 249$ N $\measuredangle 71.2°$; $\mathbf{B} = 160.8$ N ⬊ $60°$

4.20 (a) 255 N ⬊ $45°$ (b) 486 N ⬋ $70.9°$

4.24 (a) 600 N (b) $\mathbf{A} = 4$ kN ←; $\mathbf{B} = 4$ kN →

4.26 (a) 240 N ↑ (b) 1768 N →

4.28 238 mm

4.30 (a) $\mathbf{E} = 39.6$ kN ↑; $\mathbf{M}_E = 38.8$ kN $\cdot$ m
(b) $\mathbf{E} = 19.6$ kN ↑; $\mathbf{M}_E = 62.8$ kN $\cdot$ m

4.32 58.3 kN $\leqslant T \leqslant 141.7$ kN

4.34 $\theta = \sin^{-1}(2M \cot \alpha/Wl)$

4.36 (a) $\theta = 2 \cos^{-1}\left[\frac{1}{4}\left(\frac{W}{P} + \sqrt{\frac{W^2}{P^2} + 8}\right)\right]$. (b) $65.1°$

4.40 (a) $2 \sin \theta - \tan \theta = W/ka$ (a) 704 N/m.

4.42 (1) Completely constrained; determinate;
$\mathbf{A} = \mathbf{C} = 196.2$ N ↑. (2) Completely constrained; determinate; $\mathbf{B} = 0$, $\mathbf{C} = \mathbf{D} = 196.2$ N ↑.
(3) Completely constrained; indeterminate;

$\mathbf{A}_x = 294$ N $\rightarrow$, $\mathbf{D}_x = 294$ N $\leftarrow$. (4) Partially constrained; determinate; equal.; $\mathbf{C} = \mathbf{D} = 196.2$ N $\uparrow$. (5) Completely constrained; determinate; $\mathbf{B} = 294$ N $\rightarrow$, $\mathbf{D} = 491$ N $\seardownarrow$ 53.1°. (6) Improperly constrained; indeterminate; no equil. (9) Completely constrained; indeterminate; $\mathbf{B} = 196.2$ N $\uparrow$, $\mathbf{D}_y = 196.2$ N $\uparrow$.

4.44 $\mathbf{B} = 501$ N $\searrow$ 56.3°; $\mathbf{C} = 324$ N $\nwarrow$ 31.0°

4.48 $\mathbf{A} = 185.3$ N $\nearrow$ 62.4°; $T = 92.8$ N

4.54 $\mathbf{A} = 170$ N $\nearrow$ 56.1°; $\mathbf{C} = 300$ N $\nearrow$ 28.1°

4.56 (a) $T = 4P - 3Q$ (b) 150.0 N

4.58 $\theta = \sin^{-1}(a/L)^{1/3}$

4.60 (a) 81.3 N $\searrow$ 39.3° (b) 407 N $\nearrow$ 72.0°

4.62 23.2°

4.64 $\mathbf{A} = (120.0$ N$)\mathbf{j} + (133.3$ N$)\mathbf{k}$; $\mathbf{D} = (60.0$ N$)\mathbf{j} + (166.7$ N$)\mathbf{k}$

4.66 (a) 480 N (b) $\mathbf{A} = (12.00$ N$)\mathbf{j}$; $\mathbf{B} = (1068$ N$)\mathbf{j}$

4.68 (a) 1039 N (b) $\mathbf{C} = (346$ N$)\mathbf{i} + (1200$ N$)\mathbf{j}$; $\mathbf{D} = -(1386$ N$)\mathbf{i} - (480$ N$)\mathbf{j}$

4.70 $T_A = 128.8$ N; $T_B = 42.9$ N; $T_C = 171.7$ N

4.72 10 kg; $x = 500$ mm, $z = 375$ mm

4.74 $T_{BE} = 6.62$ kN; $T_{BF} = 25.1$ kN; $\mathbf{A} = -(6.34$ kN$)\mathbf{i} + (20.3$ kN$)\mathbf{j} + (2.96$ kN$)\mathbf{k}$

4.76 (a) $T_{BE} = 11.47$ kN; $T_{BD} = 8.24$ kN (b) $\mathbf{A} = (17.65$ kN$)\mathbf{i}$

4.78 (a) 38.7° (b) 51.3°

4.80 (a) 848 N (b) $\mathbf{A} = -(436$ N$)\mathbf{j} - (614$ N$)\mathbf{k}$; $\mathbf{B} = (147.2)\mathbf{j}$

4.82 (a) 2.40 kN (b) -0.600 kN

4.84 (a) 2330 N (b) $-(141.5$ N$)\mathbf{j} + (1415$ N$)\mathbf{k}$

4.86 (a) $T_{CE} = 2110$ N; $T_{DE} = 272$ N (b) $\mathbf{A} = (1415$ N$)\mathbf{k}$; $\mathbf{B} = -(490$ N$)\mathbf{i} + (1226$ N$)\mathbf{j} + (424$ N$)\mathbf{k}$

4.88 $\mathbf{A} = -(685$ N$)\mathbf{i} + (878$ N$)\mathbf{j} - (439$ N$)\mathbf{k}$; $\mathbf{M}_A = (1053$ N $\cdot$ m$)\mathbf{i} + (395$ N $\cdot$ m$)\mathbf{j}$; $F_{CE} = 1181$ N

4.90 (a) 1292 N (b) $\mathbf{A} = (429$ N$)\mathbf{i} + (1226$ N$)\mathbf{j} + (1839$ N$)\mathbf{k}$; $\mathbf{M}_A = -(1104$ N $\cdot$ m$)\mathbf{j} + (1809$ N $\cdot$ m$)\mathbf{k}$

4.92 $T_{BD} = 3.9$ kN; $T_{BE} = 3.25$ kN; $T_{CF} = 3.25$ kN; $\mathbf{A} = (9.6$ kN$)\mathbf{i} - (1.5$ kN$)\mathbf{k}$

4.94 $x = -1.144$ m; $z = +1.925$ m

4.98 $T_{BD} = 0$; $T_{BE} = 3.96$ kN; $T_{CD} = 3.00$ kN

4.100 239 N

4.102 450 N

4.104 $(375$ N$)\mathbf{i}$

4.106 (a) 1.530 kN (b) $\mathbf{A} = 2.42$ kN $\nearrow$ 21.8°

4.108 (a) 13.73 N (b) $\mathbf{A} = -(13.46$ N$)\mathbf{i} + (31.6$ N$)\mathbf{j}$; $\mathbf{B} = (34.3$ N$)\mathbf{j}$

4.112 (a) 59.2° (b) $T_{AB} = 0.596$ W; $T_{CD} = 1.164$ W

4.114 (a) $\mathbf{A} = 0.745$ P $\searrow$ 63.4°; $\mathbf{D} = 0.471$ P $\nearrow$ 45° (b) $\mathbf{A} = P \rightarrow$; $\mathbf{D} = 1.414$ P $\searrow$ 45°

(c) $\mathbf{A} = 0.471$ P $\nearrow$ 45°; $\mathbf{D} = 0.745$ P $\searrow$ 63.4° (d) $\mathbf{A} = 0.707$ P $\nearrow$ 45°; $\mathbf{C} = 0.707$ P $\nearrow$ 45°; $\mathbf{D} = P \uparrow$

4.116 (a) $\alpha = 60°$ (b) $a = 84$ mm (c) $a = 40$ mm (d) $\alpha = 63.4°$ (e) 63.4°

4.C1 (a) $\theta = 25°$: $\alpha = 40.0°$ $\nwarrow$; $\theta = 75°$: $\alpha = 60.0°$ $\nearrow$ (b) $\theta = 25°$: $\alpha = 22.0°$ $\nwarrow$; $\theta = 75°$: $\alpha = 67.4°$ $\nearrow$

4.C2 $\theta = 25°$: $P = 42.3$ N; $\theta = 65°$: $P = 78.3$ N

4.C3 $\phi = 12°$: $T_{BB} = 11.63$ kN, $T_{BE} = 20.8$ kN; $\phi = 24°$: $T_{BD} = 6.16$ kN, $T_{BE} = 24.2$ kN

4.C4 $y = 400$ mm: $T = 650$ N; $y = 800$ mm: $T = 523$ N

CHAPTER 5

5.2 $\overline{X} = 81.8$ mm. $\overline{Y} = 104.5$ mm

5.4 $\overline{X} = 175.6$ mm, $\overline{Y} = 94.4$ mm

5.6 $\overline{X} = 46.2$ mm, $\overline{Y} = 47.8$ mm

5.8 $\overline{X} = 0$ mm, $\overline{Y} = 79.2$ mm

5.10 $\overline{X} = -62.4$ mm, $\overline{Y} = 0$

5.12 $\overline{X} = 120$ mm, $\overline{Y} = 60$ mm

5.14 $\overline{X} = 253$ mm, $\overline{Y} = 96.8$ mm

5.16 $\overline{X} = \dfrac{4r \sin^3 \alpha}{3\, 2\alpha - \sin 2\alpha}$

5.18 $\overline{X} = -(4/3\pi)[(r_2^2 + r_1 r_2 + r_1^2)/(r_2 + r_1)]$, $\overline{Y} = 0$

5.20 0.508

5.22 648 N

5.24 3680 mm^3 and -3680 mm^3

5.26 $\overline{X} = 84.5$ mm, $\overline{Y} = 101.8$ mm

5.28 $\overline{X} = 172.5$ mm, $\overline{Y} = 97.5$ mm

5.30 (a) 25.0 N (b) 46.5 N $\searrow$ 57.5°

5.32 249 mm

5.34 (a) $0.513b$ (b) $0.691b$

5.36 50 mm

5.38 $0.7667a$; 2.23%

5.40 $\overline{x} = 2b/3$, $\overline{y} = h/3$

5.42 $\overline{x} = 8a/15$, $\overline{y} = 8b/21$

5.50 $\overline{x} = 2L/5$

5.52 $\overline{x} = 0.549$ R, $\overline{y} = 0$

5.54 25.7 mm

5.56 (a) $\overline{x} = 4.59 \times 10^6$ mm^3 (b) 3.68×10^6 mm^3

5.58 (a) $\pi a h^2/5$ (b) $\pi a^2 h/6$

5.62 (a) 0.226 m^3 (b) 131.2 kg

5.64 255×10^3 mm; 37.5×10^3 mm^2

5.66 54700 mm; 0.463 kg

5.68 120.1 mm

5.70 (a) 120×10^3 mm^3 (b) 12.2×10^3 mm^2

5.72 (a) $\pi R h^2$ (b) $2\pi R h^2/3$ (c) $8\pi R h^2/15$ (d) $\pi R h^2/3$ (e) $\pi R h^2/5$

5.74 $\mathbf{R} = 4400$ N $\downarrow$, 1.727 m to the right of A; $\mathbf{A} = 2500$ N $\uparrow$; $\mathbf{B} = 1900$ N $\uparrow$

5.76 $\mathbf{A} = 4.60$ kN $\uparrow$; $\mathbf{M}_A = 1.520$ kN $\cdot$ m γ·

5.80 $\mathbf{A} = 675$ N $\uparrow$; $\mathbf{B} = 1350$ N $\downarrow$

5.82 (a) 3.00 kN/m (b) 36.0 kN $\uparrow$

5.84 (a) 0.420 m (b) 42.0 kN/m

5.86 (a) $\mathbf{H} = 1766$ kN $\rightarrow$, $\mathbf{V} = 910$ kN $\uparrow$; 2.32 m to the right of A. (b) $\mathbf{R} = 236$ kN $\nearrow$ 41.6°

5.88 1.763 m

5.90 100.0 mm

5.92 $\mathbf{A} = 118.1$ kN $\nearrow$ 68.5°; $\mathbf{B} = 113.9$ kN $\uparrow$

5.96 1.490 m

5.98 3.46 m

5.100 462 mm

5.102 (a) 0.448 h (b) 0.425 h

5.104 $-3a/2\pi$

5.106 30.2 mm

5.110 40.3 mm

5.112 $\overline{X} = \overline{Z} = 105.2$ mm, $\overline{Y} = 175.8$ mm

5.114 $\overline{X} = \overline{Y} = 57.8$ mm, $\overline{Z} = -75$ mm

5.116 $\overline{X} = 205$ mm, $\overline{Y} = 255$ mm, $\overline{Z} = 75$ mm

5.118 85.2 mm above lower edge of base

5.120 34.9 mm above the base

5.124 $\bar{x} = 5h/6, \bar{y} = \bar{z} = 0$

5.126 $\bar{x} = \bar{z} = 0, \bar{y} = 7a/8$

5.128 $\bar{x} = \bar{z} = 0, \bar{y} = (\pi + 2)h/16$

5.132 94.4 mm

5.134 $\bar{x} = 0, \bar{y} = 5h/16, \bar{z} = -a/4$

5.138 38.9×10^3 mm^2

5.140 $\bar{x} = 135$ mm; $\bar{y} = 22.5$ mm; $\bar{z} = 90$ mm

5.142 $\bar{x} = -r/2, \bar{y} = \bar{z} = 0$

5.144 $\overline{X} = 24.3$ mm, $\overline{Y} = 47.8$ mm

5.C1 (b) $\overline{X} = 51.25$ mm, $\overline{Y} = 11.04$ mm
(c) $\overline{X} = 239$ mm, $\overline{Y} = 59.5$ mm

5.C2 (a) 213×10^3 mm^2 (b) 384×10^3 mm^2
(c) 846×10^3 mm^2

5.C3 $d = 0.6$ m: $\mathbf{A} = 11.54$ kN $\nearrow 72.2°$,
$\mathbf{B} = 10.99$ kN $\uparrow$; $d = 2.1$ m:
$\mathbf{A} = 118.1$ kN $\nearrow 68.5°$, $\mathbf{B} = 113.9$ kN $\uparrow$

5.C4 (a) $\overline{X} = \overline{Z} = 168.6$ mm, $\overline{Y} = 69.4$ mm
(b) $\overline{X} = \overline{Z} = 147.7$ mm, $\overline{Y} = 217$ mm
(c) $\overline{X} = 135.4$ mm, $\overline{Y} = 141.0$ mm; $\overline{Z} = 163.4$ mm

CHAPTER 6

6.2 $F_{AB} = 52$ kN T; $F_{AC} = 64$ kN T; $F_{BC} = 80$ kN C.

6.4 $F_{AB} = 5400$ N T; $F_{AC} = 9000$ N C;
$F_{BC} = 5850$ N C

6.6 $F_{AB} = F_{BC} = 0$; $F_{AD} = F_{CF} = 5$ kN C;
$F_{BD} = F_{BF} = 34$ kN C; $F_{BE} = 12$ kN T;
$F_{DE} = F_{EF} = 30$ kN T

6.8 $F_{AB} = 60$ kN C; $F_{AC} = 25$ kN C; $F_{AD} = 65$ kN T;
$F_{BD} = 0$; $F_{CD} = 150$ kN C; $F_{CE} = 87.5$ kN C;
$F_{CF} = 162.5$ kN T

6.10 $F_{AB} = F_{BC} = F_{CD} = 120$ kN T;
$F_{AE} = 192$ kN T; $F_{AF} = 150$ kN C;
$F_{BF} = F_{BG} = F_{CG} = F_{CH} = 0$;
$F_{DH} = F_{GH} = F_{FG} = 130$ kN C;
$F_{EF} = 120$ kN C

6.12 $F_{AC} = 80$ kN T; $F_{BC} = 19$ kN C;
$F_{BD} = F_{DE} = 51$ kN C; $F_{CE} = 45$ kN T;
$F_{CD} = 48$ kN T

6.14 Trusses of Probs. 6.11 and 6.15 are simple trusses; others are not simple trusses.

6.16 $BC, CD, IJ, IL, KL, LM, MN$.

6.18 $F_{AB} = F_{AC} = F_{AD} = P/\sqrt{6} \ comp.$;
$F_{BC} = F_{CD} = F_{DB} = P/3\sqrt{6} \ ten$

6.20 (a) $\mathbf{B} = (3000$ N$)\mathbf{j}$; $\mathbf{C} = \mathbf{D} = (1200$ N$)\mathbf{j}$
(b) $F_{AB} = 3400$ N C; $F_{AC} = F_{AD} = 1520$ N C;
$F_{BC} = F_{BD} = 843$ N T; $F_{CD} = 213$ N T

6.22 $F_{CD} = 9$ kN C; $F_{DF} = 12$ kN T

6.24 $F_{FG} = 70$ kN C; $F_{FH} = 240$ kN T

6.26 $F_{DE} = 125$ kN T; $F_{DF} = 65$ kN C

6.28 $F_{DE} = 38.6$ kN C; $F_{DF} = 91.5$ kN T

6.30 $F_{BD} = 240$ kN T; $F_{DE} = 300$ kN T

6.32 133.3 kN T

6.34 $F_{DF} = 40$ kN T; $F_{EF} = 12$ kN T; $F_{EG} = 60$ kN C

6.36 $F_{AD} = 16.9$ kN C; $F_{CD} = 0$; $F_{CE} = 70.2$ kN T

6.42 $F_{AB} = 161.6$ kN C; $F_{AD} = 190.1$ kN T

6.44 $F_{DB} = 0$; $F_{BE} = 62.5$ kN T; $F_{EF} = 12.5$ kN T

6.46 (a) Completely constrained, indeterminate
(b) Completely constrained, determinate
(c) Partially constrained

6.48 (a) Partially constrained.
(b) Completely constrained, determinate
(c) Completely constrained, indeterminate

6.50 $F_{BD} = 255$ N C; $\mathbf{C}_x = 120.0$ N $\rightarrow$, $\mathbf{C}_y = 625$ N $\uparrow$

6.52 $\mathbf{A}_x = 600$ N $\rightarrow$, $\mathbf{A}_y = 150$ N $\uparrow$; $\mathbf{B}_x = 600$ N $\leftarrow$;
$\mathbf{B}_y = 400$ N $\downarrow$; $\mathbf{C} = 150$ N $\downarrow$; $\mathbf{D} = 400$ N $\uparrow$

6.54 (a) 2.44 kN $\nwarrow 8.4°$ (b) 1.930 kN $\nwarrow 51.3°$

6.56 $\mathbf{A} = 750$ N $\rightarrow$; $\mathbf{B}_x = 750$ N $\leftarrow$, $\mathbf{B}_y = 300$ N $\uparrow$;
$\mathbf{C} = 100$ N $\uparrow$; $\mathbf{D} = 400$ N $\downarrow$

6.58 7.36 kN C

6.60 $\mathbf{B} = 760$ N $\downarrow$; $\mathbf{C}_x = 300$ N $\leftarrow$, $\mathbf{C}_y = 1000$ N $\uparrow$;
$\mathbf{D}_x = 300$ N $\rightarrow$, $\mathbf{D}_y = 210$ N $\uparrow$

6.62 (a) $\mathbf{D}_x = 750$ N $\rightarrow$, $\mathbf{D}_y = 250$ N $\downarrow$;
$\mathbf{E}_x = 750$ N $\leftarrow$, $\mathbf{E}_y = 250$ N $\uparrow$
(b) $\mathbf{D}_x = 375$ N $\rightarrow$, $\mathbf{D}_y = 250$ N $\downarrow$;
$\mathbf{E}_x = 375$ N $\leftarrow$, $\mathbf{E}_y = 250$ N $\uparrow$

6.64 (a) $\mathbf{A} = 332$ N $\nearrow 22.6°$; $\mathbf{C} = 613$ N $\rightarrow$;
$\mathbf{G} = 307$ N $\leftarrow$; $\mathbf{I} = 127.8$ N $\uparrow$
(b) $\mathbf{A} = 332$ N $\nearrow 22.6°$; $\mathbf{C} = 307$ N $\rightarrow$; $\mathbf{G} = 0$;
$\mathbf{I} = 127.8$ N $\uparrow$

6.66 (a) 200 N $\nwarrow 60°$ (b) 574 N $\searrow 89.0°$

6.68 $\mathbf{A}_x = 45$ N $\leftarrow$, $\mathbf{A}_y = 30$ N $\downarrow$; $\mathbf{B}_x = 45$ N $\rightarrow$,
$\mathbf{B}_y = 270$ N $\uparrow$

6.70 (a) $\mathbf{E}_x = 4320$ N ←, $\mathbf{E}_y = 5760$ N ↑
(b) $\mathbf{C}_x = 11880$ N ←, $\mathbf{C}_y = 15840$ N ↑

6.72 (a) $\mathbf{A} = 78.8$ kN ↑ ; $\mathbf{B} = 131.0$ kN ↑
(b) $\mathbf{C} = 173.0$ kN ← ; $\mathbf{D}_x = 173.0$ kN → ;
$\mathbf{D}_y = 12.40$ kN ↓

6.74 (a) $\mathbf{A} = 3980$ N ↑ ; $\mathbf{B} = 4170$ N ↑ ;
$\mathbf{C} = 2890$ N ↑
(b) $\Delta B = +1326$ N; $\Delta C = -398$ N

6.76 $\mathbf{B}_x = 3600$ N ←, $\mathbf{B}_y = 1800$ N ↓ ; $\mathbf{E}_x = 1200$ N →,
$\mathbf{E}_y = 0$; $\mathbf{G}_x = 2400$ N →, $\mathbf{G}_y = 1800$ N ↑ ; $\mathbf{H} = 0$

6.78 $\mathbf{A}_x = 10.80$ kN ←, $\mathbf{A}_y = 7.00$ kN ↑ ;
$\mathbf{B}_x = 16.20$ kN ←, $\mathbf{B}_y = 0.50$ kN ↓ ;
$\mathbf{D}_x = 27.0$ kN →, $\mathbf{D}_y = 6.50$ kN ↓ .

6.80 $\mathbf{A}_x = 3300$ N ←, $\mathbf{A}_y = 1200$ N ↑ ; $\mathbf{B}_x = 3300$ N ←,
$\mathbf{B}_y = 1600$ N ↓ ; $\mathbf{D}_x = 6600$ N →, $\mathbf{D}_y = 400$ N ↑

6.84 (a) $\mathbf{C}_x = 630$ kN ←, $\mathbf{C}_y = 516$ kN ↑
(b) $\mathbf{B}_x = 630$ kN ←, $\mathbf{B}_y = 30.0$ kN ↓

6.86 $F_{AF} = 3M_0/4a$ comp.; $F_{BG} = M_0/\sqrt{2}a$ ten.;
$F_{DG} = M_0/\sqrt{2}a$ ten.; $F_{EH} = M_0/4a$ comp.

6.88 $F_{AF} = M_0/6a$ ten.; $F_{BG} = \sqrt{2}M_0/6a$ ten.;
$F_{DG} = \sqrt{2}M_0/3a$ ten.; $F_{EH} = M_0/6a$ comp.

6.90 $F_{BF} = 7.20$ kN T; $F_{DG} = 3.00$ kN C

6.92 $\mathbf{A} = 1875$ N → ; $\mathbf{C} = 375$ N ← ;
$\mathbf{D}_x = 1500$ N →; $\mathbf{D}_y = 750$ N ↑ ; $\mathbf{F} = 3000$ N ←

6.94 $\mathbf{A} = P/7$ ↑ ; $\mathbf{D} = 2P/7$ ↑ ; $\mathbf{F} = 4P/7$ ↑

6.96 (a) $\mathbf{A} = P$ ↑ ; $\mathbf{B} = P$ ↓ ; $\mathbf{C} = P$ ↑ ; frame is rigid
(b) Frame is not rigid
(c) $\mathbf{A}_x = 2P$ →, $\mathbf{A}_y = P/2$ ↑ ;
$\mathbf{B}_x = 2P$ ←, $\mathbf{B}_y = P/2$ ↑ ; frame is rigid

6.98 (a) 2860 N ↓ (b) $\mathbf{C} = 2700$ N ⬈ 68.5°

6.100 $T_{DE} = 60.0$ N; $\mathbf{B} = 160.0$ N ↓

6.102 45.6 kN C

6.104 $\mathbf{C} = 20.5$ kN →; $\mathbf{E} = 27.1$ kN ⬈ 40.7°

6.106 (a) $F_{AB} = 13.15$ kN C; $F_{DE} = 39.2$ kN C
(b) $\mathbf{C} = 16.26$ kN ⬋ 40.8°

6.108 (a) 252 N · m ↙ . (b) 108.0 N · m ↙ .

6.110 (a) $\mathbf{M}_c = 50.4$ N · m ↖ .
(b) $\mathbf{C}_x = 217$ N ←, $\mathbf{C}_y = 86.8$ N ↑

6.112 1200 N

6.114 2220 N

6.116 3620 N

6.118 $\mathbf{Q} = 1553$ N →

6.120 $\mathbf{P} = 260$ N ←

6.124 (a) 7.68 kN C (b) 21.7 kN C

6.126 (a) 12.50 kN T
(b) $\mathbf{H}_x = 10$ kN ←, $\mathbf{H}_y = 20$ kN ↓

6.128 (a) $3.2M_A$ ↖ . (b) $2.2M_A$ ↙ .

6.130 (a) 27.2 N · m (b) $\mathbf{B} = -(105.7$ N$)\mathbf{i}$;
$\mathbf{C} = (190.2$ N$)\mathbf{i}$; $\mathbf{E} = -(84.5$ N$)\mathbf{i}$

6.132 $\mathbf{E}_x = 108.4$ kN →, $\mathbf{E}_y = 159.1$ kN ↑ ;
$\mathbf{F}_x = 29.9$ kN →, $\mathbf{F}_y = 119.9$ kN ↓ ;
$\mathbf{H}_x = 138.3$ kN ←, $\mathbf{H}_y = 39.2$ kN ↓

6.134 3.54 kN C

6.136 (a) 117.8 N · m ↖ . (b) 47.9 N · m' ↖ .

6.138 $F_{DE} = 7.98$ kN C; $F_{EF} = 17.66$ kN T

6.140 $\mathbf{A} = 160.0$ N ↑ ; $\mathbf{C}_x = 1440$ N →,
$\mathbf{C}_y = 160.0$ N ↓ ; $\mathbf{D} = 1440$ N ←

6.142 $F_{FG} = 22.7$ kN T; $F_{FH} = 53.4$ kN T

6.144 136.3 N

6.146 (1) (a) $\mathbf{A}_x = 0$, $\mathbf{A}_y = 7.85$ kN ↑
$\mathbf{M}_A = 15.70$ kN · m ↖ . (b) $\mathbf{D} = 22.2$ kN ⬈ 45°
(2) (a) $\mathbf{A}_x = 0$, $\mathbf{A}_y = 3.92$ kN ↑ ,
$\mathbf{M}_A = 8.34$ kN · m ↖ . (b) $\mathbf{D} = 11.10$ kN ⬈ 45°
(3) (a) $\mathbf{A}_x = 0$, $\mathbf{A}_y = 3.92$ kN ↑ ,
$\mathbf{M}_A = 8.34$ kN · m ↖ . (b) $\mathbf{D} = 18.95$ kN ⬈ 45°
(4) (a) $\mathbf{A}_x = 3.92$ kN →, $\mathbf{A}_y = 3.92$ kN ↑ ,
$\mathbf{M}_A = 2.35$ kN · m ↘ . (b) 11.10 kN ⬈ 45°.

6.C1 $\theta = 15°$: $F_{AB} = 12.08$ kN T; $F_{AC} = 11.31$ kN C;
$F_{BC} = 10.44$ kN T; $\theta = 65°$: $F_{AB} = 9.00$ kN T;
$F_{AC} = 10.75$ kN C; $F_{BC} = 9.92$ kN T

6.C2 $h = 6$ m: $F_{FH} = 17.50$ kN C; $F_{GH} = 1.601$ kN C;
$F_{GI} = 17.50$ kN T

6.C3 (a) $a = 0.1$ m: $F_{CF} = 22.3$ kN T,
$F_{DG} = 12.00$ kN C; $a = 0.2$ m: $F_{CF} = 24.2$ kN C,
$F_{DG} = 15.00$ kN T. (b) Improper constraints.

6.C4 (a) $\theta = 60°$: $\mathbf{M} = 149.1$ N · m ↖ ; $\theta = 135°$:
$\mathbf{M} = 84.2$ N · m ↖ . (b) 75.1°, $\mathbf{M}_{max} = 156.0$ N · m ↖ .

CHAPTER 7

7.2 (On JD) $\mathbf{F} = 0$; $\mathbf{V} = 400$ N ↑ ; $\mathbf{M} = 60$ N · m ↖ .

7.4 (On KC) $\mathbf{F} = 200$ N ↘ ; $\mathbf{V} = 150$ N ↗ ;
$\mathbf{M} = 15$ N · m ↖ .

7.6 (On JB) $\mathbf{F} = 125$ N ↗ ; $\mathbf{V} = 300$ N ↘ ;
$\mathbf{M} = 156$ N · m ↓ .

7.10 (a) (On CA) $\mathbf{F} = 480$ N ←; $\mathbf{V} = 576$ N ↑ ; $\mathbf{M} = 0$.
(b) (On JA) $\mathbf{F} = 480$ N ←; $\mathbf{V} = 576$ N ↑ ;
$\mathbf{M} = 57.6$ N · m ↖ .

7.12 (a) (On BA) $\mathbf{F} = 0.333$ P →; $\mathbf{V} = 0.333$ P ↑ ;
$\mathbf{M} = 0.667$ Pa ↖ . (b) (On BA) $\mathbf{F} = P$ ←; $\mathbf{V} = P$ ↑ ;
$\mathbf{M} = 0$ (c) (On BA) $\mathbf{F} = 0.3333$ P ←;
$\mathbf{V} = 0.667$ P ↑ ; $\mathbf{M} = 0.333$ Pa ↖ .

7.14 $M_{max} = \frac{1}{4}PL$ at $a = \frac{1}{2}L$

7.16 (On JC) $\mathbf{M} = 4.22$ N · m ↖ .

7.18 (On JC) $\mathbf{F} = (W\theta/\pi) \cos \theta$ ↗ ;
$\mathbf{V} = (W\theta/\pi) \sin \theta$ ↖ ;
$\mathbf{M} = (Wr/\pi)(\sin \theta - \theta \cos \theta)$ ↖ .

7.20 $M_B = +Pab/L$

7.22 $M_B = -\frac{1}{2}wL^2$

7.24 $M_B = -\frac{1}{6}w_0L^2$

7.26 $M_C = +6.59$ kN · m

7.32 $M = +9$ kN · m at center

7.34 $M_C = +18$ kN · m

7.36 Just to the right of C: $V = +60$ N;
$M = +12$ N · m

8.112	(a) 918 N (b) 212 N		**9.60**	-800×10^3 mm^4
8.114	91.6 N $\cdot$ m		**9.62**	-1.165×10^6 mm^4
8.116	(a) $T_A = 42.0$ N; $T_B = 98.0$ N (b) 0.270		**9.64**	(a) $(\pi - \sqrt{3})a^4/16$; $(\pi + \sqrt{3})a^4/16$; $+ a^4/16$

8.112 (a) 918 N (b) 212 N
8.114 91.6 N $\cdot$ m
8.116 (a) $T_A = 42.0$ N; $T_B = 98.0$ N (b) 0.270
8.118 51.9 N $\cdot$ m $\nwarrow$.
8.120 91.3 N $\cdot$ m $\swarrow$.
8.122 1.557
8.124 (a) 45.0 kg (b) 28.1 kg (c) 45.0 kg
8.126 0.231
8.130 62.2 mm
8.132 12.27 kN
8.134 (a) $16.9° \leqslant \theta \leqslant 73.1°$ (b) $0 \leqslant \theta \leqslant 53.1°$
8.136 1.025 kN $\downarrow$
8.138 (a) 69.5° (b) 507 N
8.140 $L/a \geqslant 3.39$
8.C1 $\mu_s = 0.15 : \theta = 25.8°$; $\mu_s = 0.50 : \theta = 90.0°$
8.C2 $m_A = 10$ kg $: \theta = 28.8°$; $m_A = 40$ kg $: \theta = 55.4°$
8.C3 (b) (1) $\theta = 20° : \mu_s = 0.285$; (2) $\theta = 20° :$
$\mu_s = 0.219$. (c) (1) $\theta = 22.0°$; (2) $\theta = 28.7°$
8.C4 (a) $x_0 = 0.600L$; $x_m = 0.604L$; $\theta_1 = 5.06°$
(b) $\theta_2 = 55.4°$

CHAPTER 9
9.2 $a^3b/(n + 3)$
9.4 $a^3(h_1 + 3h_2)/12$
9.6 $(ab^3/3)/(3n + 1)$
9.8 $a(h_1^2 + h_2^2)(h_1 + h_2)/12$
9.10 $\pi ab^3/8$; $\frac{1}{2}b$
9.12 $\pi a^3b/8$; $\frac{1}{2}a$
9.14 $0.0945ah^3$; $0.402h$
9.16 (a) $4a^4/3$; $a\sqrt{\frac{2}{3}}$ (b) $17a^4/6$; $a\sqrt{\frac{17}{12}}$
9.18 $0.1804a^4$; $0.645a$
9.20 (b) -10.56%; -2.99%; -0.125%
9.22 614×10^3 mm^4; 19.01 mm
9.24 1.059×10^7 mm^4; 56.6 mm
9.26 $\overline{I}_x = 1.268 \times 10^6$ mm^4; $\overline{I}_y = 339 \times 10^3$ mm^4
9.28 3000 mm^2; 325×10^3 mm^4
9.30 $\overline{I}_x = 1.500 \times 10^6$ mm^4; $\overline{I}_y = 3.00 \times 10^6$ mm^4
9.32 $\overline{I}_x = 2.16 \times 10^7$ mm^4; 2.13×10^6 mm^4
9.34 (a) 11.57×10^6 mm^4 (b) 7.81×10^6 mm^4
9.36 (a) 2.13×10^8 mm^4 (b) 1.522×10^8 mm^4
9.38 $\overline{I}_x = 186.9 \times 10^6$ mm^4, $\overline{I}_y = 167.9 \times 10^6$ mm^4;
$\overline{k}_x = 118.6$ mm, $\overline{k}_y = 112.4$ mm
9.40 $\overline{I}_x = 3.79 \times 10^6$ mm^4; $\overline{I}_y = 4.06 \times 10^7$ mm^4
9.42 $\overline{I}_x = 7.34 \times 10^6$ mm^4; $\overline{I}_y = 101.3 \times 10^6$ mm^4
9.44 $\frac{1}{2}h$
9.46 $(a + 3b)h/(2a + 4b)$
9.48 $B = 4.44$ kN; $C = D = 6.10$ kN
9.50 $5a/4$
9.54 $b^2h^2/8$
9.56 $a^4/8$
9.58 $+19.4 \times 10^6$ mm^4

9.60 -800×10^3 mm^4
9.62 -1.165×10^6 mm^4
9.64 (a) $(\pi - \sqrt{3})a^4/16$; $(\pi + \sqrt{3})a^4/16$; $+ a^4/16$
(b) $(\pi - 2)a^4/16$; $(\pi + 2)a^4/16$; 0
9.66 7.79×10^5 mm^4; 4.22×10^6 mm^4;
6.54×10^5 mm^4
9.68 $+18.4°$; 84.2×10^6 mm^4, 19.46×10^6 mm^4
9.70 $-25.7°$; 2.28×10^6 mm^4, 0.230×10^6 mm^4
9.72 $-19.6°$; 4.34×10^6 mm^4, 6.59×10^5 mm^4
9.74 (a) $(\pi - \sqrt{3})a^4/16$; $(\pi + \sqrt{3})a^4/16$
(b) $(\pi - 2)a^4/16$; $(\pi + 2)a^4/16$; 0
9.76 7.79×10^5 mm^4; 4.22×10^6 mm^4;
6.54×10^5 mm^4
9.78 $+18.4°$; 84.2×10^6 mm^4, 19.46×10^6 mm^4
9.80 $-25.7°$; 2.28×10^6 mm^4, 0.230×10^6 mm^4
9.82 $-19.6°$; 4.34×10^6 mm^4, 6.59×10^5 mm^4
9.88 (a) $0.0699 ma^2$ (b) $0.320 ma^2$
9.90 (a) $I_{AA} = mb^2/24$; $I_{BB} = mh^2/18$
(b) $m(3b^2 + 4h^2)/72$
9.92 (a) $ma^2/3$ (b) $3ma^2/2$
9.94 $\frac{1}{2}ma^2(2n + 1)/(4n + 1)$
9.96 $m(3a^2 + 2h^2)/20$; $\sqrt{(3a^2 + 2h^2)/20}$
9.98 $m(b^2 + 3h^2)/5$
9.100 $\frac{1}{3}mR^2(1 - \cos\phi)(2 + \cos\phi)$
9.102 1.514 kg $\cdot$ m^2; 155.7 mm
9.104 $2mr^2/3$; $0.816r$
9.106 (a) $r_a = 176.9$ mm (b) 87.8 mm
9.108 (a) $\frac{1}{2}\rho\pi h(a_2^4 + 2a_2^2a_1^2 - 3a_1^4)$ (b) $a_2/\sqrt{3}$
(c) $\frac{2}{3}\rho\pi ha_2^4$
9.110 (a) 5.14×10^{-3} kg $\cdot$ m^2 (b) 7.54×10^{-3} kg $\cdot$ m^2
(c) 3.47×10^{-3} kg $\cdot$ m^2
9.112 $\overline{I}_x = \overline{I}_z = 4.65 \times 10^{-2}$ kg $\cdot$ m^2
$\overline{I}_y = 3.87 \times 10^{-2}$ kg $\cdot$ m^2
9.114 0.883 g $\cdot$ m^2
9.116 3.89×10^{-2} kg $\cdot$ m^2
9.118 (a) 9.97 kg $\cdot$ m^2 (b) 4.96 kg $\cdot$ m^2
9.120 $I_{xy} = I_{zx} = 0$; $I_{yz} = 4.43 \times 10^{-3}$ kg $\cdot$ m^2
9.122 $I_{xy} = 14.13$ g $\cdot$ m^2; $I_{yz} = 37.7$ g $\cdot$ m^2;
$I_{zx} = 113.0$ g $\cdot$ m^2
9.124 $I_{xy} = I_{yz} = 8.65 \times 10^{-3}$ kg $\cdot$ m^2
$I_{zx} = 2.88 \times 10^{-3}$ kg $\cdot$ m^2
9.128 $(3ma^2/20)(a^2 + 6h^2)/(a^2 + h^2)$
9.132 (a) $I_{xy} = \frac{1}{4}ma^2$; $I_{yz} = 0$; $I_{zx} = -\frac{1}{4}ma^2$ (b) $2ma^2/3$
9.134 $17ma^2/54$
9.136 (a) 2 (b) $\frac{1}{2}$
9.142 (a) $2ab^3/7$ (b) $2a^3b/15$
9.144 1.300×10^6 mm^4
9.148 13.78×10^{-3} kg $\cdot$ m^2; 114.5 mm
9.150 $m(3a^2 + 2h^2)/6$
9.152 (a) $I_{AA'} = ma^2/24$; $I_{BB'} = ma^2/24$ (c) $ma^2/12$
9.C2 (a) $+23.8°$, 524×10^3 mm^4, 92.5×10^3 mm^4
9.C3 (b) $I_x = 315 \times 10^3$ mm^4, $k_x = 13.23$ mm;

$I_y = 5.70 \times 10^6 \text{ mm}^4, k_y = 56.3 \text{ mm}$
(c) $I_x = 281 \times 10^6 \text{ mm}^4, k_x = 69.9 \text{ mm};$
$I_y = 4.64 \times 10^9 \text{ mm}^4, k_y = 284 \text{ mm}$
9.C4 (b) $0.423 \text{ kg} \cdot \text{m}^2; 117.7 \text{ mm}$

CHAPTER 10

10.2 $\mathbf{P} = 600 \text{ N} \uparrow$
10.4 $\mathbf{P} = 82.5 \text{ N} \downarrow$
10.6 $M = 165 \text{ N} \cdot \text{m} \,\curvearrowright\cdot$
10.8 $Q = (P \cos \theta)/\sin(\theta/2)$
10.10 $Q = P[(l/a)\sin^3 \theta - 1]$
10.12 $M = \frac{1}{2}Wl \tan \alpha \sin \theta$
10.14 (a) $199.6 \text{ N} \cdot \text{m}$ (b) $100.4 \text{ N} \cdot \text{m}$
10.20 $69.4°$
10.22 $57.5°$
10.24 $(1 - \cos \theta)\tan \theta = W/4kl$
10.26 390 mm
10.28 $55.6°$
10.30 $54.9°$
10.32 11.86 kN
10.36 $\eta = 1/(1 + \mu \cot \alpha)$
10.38 $M_{\max} = Pl/[2(\tan \theta - \mu)]$
10.40 $7.75 \text{ kN} \uparrow$
10.42 11.90 mm
10.44 5.65 mm
10.46 $20.8 \text{ mm} \downarrow$
10.54 $45°$, stable; $-135°$, unstable

10.56 $22.0°$ and $158.0°$, stable; $90°$ and $270°$, unstable
10.58 $54.9°$, stable
10.60 $69.3°$
10.62 (a) $y(1 - a\sqrt{a^2 + y^2}) = W/k$
(b) 400 mm, stable
10.64 $12.5°$ and $90°$, stable; $30.8°$, unstable
10.66 (a) $(1 - \cos \theta)\tan \theta = 2mg/kl$ (b) $52.0°$, stable
10.68 (a) $\theta = 2 \sin^{-1}[kl/2(kl - P)]$ and $\theta = 180°$
(b) $88.6°$, stable; $180°$, unstable
10.70 (a) $\theta = \tan^{-1}(P/kl)$
(b) $63.4°$, stable; $24.3°$, unstable
10.72 $k > 2.45 \text{ kN/m}$
10.74 $P < kl/2$
10.76 $P < kl/2$
10.78 $P < 2.51 \text{ kN}$
10.82 $16.7°$, stable; $73.3°$, unstable
10.86 $M = Pl \cos (\theta/2)$
10.88 (a) and (b) $P < ka^2/2l$
10.90 $P < kl/3$
10.92 (a) $T = W/2(1 - \tan \theta)$ (b) $36.9°$
10.C1 $\theta = 40°: F_{CD} = 9.36 \text{ kN } T;$
$\theta = 80°: F_{CD} = 22.2 \text{ kN } T.$
10.C2 $\theta = 40°: 62.5 \text{ mm}; \theta = 80°: 79.0 \text{ mm};$
$\theta = 120°: 52.1 \text{ mm}$
10.C3 (b) $\theta = 20°: V = 64.1 \text{ J}; \theta = 40°: V = 46.4 \text{ J}$
(c) and (d) $9.59°$, unstable; $40.3°$, stable
10.C4 (b) $\theta = 40°: W = 353 \text{ N}; \theta = 60°: W = 1559 \text{ N}$
(c) $52.2°$

Centroids of Common Shapes of Areas and Lines

Shape		$\bar{x}$	$\bar{y}$	Area
Triangular area			$\dfrac{h}{3}$	$\dfrac{bh}{2}$
Quarter-circular area		$\dfrac{4r}{3\pi}$	$\dfrac{4r}{3\pi}$	$\dfrac{\pi r^2}{4}$
Semicircular area		0	$\dfrac{4r}{3\pi}$	$\dfrac{\pi r^2}{2}$
Semiparabolic area		$\dfrac{3a}{8}$	$\dfrac{3h}{5}$	$\dfrac{2ah}{3}$
Parabolic area		0	$\dfrac{3h}{5}$	$\dfrac{4ah}{3}$
Parabolic span-drel		$\dfrac{3a}{4}$	$\dfrac{3h}{10}$	$\dfrac{ah}{3}$
Circular sector		$\dfrac{2r\sin\alpha}{3\alpha}$	0	αr^2
Quarter-circular arc		$\dfrac{2r}{\pi}$	$\dfrac{2r}{\pi}$	$\dfrac{\pi r}{2}$
Semicircular arc		0	$\dfrac{2r}{\pi}$	πr
Arc of circle		$\dfrac{r\sin\alpha}{\alpha}$	0	$2\alpha r$

Moments of Inertia of Common Geometric Shapes

Rectangle

$$\bar{I}_{x'} = \tfrac{1}{12}bh^3$$
$$\bar{I}_{y'} = \tfrac{1}{12}b^3h$$
$$I_x = \tfrac{1}{3}bh^3$$
$$I_y = \tfrac{1}{3}b^3h$$
$$J_C = \tfrac{1}{12}bh(b^2 + h^2)$$

Triangle

$$\bar{I}_{x'} = \tfrac{1}{36}bh^3$$
$$I_x = \tfrac{1}{12}bh^3$$

Circle

$$\bar{I}_x = \bar{I}_y = \tfrac{1}{4}\pi r^4$$
$$J_O = \tfrac{1}{2}\pi r^4$$

Semicircle

$$I_x = I_y = \tfrac{1}{8}\pi r^4$$
$$J_O = \tfrac{1}{4}\pi r^4$$

Quarter circle

$$I_x = I_y = \tfrac{1}{16}\pi r^4$$
$$J_O = \tfrac{1}{8}\pi r^4$$

Ellipse

$$\bar{I}_x = \tfrac{1}{4}\pi ab^3$$
$$\bar{I}_y = \tfrac{1}{4}\pi a^3b$$
$$J_O = \tfrac{1}{4}\pi ab(a^2 + b^2)$$

Mass Moments of Inertia of Common Geometric Shapes

Slender rod

$$I_y = I_z = \tfrac{1}{12}mL^2$$

Thin rectangular plate

$$I_x = \tfrac{1}{12}m(b^2 + c^2)$$
$$I_y = \tfrac{1}{12}mc^2$$
$$I_z = \tfrac{1}{12}mb^2$$

Rectangular prism

$$I_x = \tfrac{1}{12}m(b^2 + c^2)$$
$$I_y = \tfrac{1}{12}m(c^2 + a^2)$$
$$I_z = \tfrac{1}{12}m(a^2 + b^2)$$

Thin disk

$$I_x = \tfrac{1}{2}mr^2$$
$$I_y = I_z = \tfrac{1}{4}mr^2$$

Circular cylinder

$$I_x = \tfrac{1}{2}ma^2$$
$$I_y = I_z = \tfrac{1}{12}m(3a^2 + L^2)$$

Circular cone

$$I_x = \tfrac{3}{10}ma^2$$
$$I_y = I_z = \tfrac{3}{5}m(\tfrac{1}{4}a^2 + h^2)$$

Sphere

$$I_x = I_y = I_z = \tfrac{2}{5}ma^2$$